THE

# INTERNATIONAL SERIES
OF
# MONOGRAPHS ON PHYSICS

GENERAL EDITORS

R. H. FOWLER AND P. KAPITZA

OXFORD UNIVERSITY PRESS
AMEN HOUSE, E.C. 4
LONDON EDINBURGH GLASGOW
LEIPZIG NEW YORK TORONTO
MELBOURNE CAPETOWN BOMBAY
CALCUTTA MADRAS SHANGHAI
HUMPHREY MILFORD
PUBLISHER TO THE
UNIVERSITY

PRINTED IN GREAT BRITAIN

# THE
# THEORY
## OF
# ELECTRIC AND MAGNETIC
# SUSCEPTIBILITIES

BY

## J. H. VAN VLECK

PROFESSOR OF THEORETICAL PHYSICS IN
THE UNIVERSITY OF WISCONSIN

**OXFORD**
**AT THE CLARENDON PRESS**
1932

*J. Francis Southgate*

TO MY FATHER

# EDWARD BURR VAN VLECK

EMERITUS PROFESSOR OF MATHEMATICS

THE UNIVERSITY OF WISCONSIN

# PREFACE

THE new quantum mechanics is perhaps most noted for its triumphs in the field of spectroscopy, but its less heralded successes in the theory of electric and magnetic susceptibilities must be regarded as one of its great achievements. At the same time the accomplishments of classical mechanics in this field must not be overlooked, and so the first four chapters are devoted to purely classical theory. Most of the comparison with experiment regarding dielectric constants is included in one of these (Chap. III). This can be done without making the comparison obsolete because the new quantum mechanics has restored the validity of many classical theorems violated in the old quantum theory. On the other hand, the analysis of experimental magnetic susceptibilities cannot be attempted until the quantum chapters, since the numerical values of magnetic susceptibilities are inextricably connected with the quantization of angular momentum. At the outset I intended to include only gaseous media, but the number of paramagnetic gases is so very limited that any treatment of magnetism not applicable to solids would be rather unfruitful. Therefore, salts of the rare earth and iron groups are examined in considerable detail. A theory is developed to explain why, as conjectured by Stoner, inter-atomic forces obliterate the contribution of the orbital angular momentum to the magnetic moment in the iron group. Chapter XII includes the aspects of ferromagnetism so far amenable to the Heisenberg theory, which has at last divested the Weiss molecular field of its mystery. This means that here the discussion is centred on the thermal behaviour of the saturation, rather than on hysteresis and retentivity. As far as practicable, I have striven throughout the volume to avoid duplication of the existing literature, especially Debye's *Polar Molecules* and Stoner's *Magnetism and Atomic Structure*.

In the preface to a book on theoretical physics it is customary for the author to express the laudable but, alas, usually unwarranted hope that the volume will prove simultaneously rigorous to mathematical readers and intelligible to the non-mathematical, at least provided the latter omit the particular sections where the density of equations is excessive. At any rate this has been the aim of the present volume, and I hope that it has not fallen too far short. A detailed knowledge of quantum mechanics or of spectroscopic nomenclature has not been presupposed—only an elementary acquaintance with the Schrödinger wave equation. The necessary perturbation theory and theorems of spectro-scopic stability are developed in Chapter VI. Here I have tried to correlate and intermingle the use of wave functions and of matrices, rather than relying exclusively on the one or the other, as is too often done. It is hoped that this chapter may be helpful as a presentation of the perturbation machinery of quantum mechanics, quite irrespective of the magnetic applications.

I am much indebted to the Guggenheim Memorial Foundation for a travelling fellowship which enabled me to visit many European institutes for theoretical physics. I wish to take this occasion to thank the staffs of these institutes for their cordiality and helpful discussions. The list is rather extensive—Cambridge, Leipzig, Munich, Göttingen, Berlin, Zurich, Copenhagen, Leiden, Utrecht, Groningen, Bristol, Paris. I am also indebted to the University of Wisconsin for extension of leave which permitted me to attend the sixth Solvay Congress, devoted to magnet-ism, and to Professors W. Weaver and J. W. Williams of this university for valuable criticisms on Chapters I and III respectively. I also wish to thank Miss A. Frank and Mr. R. Serber for assistance in some of the computations and in proof-reading.

J. H. V. V.

DEPARTMENT OF PHYSICS,
UNIVERSITY OF WISCONSIN,
        *June, 1931.*

# CONTENTS

## XI. THE PARAMAGNETISM OF SOLIDS, ESPECIALLY SALTS OF THE IRON GROUP

## XII. HEISENBERG'S THEORY OF FERROMAGNETISM; FURTHER TOPICS IN SOLIDS

## XIII. BRIEF SURVEY OF SOME RELATED OPTICAL PHENOMENA

# SYLLABUS OF NOTATION

BESIDES symbols which are standard usage, such as $e$, $h$, $m$, $E$, $H$, the following notation commonly occurs in the present volume:

$\alpha =$ constant term in the Langevin-Debye formula $\chi = N\left(\alpha + \dfrac{\mu^2}{3kT}\right)$. Usually $\alpha$ arises from induced polarization or diamagnetic induction.

$\beta =$ Bohr magneton $= 0\cdot9174 \times 10^{-20}$ e.m.u. ($= 4\cdot95$ Weiss magnetons). (The so-called 'molar' Bohr magneton number is $L\beta = 5564$ e.m.u.)

$e_i, m_i =$ arbitrary charge or mass, whereas $e = 4\cdot77 \times 10^{-10}$ e.s.u., $m = 9\cdot04 \times 10^{-28}$ gm.

$\mathscr{H} =$ Hamiltonian function (to be distinguished from the magnetic field $H$).

$\kappa =$ 'molar polarizability' $4\pi LP/3NE$.

$L =$ Avogadro number $6\cdot064 \times 10^{23}$. (Occasionally $L$ is also used for the Lagrangian function or for the azimuthal quantum number.)

$m_H$ (or $m_z$) $=$ component of an individual molecule's total magnetic moment, inclusive of both induced and permanent parts, in direction of the applied field $H$ (or of the $z$ axis).

$M = N\overline{\overline{m}}_H =$ magnetic moment per unit-volume. ($B = H + 4\pi M$.)

$\mu =$ permanent moment of the molecule. (On pp. 1–17 only, $\mu$ instead denotes the magnetic permeability.)

$\mu_{\text{eff}} =$ 'effective Bohr magneton number', defined in terms of the susceptibility by the relation $\mu_{\text{eff}} = \sqrt{(3kT\chi/N\beta^2)}$. We throughout use Bohr rather than Weiss magneton numbers because of the former's more elemental physical significance. Note that the empirical number $\mu_{\text{eff}}$ has no connexion with the permanent moment $\mu$ except when Curie's law is obeyed.

$N =$ number of molecules per unit-volume ($= 2\cdot706 \times 10^{19}$ per c.c. at $0^\circ$ C., 76 cm.).

$p_E =$ component of an individual molecule's total electric moment in direction of the applied field $E$.

$P = N\overline{\overline{p}}_E =$ electric moment per unit-volume. ($D = E + 4\pi P$.)

$S' =$ spin quantum number for entire crystal (used in Chap. XII) to be distinguished from spin $S$ of a single atom.

$\chi =$ susceptibility per unit-volume (electric or magnetic). $\chi_{\text{mol}} = L\chi/N =$ susceptibility per gramme mol.

Expressions in bold-face type are vectors. Single bars denote time average for a single molecule. Double bars denote statistical average over a very large number of molecules. Equations involving entire matrices are numbered in angular parentheses, e.g. Eq. $\langle 12 \rangle$. A dotted equality such as $p_\phi \doteq m_l h/2\pi$ means that $p_\phi$ is a diagonal matrix whose characteristic values are $m_l h/2\pi$, i.e.

$$p_\phi(n; n') = \delta(n; n') m_l h/2\pi.$$

For explanation of spectroscopic nomenclature and quantum numbers see § 40 (atoms) and § 63 (molecules).

# I
## CLASSICAL FOUNDATIONS

### 1. The Macroscopic versus Microscopic Field Equations

The conventional Maxwell equations are

$$\operatorname{curl} \mathbf{E} = -\frac{1}{c}\frac{\partial \mathbf{B}}{\partial t}, \qquad \operatorname{curl} \mathbf{H} = \frac{1}{c}\left(4\pi \mathbf{i} + \frac{\partial \mathbf{D}}{\partial t}\right), \tag{1}$$

together with $\qquad \operatorname{div} \mathbf{D} = 4\pi\rho, \qquad \operatorname{div} \mathbf{B} = 0.$ (2)

We shall term these the 'macroscopic field equations' as they do not aim to take direct cognizance of the atomicity of matter or electricity. Throughout the volume all expressions printed in bold-face type are vectors. Between the four field vectors there exist the so-called constitutive relations

$$\frac{\mathbf{D}}{\mathbf{E}} = \epsilon, \qquad \frac{\mathbf{B}}{\mathbf{H}} = \mu, \tag{3}$$

which may be regarded as defining the dielectric constant $\epsilon$ and the permeability $\mu$.[1] The ratios $\epsilon$ and $\mu$ are, except for ferromagnetic media,

---

[1] The logically minded will immediately object that Eqs. (3) do not really define $\epsilon$ and $\mu$, inasmuch as the solutions of Eqs. (1) and (2) and hence the left sides of (3) are not *per se* unique, because (1), (2) involve four unknown vectors $\mathbf{E}, \mathbf{H}, \mathbf{D}, \mathbf{B}$ rather than two as *in vacuo*. The solutions of (1), (2) become unique as soon as we know something about the nature of the ratios (3), but this is clearly arguing in a circle, and (3) cannot serve simultaneously as an auxiliary relation and as a definition. This inability to give a simple and rigorous definition of $\epsilon$ and $\mu$ is inherent in the macroscopic field equations, but is a purely academic difficulty, as from a practical standpoint there never seems to have been any particular ambiguity in knowing in simple cases what is meant by a dielectric constant or magnetic permeability. Two ways of avoiding the looseness in definition immediately suggest themselves. One is to assume, as one always does, that $\epsilon$ and $\mu$ are independent of position in homogeneous media, and also of time in static or in monochromatic phenomena. For electromagnetic waves of given frequency the expressions $\epsilon$ and $\mu$ are then constants of the homogeneous body, which are not calculable from (1), (2) but which can be determined once for all by observing once through experiment which particular values of the constants are true experimentally—i.e. verifying which values of the otherwise indeterminate ratios $\mathbf{B}/\mathbf{H}$ and $\mathbf{D}/\mathbf{E}$ are actually realized. We then regard $\epsilon$ and $\mu$ at a given point in a non-homogeneous body to be the same as they would in a homogeneous body of the same density and material throughout as at the given point. If the electromagnetic waves are not monochromatic we would have to make a harmonic analysis into the various Fourier components, and knowing the $\epsilon$ and $\mu$ for each component, find the total solution by the principle of superposition. The other way of avoiding the looseness is to appeal to the microscopic point of view and define $\epsilon$ and $\mu$ by means of (8), (11), and (12). Although this is more rigorous from a postulational standpoint, it does not seem as desirable to follow, since most physicists have felt in the past, and still feel, that the task of the microscopic theory is to explain dielectric constants and magnetic permeabilities already measured macroscopically rather than to define something not already known. We therefore aim in the present chapter to analyse or dissect the macroscopic equations from the microscopic standpoint, rather than to synthesize from microscopic to macroscopic phenomena.

independent of the field strength for sufficiently small fields, and in general we must have such an independence, or at least a known dependence on the field strength, before Eqs. (1), (2) become unambiguous enough to be useful. We suppose throughout the volume that the medium is isotropic; in crystalline media directional effects make it necessary to use six dielectric constants or permeabilities instead of one, and **D**, **B** cease in general to be parallel to **E**, **H** respectively as presupposed by (3).

Of course $\epsilon$ and $\mu$ depend on many factors, notably on the temperature, density, chemical constitution, and frequency, as well as on the field strength if great. The theoretical description of their modes of dependence is the main aim of the present volume. This description is accomplished by means of the molecular theory of matter, and especially by means of the dynamics governing the electrons within each atom or molecule. The dawn of the twentieth century brought to light the electrical origin of matter, unknown to Maxwell when he developed his macroscopic equations in 1861–73. This electrical origin implied that by probing down to sub-atomic distances it should be possible to formulate the equations of electrodynamics in terms of charges *in vacuo* without the introduction of ponderable dielectric and magnetic media. H. A. Lorentz[2] therefore proposed and studied what we shall term the 'microscopic field equations'

$$\operatorname{curl}\mathbf{e} = -\frac{1}{c}\frac{\partial\mathbf{h}}{\partial t}, \qquad \operatorname{curl}\mathbf{h} = \frac{1}{c}\left(4\pi\rho'\mathbf{v} + \frac{\partial\mathbf{e}}{\partial t}\right), \tag{4}$$

$$\operatorname{div}\mathbf{e} = 4\pi\rho', \qquad \operatorname{div}\mathbf{h} = 0, \tag{5}$$

which are similar in structure to the macroscopic equations *in vacuo* (where, of course, $\mathbf{B} = \mathbf{H}$, $\mathbf{D} = \mathbf{E}$), except that instead of the ponderable current density **i** Lorentz introduced the convection current density $\rho'\mathbf{v}$ due to motion of the charge density $\rho'$ with the vector velocity **v**. The microscopic fields **e**, **h** and charge $\rho'$ are not the same as the macroscopic fields or charge, and have therefore been printed in small letters or else designated by a prime. Eqs. (4), (5) are more fundamental than (1), (2), (3), as (4), (5) are supposed to hold at every point either inside or outside the molecule, whereas (1), (2), (3) are essentially statistical in nature, and the expressions **E**, **D**, **H**, **B**, $\rho$ which they involve must be correlated in some way with averages of microscopic fields and charges over a large number of molecules. How this correlation is achieved will be discussed in the two following sections.

[2] Cf., for instance, H. A. Lorentz, *The Theory of Electrons* (Leipzig, 1916). His original papers were published considerably earlier in the *Proceedings of the Amsterdam Academy*.

## 2. Correlation of the Microscopic and Macroscopic Equations. The Fundamental Lemma on the Significance of Molecular Moments

Let $\bar{\bar{\mathbf{e}}}$ and $\bar{\bar{\mathbf{h}}}$ denote the averages of $\mathbf{e}$ and $\mathbf{h}$ over a 'physically small' element of volume; i.e. an element too small to be accessible to ordinary methods of measurement but nevertheless large enough to contain a very great number of molecules. Throughout the volume we shall use double bars to designate statistical averages involving a large number of molecules, to avoid confusion with time averages for a single molecule, for which a single bar is used. It turns out (see § 3) that $\mathbf{E}$ and $\mathbf{B}$ are identical with the microscopic fields averaged over such a volume element, so that

$$\mathbf{E} = \bar{\bar{\mathbf{e}}}, \qquad \mathbf{B} = \bar{\bar{\mathbf{h}}}. \tag{6}$$

It is to be noted that the electric and magnetic cases are not entirely parallel, as by analogy with the electric one we should expect $\mathbf{H}$ rather than $\mathbf{B}$ to enter in (6).[3]

In order to describe the statistical significance of $\mathbf{D}$ and $\mathbf{H}$ or of the constitutive relations (3) in terms of the microscopic theory, let us, as customary, write

$$\mathbf{D} = \mathbf{E} + 4\pi\mathbf{P}, \qquad \mathbf{B} = \mathbf{H} + 4\pi\mathbf{M}. \tag{7}$$

The expressions $\mathbf{P}$ and $\mathbf{M}$ so defined are called respectively the electric and magnetic polarizations (or intensity of magnetization), while the quotients

$$\frac{\mathbf{P}}{\mathbf{E}} = \frac{\epsilon - 1}{4\pi} = \chi_e, \qquad \frac{\mathbf{M}}{\mathbf{H}} = \frac{\mu - 1}{4\pi} = \chi_m \tag{8}$$

are the electric and magnetic susceptibilities $\chi_e$ and $\chi_m$. Let us form the expressions

$$e_{\mathrm{mol}} = \iiint_{1M} \rho' \, dv, \tag{9}$$

and

$$\mathbf{p} = \iiint_{1M} \rho' \mathbf{r} \, dv, \qquad \mathbf{m} = \frac{1}{2c} \iiint_{1M} \rho' [\mathbf{r} \times \mathbf{v}] \, dv, \tag{10}$$

in which the integration is to include only the charge which belongs to a single molecule, as indicated by the subscript $_{1M}$. In general molecules may overlap each other, but we are to suppose that the charges pertaining to individual molecules can still be identified as such. The origin for the radius vector $\mathbf{r}$ is to be taken at the centre of gravity of the

---

[3] The appearance of $\mathbf{B}$ rather than $\mathbf{H}$ in (6) shows that $\mathbf{B}$ rather than $\mathbf{H}$ is the fundamental field vector, so that it would seem preferable to write the microscopic equations with the notation $\mathbf{b}$ instead of $\mathbf{h}$, and to retain $\mathbf{B}$ rather than $\mathbf{H}$ to denote the common value of $\mathbf{B}$ and $\mathbf{H}$ *in vacuo*. However, we do not make these changes, in order to conform more closely to most of the existing literature, which regards $\mathbf{H}$ as the fundamental magnetic field vector.

molecule, whose velocity we shall suppose negligible. If the molecule is electrically neutral, the integral in (9) vanishes and the origin for $r$ is then, as a matter of fact, immaterial in the first integral of (10). The expressions $\mathbf{p}$ and $\mathbf{m}$ defined by (10) are called the electric and magnetic moments of the molecule. The integrands of (9), (10), of course, vanish except where the element of integration falls inside an electron or nucleus of the molecule. In the conventional electron theory it is customary to think of the dimensions of the electrons and nuclei as negligible. Then the integrations may be replaced by a summation over all the discrete charges $e_i$ constituting the molecule, making

$$e_{\mathrm{mol}} = \sum e_i, \qquad \mathbf{p} = \sum e_i \mathbf{r}_i, \qquad \mathbf{m} = \frac{1}{2c} \sum e_i [\mathbf{r}_i \times \mathbf{v}_i]. \qquad (11)$$

Throughout the volume $e_i$ is used to denote a discrete charge of undetermined sign and magnitude, while $e$ without a subscript is used for the numerical magnitude $4 \cdot 770 \times 10^{-10}$ e.s.u. of the charge of an electron. Thus $e_i$ is equal either to $-e$ or $+Ze$ according as the discrete particle is an electron or a nucleus of atomic number $Z$. The contribution of a particle to the magnetic moment is seen to differ from its angular momentum $m_i[\mathbf{r}_i \times \mathbf{v}_i]$ only by a factor $e_i/2m_ic$ equal to half the ratio of its charge $e_i$ to the product of its mass $m_i$ and the velocity of light $c$. We shall later see (end of § 33) that in many respects the time average of the electronic distribution in the new quantum mechanics can be treated like a classical 'smeared out' or continuously distributed charge pervading all space. Consequently the use of the integration (9), (10) in place of the summation (11) no longer seems an abstract academic refinement, as it did prior to Schrödinger's work.

It will be proved in § 3 that the expressions $\mathbf{P}$ and $\mathbf{M}$ defined in (7) are equal respectively to the average electric and magnetic moments $\bar{\bar{\mathbf{p}}}$ and $\bar{\bar{\mathbf{m}}}$ per molecule multiplied by the number $N$ of molecules per c.c., so that

$$\mathbf{P} = N\bar{\bar{\mathbf{p}}}, \qquad \mathbf{M} = N\bar{\bar{\mathbf{m}}}. \qquad (12)$$

This immediately furnishes the desired correlation formulae for $\mathbf{D}$ and $\mathbf{H}$, as by (6), (7), and (12),

$$\mathbf{D} = \bar{\bar{\mathbf{e}}} + 4\pi N\bar{\bar{\mathbf{p}}}, \qquad \mathbf{H} = \bar{\bar{\mathbf{h}}} - 4\pi N\bar{\bar{\mathbf{m}}}.$$

By the term average moment per molecule we mean the molecular moment averaged over all the molecules in a 'physically small' element of volume. This is equivalent to the time average moment for an individual molecule if all the molecules are alike except for phase. If they are of several different classes, i.e. form a chemical mixture, the average denoted by the bars in (12) can be regarded as the mean of the time averages for single molecules of the various classes, weighted according to their relative abundance. In non-homogeneous media the term 'number of molecules per c.c.' is to be understood to mean the 'number-density', i.e. the number of molecules which there would be in unit volume if they were distributed throughout a unit volume with the same density as that with which they actually are distributed in the immediate vicinity of the point at which the polarization is being computed. The information conveyed by Eqs. (12) must be regarded as a very important lemma on the physical or macroscopic significance of the mean molecular moments, as it interprets the distinction between **D** and **E** or between **B** and **H** in terms of simple properties (10) of the molecules. Because of their simple connexion (12) with the average moments of individual molecules, the polarizations **P** and **M** are often called the specific moments per unit volume.

*Eqs.* (12) *underlie all theories of dielectric or magnetic media*, and hence are fundamental to the rest of the book. This concept of the polarization of the molecule as the cause of the departures of $\epsilon$ and $\mu$ from unity is by no means a purely twentieth-century concept, and was intimated by Faraday. In 1836 Mossotti[4] pictured the molecule as a conducting sphere of radius $a$, on which the charge would, of course, readjust or 'polarize' itself under the influence of an applied field, thus making the molecular moment different from zero. If the electric susceptibility $\chi_e$ is small compared to unity, he thereby showed that $\chi_e = Na^3$. It seems almost too hackneyed to mention that the values of $a$ obtained from this simple equation (together with the observed $N$ and $\chi_e$) are comparable in magnitude with the molecular radii in kinetic theory. This is illustrated by the following table, taken from Jeans's *Electricity and Magnetism*:

| Molecule | He | $H_2$ | $O_2$ | Ar | $N_2$ | CO | $CO_2$ | $N_2O$ | $C_2H_4$ | |
|---|---|---|---|---|---|---|---|---|---|---|
| $a$ (Mossotti) | 0·60 | 0·92 | 1·17 | 1·18 | 1·20 | 1·26 | 1·40 | 1·46 | 1·60 | $\times 10^{-8}$ cm. |
| $a$ (Kinetic Theory) | 1·12 | 1·35 | 1·82 | 1·83 | 1·91 | 1·90 | 2·30 | 2·31 | 2·78 | $\times 10^{-8}$ cm. |

The agreement is remarkably good in view of the crude nature of both values of $a$, but some similarity in orders of magnitude is perhaps not so startling after all because a freely circulating swarm of electrons probably readjust themselves somewhat like the charge on a conductor, and the rigorous quantum theory formula to be developed later proves to involve the atomic diameter dimensionally in the same way as

---

[4] O. F. Mossotti, *Sur les forces qui régissent la constitution intime des corps* (Turin 1836). An account of his theory is given in Jeans's *Electricity and Magnetism*, p. 127.

Mossotti's formula. Passing now to magnetism, Ampère's picture of a magnetic molecule as containing a continuous circulating current (instead of the more modern electron circumnavigating the nucleus) is well known, and Weber in 1854 was able to elaborate this Ampèrian concept to give the beginnings of a molecular theory of magnetic media just as did Mossotti for the electric case. We, however, shall prove Eqs. (12) with the aid of the more modern Lorentz electron theory, even though these relations were suspected and to a certain extent established at earlier dates.

To complete the correlation of the macroscopic and microscopic equations we must state how the macroscopic and microscopic currents and charges are connected. We assume that the velocity of the centre of gravity of a molecule is negligible. The convection current then arises entirely from the migration of conduction electrons, rather than of molecular ions, and the current and charge densities are given by the expressions

$$\mathbf{i} = -N_c e \bar{\bar{\mathbf{v}}}_c, \qquad \rho = N \bar{\bar{e}}_{\text{mol}} - N_c e, \tag{13}$$

where $N_c$ is the number of conduction electrons per c.c., and $\mathbf{v}_c$ is their velocity. Similarly $N$ denotes the number of molecules per c.c., and $\bar{\bar{e}}_{\text{mol}}$ is the mean value of their net charge (9). The term $N \bar{\bar{e}}_{\text{mol}}$ could, of course, be written equally well as $N_{\text{ion}} \bar{\bar{e}}_{\text{ion}}$, if now $N_{\text{ion}}$ denote the number of ions (exclusive of free electrons) per c.c., and $\bar{\bar{e}}_{\text{ion}}$ be their average charge, which is much larger than the average molecular charge as most molecules are neutral. We thus regard the conduction electrons as distinct entities from the molecules. There is actually probably no such sharp cleavage between free and bound electrons, and the conduction electrons may in reality be itinerant valence electrons which migrate from atom to atom, making transient stops at each. The use of such idealizations as perfectly free conduction electrons and stationary molecular ions does no harm as far as our investigations of dielectric and magnetic media are concerned. As a matter of fact it is possible to establish a statistical connexion between the macroscopic and microscopic equations even when the centres of the molecules are in motion. This has, indeed, been done by Lorentz.[5] It is, however, then necessary to complicate the macroscopic equations by the addition of 'convection terms' arising from the mass motion of the ponderable magnetic or dielectric media, and such considerations of the electrodynamics of moving media are unnecessary for our purposes.

[5] H. A. Lorentz, *Encyklopedie der mathematischen Wissenschaften*, Band V2, Heft 1, p. 200 ff.

## 3. Proof of the Preceding Correlation Formulae [6,7]

This proof is probably most easily given by using the macroscopic scalar and vector potentials, $\Phi$ and $\mathbf{A}$ respectively, together with the analogous microscopic potentials $\phi$ and $\mathbf{a}$. From these potentials the electric and magnetic vectors are derivable by means of the formulae

$$\mathbf{E} = -\operatorname{grad}\Phi - \frac{1}{c}\frac{\partial \mathbf{A}}{\partial t}, \qquad \mathbf{B} = \operatorname{curl}\mathbf{A};$$

$$\mathbf{e} = -\operatorname{grad}\phi - \frac{1}{c}\frac{\partial \mathbf{a}}{\partial t}, \qquad \mathbf{h} = \operatorname{curl}\mathbf{a}. \tag{14}$$

The differential equations for determining the potentials are

$$\Box\,\Phi = -4\pi[\rho - \operatorname{div}\mathbf{P}], \qquad \Box\,\mathbf{A} = -\frac{4\pi}{c}\left[\mathbf{i} + \frac{\partial \mathbf{P}}{\partial t} + c\,\operatorname{curl}\mathbf{M}\right];$$

$$\Box\,\phi = -4\pi\rho', \qquad\qquad \Box\,\mathbf{a} = -\frac{4\pi}{c}\rho'\mathbf{v}, \tag{15}$$

together with the auxiliary conditions that

$$\operatorname{div}\mathbf{A} + \frac{1}{c}\frac{\partial \Phi}{\partial t} = 0, \qquad \operatorname{div}\mathbf{a} + \frac{1}{c}\frac{\partial \phi}{\partial t} = 0. \tag{16}$$

The symbol $\Box$ denotes the d'Alembertian operator

$$\frac{\partial^2}{\partial x^2} + \frac{\partial^2}{\partial y^2} + \frac{\partial^2}{\partial z^2} - \frac{1}{c^2}\frac{\partial^2}{\partial t^2}.$$

To prove (15) one substitutes (14) in the field equations (1), (2) or (4), (5). One finds that the first set of equations in (1) or (4) is identically satisfied by the substitution (14), while the second set and (2) or (5) yield (15) by a well-known procedure (viz. taking the curl of the equations and using (16) and the identity $\operatorname{curl}\operatorname{curl}\mathbf{A} = \operatorname{grad}\operatorname{div}\mathbf{A} - \nabla^2\mathbf{A}$).

---

[6] The formulation and proof of the statistical correlation of the macroscopic and microscopic equations is due originally to Lorentz. See, for instance, the preceding reference. Our method of proof is, however, somewhat different from his, although both invoke the aid of the scalar and vector potentials in the fashion (21). We use the Taylor's expansion (24) rather than a somewhat artificial comparison of positive and negative charge elements at the same point. In this particular respect our treatment resembles that in Mason and Weaver, *The Electromagnetic Field*, though obtained independently. For still other proofs of the correlation see Abraham, *Theorie der Elektrizität*, 4th ed., vol. ii, pp. 224–38; Swann, *Electrodynamics of Moving Media*, pp. 44–54; Frenkel, *Lehrbuch der Elektrodynamik*, ii, p. 10.

[7] Throughout the present section in considering the macroscopic equations we do not include surface phenomena such as surfaces of discontinuity between two media, conducting surfaces, surface charges, &c. The surface terms could, of course, be added, but would only make the equations more cumbersome, and their omission involves no loss of generality, as surface discontinuities can always be regarded as limiting cases of continuous volume changes.

The solutions of (15) are

$$\Phi = \int\int\int \frac{\{\rho - \operatorname{div}\mathbf{P}\}}{R}\,dv, \qquad \mathbf{A} = \int\int\int \frac{\{\mathbf{i} + \partial\mathbf{P}/\partial t + c\operatorname{curl}\mathbf{M}\}}{cR}\,dv,$$

$$\phi = \int\int\int \frac{\{\rho'\}}{R}\,dv, \qquad \mathbf{a} = \int\int\int \frac{\{\rho'\mathbf{v}\}}{cR}\,dv, \tag{17}$$

where the brackets { } enclose functions that are to be evaluated at the retarded time $t - R/c$, and where $R$ denotes the distance from the element of integration $dv$ to the point at which the potentials are being calculated.

*Proof of the Solutions* (17). The scalar equations and scalar components of the vector equations in (15) are all of the type form $\Box\psi = -4\pi q(x, y, z, t)$. Now an equation of this type form is identically satisfied by $\psi = \iiint\{q\}/R\,dv$. Without giving a rigorous proof of this solution, we may note with Jeans[8] that it becomes quite evident when we observe that $\psi = Q(t - R/c)/R$ is a solution of $\Box\psi = 0$, and corresponds to a point charge $q(t)$ at the origin, as $\psi$ becomes infinite there like $Q(t)/R$, the retardation effects disappearing on account of $R = 0$. Similarly the solution corresponding to a series of charges $Q_i$ at various points distant $R_i$ from the point of observation is $\Sigma\, Q_i(t - R_i/c)/R_i$, and passage from discrete point singularities to a continuous charge distribution yields the desired integral formula.

It remains to show that the solutions (17) fulfil the auxiliary conditions (16). We shall consider only the microscopic case, as the macroscopic is analogous. We must prove that

$$\int\int\int \operatorname{div}_P\left[\frac{\{\rho'\mathbf{v}\}}{R}\right]dv + \int\int\int \frac{\{\partial\rho'/\partial t\}}{R}\,dv = 0, \tag{18}$$

where the subscript $P$ means that the differentiations involved in taking the divergence are with respect to the coordinates of the terminal point of the vector $R$ drawn from $Q$ at $dv$ to $P$, the point of observation. Similarly, the subscript $Q$ will denote differentiation at the initial point. Now at $P$ the expression $\{\rho'\mathbf{v}/R\}$ involves the coordinates of the terminal point $P$ only through the denominator $R$ and implicitly through $R$ in the retarded time $t - R/c$. On the other hand, this expression involves the coordinates $x$, $y$, $z$ of the initial point $Q$ through $\rho\mathbf{v}'$ as well as through $R$ in the two fashions just described. Hence

$$\operatorname{div}_P\left[\frac{\{\rho'\mathbf{v}\}}{R}\right] = -\operatorname{div}_Q\left[\frac{\{\rho'\mathbf{v}\}}{R}\right] + \frac{1}{R}\{\operatorname{div}_Q\rho'\mathbf{v}\}, \tag{19}$$

where the brackets outside the div mean that the retarded value of the time is to be substituted after, rather than before, the differentiation. Now the equation of continuity or indestructibility of charge is

$$\{\operatorname{div}_Q\rho'\mathbf{v}\} + \left\{\frac{\partial\rho'}{\partial t}\right\} = 0. \tag{20}$$

When we substitute (19) in (18) and use (20) all terms cancel except that coming from the first right-hand member of (19), and this integrates to zero, since by Green's theorem the volume integral over all space vanishes if the integrand is the divergence of a vector which vanishes properly at infinity.

[8] J. H. Jeans, *Electricity and Magnetism*, 4th ed., pp. 571–2.

The desired statistical correlation of the microscopic and macroscopic theories is obtained by assuming that the macroscopic potentials equal the microscopic ones averaged over a 'physically small' (cf. p. 3) element of volume. This means that

$$\Phi = \bar{\bar{\phi}}, \qquad \mathbf{A} = \bar{\bar{\mathbf{a}}}. \tag{21}$$

Formulae (6) are direct consequences of (21) and (14), as it is easily established that the order of averaging and of space or time differentiation is interchangeable.

The interchangeability of the averaging and time differentiation is obvious since the space and time coordinates are independent. To prove[9] the interchangeability with space differentiation take the 'physically small' region over which the average is evaluated as a sphere of volume $\theta$ with centre at $x_0, y_0, z_0$. Let $x', y', z'$ be coordinates with origin at this centre and let $f(x,y,z,t)$ be any function (including the components of a vector) which we are interested in averaging. Now the macroscopic differentiations, i.e. differentiations after averaging, involve small virtual displacements of the centre of the sphere without changing the range of values of the coordinates $x', y', z'$ relative to the centre. Hence

$$\frac{\partial \bar{\bar{f}}}{\partial x} = \frac{\partial}{\partial x_0} \frac{1}{\theta} \iiint f \, dx' dy' dz' = \frac{1}{\theta} \iiint \frac{\partial f}{\partial x_0} dx' dy' dz' \text{ while } \overline{\overline{\frac{\partial f}{\partial x}}} = \frac{1}{\theta} \iiint \frac{\partial f}{\partial x'} dx' dy' dz'.$$

The identity of the two expressions is now an immediate consequence of the fact that the function $f$ is of the form $f(x_0+x', y_0+y', z_0+z', t)$.

It remains to show that (12) and (13) also follow from (21). The first step in doing this is to transform the formulae for the macroscopic potentials by means of the two following vector identities:[10, 11]

$$\iiint \left( \mathbf{P} \cdot \mathrm{grad}\, \frac{1}{R} + \frac{1}{R} \mathrm{div}\, \mathbf{P} \right) dv = \iiint \mathrm{div}\left( \frac{\mathbf{P}}{R} \right) dv = \iint \frac{\mathbf{n} \cdot \mathbf{P}}{R} \, dS,$$

$$\iiint \left( \frac{1}{R} \mathrm{curl}\, \mathbf{M} - \mathbf{M} \times \mathrm{grad}\, \frac{1}{R} \right) dv = \iiint \mathrm{curl}\, \frac{\mathbf{M}}{R} \, dv = \iint \frac{\mathbf{n} \times \mathbf{M}}{R} \, dS, \tag{22}$$

in which $\mathbf{n}$ denotes a unit vector along the exterior normal to the surface element $dS$. The surface integrals disappear, as we may suppose the magnetic and dielectric matter bounded in extent, so that $\mathbf{P} = \mathbf{M} = 0$ on the surface of a sufficiently great sphere. Thus the first part of (17) becomes

$$\Phi = \iiint \left\{ \frac{\rho}{R} + \mathbf{P} \cdot \mathrm{grad}\, \frac{1}{R} \right\} dv,$$

$$\mathbf{A} = \iiint \left\{ \frac{\mathbf{i} + \partial \mathbf{P}/\partial t}{cR} + \mathbf{M} \times \mathrm{grad}\, \frac{1}{R} \right\} dv. \tag{23}$$

[9] This proof is taken from Frenkel, *Lehrbuch der Elektrodynamik*, ii, p. 4.

[10] For proof of the second identity of (22), which is not a particularly common one, see Abraham, *Theorie der Elektrizität*, 4th ed., vol. i, p. 76.

[11] All the differentiations in Eq. (22) *et seq.* are to be taken at the element of integration $dv$, but for brevity we no longer write in the subscript $Q$ used in (19), (20).

We must now throw the microscopic formulae for $\phi$ and $\mathbf{a}$ into a form somewhat analogous to (23). Let us consider the portion of the microscopic potentials which results from integration over a single molecule, indicated by the subscript $_{1M}$. The radius vector $\mathbf{R}$ from $Q$, the position of an element (of integration) of the molecule to the point of observation $P$, is the vector-difference of the radius vector $\mathbf{R_0}$ from the centre of gravity of the molecule to $P$ and the radius vector $\mathbf{r} = \mathbf{i}x + \mathbf{j}y + \mathbf{k}z$ from this centre to the given element. As $r/R$ is small, we may develop $1/R$ in a Taylor's series:

$$\frac{1}{R} = \frac{1}{R_0} + \left( x \frac{\partial}{\partial x} \frac{1}{R} + y \frac{\partial}{\partial y} \frac{1}{R} + z \frac{\partial}{\partial z} \frac{1}{R} \right)_{R=R_0} + \dots = \frac{1}{R_0} + \mathbf{r} \cdot \mathrm{grad} \frac{1}{R_0} + \dots$$

Thus by (17)

$$\phi_{1M} = \iiint \left\{ \frac{\rho'}{R_0} + \rho' \mathbf{r} \cdot \mathrm{grad} \frac{1}{R_0} \right\} dv, \tag{24}$$

$$\mathbf{a}_{1M} = \frac{1}{c} \iiint \left\{ \rho' \mathbf{v} \left( \frac{1}{R_0} + \mathbf{r} \cdot \mathrm{grad} \frac{1}{R_0} \right) \right\} dv. \tag{25}$$

Using the definitions (9) and (10), and the fact that $R_0$ is constant with respect to the integration, we now see that

$$\phi_{1M} = \left\{ \frac{e_{\mathrm{mol}}}{R_0} \right\} + \left\{ \mathbf{p} \cdot \mathrm{grad} \frac{1}{R_0} \right\}. \tag{26}$$

A convenient formula for $\mathbf{a}$ analogous to (26) is obtained only after a certain amount of juggling involved in using the relations

$$\frac{\partial \mathbf{p}}{\partial t} = \iiint \frac{\partial \rho'}{\partial t} \mathbf{r}\, dv = - \iiint (\mathrm{div}\, \rho' \mathbf{v}) \mathbf{r}\, dv = \iiint \rho' \mathbf{v}\, dv, \tag{27a}$$

$$\frac{\partial \mathbf{k}}{\partial t} = - \iiint (\mathrm{div}\, \rho' \mathbf{v}) \mathbf{r} \left( \mathbf{r} \cdot \mathrm{grad} \frac{1}{R_0} \right) dv$$

$$= \iiint \rho' \left[ \mathbf{v} \left( \mathbf{r} \cdot \mathrm{grad} \frac{1}{R_0} \right) + \mathbf{r} \left( \mathbf{v} \cdot \mathrm{grad} \frac{1}{R_0} \right) \right] dv, \tag{27b}$$

$$2c \left[ \mathbf{m} \times \mathrm{grad} \frac{1}{R_0} \right] = \iiint \rho' \left[ \mathbf{v} \left( \mathbf{r} \cdot \mathrm{grad} \frac{1}{R_0} \right) - \mathbf{r} \left( \mathbf{v} \cdot \mathrm{grad} \frac{1}{R_0} \right) \right] dv, \tag{27c}$$

where

$$\mathbf{k} = \iiint \rho' \mathbf{r} \left( \mathbf{r} \cdot \mathrm{grad} \frac{1}{R_0} \right) dv, \tag{28}$$

and where $\mathbf{p}$ and $\mathbf{m}$ are defined as in (10). The velocity $\mathbf{v}$ in (10), to be sure, was defined as relative to the centre of gravity of the molecule rather than relative to a fixed system of reference as in (17), but this distinction is of no consequence, as we have supposed the velocities of the centres of gravity of the molecules to be negligible. The intermediate forms of (27 a, b) follow from the equation of continuity (20), and the final forms by partial integration.[12]   Eq. (27 c) is obtained from the second expression of (10) by using the vector identity

$$\mathbf{A}\times[\mathbf{B}\times\mathbf{C}] = \mathbf{B}(\mathbf{A}\cdot\mathbf{C})-\mathbf{C}(\mathbf{A}\cdot\mathbf{B}).$$

After use of (27 a, b, c), the second equation of (25) may be written

$$\mathbf{a}_{1M} = \left\{\frac{1}{cR_0}\frac{\partial\mathbf{p}}{\partial t}\right\} + \left\{\mathbf{m}\times\mathrm{grad}\,\frac{1}{R_0}\right\} + \frac{1}{2c}\left\{\frac{\partial\mathbf{k}}{\partial t}\right\}. \tag{29}$$

We have so far considered only the contribution of one molecule. Actually we desire the total contribution of all molecules in a 'physically small' volume element $dv$. This total contribution is the average contribution of one molecule multiplied by the number $Ndv$ of molecules in $dv$. The term 'average' as here used means the space average over the different molecules in $dv$, but if the various molecules differ only in phase, it is the time average for a single molecule over a very long time interval. If there are several classes of molecules it may be considered the weighted mean of the time averages for the different molecules. When such an average is made, the last term in (29) becomes negligible, for $\overline{\partial\mathbf{k}/\partial t} = [\mathbf{k}]_{t_1}^{t_2}/(t_2-t_1)$, and this is exceedingly small if $t_2-t_1$ is made very large and if $\mathbf{k}$ remains bounded in magnitude, as it will in virtue of the definition (28) (certainly at least in periodic or multiply periodic phenomena). Similar considerations would also permit the omission of the first term of (29), but this is unnecessary for the establishment of the correlation, and if the assumption of haphazard phases is not fulfilled the omission of the first term of (29) would be a more serious offence than that of the third, as it is of lower order in $1/R$. Having found the contribution from $dv$, we must next sum over all the 'physically small' volume elements $dv$. Without appreciable error this summation may be replaced by a macroscopic integration, to be carefully distinguished from the previous microscopic integration

---

[12] The formulae obtained by partial integration seem to be most easily verified by writing out the components of the integrand in scalar notation rather than by manipulating the integrand by the appropriate vector identities, which would be rather complicated. The simplicity in the scalar method results from the fact that the components of $\mathbf{r}$ are merely $x, y, z$. The integrand of the $x$ component of (27 a) before the partial integration for instance, is $-x\left(\dfrac{\partial\rho'v_x}{\partial x} + \dfrac{\partial\rho'v_y}{\partial y} + \dfrac{\partial\rho'v_z}{\partial z}\right)$, and the final form is obtained by integrating the first, second, and third terms of this integrand partially with respect to $x, y, z$ respectively. The surface integrals in the partial integration of course disappear for the same reason as in (22). The necessity for the partial integrations in (27 a, b) and also in (18) can be avoided if one uses point singularities rather than continuous distributions, i.e. (11) rather than (9), (10). If this is done, it is convenient in performing the time differentiation to travel with a particle rather than remain at a fixed element $dv$, so that the charge is to be regarded as independent of $t$, whereas $R$ is to be considered as varying with $t$ in the fashion $\mathbf{v} = d\mathbf{R}/dt$.

over one molecule. In this new integration, expressions such as $R_0$, $\mathbf{p}$, $\mathbf{m}$ may be considered to vary continuously with the macroscopic co-ordinates fixing $dv$, even though these expressions were previously defined in a discrete fashion.[13] As all parts of molecules in $dv$ are, from a macroscopic standpoint, located at virtually the same distance from the point of observation $P$, the subscript may be omitted from $R_0$. At the same time that we perform this macroscopic integration we must add in the contribution of the conduction electrons, for which the Taylor's expansion is unnecessary, as their dimensions, and hence their moments,[14] may be considered negligible. In this way we find that

$$\bar{\bar{\phi}} = \int\int\int \frac{\{N\bar{\bar{e}}_{\text{mol}} - N_c\bar{\bar{e}}\}}{R}\, dv + \int\int\int \left\{N\bar{\bar{\mathbf{p}}}\cdot\text{grad}\,\frac{1}{R}\right\} dv,$$

$$\bar{\bar{\mathbf{a}}} = \int\int\int \frac{\{-N_c e\bar{\bar{\mathbf{v}}}_c + N\partial\bar{\bar{\mathbf{p}}}/\partial t\}}{cR}\, dv + \int\int\int \left\{N\bar{\bar{\mathbf{m}}}\times\text{grad}\,\frac{1}{R}\right\} dv. \quad (30)$$

The desired results (12) and (13) now follow on using (21) and comparing the structure of (23) and (30).

The reader has perhaps noticed that all the foregoing correlation of the microscopic and macroscopic electromagnetic theories is only approximate, due to neglect of terms beyond $1/R^2$ in the Taylor's expansion. Such terms are usually unimportant[15] because molecular radii are small compared to distances of observation. Otherwise the ordinary macroscopic equations would presumably not be found to be valid experimentally. The omitted terms are sometimes characterized as representing 'multipoles'. The omitted term in $\phi$ of lowest order, for instance, is readily shown to be $Nq/R^3$, where $q$ is the 'quadrupole moment'

$$\int\int\int \rho' r^2(\tfrac{3}{2}\cos^2\theta - \tfrac{1}{2})\, dv,$$

[13] One is perhaps a bit solicitous about the error incurred in treating $R$, $\mathbf{p}$, $\mathbf{m}$, &c. as continuous functions in view of the fact that molecules are discretely and irregularly distributed, especially in a gas. Statistical theory shows that the root mean square deviation of the number of molecules in $dv$ from its mean value $Ndv$ is $(Ndv)^{\frac{1}{2}}$. The relative error involved in ironing out the fluctuations and substituting a continuum is thus at most of the order $(1/Ndv)^{\frac{1}{2}}$, and requires that $dv$ be not too small or the medium too rarefied. For this reason $dv$ cannot well be reduced beyond a certain value $dv_0$, but then there is a relative error of the order $(dv_0)^{\frac{1}{2}}/R$ in substituting an integral for the sum. As $N$ is of the order $10^{19}$ in gases, and as $R$ is 1 cm. or greater in most macroscopic problems of interest, both $(1/Ndv)^{\frac{1}{2}}$ and $(dv)^{\frac{1}{2}}/R$ may be made small by taking $dv$ about $10^{-12}$. For further discussion of the legitimacy of the substitution of macroscopic integrations for summations see Mason and Weaver, *The Electromagnetic Field*, Chap. I, Part III.

[14] We do not introduce the spinning electron, with its finite magnetic moment, until the quantum chapters.

[15] Retention of these higher order terms is, however, vital in molecular theories of the equation of state.

$\theta$ being the angle between $\mathbf{r}$ and $\mathbf{R}$. The terms of highest order in $1/R$ which have been retained are of order $1/R^2$, and are the 'dipole' ones, as the potential due to a discrete dipole of vector moment $\mathbf{P}$ is

$$\mathbf{P} \cdot \operatorname{grad} \frac{1}{R}. \tag{31}$$

Instead of tracing through the details of the connexion with the microscopic theory, it is seen by direct comparison of (23) and (31) that the term in $\Phi$ which is the correction for dielectric action can be interpreted as due to a continuous space distribution of dipoles of specific moment $\mathbf{P}$ per unit volume. This explains why the existence of molecular dipoles in dielectrics could be inferred in the nineteenth century before the advent of the Lorentz electron theory. Similar remarks apply to the magnetic case, as the vector potential of a discrete magnetic dipole of moment $\mathbf{M}$ is $\mathbf{M} \times \operatorname{grad}(1/R)$.

## 4. Relation between Index of Refraction and Dielectric Constant

It is a matter of common knowledge that the index of refraction $n$ is connected with the dielectric constant $\epsilon$ and magnetic permeability $\mu$ according to the relation

$$n^2 = \epsilon\mu, \tag{32}$$

provided we use the term dielectric constant, as we already tacitly have throughout the chapter, in a generalized sense to mean the ratio of $\mathbf{D}$ to $\mathbf{E}$ in periodic fields rather than in the restricted sense to denote just this ratio in static phenomena. Now gases of a high refractivity usually show very little magnetic polarization, so that without much error we may take $\mu = 1$. In other words, in gases the magnetic susceptibility is usually small compared to the electric, and then (32) becomes

$$n^2 = \epsilon. \tag{33}$$

Discussion of the experimental confirmation of (33) will be deferred until Chapter III. The theoretical validity of (32) can be seen as follows. Let us suppose that the radiation is monochromatic, and that the medium is homogeneous and infinite in extent. This is somewhat of an idealization, as a dielectric or magnetic medium never extends to infinity, but in a sufficiently large homogeneous medium the velocity of propagation of disturbances is virtually the same as though the medium extended indefinitely. In such an ideal medium $\epsilon$ and $\mu$ may be regarded as constants independent of $x$, $y$, $z$, $t$, so that

$$\partial \mathbf{D}/\partial t = \epsilon \partial \mathbf{E}/\partial t, \qquad \operatorname{curl} \mathbf{B} = \mu \operatorname{curl} \mathbf{H}, \qquad \&c.$$

If we make the substitutions $\mathbf{E}' = \epsilon^{\frac{1}{2}} \mathbf{E}$, $\mathbf{H}' = \mu^{\frac{1}{2}} \mathbf{H}$, $\rho' = \rho/\epsilon^{\frac{1}{2}}$, $\mathbf{i}' = \mathbf{i}/\epsilon^{\frac{1}{2}}$, which may be regarded as changing the scale of measurement of unit magnetic and electric poles, the field equations (1, 2) reduce to

$$\operatorname{curl} \mathbf{E}' = -\frac{1}{c'}\frac{\partial \mathbf{H}'}{\partial t}, \quad \operatorname{curl} \mathbf{H}' = \frac{1}{c'}\left(4\pi\mathbf{i}' + \frac{\partial \mathbf{E}'}{\partial t}\right), \operatorname{div} \mathbf{E}' = 4\pi\rho', \operatorname{div} \mathbf{H}' = 0,$$

provided $c' = c/(\epsilon\mu)^{\frac{1}{2}}$. These are equations of the same type form as for a vacuum except for the change of scale just noted, and for the fact that the effective velocity of propagation is $c/(\epsilon\mu)^{\frac{1}{2}}$. Now the index of refraction $n$ is defined as the quotient of the velocity of propagation $c$ *in vacuo* to that $c'$ in the material medium—hence Eq. (32).

## 5. The Local Field

It is desirable to know the effective average field to which a molecule is subjected when a macroscopic field **E** is applied. This effective field is not the same, even in the mean, as the macroscopic **E** despite the fact that by (6) the vector **E** is the space average of the microscopic field **e** over a 'physically small' volume element. The explanation of this paradox is that the effective field in which we are interested is that in the interior of a molecule, whereas the space averaging presupposed in the relation $\mathbf{E} = \bar{\bar{\mathbf{e}}}$ is over regions both exterior and interior to molecules. The effective field within a molecule may be resolved into two parts: first, the internal field exerted by other charges within the same molecule, and second, the remainder due not only to the applied electric field but also to the attractions and repulsions by other molecules, usually polarized under the influence of the external field. The first part is not our present concern, and could, of course, be calculated from the Coulomb law immediately we knew the configurations of the charges in the molecule. The second part we shall term the local field. Under certain simplifying assumptions the local field can be shown to be

$$\mathbf{e}_{\text{loc}} = \mathbf{E} + \frac{4\pi\mathbf{P}}{3}. \tag{34}$$

The expression (34) is sometimes called the Clausius-Mossotti formula for the local field. We shall not prove (34), as this is tedious and is frequently done in the literature.[16] The usual derivations assume that the molecule in question can be considered to be located at the centre of a spherical cavity in the dielectric, and that further the diameter of the cavity is large compared to the size of a molecule. The reader will recall that the field within a cavity is a function of the shape of the cavity. It has the value (34) at the centre of a spherical cavity, whereas it equals **E** within a needle-shaped cavity whose axis is parallel to **E**, and $\mathbf{D} = \mathbf{E} + 4\pi\mathbf{P}$ within a slab-shaped cavity whose surfaces are perpendicular to **E**. The term $4\pi\mathbf{P}/3$ in (34) is sometimes spoken of as the 'inter-molecular field', and is a correction for the fact that the other molecules of the dielectric exert an average force on the given molecule when the dielectric is subject to an electric field. This is due, of course,

[16] Cf., for instance, H. A. Lorentz, *The Theory of Electrons*, section 117 and note 54.

to their acquisition of an electric polarity, so that the resultant field which they exert at the centre of a spherical cavity no longer vanishes on the average as it would by symmetry (at least in isotropic media) without an external field to create a preferred direction. We here, as elsewhere in the book, assume that there is no residual polarization when the applied field vanishes. Otherwise it would be necessary to add a constant term to the right side of (34). Residual or permanent polarization of a dielectric, which would be the electric analogue of 'hard magnetism', is not an unknown phenomenon, but is usually feeble and found only in complicated solids, a discussion of which is beyond the scope of the present volume.

An important and simple experimental confirmation of (34) is furnished by the variation of the index of refraction with density in gases. At ordinary field strengths the average electrical moment may be taken proportional to the local field:

$$\bar{\bar{\mathbf{p}}} = \alpha \mathbf{e}_{\mathrm{loc}} = \alpha\left(\mathbf{E} + \frac{4\pi\mathbf{P}}{3}\right), \tag{35}$$

where $\alpha$ is a constant independent of the density. On elimination of $\mathbf{p}$, $\mathbf{P}$ by means of (8), (12) and use of (33) the relation (35) becomes

$$\frac{1}{4\pi N}(n^2 - 1)\mathbf{E} = \alpha(1 + \tfrac{1}{3}n^2 - \tfrac{1}{3})\mathbf{E}.$$

The number $N$ of molecules per c.c. is proportional to the density $\rho$. Hence

$$\frac{1}{\rho}\frac{n^2 - 1}{n^2 + 2} = \frac{4\pi N\alpha}{3\rho}, \text{ a constant independent of density.} \tag{36}$$

This is the so-called Lorenz-Lorentz formula, as it was proposed independently by L. Lorenz and H. A. Lorentz, both in 1880.[17] The most thorough experimental test of (36) has perhaps been made by Magri,[18] who varied the density by using pressures of from 1 to 200 atmospheres. According to Magri's data, the left side of (36) has the following values at different densities:

| Density | 1 | 14·84 | 42·13 | 69·24 | 96·16 | 123·04 | 149·53 | 176·27 |
|---|---|---|---|---|---|---|---|---|
| $\dfrac{1}{\rho}\dfrac{n^2-1}{n^2+2}\times 10^7$ | 1953 | 1947 | 1959 | 1961 | 1961 | 1956 | 1956 | 1953 |
| $\dfrac{1}{\rho}\dfrac{n^2-1}{3}\times 10^7$ | (1953) | (1953) | (1976) | (1988) | (1998) | (2005) | (2015) | (2023) |

[17] H. A. Lorentz, *Ann. Phys. Chem.* **9**, 641 (1880); L. Lorenz, *ibid.* **11**, 70 (1880).

[18] L. Magri, *Phys. Zeits.* **6**, 629 (1905). The various measurements given in the above table were all made at 14°–15° C. except that the reading at unit density is at 0° C. Thus practically all the change in density is from varying the pressure rather than temperature.

The unit of density is the density of air under standard conditions. The values in parentheses are those which would be obtained by taking the local field to be identical with the macroscopic field $\mathbf{E}$, thereby making the denominator 3 instead of $n^2+2$. It is seen that the rigorous or first formula yields values which are much more nearly constant than with the second formula, thus confirming the correction term $4\pi\mathbf{P}/3$ for the inter-molecular field in (35). Formula (36) as applied to dielectric constants (i.e. with $n^2$ replaced by $\epsilon$) has also been verified for several gases up to 100 atmospheres by Tangl and others.[19]

A much more severe, in fact unreasonably hard, test of (36) is obtained by examination of whether its left side has the same value in the liquid and vapour states. The agreement in the two states is surprisingly good in view of the fact that (36) cannot be expected to hold accurately in liquids because of association effects and the like. In water, for instance, it is found that at optical wave-lengths the left side of (36) changes by only about 10 per cent. in passing from the liquid to the vapour state, whereas the density changes by a factor over 1,000. In the static case of infinite wave-lengths, however, all traces of agreement between the two states are lost in polar materials like water. For non-polar substances the change in (36) between the two states is practically negligible (see p. 59 for numerical data).

Our primary concern is gaseous media, and at any ordinary pressures (up to 10 atmospheres or more) the term $n^2+2$ in the denominator of (36) can be equated to 3 in gases, thereby making the left side of (36) become $4\pi\chi_e/3\rho$ (cf. Eq. (8)). Consequently we shall, for simplicity, henceforth make this approximation throughout the volume, unless otherwise stated. If, however, one should wish at any time to make the above 'Clausius-Mossotti' correction resulting from the difference between the macroscopic and local fields, one has only to substitute $3(\epsilon-1)/4\pi(\epsilon+2)$ for the susceptibility $\chi_e$ in the formulae for susceptibilities given throughout the book. This remark applies to all formulae except those which relate to saturation effects and which thus do not take the polarization as proportional to field strength. In the study of liquids the correction for the difference between the local and macroscopic fields is important. In some instances a formula such as (36) seems to be applicable to liquids, but our feelings must not be hurt when we discover that (36) fails completely, at least in the static case, in the

[19] Tangl, *Ann. der Physik*, **10**, 748 (1903); **23**, 559 (1907); **26**, 59 (1908); also Occhialini, *Phys. Zeits.* **6**, 669 (1905); Waibel, *Ann. der Physik*, **72**, 160 (1923); Occhialini and Bodareu, *Ann. der Physik*, **42**, 67 (1913); K. Wolf, *Phys. Zeits.* **27**, 588 and 830 (1926).

so-called polar liquids where agglomeration or association effects are important. The formula (34), on which Eq. (36) is based, is derived on the assumption that the arrangement of molecules is haphazard and that the inter-molecular distances are large compared to molecular diameters. These assumptions are clearly not legitimate in such polar liquids.

We have so far considered only the local electric fields. Under the same assumptions as are made in the usual derivation of (34), the local magnetic field can be shown to be $\mathbf{h}_{\text{local}} = \mathbf{H} + (4\pi\mathbf{M}/3)$. The expression $(\mu-1)/\rho(\mu+2)$ should then be independent of the density. However, in gases the permeability is so nearly unity, and magnetic measurements are so difficult that there is no experimental material adequate to test whether $\mu+2$ should occur in place of 3 in the denominator. On the other hand, in solid magnetic bodies local fields are apparently encountered which are tremendously larger than $\mathbf{H} + (4\pi\mathbf{M}/3)$; otherwise we would never have ferromagnetism, and the cause for this will be discussed in Chapter XII. Thus in the magnetic case a correction of the type considered above in the electric case is either negligible or inapplicable. Consequently we shall not go to the refinement of making this correction and writing $3(\mu-1)/4\pi(\mu+2)$ in place of $\chi_m$ in the formulae for the paramagnetic and diamagnetic susceptibilities given later in the book.

## 6. The Force Equation

To formulate a dynamics governing the motion of the charges within the molecule it is first necessary to have an expression for the forces exerted upon them. This is furnished by the fundamental 'force equation'

$$\mathbf{F}_i = e_i\mathbf{e} + \frac{e_i}{c}[\mathbf{v}_i \times \mathbf{h}], \tag{37}$$

postulated by the electron theory as the vector force $\mathbf{F}_i$ exerted on a charge (electron or nucleus) moving with the velocity $\mathbf{v}_i$ and subject to electric and magnetic fields $\mathbf{e}$ and $\mathbf{h}$ respectively. We here and for the balance of the chapter regard the dimensions of the electrons and nuclei as negligible, so that they can be treated as point charges. The total fields $\mathbf{e}$ and $\mathbf{h}$ may be resolved into two parts, viz. the internal or 'intra-molecular' portions exerted by other charges in the same molecule, and the remaining or external parts exerted by the rest of the universe.

If we neglect retarded time effects, the internal fields at the point occupied by the charge $e_i$ can be derived in the usual fashion (14) from the scalar and vector potentials

$$\phi_i^{\text{int}} = \sum_{j \neq i} \frac{e_j}{r_{ij}}, \qquad \mathbf{a}_i^{\text{int}} = \sum_{j \neq i} \frac{e_j \mathbf{v}_j}{c r_{ij}}$$

(cf. Eq. (17)), where $r_{ij}$ denotes the distance between the charges $e_i$ and $e_j$. It is seen from Eqs. (14) and (37) that the terms in the force which arise from the internal vector potential are of order $1/c^2$ in the velocity of light $c$, even though the vector potential itself is of order $1/c$. Terms of this order are usually very small, and, in fact, are comparable with the relativity corrections and retardation effects in the scalar potential $\phi$, so that for our purposes we are fully warranted in dropping them, and it would be deceptive to include them without including the other effects of the same order. With their neglect the internal forces become entirely electrical in nature and can be expressed in the simple fashion

$$\mathbf{F}_i = -\text{grad}_i V \tag{38}$$

in terms of the electrostatic potential energy function

$$V = \sum_{i < j} \frac{e_i e_j}{r_{ij}} = \tfrac{1}{2} \sum_j e_j \phi_j^{\text{int}} \tag{39}$$

as $e_i \, \text{grad} \, \phi_i^{\text{int}} = \text{grad}_i V$. Here the subscript in $\text{grad}_i$ indicates that the differentiation in the gradient operator is with respect to the coordinates $x_i$, $y_i$, $z_i$ of the charge $e_i$. Use of $V$ instead of the $\phi_i^{\text{int}}$ has the great advantage that it is necessary to use only one potential function for the whole molecule rather than one for each charge.

The external part of the field will fluctuate with the approach and recession of other molecules, especially at the time of the so-called collisions of kinetic theory. However, we have mentioned in the preceding section that in gases the average values of the external fields are equal to the expressions for the local fields given in (34) (and an analogous magnetic expression). As gases usually have small polarizations, we agreed to neglect the differences between the local fields and the macroscopic fields. The combined internal and external force can therefore be considered to be

$$\mathbf{F}_i = -\text{grad}_i V - e_i \, \text{grad} \, \Phi_i - \frac{e_i}{c} \frac{\partial \mathbf{A}_i}{\partial t} + \frac{e_i}{c} [\mathbf{v}_i \times \text{curl} \, \mathbf{A}_i],$$

where $\Phi_i$, $\mathbf{A}_i$ are the macroscopic scalar and vector potentials evaluated at the point $x_i$, $y_i$, $z_i$, at which the charge $e_i$ is located. If we equate force to mass times acceleration, the explicit formula in scalar notation for the $x$ component of motion is, for instance,

$$m_i \ddot{x}_i = -\frac{\partial V}{\partial x_i} - e_i \frac{\partial \Phi_i}{\partial x_i} - \frac{e_i}{c} \frac{\partial A_{xi}}{\partial t} + \frac{e_i}{c} \left[ \dot{y}_i \left( \frac{\partial A_{yi}}{\partial x_i} - \frac{\partial A_{xi}}{\partial y_i} \right) - \dot{z}_i \left( \frac{\partial A_{xi}}{\partial z_i} - \frac{\partial A_{zi}}{\partial x_i} \right) \right].$$

(40)

## 7. The Lagrangian and Hamiltonian Functions

The differential equations of motion (40), together with the analogous $y$ and $z$ equations, are equivalent to the Lagrangian system of equations

$$\frac{d}{dt} \frac{\partial L}{\partial \dot{q}_k} - \frac{\partial L}{\partial q_k} = 0$$

(41)

provided we take the Lagrangian function to be

$$L = \tfrac{1}{2} \sum_i m_i \mathbf{v}_i^2 - V - \sum_i e_i \Phi_i + \sum_i \frac{e_i}{c} (\mathbf{v}_i \cdot \mathbf{A}_i).$$

(41 a)

The number of coordinates $q_k$ is, of course, three times the number $\eta$ of particles constituting the atom or molecule. The identity of (40) and (41) can be established immediately by specializing the $q_k$ to be Cartesian coordinates $x_1, ..., x_\eta, y_1, ..., y_\eta, z_1, ..., z_\eta$; then

$$\frac{\partial}{\partial x_i} (\mathbf{v}_i \mathbf{A}_i) = \dot{x}_i \frac{\partial A_{xi}}{\partial x_i} + \dot{y}_i \frac{\partial A_{yi}}{\partial x_i} + \dot{z}_i \frac{\partial A_{zi}}{\partial x_i}$$

$$\frac{d}{dt} \frac{\partial}{\partial \dot{x}_i} (\mathbf{v}_i \mathbf{A}_i) = \frac{dA_{xi}}{dt} = \frac{\partial A_{xi}}{\partial t} + \dot{x}_i \frac{\partial A_{xi}}{\partial x_i} + \dot{y}_i \frac{\partial A_{xi}}{\partial y_i} + \dot{z}_i \frac{\partial A_{xi}}{\partial z_i}$$

(42)

With these relations Eqs. (41) follow directly from (40). The last part of (42) expresses the fact that in the total differentiation with respect to $t$, the vector potential $\mathbf{A}$ must be supposed to involve the time not only explicitly through $t$ but also through the position $x, y, z$. As the Lagrangian form of the equations of motion is preserved under any point transformation, Eqs. (41) will also be valid in any system of generalized coordinates since they are valid for Cartesian coordinates.

If we introduce the generalized momenta

$$p_k = \frac{\partial L}{\partial \dot{q}_k},$$

(43)

and if we express the function

$$\mathscr{H} = \sum_k p_k \dot{q}_k - L$$

in terms of the $q_k$ and $p_k$ rather than the $q_k$ and $\dot{q}_k$, then $\mathscr{H}$ is called the Hamiltonian function. To avoid confusion with the magnetic field $H$, we throughout print the Hamiltonian function in script type. It is immediately seen that in Cartesian coordinates

$$\mathcal{H} = \sum_{i=1}^{n} \frac{1}{2m_i}\left[\left(p_{x_i} - \frac{e_i}{c}A_{x_i}\right)^2 + \left(p_{y_i} - \frac{e_i}{c}A_{y_i}\right)^2 + \right.$$
$$\left. + \left(p_{z_i} - \frac{e_i}{c}A_{z_i}\right)^2\right] + V + \sum e_i\Phi_i \quad (44)$$

as in the Cartesian system by (41 a), (43)

$$p_{x_i} = m_i\dot{x}_i + \frac{e_i}{c}\boldsymbol{A}_{x_i}. \quad (45)$$

General dynamical theory [20] tells us that the $3\eta$ second-order equations (41) are equivalent to the $6\eta$ first-order Hamiltonian equations

$$\frac{dq_k}{dt} = \frac{\partial \mathcal{H}}{\partial p_k}, \qquad \frac{dp_k}{dt} = -\frac{\partial \mathcal{H}}{\partial q_k}. \quad (46)$$

Without appealing to the general theorems of dynamics, the identity of (46) with (40) or (41) can immediately be established by writing out the equations (46) explicitly in Cartesian coordinates, where $\mathcal{H}$ has the form (44). The first set of the Eqs. (46) then give us the definitions (43) of the momenta. When these definitions are substituted in the second set of Eqs. (46), we immediately obtain (41) if in the term $dp_{x_i}/dt = m_i d^2x_i/dt^2 + e_i dA_{x_i}/cdt$ we remember to introduce the total $t$ derivative after the fashion (42).

The preceding equations are rather more general than needed for most of our work, as they apply to variable and non-homogeneous impressed fields, which can be simultaneously electric and magnetic, whereas our main interest is in constant fields. If we assume that the applied electric and magnetic fields both have the $z$ direction and have constant magnitudes $E$ and $H$ independent both of time and position, then [21]

$$\Phi = -Ez, \qquad A_x = -\tfrac{1}{2}Hy, \qquad A_y = \tfrac{1}{2}Hx, \qquad A_z = 0, \quad (47)$$

and (44) becomes

$$\mathcal{H} = \sum_{i=1}^{\eta}\left\{\frac{1}{2m_i}(p_{x_i}^2 + p_{y_i}^2 + p_{z_i}^2) - Ee_iz_i - \right.$$
$$\left. - \frac{He_i}{2m_ic}(x_ip_{y_i} - y_ip_{x_i}) + \frac{H^2e_i^2}{8m_ic^2}(x_i^2 + y_i^2)\right\} + V. \quad (48)$$

[20] E. T. Whittaker, *Analytical Dynamics*, Chap. x.

[21] The choice of potentials in (47) is not the only one which will yield the desired constant fields $E$, $H$. We could, for instance, take $A_x = 0$, $A_y = Hx$, $A_z = 0$. The latter choice would, however, make the Hamiltonian function have a more complicated and less illuminating form, although it would still equal the energy (51). The choice (47) is the simplest, probably because it makes the scalar magnitude of $\mathbf{A}$ independent of a

That (47) gives the potentials appropriate to this special case can immediately be verified by substitution in (14). Even the case of parallel coexistent constant electric and magnetic fields is more general than usually needed, as we usually deal with entirely electric or entirely magnetic applied fields. It is, however, convenient to include both cases in a single equation. The Hamiltonian function appropriate to a purely magnetic constant field $H$ can, of course, be obtained by setting $E = 0$ in (48), and vice versa.

Our main interest throughout the book is in the electric and magnetic moments $\mathbf{p}$, $\mathbf{m}$ defined in Eqs. (11), and especially in their components $p_E$, $m_H$ in the direction of the applied field.[22] Fortunately these are obtainable from the Hamiltonian function by simple differentiations, as

$$p_E = -\frac{\partial \mathcal{H}}{\partial E}, \qquad m_H = -\frac{\partial \mathcal{H}}{\partial H}. \tag{49}$$

The first of these relations is immediately obvious from (48), as by (11) $p_E = \sum e_i z_i$. The second is only a trifle more difficult to establish, as in Cartesian coordinates

$$-\frac{\partial \mathcal{H}}{\partial H} = \sum \left\{ \frac{e_i}{2m_i c}(x_i p_{y_i} - y_i p_{x_i}) - \frac{H e_i^2}{4m_i c^2}(x_i^2 + y_i^2) \right\}$$
$$= \sum \frac{e_i}{2c}(x_i \dot{y}_i - y_i \dot{x}_i) = m_z \tag{50}$$

by (45), (47), (11). The relations (49) will apply not merely in Cartesian coordinates, but also in any set of 'canonical coordinates' that preserve the Hamiltonian form (46), provided the formulae of transformation from the Cartesian to the new coordinates and momenta do not involve the fields $E$ or $H$. This proviso is necessary in order that holding fast the Cartesian coordinates and momenta in the differentiation be equivalent to holding fast the new ones. It is met in the case of the usual 'positional coordinates' and momenta defined by an 'extended

rotation around the $z$ axis. The lack of uniqueness in the definition of $\mathbf{A}$, $\Phi$, and so of the Hamiltonian function in electric and magnetic fields occasions no real difficulty, as the different choices merely yield different fully equivalent canonical forms which can be obtained from each other by a contact transformation (and in some cases a shift of the origin for the energy).

[22] We use the notation $p_E$, $m_H$ rather than $p_z$, $m_z$ for the components of the moments $\mathbf{p}$, $\mathbf{m}$ in the direction of the applied fields in order to avoid confusion with the Cartesian momenta $p_{z_i}$. In writing our Hamiltonian functions we use a scalar rather than vector notation for the electric and magnetic fields. This is something of a change from the vector notation used in the preceding sections, but the various vector relations are usually of no particular interest in our use of the Hamiltonian technique, and so it seems simpler to restrict $\mathbf{E}$ and $\mathbf{H}$ to directions along the $z$ axis rather than to complicate our Hamiltonian functions with scalar and vector products.

point transformation'

$$q_k = q_k(x_1,...,z_\eta), \qquad p_k = \sum_i \left( \frac{\partial x_i}{\partial q_k} p_{x_i} + \frac{\partial y_i}{\partial q_k} p_{y_i} + \frac{\partial z_i}{\partial q_k} p_{z_i} \right),$$

as such a transformation obviously does not depend on the fields $E$ or $H$ in any way.

The numerical value of the Hamiltonian function (44) or (48) is the same as that of the ordinary total, i.e. kinetic plus scalar potential energy
$$T+V+\sum e_i\Phi_i = \tfrac{1}{2} \sum m_i \mathbf{v}_i^2 + V + \sum e_i\Phi_i, \tag{51}$$
as can be verified by substitution of (45) in (44). The reason why the energy formula (51) has no terms containing the magnetic field $H$ is, of course, that magnetic forces do no work, so that the constancy of energy can be secured without the addition of such terms. This may at first seem contrary to the fact that the Zeeman effect shows that the energy of an atom is not the same in a magnetic field as in its absence, but the solution of the paradox is that during the creation of the field, when $dH/dt \neq 0$, the field equations (1) demand that there be a concomitant electric field, which does work just sufficient to account for the energy displacements in the field. It may also seem strange that the field $H$ is involved in (48) but not in (51). This difference is due to the fact that in a magnetic field the canonical momenta necessary to preserve the Hamiltonian form are $\partial L/\partial \dot{q}_k$ and not $\partial T/\partial \dot{q}_k$, i.e. in Cartesian coordinates are $m_i\dot{x}_i + e_i A_{x_i}/c$ and not $m_i\dot{x}_i$ (cf. Eq. (45)). This distinction is nicely illustrated in Larmor's theorem.

## 8. Larmor's Theorem[23]

This theorem states that for a monatomic molecule in a magnetic field the motion of the electrons is, to a first approximation in $H$, the same as a motion in the absence of $H$ except for superposition of a common precession of frequency $He/4\pi mc$. This may be proved as follows. Let us specify the $Z$ electrons of the atom by cylindrical coordinates $\rho_i, z_i, \phi_i$, whose axis is the direction of $H$ and whose origin is at the centre of gravity. We suppose the nucleus to have such a large mass that it can be regarded as coinciding with the centre of gravity. The Lagrangian function is by (41 a) and (47), supposing $E = 0$,

$$L = \sum_{i=1}^{Z} \frac{m_i}{2}(\dot{z}_i^2 + \dot{\rho}_i^2 + \rho_i^2\dot{\phi}_i^2) + \sum \frac{He_i}{2c}\rho_i^2\dot{\phi}_i - V.$$

In place of the $\phi$'s, let us introduce new coordinates:

$$\gamma_1 = \phi_1, \qquad \gamma_2 = \phi_2 - \phi_1, \qquad \gamma_3 = \phi_3 - \phi_1,.... \tag{52}$$

[23] J. Larmor, *Aether and Matter*, p. 341.

The Hamiltonian function is then

$$\mathcal{H} = \sum_{i \neq 1} \frac{1}{2m_i}\left(p_{z_i}^2 + p_{\rho_i}^2 + \frac{p_{\gamma_i}^2}{\rho_i^2}\right) + \frac{1}{2m_1}(p_{z_1}^2 + p_{\rho_1}^2) +$$

$$+ \frac{1}{2m_1\rho_1^2}\left(\dot{p}_{\gamma_1} - \sum_{i\neq 1} p_{\gamma_i}\right)^2 + \frac{He}{2mc}p_{\gamma_1} + \frac{H^2e^2}{8mc^2}\sum_{i=1}^{Z}\rho_i^2 + V, \quad (53)$$

since all the electrons have the same value $-e/m$ of $e_i/m_i$, and since

$$p_{\gamma_i} = \frac{\partial L}{\partial \dot{\gamma}_i} = m_i\rho_i^2\left(\dot{\gamma}_i + \dot{\gamma}_1 + \frac{He_i}{2m_ic}\right) \quad (i \neq 1), \qquad p_{\rho_i} = m_i\dot{\rho}_i, \qquad p_{z_i} = m_i\dot{z}_i,$$

$$p_{\gamma_1} = m_1\rho_1^2\left(\dot{\gamma}_1 + \frac{He_1}{2m_1c}\right) + \sum_{i\neq 1} m_i\rho_i^2\left(\dot{\gamma}_i + \dot{\gamma}_1 + \frac{He_i}{2m_ic}\right) = \sum_{i=1}^{Z} m_i\rho_i^2\left(\phi_i - \frac{He}{2mc}\right).$$

$$(54)$$

Now the potential energy $V(\rho_1, ..., z_1, ..., \gamma_2, ...)$ does not involve $\gamma_1$, as it depends only on the relative positions of the coordinates. Thus $\partial \mathcal{H}/\partial \gamma_1$ vanishes, making $\gamma_1$ an 'ignorable coordinate', and $\dot{\gamma}_1$ hence has a constant value independent of $t$ (cf. Eq. (46)). If we disregard terms in $H^2$, then with any given value of $p_{\gamma_1}$ the equations of motion for the other $3Z-1$ pairs of canonical variables are precisely the same as in the absence of the field. Hence, neglecting quadratic terms in $H$, there exists a solution in which $\rho_1, ..., z_1, ..., \gamma_2, ...$ are the same functions of the time as in the absence of the field. However, the angular velocity $\dot{\gamma}_1 = \partial \mathcal{H}/\partial p_{\gamma_1}$ is now $\dfrac{1}{m_1\rho_1^2}\left(p_{\gamma_1} - \displaystyle\sum_{i\neq 1} p_{\gamma_i}\right) + \dfrac{He}{2mc}$. The addition of the term involving $H$ means that with a given value of $p_{\gamma_1}$ and a given solution for the other $3Z-1$ pairs of canonical variables, the value of the angular velocity of electron 1 is augmented by an amount $He/2mc$. As the angular displacements $\gamma_2, ...$ of the other electrons are measured relative to an apse line containing electron 1, it follows that the entire system precesses about the axis of the field with an angular velocity $He/2mc$. The corresponding frequency of precession is, of course, $He/4\pi mc$. Thus Larmor's theorem has been established, but it has been necessary to (a) disregard squares of the field $H$, (b) neglect the motion of the nucleus, and (c) suppose the molecule to be monatomic, as it was assumed in (53) that all particles not on the coordinate axis have a common value $-e/m$ of $e_i/m_i$. It is seen that the Larmor precession is essentially a correction for the different significance of the canonical momenta in terms of velocities with and without the field. It can be shown [24] that if the magnetic field is applied slowly and uniformly, then $p_{\gamma_i}$ does not

[24] P. A. M. Dirac, Proc. Cambr. Phil. Soc. 33, 69 (1926).

change, i.e. is an 'adiabatic invariant' during the creation of the field, whereas the ordinary angular momentum $\sum m_i \rho_i^2 \dot{\phi}_i$, which differs from (54), is not. When the field is thus adiabatically applied, the motion in the field can be proved[24, 25] the same (neglecting $H^2$) as the actual motion before the existence of the field, except for the superposition of the Larmor precession. We proved above merely that it resembled, except for this precession, some dynamically permissible motion for $H = 0$, not necessarily the actual original motion.

### 9. The Fundamental Theorem of Statistical Mechanics

The theoretical formulae for the electric or magnetic susceptibilities, which result from substitution of (12) in (8), involve the average moments $\bar{\bar{\mathbf{p}}}$ or $\bar{\bar{\mathbf{m}}}$ of a large number of molecules not necessarily all in a similar condition. Such averages can be calculated if we know the statistical 'distribution function' or probability that the molecule have any particular configuration. To determine such a distribution function is a problem in statistical mechanics. A probe into the foundations of classical statistical mechanics[26] is beyond our scope, and we shall be content to give the fundamental result without proof. Let $q_1,..., q_f$, $p_1,..., p_f$ be any set of 'canonical' coordinates and momenta, i.e. a set which satisfies Hamilton's equations (46) and which suffices to determine the positions and velocities of the various particles composing the molecule. Then the probability that a molecule be in the configuration

$$(q_1, q_1+dq_1)...(p_f, p_f+dp_f)$$

is

$$Ce^{-\mathcal{H}/kT}dq_1...dq_f dp_1...dp_f, \tag{55}$$

where $(q_1, q_1+dq_1)$ means that $q_1$ falls between $q_1$ and $q_1+dq_1$, &c., and where $\mathcal{H}$ is the Hamiltonian function. This is the so-called Boltzmann distribution formula. The value of the constant $C$ is determined by the requirement that the total probability be unity, and hence

$$\frac{1}{C} = \int...\int e^{-\mathcal{H}/kT}dq_1...dq_f dp_1...dp_f. \tag{56}$$

An immediate corollary of (55) is that the average value of any function $f$ of the $p$'s and $q$'s is

$$\bar{f} = C\int...\int fe^{-\mathcal{H}/kT}\,dq_1...dq_f dp_1...dp_f. \tag{57}$$

Most often we shall want the function $f$ to be either the electric or magnetic moment defined in Eq. (11). Thus by (8), (12), and (49) the

[25] J. H. Van Vleck, *Quantum Principles and Line Spectra*, p. 303.
[26] See, for instance, R. H. Fowler, *Statistical Mechanics*, Chap. II.

electric susceptibility is

$$\chi_e = \frac{\mathbf{P}}{\mathbf{E}} = \frac{N\bar{\bar{p}}_E}{E} = -\frac{NC}{E} \int ... \int \frac{\partial \mathcal{H}}{\partial E} e^{-\mathcal{H}/kT} dq_1...dp_f, \qquad (58)$$

with an analogous formula for the magnetic susceptibility. This result may also be written

$$\chi_e = \frac{NkT}{E} \frac{\partial \log Z}{\partial E} \qquad \text{where} \quad Z = \int ... \int e^{-\mathcal{H}/kT} dq_1...dp_f. \qquad (59)$$

The expression $Z$ is called by Darwin and Fowler the 'partition function', and is also sometimes termed the 'sum of states', as a translation of the name 'Zustandssumme' which it is given by German writers.

A feature particularly to be emphasized in connexion with Eqs. (55)–(58) is that it is immaterial how we choose the coordinates and momenta $q_1,..., p_f$ as long as they be a 'canonical set' satisfying Hamilton's equations (46). They might, for example, be Cartesian, polar, or parabolic coordinates and momenta, or the more general 'action and angle variables' used in perturbation theory. This indifference of (55)–(58) to the choice of coordinates is due to the well-known fact that any contact transformation,[27] i.e. any transformation which preserves the validity of the Hamiltonian form (46), has unit functional determinant. Hence

$$dq_1...dp_f = dQ_1...dP_f, \qquad (60)$$

where $p$, $q$ and $P$, $Q$ are respectively the old and new variables.

It can be objected that the derivations of the Boltzmann distribution formula (55) given in statistical mechanics are not without loopholes if one looks hard enough for them. The fundamental assumption made to obtain (55) is that the 'picking out' of numerical values for coordinates and momenta for any particular molecule is a lottery or random proposition, subject only to the requirement that the total energy of an assembly of molecules (e.g. box of gas) has a given value. On this basis it can be shown that the Boltzmann distribution is not merely the most probable, but that it is infinitely the most probable, and hence is what Jeans terms a 'normal property' of the system.[28] Many of the common brief treatments of statistical mechanics, to be sure, merely calculate the most probable configuration without demonstrating its overwhelming probability or normal property, but

---

[27] W. Gibbs, *Elementary Principles in Statistical Mechanics*, Chap. I (extended point transformations only); A. Szarvassi, *Ann. der Physik*, **60**, 501 (1919).

[28] According to the so-called 'ergodic hypothesis', which supposes that all assemblies having the same energy have the same life-history, the Boltzmann formula would be inescapable. Unfortunately, Plancherel and also Rosenthal have demonstrated the impossibility of ergodic systems (*Ann. der Physik*, **42**, 796 and 1061, 1913).

recent very complete and elegant work of Darwin and Fowler [29] shows very convincingly that the Boltzmann distribution is always a normal property. Thus this distribution is inescapable unless we assume that nature has a peculiar preference for configurations which would be abnormally improbable in the lottery described above.[30] As long as we retain a classical theory with continuous distributions rather than use a discrete quantum mechanics, we can therefore feel reasonably safe in resting our calculations of the susceptibility on (59).

[29] C. G. Darwin and R. H. Fowler, *Phil. Mag.* **44**, 450 and 823 (1922) and several later papers, especially by Fowler. A detailed account is given in Fowler's book *Statistical Mechanics*.

[30] The Pauli exclusion principle and Fermi-Dirac statistics in the new quantum mechanics do indeed show that only configurations corresponding to antisymmetric wave functions are realized physically despite the fact that they oftentimes represent but a small fraction of the classical phase space. This restriction, however, is usually unimportant for our purposes, as we shall deal mainly with media sufficiently rarefied to make the Fermi-Dirac interference effects unimportant, and so we use Boltzmann statistics throughout except in §§ 80–1.

# CLASSICAL THEORY OF THE LANGEVIN-DEBYE FORMULA

## 10. Polar versus Non-Polar Molecules

In the study of dielectric phenomena, molecules are commonly divided into two categories called 'polar' and 'non-polar', also sometimes termed 'homopolar' and 'heteropolar'. A molecule may be defined as polar if it has a permanent electrical moment, i.e. an electrical moment which is on the time average different from zero even in the absence of external fields. A molecule without such a permanent moment is termed non-polar. To find the permanent moment one must retain out of the total moment $\sum e_i \mathbf{r}_i$ only the constant part which remains on averaging over the 'internal' motions of the electrons relative to the nuclei.[1] All atoms and molecules contain instantaneous moments which fluctuate with the positions of the electrons. Hence the mean square of the electric moment is never zero, but on the other hand the square of the mean may vanish, and if it does the molecule is non-polar.

As a simple example of this classification, we may mention that all diatomic molecules composed of two identical atoms, such as $N_2$, $O_2$, &c., are non-polar. This is quite obvious from symmetry considerations. Diatomic molecules composed of unlike atoms, e.g. HCl, are in general polar, as the charge therein will not distribute itself symmetrically with respect to the two ends of the molecule. Triatomic molecules are ordinarily polar. A few exceptions such as $CO_2$ will be discussed in § 20. Molecules with more than three atoms may be non-polar if highly symmetrical, as in e.g. $CCl_4$, $CH_4$ (see §§ 19–20). Monatomic molecules are always non-polar, as on the average the electrons are symmetrically located with respect to any plane containing the single nucleus.

We have not yet mentioned how to decide experimentally whether or not a molecule is polar, instead of appealing to our preconceived ideas of a molecular model. There are many experiments, both physical and chemical, which furnish tests for the existence of permanent moments, but probably the best of these consists in the measurement of dielectric constants. If the field is not so extremely strong that it requires consideration of 'saturation effects', i.e. if we can treat the dielectric constant as independent of field strength, then it will be shown that

---

[1] This permanent moment is to be measured relative to axes fixed in the molecule, for the 'external' rotations of a molecule as a whole make the axis of molecular polarity continually point in a different direction relative to axes fixed in space.

the electric susceptibility $\chi_e = (\epsilon - 1)/4\pi$ is given by the expression

$$\chi_e = N\left(\alpha + \frac{\mu^2}{3kT}\right), \tag{1}$$

which we shall call the Langevin-Debye formula. Here $N$ is the number of molecules per c.c., $T$ is the absolute temperature, and $\alpha$ is a constant. The permanent electrical moment will throughout be denoted by $\mu$, and hence the existence of a non-vanishing second term in (1) is a criterion for a polar molecule. We shall henceforth omit the subscript $e$ or $m$ from $\chi$, as ordinarily it will be clear from the context whether we are studying an electric or magnetic susceptibility. Eq. (1) assumes that $\chi$ is small compared to unity, as it ordinarily is in gases; otherwise $\chi$ should be replaced by $3(\epsilon-1)/4\pi(\epsilon+2)$ in accordance with the correction for the local field given in § 5.

The second term of (1) disappears if the molecule has no permanent moment. Hence the dielectric constant of a non-polar gas should be independent of temperature provided the density is maintained constant. It is often convenient to work at constant pressure rather than constant density when $T$ is varied, and then the number $N$ of molecules per c.c. is a function of $T$. The part of the temperature variation of the dielectric constant due merely to changes in density may be eliminated by using the quotient $\chi/N$, which is the 'susceptibility per molecule', or else the expression $L\chi/N$, which is the 'susceptibility per gram mol' or 'molar susceptibility'. Here $L$ has been used to denote the Avogadro number. One therefore has the following fundamental result: in a non-polar gas the molar susceptibility should be independent of $T$, while in a polar gas it should be a linear function $a + b(1/T)$ of $1/T$. This agrees well with experiment. From the experimental values of the coefficient $b$ together with the relation $b = L\mu^2/3k$ following from (1), it is possible to deduce quantitatively the permanent electrical moment of the molecule. The numerical values of the moments so obtained will be considered in § 19.

Before proceeding to the mathematical derivation of (1) it is perhaps illuminating first to discuss qualitatively the physical nature of the phenomena responsible for each of the two terms of (1). The existence of a susceptibility requires that the molecules have an average electrical moment in the direction of the applied field. This does not require an average or permanent moment before the field is applied, as the introduction of the field may distort or 'polarize' the molecule, since the positive charges are attracted in the direction of the field, and the negative ones repelled. The electrical centres of gravity of the positive and negative charges will then no longer coincide, as they did before the field was applied if the molecule is non-polar. Due to this deformation effect, the molecule thus acquires what is termed an 'induced moment' or 'elastic polarization'. In addition there will be a contribution to the susceptibility resulting from the permanent moment of the molecule, if it is polar. Even the mean electrical moment of an assembly of polar molecules is zero in the absence of external fields, since in the absence of orienting influences the molecular axes will have a random spacial distribution. To a given number of molecules oriented in one direction there will be an equal number oriented in the diametrically opposite direction. Hence, on averaging over a very large number of molecules the net moment is zero. Not so after the field is applied. Each polar molecule will be subject to a torque which tends to aline its axis of polarity parallel to the field. All the permanent molecular moments would aline themselves perfectly parallel to the field, were they not prevented by the centrifugal or gyroscopic forces due to molecular rotation, and also perhaps by the disturbing influences of molecular collisions. Both these influences which prevent perfect alinement become more potent with increasing temperature, and will usually be referred to as 'temperature agitation'. Fortunately, an exact examination of the forces arising from the temperature agitation is unnecessary, as the great beauty of the method of statistical mechanics is that it yields the state of equilibrium between the orienting influence of the field and the temperature agitation without specializing the mechanism by which the equilibrium is secured. Although there is perfect alinement only at $T = 0$, at any other temperature there is a predominance of the parallel over the anti-parallel alinements of the axes of polarity with respect to the field, as the former have a lower potential energy and hence a larger Boltzmann probability factor. Thus the orientation effect always enhances the susceptibility if the molecule has a permanent moment.

From the foregoing discussion one immediately suspects that the first term of (1), which is independent of the temperature and which is found in both polar and non-polar molecules, is due to the induced polarization; and that the second term, which disappears at $T = \infty$ and which is found only in polar molecules, is due to the orientation of the permanent dipoles. This indeed turns out to be the case. Incidently, Eq. (1) would make it appear that the susceptibility became infinite in polar molecules at the absolute zero, but this is not really the case, as at low temperatures higher powers of the field and the resulting saturation effects not included in (1) must be considered.

The idea of induced polarization is an old one, as it was even used, for instance, in Mossotti's theory discussed in § 2. The suggestion that part of the electric susceptibility might be due to alinement of permanent moments, resisted by temperature agitation, does not appear to have been made until 1912, by Debye.[2] A magnetic susceptibility due entirely to orientation of permanent moments was suggested some time previously, in 1905, by Langevin,[3] and the second term of (1) is thus an adaptation to the electric case of Langevin's magnetic formula. Hence we term (1) the Langevin-Debye formula. (In the electric case, a formula such as (1) is commonly called just the Debye formula, but we use the compound title Langevin-Debye in order to emphasize that the mathematical methods which we use to derive the second term of (1) apply equally well to magnetic or electric dipoles.) Despite the earlier appearance of the orientation theory in the magnetic case, we nevertheless first present this theory in the present chapter on electric polarization. We do this in order to defer until a later chapter certain rather delicate points in the classical theory of magnetic susceptibilities.

## 11. Rudimentary Proof of the Langevin-Debye Formula

We shall first give the conventional, rather crude derivation of (1). To obtain the first term of (1) we may follow the usual line of least resistance in classical theory and regard each charge in the atom or molecule as having a position of static equilibrium and subject to an isotropic linear restoring force when displaced therefrom. This naïve depicture of an atom or molecule as a collection of harmonic oscillators is not in agreement with modern views of atomic structure as exemplified in the Rutherford atom, but yields surprisingly fruitful results. The restoring force on a harmonically bound charge $e_i$ is $-a_i(\mathbf{r}_i - \mathbf{r}_{i0})$, where $a_i$ is a constant and $\mathbf{r}_i - \mathbf{r}_{i0}$ is its vector displacement from the equilibrium position. The force on the charge in an electric field $\mathbf{E}$ is $e_i\mathbf{E}$. Hence for static equilibrium between the internal restoring and external electric forces, $\mathbf{r}_i - \mathbf{r}_{i0}$ equals $e_i\mathbf{E}/a_i$, and the induced electrical moment $e_i(\mathbf{r}_i - \mathbf{r}_{i0})$ is $\mathbf{E}e_i^2/a_i$. The total induced moment in the molecule is then $\mathbf{E}\sum e_i^2/a_i$, where the summation extends over all the charges in the molecule capable of displacement from equilibrium positions. Since the susceptibility is the total moment per c.c. divided by field strength (Eqs. (8) and (12), Chap. I) the susceptibility arising from the induced polarization of the elastically bound charges is $N\alpha$, where $\alpha$ is an

[2] P. Debye, *Phys. Zeits.* **13**, 97 (1912).
[3] P. Langevin, *J. de Physique*, **4**, 678 (1905); *Annales de Chimie et Physique*, **5**, 70 (1905).

abbreviation for $\sum e_i^2/a_i$, a constant which is obviously independent of temperature. We have thus obtained an expression of the same form as the first term of (1).

To obtain the second term we suppose that the molecule has also a permanent moment $\mu$, or in other words an electrical polarity even when the charges are at their equilibrium positions. If $\theta$ be the angle between the axis of polarity (i.e. direction of the permanent moment) and the applied field, then the part of the susceptibility arising from the permanent moment is clearly

$$\frac{N}{E}\mu\,\overline{\overline{\cos\theta}},\qquad(2)$$

where the double bar means an average over all the molecules in a physically small element of volume (cf. Chap. I). In the absence of the field, positive and negative values of $\cos\theta$ are equally probable, as already mentioned, and the expression (2) vanishes. Let us boldly omit the kinetic energy of the molecule and regard the Hamiltonian function as consisting merely of the potential energy $-\mu E\cos\theta$ of the permanent moment of the molecule in the applied field $E$. Then by a rather loose application of the Boltzmann distribution formula (55), Chap. I, the probability that a dipole axis fall within an element of solid angle $d\Omega = \sin\theta\,d\theta d\phi$ is proportional to $e^{\mu E\cos\theta/kT}d\Omega$, and (2) becomes (cf. Eqs. (56) and (57), Chap. I)

$$\frac{N\mu \iint \cos\theta\, e^{\mu E\cos\theta/kT}\,d\Omega}{E \iint e^{\mu E\cos\theta/kT}\,d\Omega} = \frac{N\mu \iint (\cos\theta + \mu E\cos^2\theta/kT + ...)\,d\Omega}{E \iint (1+...)\,d\Omega}.\qquad(3)$$

Here on the right side we have developed the exponents as power series in $E$, and have carried the expansion only far enough to include the first term which does not vanish on integration. As the average value of $\cos\theta$ over a sphere is zero, the quotient of the two integrals on the right side of (3) is, except for a factor $\mu E/kT$, merely the average of $\cos^2\theta$ over a sphere. This average is $1/3$, and hence the approximate value of (3) is $N\mu^2/3kT$, which is the second term of (1), thus finishing the proof.

As a matter of fact, the integrals in (3) are readily evaluated in closed form without resorting to a series development. If we make the substitution $q = \mu E\cos\theta/kT$ and cancel the trivial integral over $\phi$ from numerator and denominator, the left side of (3) becomes

$$\frac{N\mu \int_{-x}^{+x} qe^q\,dq}{Ex \int_{-x}^{+x} e^q\,dq} = \frac{N\mu}{E}\left[\coth x - \frac{1}{x}\right] = \frac{N\mu}{E}\,L(x),\qquad(4)$$

where $\coth x = (e^x + e^{-x})/(e^x - e^{-x})$ and where $x$ is an abbreviation for the dimensionless ratio $\mu E/kT$. The expression enclosed in square brackets is often called a Langevin function and commonly denoted by $L(x)$. The series expansion of $L(x)$ for small values of $x$ is $\frac{1}{3}x - \frac{1}{45}x^3 + \dots$ and hence (4) agrees with the second part of (1) when we keep only the first term in this development. On the other hand, for very large values of $x$, the asymptotic value of $\coth x$, and hence of $L(x)$, is unity. It thus follows that the polarization due to orientation, viz. $E\chi = N\mu L(x)$, becomes $N\mu$ if the field strength is enormously great or if the temperature is exceedingly low. This limiting or 'saturation' value $N\mu$ is what we should expect, as under such extreme conditions the dipole axes all aline themselves parallel to the field, making the cosine factor unity in (2). A graph of the Langevin function is shown in Fig. 1. Near the origin the curve is a straight line, so that the polarization is linear in the field strength if not too great. This is the

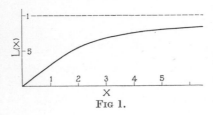

FIG 1.

portion of the curve in which only the first term in the expansion need be considered, and in which (4) can be replaced by the second part of (1). On the other hand, the fact that for large $x$ the curve is asymptotic to a horizontal line shows that the polarization by orientation cannot exceed the saturation value $N\mu$.

## 12. More Complete Derivation of the Langevin-Debye Formula[4]

The preceding proof of the Langevin-Debye formula cannot be regarded as satisfactory, since in forming the Boltzmann distribution factor $e^{-\mathscr{H}/kT}$ the kinetic energies of rotation and vibration were entirely omitted from the Hamiltonian function $\mathscr{H}$. In dealing with the induced polarization, the charges were supposed in static equilibrium between the forces of restitution and the applied field. On the other hand, in order to make possible the Boltzmann distribution in the orientation, it was necessary to suppose a 'kinetic statistical equilibrium' between the impressed electrical forces and the forces of temperature agitation. The only position of static equilibrium for the permanent dipoles would be when they are all parallel to the applied field; hence the assumption

---

[4] In writing the present section the writer has been aided by the discussion of distribution functions and Gans's theories of magnetism given by Wills in *Theories of Magnetism* (Bulletin No. 18 of the National Research Council). Gans's mathematical transformations and use of momentoids show considerable resemblance to the devices which we employ, but he treated rather different problems and assumed more symmetry in the molecule.

of static equilibrium would yield the saturation moment $N\mu$ even for infinitesimal fields, an absurdity. It is clearly illogical to include the temperature agitation in the rotational problem connected with the permanent dipoles, as one must of necessity, but to neglect this agitation in the vibrational problem connected with the induced polarization. Furthermore, although the temperature agitation was implicitly recognized in the orientation or rotational problem, it was explicitly neglected in omitting the kinetic energy of molecular rotation from the Hamiltonian function. This omission is made in much of the literature, including Langevin's original paper, and it is fortunate that the Langevin-Debye formula (1) is obtainable regardless of whether one is painstaking enough to include the kinetic energy terms in the Hamiltonian function.

We shall therefore begin afresh and re-derive (1), taking cognizance of the kinetic energy. Also we shall free ourselves from the restriction that the forces binding the charges to their equilibrium configurations be isotropic. This restriction was a bad one, as few, if any, molecules have such perfect symmetry that displacements in all directions can be regarded as equivalent. Let the small vibrations of the charges about their equilibrium configurations be specified by a set of normal coordinates $\xi_1, \xi_2, ..., \xi_s$, equal in number, of course, to the number of degrees of freedom of the elastic vibrations. We may suppose the electrical moments $\mathfrak{p}_{x'}, \mathfrak{p}_{y'}, \mathfrak{p}_{z'}$ along the principal axes of inertia $x', y', z'$ to be linear functions of the normal coordinates, so that

$$\mathfrak{p}_{x'} = \mu_{x'} + \sum_{i=1}^{s} c_{x'i}\xi_i \tag{5}$$

with analogous formulae for the moments along the $y'$ and $z'$ directions. Here $\mu_{x'}, \mu_{y'}, \mu_{z'}$, which are the terms remaining when the displacements $\xi_i$ vanish, are, of course, the components of the permanent moment along the three principal axes. The other terms, which are inside the summation sign, represent polarization acquired in virtue of the elastic vibrations.

Let $\theta, \phi, \psi$ be a set of Eulerian angles specifying the position of the principal axes of inertia $x', y', z'$ which are fixed in the molecule, relative to another set of axes $x, y, z$ which are fixed in space. Here $\theta$ is the angle between the $z$ and $z'$ axes, while $\phi, \psi$ are respectively the angles between the nodal line (i.e. intersection of the $xy$ and $x'y'$ planes) and the $x$ and $x'$ axes respectively. We suppose the field in the $z$ direction. The coordinate $z$ is connected with $x', y', z'$ according to the relation

$$z = \sin\theta\sin\psi\, x' + \sin\theta\cos\psi\, y' + \cos\theta\, z'. \tag{6}$$

D

The kinetic energy of rotation of the molecule regarded as a rigid body is

$$T_{\text{rot}} = \tfrac{1}{2}[A_x\Omega_x^2 + A_y\Omega_y^2 + A_z\Omega_z^2], \tag{7}$$

where $A_{x'}$, $A_{y'}$, $A_{z'}$ are the principal moments of inertia, and $\Omega_{x'}$, $\Omega_{y'}$, $\Omega_{z'}$ are the $x'$, $y'$, $z'$ components of angular velocity. The expressions for these components of angular velocity in terms of the Eulerian angles and related velocities are as follows:[5]

$$\Omega_{x'} = \dot{\theta}\cos\psi + \dot{\phi}\sin\theta\sin\psi, \quad \Omega_{y'} = \dot{\phi}\cos\psi\sin\theta - \dot{\theta}\sin\psi, \quad \Omega_{z'} = \dot{\psi} + \dot{\phi}\cos\theta. \tag{8}$$

The Hamiltonian function is

$$\mathcal{H} = \left(\frac{1}{2A_{x'}}P^2 + \frac{1}{2A_{y'}}Q^2 + \frac{1}{2A_{z'}}R^2\right) + \tfrac{1}{2}\sum b_i p_{\xi_i}^2 + \tfrac{1}{2}\sum a_i \xi_i^2 - \tag{9}$$

$$- E[(\mu_{x'} + \sum c_{x'i}\xi_i)\sin\theta\sin\psi + (\mu_{y'} + \sum c_{y'i}\xi_i)\sin\theta\cos\psi +$$
$$+ (\mu_{z'} + \sum c_{z'i}\xi_i)\cos\theta],$$

where
$$P = \cos\psi\, p_\theta + \sin\psi\,\mathrm{cosec}\,\theta\,(p_\phi - \cos\theta\, p_\psi), \tag{10}$$
$$Q = -\sin\psi\, p_\theta + \cos\psi\,\mathrm{cosec}\,\theta\,(p_\phi - \cos\theta\, p_\psi), \qquad R = p_\psi.$$

The first term of (9) is the kinetic energy of rotation of the molecule regarded as a rigid body, sometimes dubbed the 'asymmetrical top'. It is obtained in the usual way by first expressing (7) in terms of $\dot{\theta}$, $\dot{\phi}$, $\dot{\psi}$, $\theta$, $\phi$, $\psi$ by means of (8), and then passing from $\dot{\theta}$, $\dot{\phi}$, $\dot{\psi}$ to the canonical momenta $p_\theta$, $p_\phi$, $p_\psi$ defined by the relations $p_\theta = \partial T_{\text{rot}}/\partial\dot{\theta}$, &c. The next two terms are the kinetic and potential energies of the small vibrations, and of course consist entirely of the sum of squares. The remainder of (9) is the potential energy

$$- E[\mathfrak{p}_{x'}\cos(x',z) + \mathfrak{p}_{y'}\cos(y',z) + \mathfrak{p}_{z'}\cos(z',z)] \tag{11}$$

due to the applied electrical field. In writing this electrical potential energy in (9) we have utilized (5) and have expressed the direction cosines involved in (11) in terms of the Eulerian angles by means of (6).

Even the rather formidable expression (9) is not a rigorous Hamiltonian function, as it assumes that the vibrational and rotational kinetic energies enter in a strictly additive fashion, which is not true. Actually the molecular distortion accompanying the small vibrations will constantly cause slight variations in the moments of inertia $A_{x'}$, $A_{y'}$, $A_{z'}$, so that they are not really constants of the molecule. Also, reciprocally, the centrifugal forces from molecular rotation ought really to be added to the linear restoring forces acting on the coordinates $\xi_1$, $\xi_2$,... A rigorous Hamiltonian would, among other things, involve 'cross products' in the momenta of the form $d_{i\alpha}p_{\xi_i}p_\alpha$, where $p_\alpha$ denotes any of the rotational momenta $p_\theta$, $p_\phi$, $p_\psi$, and where the coefficients $d_{i\alpha}$ are functions of the various positional coordinates. However, all these corrections for the mutual interaction

[5] Cf., for instance, Born, *Atommechanik*, p. 30, or Webster, *Dynamics*, p. 275. The notation of these writers differs from ours in an interchange of the angles denoted by $\phi$, $\psi$.

of the rotation and vibration are small if the stiffness coefficients $a_i$ for the normal vibrations are so large that the amplitudes of these vibrations are small. Hence (9) involves no serious error if the elastic vibrations are supposed small, and without such a supposition the dynamical problem would, of course, be unmanageable.

Eq. (59) of the preceding chapter shows that the susceptibility is determined as soon as we evaluate the 'partition function'

$$Z = \int\int ... \int e^{-\mathcal{H}/kT} \, dp_{\xi_1} dp_{\xi_2} ... dp_\theta dp_\phi dp_\psi d\xi_1 d\xi_2 ... d\theta d\phi d\psi. \qquad (12)$$

It is convenient to change three of the variables of integration from $p_\theta$, $p_\phi$, $p_\psi$ to new variables $P$, $Q$, $R$, which are given in terms of $p_\theta$, $p_\phi$, $p_\psi$ in (10). The expressions $P$, $Q$, $R$ are sometimes called 'momentoids'.[6] They are not canonically conjugate to $\theta$, $\phi$, $\psi$, but equal the instantaneous angular momenta about the three principal axes of the molecule. For this reason the rotational kinetic energy takes the exceedingly simple form given in the first term of (9) when expressed in terms of $P$, $Q$, $R$, whereas (10) shows that it would be exceedingly cumbersome if expressed explicitly in terms of the true canonical momenta. The functional determinant of the transformation to the momentoids is most easily evaluated by calculating its reciprocal[7]

$$\frac{1}{\Delta} = \frac{\partial(P,Q,R)}{\partial(p_\theta,p_\phi,p_\psi)} = \begin{vmatrix} \cos\psi & \sin\psi \operatorname{cosec}\theta & -\sin\psi\cot\theta \\ -\sin\psi & \cos\psi \operatorname{cosec}\theta & -\cos\psi\cot\theta \\ 0 & 0 & 1 \end{vmatrix} - \frac{1}{\sin\theta}.$$

The expression (9) for the energy is of the form

$$f(P,Q,R,p_{\xi_1},...) + g(\theta,\phi,\psi,\xi_1,...,E). \qquad (13)$$

It is this separability into two parts, depending respectively on the momentoids together with the vibrational momenta, and on the coordinates, which makes the momentoids so useful. If the true momenta $p_\theta$, $p_\phi$, $p_\psi$ were introduced as variables in place of $P$, $Q$, $R$, this separation would not be possible, as (9) shows that then $\theta$, $\phi$, $\psi$ would be involved in the kinetic energy. The partition function now factors as follows:

$$Z = Z_1 Z_2, \qquad Z_1 = \int ... \int e^{-f/kT} \, dP dQ dR dp_{\xi_1} dp_{\xi_2}...,$$

$$Z_2 = \int ... \int e^{-g/kT} \sin\theta \, d\theta d\phi d\psi d\xi_1 d\xi_2....$$

---

[6] Cf. Jeans, *The Dynamical Theory of Gases*, 3rd ed., p. 97.

[7] The transformation equations (10) involve the variables $\theta$, $\phi$, $\psi$ as well as $p_\theta$, $p_\phi$, $p_\psi$, $P$, $Q$, $R$, but it is immediately verified that the complete sixth order Jacobian $\partial(p_\theta, p_\phi, p_\psi, \theta, \phi, \psi)/\partial(P, Q, R, \theta, \phi, \psi)$ is the same as the third order one $\partial(p_\theta, p_\phi, p_\psi)/\partial(P, Q, R)$ in view of the fact that the old and new $\theta$, $\phi$, $\psi$ are identical. This makes a third order under-determinant in one corner of the sixth order one equal to zero, and the sixth order determinant factors into two third order ones equal respectively to unity and $\sin\theta$.

The important thing is that the factor $Z_1$ is independent of $E$, and so makes no contribution to the susceptibility, for Eq. (59), Chap. I, is

$$\chi = \frac{NkT}{E} \frac{\partial \log Z}{\partial E} = \frac{NkT}{E} \frac{\partial (\log Z_1 + \log Z_2)}{\partial E}. \tag{14}$$

The factor $Z_1$ can henceforth be omitted entirely. The physical meaning of this result is that the susceptibility is the same as though the kinetic energy were omitted entirely, provided we retain the 'weight function' $\sin \theta$ in the integrand of $Z_2$. In the present problem this weight function arises from transformation of the kinetic part of the problem, as in the original system of canonical variables the volume element was $dp_\theta dp_\phi dp_\psi dp_{\xi_1}...d\theta d\phi d\psi d\xi_1...$, whereas after the transformation it becomes $\sin \theta \, dP dQ dR dp_{\xi_1}...d\theta d\phi d\psi d\xi_1....$ In the conventional Langevin theory (§ 11) this weight function is inserted because an element of solid angle is of the form $d\Omega = \sin \theta \, d\theta d\phi$ (cf. Eq. (3)). However, rigorous statistical mechanics do not allow us to proceed in such a fashion without justification, as the statistical theory tells us that the weight function is unity (or some other constant) in the complete macroscopic phase space involving both the position and momentum variables, but tells us nothing about distributions in a space of half as many dimensions involving only the coordinates of position. There is thus quite an amusing and illuminating contrast between the way the factor $\sin \theta$ makes its appearance in the present section and in the preceding one (§ 11).

In order to evaluate the term in the moment which is proportional to $E$, we must expand $Z_2$ to terms in $E^2$. To this approximation we have

$$Z_2 = \int ... \int e^{-\Sigma a_i \xi_i^2/2kT} \left[ 1 + \frac{E(\lambda_{x'} \mathfrak{p}_{x'} + \lambda_{y'} \mathfrak{p}_{y'} + \lambda_{z'} \mathfrak{p}_{z'})}{kT} + \right.$$
$$\left. + \frac{E^2(\lambda_{x'} \mathfrak{p}_{x'} + ...)^2}{2k^2 T^2} + ... \right] \sin \theta \, d\theta d\phi d\psi d\xi_1... \tag{15}$$

by (9) and (11). Here we have used $\lambda_{x'}, \lambda_{y'}, \lambda_{z'}$ as abbreviations for the three direction cosines in (11). The integration over the Eulerian angles $\theta, \phi, \psi$ is readily performed, either by substituting the explicit formulae for $\lambda_{x'}, \lambda_{y'}, \lambda_{z'}$ in terms of $\theta, \phi, \psi$ by means of (6) or without doing this by observing that the mean square of any direction cosine is $1/3$, while the mean of the first power of a direction cosine or of the product of two different direction cosines is zero. Furthermore,

$$\int\limits_{-\infty}^{+\infty} \xi_i e^{-\beta \xi_i^2} \, d\xi_i = 0, \qquad 2\beta \int\limits_{-\infty}^{+\infty} \xi_i^2 e^{-\beta \xi_i^2} \, d\xi_i = \int\limits_{-\infty}^{+\infty} e^{-\beta \xi_i^2} \, d\xi_i. \tag{16}$$

The first of these relations is obvious from the fact that its integrand is an odd function of $\xi_i$, while the second is obtained by partial integration. On taking $\beta = a_i/2kT$, formulae (16) show that the integral over the $\xi_i$ of $\mathfrak{p}_x^2 = [\mu_{x'} + \sum c_{x'i}\xi_i]^2$ is identical with the integral of

$$\mu_{x'}^2 + kT \sum c_{x'i}^2/a_i.$$

Hence (15) becomes

$$Z_2 = \left[1 + \frac{E^2}{6k^2T^2}\left(\mu_{x'}^2 + \mu_{y'}^2 + \mu_{z'}^2 + kT \sum \frac{c_{x'i}^2 + c_{y'i}^2 + c_{z'i}^2}{a_i}\right)\right] \times$$

$$\times \int...\int e^{-\sum a_i \xi_i^2/2kT} \sin\theta \, d\theta d\phi d\psi d\xi_1.... \quad (17)$$

It is unnecessary to evaluate the integrals in (17), as they are independent of $E$ and hence make no contribution to (14). The disappearance of the linear terms in $E$ from (17) could have been predicted, as the susceptibility and hence by (14) the partition function must depend on the magnitude but not on the sign of $E$, so that $Z_2$ can involve only even powers of $E$. From (14) and (17) it follows that the susceptibility is $2\gamma NkT/(1+\gamma E^2)$, where $1+\gamma E^2$ is an abbreviation for the factor outside the integral sign in (17). We may neglect $\gamma E^2$ in comparison with 1 in the denominator, as we have agreed to retain only the part of the susceptibility which is independent of field strength, and have already made approximations of this order. Hence

$$\chi = N \sum_{i=1}^{s} \frac{c_{x'i}^2 + c_{y'i}^2 + c_{z'i}^2}{3a_i} + \frac{N(\mu_{x'}^2 + \mu_{y'}^2 + \mu_{z'}^2)}{3kT}. \quad (18)$$

This is the desired result, the same as (1), since $\mu_{x'}^2 + \mu_{y'}^2 + \mu_{z'}^2$ is the square of the magnitude of the permanent moment $\mu$ of the molecule, and since the summation in the first part of (18) consists solely of terms independent of $T$, and so is a constant, say $\alpha$, independent of temperature. If in particular the oscillations are due to isotropically bound charges $e_i$, then $c_{x'i} = c_{y'i} = c_{z'i} = e_i$, and the expression for $N\alpha$ is $N \sum e_i^2/a_i$, the same as given in the first paragraph of § 11.

## 13. Derivation of a Generalized Langevin-Debye Formula[8]

We shall now deduce a very general form of the Langevin-Debye formula. This proof is intended, and should be very easy, for readers familiar with the use of 'action and angle variables' in dynamics and perturbation theory.[9] Suppose that we have a multiply periodic dyna-

[8] J. H. Van Vleck, *Phys. Rev.* **30**, 50 (1927).

[9] For details on the dynamical technique involved in the use of angle and action variables see Born's *Atommechanik* or Chap. XI of the author's *Quantum Principles and Line Spectra*.

mical system with $f$ degrees of freedom, specified by $2f$ canonical variables $w_1^0,..., w_f^0, J_1^0,..., J_f^0$. We assume further that the $w^0$'s and $J^0$'s are respectively true angle and action variables for the system in the absence of the field $E$. When $E = 0$ the $w_k^0$'s are thus linear functions $\nu_k^0 t + \epsilon_k^0$ of the time $t$, while the $J_k^0$'s are constants (which incidentally in the old quantum theory would be equated to integral multiples of $h$). The $z$-component of electrical moment will be a Fourier series:[10]

$$p_z = \sum_\tau p_\tau^{(z)} e^{2\pi i(\tau w^0)}. \tag{19}$$

We use the same notation as in Born's *Atommechanik* (i, p. 86, &c.). Thus $(\tau w)$ is an abbreviation for $\tau_1 w_1 + \tau_2 w_2 + ... + \tau_f w_f$, and the subscript $\tau_1 \tau_2 ... \tau_f$ is abbreviated to $\tau$. The summation is $f$-fold, and extends over all positive and negative values of the integers $\tau_1 ... \tau_f$. The complex amplitudes $p_\tau^{(z)}$ are, of course, functions of the $J^0$'s as well as the $\tau$'s, and $p_{-\tau}^{(z)}$ is the conjugate of $p_\tau^{(z)}$. Classical statistical mechanics (e.g. Eq. (57) or (58), Chap. I) shows that if an electric field $E$ is applied along the $z$ direction, the susceptibility is[11]

$$\chi = \frac{N \int ... \int p_z e^{-\mathcal{H}/kT} dJ^0 dw^0}{E \int ... \int e^{-\mathcal{H}/kT} dJ^0 dw^0}, \tag{20}$$

where $dJ^0 dw^0$ denotes an element of volume $dJ_1^0 ... dJ_f^0 dw_1^0 ... dw_f^0$ of the 'phase space'. Also $\mathcal{H}$ denotes the Hamiltonian function in the field $E$, and equals $\mathcal{H}_0 - E p_z$ (cf. Eq. (48), Chap. I), where $p_z$ is given by (19), and $\mathcal{H}_0$ is the Hamiltonian for $E = 0$. The 'unperturbed' Hamiltonian $\mathcal{H}_0$ is a function only of the $J^0$'s, whereas $\mathcal{H}$ involves also the $w^0$'s through $p_z$. It is to be clearly understood that we are keeping the *original* canonical variables $w_1^0,..., w_f^0, J_1^0,..., J_f^0$ defined in the same way as for $E = 0$. Since the transformation from a Cartesian to the $w^0, J^0$

---

[10] We henceforth use ordinary italic type $p$ for the components of electric moment. In the preceding section (§ 12) a special type ℘ was employed to avoid confusion with the generalized momenta $p_q$, &c.

[11] *Limits of Integration in Eqs.* (20), (21). If we integrated over the entire phase space in the $J^0$, $w^0$ system the limits of integration for each of the $w^0$'s in (20) or (21) would be from $-\infty$ to $+\infty$, as all of the $w^0$'s may increase without limit. However, since the system is cyclic in each of the $w^0$'s with unit period, it is clear that we will obtain the correct statistical average if we take the limits of integration for each of the $w^0$'s as zero and unity. Another way of saying the same thing is that Cartesian variables are multiple valued in the $w^0$'s, so that the entire Cartesian phase space corresponds to only one period for the $w^0$'s.

The limits of integration for the $J^0$'s can usually be taken as 0 and $+\infty$ by proper choice of the fundamental periods. (The limits, however, are $-\infty$ and $+\infty$ for $J^0$'s associated with both left- and right-handed rotations, as, for instance, in the case of a $J^0$ associated with an axial component of angular momentum.) The precise form of the limits for the $J^0$'s is immaterial for us, as the bars in (22) automatically denote an average over the entire $J^0$ space.

system is thus not modified to take account of the field $E$, the $w^0$'s and $J^0$'s will cease to be true angle and action variables, i.e. cease to be respectively linear in $t$ and constant, after the field $E$ is applied. The $w^0$'s and $J^0$'s will, however, remain canonically conjugate, and we can apply (20) because it is a fundamental theorem in statistical mechanics that the *a priori* probability is proportional to the volume occupied in the phase space, regardless of what $2f$ variables we choose as constituting the coordinates of this space provided only they are canonical; this is because all 'contact transformations' have unit functional determinant, as already explained in § 9.

Now $e^{-\mathcal{H}/kT} = e^{-(\mathcal{H}_0 - Ep_z)/kT} = e^{-\mathcal{H}_0/kT}(1 + Ep_z/kT + ...)$, and hence, if we keep only the part of the susceptibility which is independent of $E$, Eq. (20) becomes

$$\chi = \frac{N \int ... \int p_z^2 e^{-\mathcal{H}_0/kT} \, dJ^0 dw^0}{kT \int ... \int e^{-\mathcal{H}_0/kT} \, dJ^0 dw^0}. \tag{21}$$

Here we have assumed that the polarization vanishes when $E = 0$, i.e. that the numerator of (20) vanishes when $\mathcal{H}$ is replaced by $\mathcal{H}_0$. Otherwise the body would exhibit a 'permanent' or 'hard' polarization, a phenomenon not usually encountered in dielectrics, at least not to an appreciable degree, although it is quite common in ferromagnetism. Ordinarily this assumption of no residual polarization is fulfilled by reason of symmetry, as in a gaseous medium there is no preferred direction in the absence of external fields.

Now since the square of two multiple Fourier series is itself such a series, $p_z^2$ may be expressed as a multiple Fourier series in the $w^0$'s. On integrating over the $w^0$ part of the phase space, the contributions of all terms in this multiple Fourier development of $p_z^2$ vanish except the constant term $(p_z^2)_0$, for integrals of the periodic terms in the $w^0$'s taken over a period are zero. By the rules for multiplying together two Fourier series term by term, $(p_z^2)_0$ equals $\sum_{\tau} p_{\tau}^{(z)} p_{-\tau}^{(z)}$, which is, of course, a function only of the $J^0$'s. Eq. (21) now becomes

$$\chi = \frac{N \int ... \int (p_z^2)_0 e^{-\mathcal{H}_0/kT} \, dJ^0}{kT \int ... \int e^{-\mathcal{H}_0/kT} \, dJ^0} = \frac{N\overline{\overline{p_z^2}}}{kT},$$

where $\overline{\overline{p_z^2}}$ denotes the statistical mean square of $p_z^2$ in the absence of the field $E$, i.e. the average over only the $J^0$ part of the phase space, weighted according to the Boltzmann factor, of the time-average value of $p_z^2$ for a molecule having given values of the $J^0$'s. Now if the applied electric field $E$ is the only external field, all spacial orientations will be equally probable when $E = 0$, and the mean squares of the $x$, $y$, and $z$

components of moment will be equal. This will also be true even when there are other external fields (e.g. a magnetic field) besides the given electric field provided, as is usually the case, these other fields do not greatly affect the spacial distribution. We may hence replace $\overline{\overline{p_z^2}}$ by one-third the statistical mean square of the vector moment $\mathbf{p}$ of the molecule. Thus we have

$$\chi = \frac{N\overline{\overline{\mathbf{p}^2}}}{3kT} \tag{22}$$

which is a sort of generalized Langevin-Debye formula. It is much more comprehensive than the ordinary Eq. (1), since the statistical mean square moment in (22) must not be confused with the time average for an individual molecule, and is in general a function of the temperature.

Eq. (22) gives the same temperature dependence as the ordinary Langevin-Debye formula (1) only if we make certain specializing assumptions concerning the nature of the multiply periodic dynamical system, such that the mean square moment $\overline{\overline{\mathbf{p}^2}}$ becomes a linear function $AT+B$ of the temperature. Such a specialization can be achieved by assuming, as in § 12, that the molecule can be represented by a model consisting of harmonic oscillators mounted on a rigid, freely rotating framework of moments of inertia $A_{x'}, A_{y'}, A_{z'}$. Then the instantaneous moment $\mathbf{p}$ is a linear function of the normal coordinates $\xi_i$, so that the components of $\mathbf{p}$ along the principal axes of the molecule are given by expressions of the form (5). With the model of § 12 the molecule is supposed to have a permanent moment of invariant magnitude $\mu$, so that there is no distinction between $\overline{\overline{\mu^2}}$ and $\mu^2$. Furthermore,

$$\overline{\overline{\xi_i}} = 0, \qquad \overline{\overline{\xi_i \xi_j}} = 0, \qquad \tfrac{1}{2}a_i \overline{\overline{\xi_i^2}} = \tfrac{1}{2}kT. \tag{23}$$

The first two of these relations are obvious since positive and negative values of the displacements of the oscillators from their equilibrium positions are equally probable. The third relation of (23) is the well-known classical equipartition theorem that the mean of the potential energy $\tfrac{1}{2}a_i \xi_i^2$ of each normal vibration is $\tfrac{1}{2}kT$. Eqs. (5) and (23) show that $\overline{\overline{p_{x'}^2}} = \mu_{x'}^2 + kT \sum c_{x'i}^2/a_i$, &c., and so (22) becomes identical with (18), the desired result. It is seen that the present method, although requiring more dynamical background, furnishes a much briefer means of deriving (18) than that given in the preceding section (§ 12). The present method is equally rigorous, as the kinetic energy terms are included in the Hamiltonian function, although it is not even necessary to write out their explicit form. The rotational part $N\mu^2/3kT$ follows particularly easily from (22), as the calculation is not a bit more complicated for the most unsymmetrical molecule, with three unequal moments of inertia, than for symmetrical ones. We have seen fit to include both methods of deriving (18), partly because they furnish an interesting contrast, and partly because some readers may not be familiar with action and angle variables. The method of these variables is exceedingly compact and general, but for this very reason perhaps does not furnish as much physical insight as the more explicit and longer representation by means of the ordinary Eulerian and normal 'positional' coordinates and momenta used in § 12.

A model such as we have used, in which the electronic motions are represented by harmonic oscillators, is not compatible with modern knowledge of atomic structure. We know that actually the electrons are subject to inverse square rather than linear restoring forces, and move in approximately Keplerian orbits instead of executing simple harmonic vibrations about positions of static equilibrium. In fact Earnshaw's theorem in electrostatics tells us that there are no such positions for all the charges. In actual molecules, to be sure, the motions of the nuclei, in distinction from electrons, can be regarded as approximately simple harmonic motions about equilibrium, as the nuclei are sluggish because of their large masses, but for this very reason the amplitudes of their vibrations are so small that the contribution of these oscillations to the susceptibility is usually small, though not always negligible. This will be shown in § 15. Hence the part of the molecular motion which is really simple harmonic is of secondary importance for susceptibilities. Inasmuch as we have deduced a generalized Langevin-Debye formula for any multiply periodic system, the question naturally arises whether Eq. (22) cannot be specialized in a fashion appropriate to a real Rutherford atom instead of to a fictitious system of oscillators mounted on a rigid rotating framework. This, however, is not possible. The reason is that in classical statistics the energy ordinarily ranges from 0 to $\infty$, whereas in a Rutherford atom it ranges from 0 (the value for infinitely loosely bound electrons) to $-\infty$ (the value for infinitely tight binding). The numerical value of the energy is the same as that of the Hamiltonian function $\mathcal{H}$, and hence the Boltzmann probability factor $Ce^{-\mathcal{H}/kT}$ increases without limit as the energy approaches $-\infty$, so that the total integrated probability $C \int ... \int e^{-\mathcal{H}/kT} \, dw^0 dJ^0$ cannot equal unity, as required by (56), Chap. I, unless $C = 0$. Thus, although (22) summarizes rather elegantly all the results of classical statistics applied to susceptibilities, the practical advantages of the increased generality of (22) as compared to (1) or (18) are somewhat restricted because of the inherent limitations in classical theory.

# DIELECTRIC CONSTANTS, REFRACTION, AND THE MEASUREMENT OF ELECTRIC MOMENTS

## 14. Relation of Polarity to the Extrapolated Refractive Index

In the present chapter we shall examine the experimental confirmation of the Langevin-Debye formula derived in Chapter II, but it will first be necessary in §§ 14–18 to discuss some related topics in the theory of refractive indices.

In § 4 we saw that the static dielectric constant should equal the extrapolation of $n^2$, the square of the index of refraction, to infinite wave-length. That $n$ is really a function of frequency or wave-length can be seen from the following very elementary form of the Drude dispersion theory.[1] Suppose that a particle of charge $e_i$ and mass $m_i$ is harmonically and isotropically bound to a position of equilibrium. If $a_i$ and $\mathbf{r}_i - \mathbf{r}_i^0$ denote respectively the coefficient of restitution and the vector displacement from equilibrium, the particle's equation of motion when subject to an incident electromagnetic wave of frequency $\nu_0$ is

$$m_i \frac{d^2\mathbf{r}_i}{dt^2} + a_i(\mathbf{r}_i - \mathbf{r}_i^0) = e_i \mathbf{E}_0 \cos 2\pi\nu_0 t, \tag{1}$$

where $\mathbf{E}_0$ is the vector amplitude of the electric field of the wave. Eq. (1) is merely that of a forced harmonic vibrator, and as the natural oscillation frequency of the particle is $\nu_i = a_i^{\frac{1}{2}}/2\pi m_i^{\frac{1}{2}}$, the solution of (1) may be written

$$\mathbf{r}_i - \mathbf{r}_i^0 = \frac{e_i \mathbf{E}_0 \cos 2\pi\nu_0 t}{4\pi^2 m_i(\nu_i^2 - \nu_0^2)}.$$

The total induced polarization of the molecule is $\mathbf{p} = \sum e_i(\mathbf{r}_i - \mathbf{r}_i^0)$, where the summation extends over all its charges. Hence the index of refraction is given by

$$n^2 - 1 = \frac{4\pi\mathbf{P}}{\mathbf{E}} = \frac{4\pi N\mathbf{p}}{\mathbf{E}_0 \cos 2\pi\nu_0 t} = 4\pi N \sum \frac{e_i^2}{4\pi^2 m_i(\nu_i^2 - \nu_0^2)}. \tag{2}$$

Eq. (2) yields a dispersion curve of the familiar Sellmeier form characteristic of classical theory. It is well known that by proper adjustment of the natural frequencies $\nu_i$ and of the effective charges and masses $e_i$, $m_i$, Eq. (2) can be made to represent quite well the observed variation of refraction with frequency. There is, however, the difficulty that the values of $e_i$ and $m_i$ which must be assumed are not the true values of either electronic or nuclear charges and masses. We shall see in § 82

---

[1] Cf., for instance, Drude, *Theory of Optics*, Chaps. V–VII.

that the quantum mechanics also yields a dispersion curve of the Sellmeier type, but without this difficulty in the interpretation of the constants. Eq. (2) might be generalized by assuming that the restoring forces are non-isotropic, somewhat along the lines of the model used in § 12. This generalization has commonly been made in the literature,[1] and is, of course, necessary for optically anisotropic media. It will, however, be omitted here to avoid devotion of too much space to antique models based on positions of static equilibrium for the electrons.

We are interested especially in the behaviour of Eq. (2) in the region of infinitely long incident waves. Here $\nu_0 = 0$, and (2) becomes

$$n_\infty^2 - 1 = 4\pi N \sum e_i^2 / 4\pi^2 m_i \nu_i^2.$$

On comparing with the value of $\alpha$ derived for the isotropic model in the first paragraph of § 11, we see that $n_\infty^2 - 1 = 4\pi N\alpha$. Hence, according to (2) the square of the index of refraction extrapolates for infinite wave-lengths to the part $1 + 4\pi N\alpha$ of the dielectric constant arising from the induced polarization rather than to the complete dielectric constant $1 + 4\pi N(\alpha + \mu^2/3kT)$. The reason is, of course, that in the preceding paragraph we have neglected entirely all polarization by orientation. We ought therefore to add to the right side of (2) a term $O(\mu, \nu_0, T)$ representing the orientation effect, and reducing to $4\pi N\mu^2/3kT$ when $\nu_0 = 0$. We shall not give the explicit calculation of $O$, as this is more difficult in the periodic as distinct from the static case owing to the necessity of having a statistical theory of non-conservative systems. Even without such a calculation it is quite apparent that the term $O$ must be negligible at ordinary optical frequencies, since the electromagnetic forces associated with visible light oscillate so rapidly in sign that they do not act in any direction long enough to orient the molecules in that direction.[2] The orientation term $O$ would first become significant

---

[2] Simple dimensional considerations show that the orienting effect of the field on the permanent dipoles is negligible at optical wave-lengths. Optical frequencies are very large compared to the frequencies of collisions or of molecular rotations. Hence the temperature cannot enter into the contribution of the orientation to the optical index of refraction. In other words the forces resisting the orientation of dipoles by fields of high frequency are inertial rather than statistical. If $I$ and $\mu$ denote respectively the moment of inertia and electrical moment of the molecule, the part $n_{\text{rot}}^2 - 1$ of the refraction due to the orientation effect will involve the arguments $I$, $\mu$, $N$, $\nu_0$. As the dimensions of these expressions are respectively $ml^2$, $m^{1/2} l^{5/2}/t$, $l^{-3}$, $t^{-1}$ and as $n_{\text{rot}}^2 - 1$ is dimensionless and is linear in $N$, it must be given by an expression of the form const. $N\mu^2/I\nu_0^2$. This is also quite evident by comparison with (2), as $\mu$, $I$ are the rotational analogues of the expressions $e$, $m$ found in rectilinear problems. The contribution of the permanent dipoles to the static dielectric constant is of the order $N\mu^2/kT$. The orientation effect is therefore smaller in the periodic than in the static case by a ratio of the order $kT/I\nu_0^2$, or $10^{-4}$ as $kT \sim 10^{-13}$, $I \sim 10^{-39}$, $\nu_0 \sim 10^{15}$.

in gases when the incident frequency is comparable with the rotation frequencies of the molecule. This requires a frequency far in the infra-red (10 to 100 microns). Hence a series of measurements of indices of refraction made at optical frequencies will reveal practically no trace of the orientation term, and so the extrapolation of such data to infinite wave-length will yield only the part of the dielectric constant exclusive of the orientation effect.

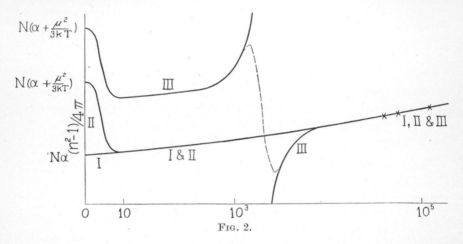

FIG. 2.

We have attempted to illustrate this graphically in Fig. 2. The curves I and II represent respectively the values of $n^2-1$ exclusive and inclusive of the orientation effect. The theoretical values of the intersection of these two curves with the axis of zero frequency are respectively $N\alpha$ and $N(\alpha+\mu^2/3kT)$. If the molecule is polar the curve II will lie con-siderably above curve I in the region of very small frequencies, as it contains a large contribution from orientation. This contribution is, however, rapidly blotted out when the frequency is increased, so that the two curves are sensibly the same when the incident frequency exceeds the natural molecular rotation frequencies. The actual disper-sion of the material is given by curve II rather than curve I, but any one attempting to extrapolate to zero frequency a series of measure-ments made in the optical region, represented by crosses in the figure, would naturally follow curve I, since the measurements do not sensibly reveal the rise in the actual curve near the origin $\nu_0 = 0$. In drawing curves I and II of Fig. 2 we have supposed that the molecule's natural frequencies all lie in the ultra-violet, in order not to complicate the curve with 'resonance catastrophes' in which some of the denominators in (2) become zero.

The fact that the natural extrapolation of optical refractivities follows curve I rather than curve II furnishes a second method of experimentally determining electrical moments which is an alternative to the first method, that of temperature variation of the dielectric constant already mentioned in § 10. Let $n_\infty^2$ be the extrapolation of the square of the index of refraction to zero frequency, exclusive of the orientation term which is undetectable in the optical region. Let $\epsilon$ be the measured static dielectric constant, which of course includes the polarization arising from orientation of permanent dipoles as well as the induced polarization. Then

$$\epsilon - n_\infty^2 = \frac{4\pi N \mu^2}{3kT} \tag{3}$$

as the Langevin-Debye formula (1), Chap. II, shows that $4\pi N\mu^2/3kT$ is the part of $\epsilon$ arising from the orientation effect. Hence, knowing $n_\infty$, $\epsilon$ and the temperature and density, the electric moment can be determined without the necessity of varying the temperature. The numerical values of the electric moments obtained by the two methods will be compared in § 19.

## 15. Effect of Infra-red Vibration Bands. The 'Atomic Polarization'.

There is sometimes considerable discrepancy between the values of the electric moments deduced by the two methods, or, what is the same thing, the value of $n_\infty^2 - 1$ deduced by extrapolation does not agree with the value of $4\pi N\alpha$ deduced from the temperature variation of the dielectric constant. To account for such disagreements it has often been suggested[3] that the dielectric constant is appreciably influenced by infra-red absorption bands associated with vibrations of the nuclei and revealed in the ordinary 'vibration spectrum' of molecules such as HCl. Suppose, for instance, that the molecule is diatomic. Let $m_{\text{eff}}$ be the effective mass $m_1 m_2/(m_1 + m_2)$ of the nuclei, $\nu_{\text{vib}}$ be the frequency of vibration of the nuclei along their line of centres, and $e_{\text{eff}}$ be the corresponding effective charge, which is defined as the rate of change $d\mu/dr$ of the magnitude of the electrical moment $\mu$ with the inter-nuclear distance $r$. The contribution of this vibration to $n^2$ is

$$\frac{N e_{\text{eff}}^2}{3\pi m_{\text{eff}}(\nu_{\text{vib}}^2 - \nu_0^2)}. \tag{4}$$

[3] Cf., for instance, Debye, *Handbuch der Radiologie*, vi. 620, 'Polar Molecules', p. 43; L. Ebert, *Die Naturwissenschaften*, **14**, 919 (1926); H. A. Stuart, *Zeits. f. Physik*, **51**, 499 (1928); Sänger and Steiger, *Hel. Phys. Acta* **2**, 144 (1929).

This can be seen from Eq. (2); the factor $\frac{1}{3}$, however, must be inserted because the vibration under consideration has only one degree of freedom rather than three as does the isotropic oscillator assumed in Eqs. (1), (2). The result (4), incidently, remains valid with quantum mechanics, as the classical and quantum theories yield identical results for the harmonic oscillator, and as there is no need of improving our model of the nuclear oscillations in the new theory inasmuch as the nuclei, in distinction from electrons, really do have positions of static equilibrium.[4] By (4) the contribution of the infra-red vibration to the static dielectric constant, corresponding to $\nu_0 = 0$, is $Ne_{\text{eff}}^2/3\pi m_{\text{eff}}\nu_{\text{vib}}^2$. Because of their large masses, the nuclei vibrate slowly, so that the frequency $\nu_{\text{vib}}$ is in the infra-red, and very small compared to the incident frequency $\nu_0$ if $\nu_0$ is in the visible region. By (4) the contribution of the nuclear vibration to $n^2$ in the latter region is approximately $-Ne_{\text{eff}}^2/3\pi m_{\text{eff}}\nu_0^2$, and hence negligible in comparison with its contribution to the static dielectric constant. Thus the apparent extrapolation of measured optical refractivities to zero frequency will not include the effect of the infra-red vibration band, besides also, of course, omitting the polarization by orientation of permanent dipoles, as previously mentioned. This is illustrated by curve III of Fig. 2, p. 44. This curve is drawn inclusive of the contribution of this band, while the other curves are exclusive. Optical measurements indicated by crosses would clearly not reveal the difference between curve III and I or II. The curve III, of course, shows a discontinuity at the resonance point $\nu_0 = \nu_{\text{vib}}$. The part of the polarization arising from the difference between curves III and II is sometimes termed 'the atomic polarization', as it is due to oscillations in the positions of the atomic masses (or more accurately nuclei) within the molecule, in contrast to the 'electronic polarization' due to changes in the electronic positions without appreciable motion of the nuclei.

The foregoing shows that because of the infra-red nuclear vibration, the term $4\pi N\alpha$ in the static dielectric constant should exceed $n_\infty^2 - 1$ by an amount

$$4\pi N\alpha - (n_\infty^2 - 1) = \frac{Ne_{\text{eff}}^2}{3\pi m_{\text{eff}}\nu_{\text{vib}}^2}. \tag{5}$$

The predicted sign of this difference is that found experimentally in the majority of cases. In HCl, for instance, Zahn[5] finds $4\pi N\alpha = 0\cdot001040$

---

[4] Strictly speaking this statement is not true, as there are always rapidly varying instantaneous forces on the nuclei due to the continual changes in the positions of the electrons. Such forces, however, vanish on averaging over the electronic periods of motion, which are very short, and hence are inconsequential.

[5] C. T. Zahn, *Phys. Rev.* **24**, 400 (1924).

at 0° C., 76 cm., whereas extrapolation of C. and M. Cuthbertson's[6] dispersion data gives the smaller value $n_\infty^2 - 1 = 0 \cdot 000871$.

*Determination of $e_{\text{eff}}$ from Absorption Intensities.* In order to evaluate (5) it is necessary to know the magnitude of $e_{\text{eff}}$, which need not be at all like the charge of an electron or nucleus, as it is by definition not the charge of a single particle, but rather the differential coefficient $d\mu/dr$ of the total molecular moment by inter-nuclear distance. For a non-polar diatomic molecule, for instance, $e_{\text{eff}}$ is zero. One method of determination of $e_{\text{eff}}$ is by measurement of the absolute intensities of infra-red vibration bands, usually studied in absorption rather than emission. The absorption coefficient is proportional to $(\mu - \mu_0)^2$, and hence very approximately to $e_{\text{eff}}^2(r - r_0^2)$. The most accurate infra-red intensity measurements are probably those of Bourgin[7] for HCl, who finds that here $e_{\text{eff}} = 0 \cdot 86 \times 10^{-10}$ e.s.u. Introducing this value of $e_{\text{eff}}$ and the values $m_{\text{eff}} = 1 \cdot 62 \times 10^{-24}$, $\nu_{\text{vib}} = 8 \cdot 82 \times 10^{13}$ of the effective mass and vibrational frequency of HCl, we find that the right side of (5) is only $1 \cdot 5 \times 10^{-6}$, whereas we have seen that the experimental value of the left side is $1 \cdot 7 \times 10^{-4}$. Values of the effective charge have also been calculated by Dennison[8] for HBr, CO, $CO_2$, $NH_3$, $CH_4$ from various intensity measurements. These values are all less than one-fifth the charge $4 \cdot 77 \times 10^{-10}$ of an electron; correspondingly, the expression (5) should be of the order $10^{-6}$, and hence negligible.[9] Of course, absolute intensities and hence values of the effective charge are hard to measure with precision, but to account for a discrepancy between $4\pi N\alpha$ and $n_\infty^2 - 1$ as large as that $1 \cdot 7 \times 10^{-4}$ in HCl, for instance, the effective charge would have to be about $8 \cdot 7 \times 10^{-10}$ instead of $0 \cdot 86 \times 10^{-10}$ e.s.u. Since the absorption coefficient varies as $e_{\text{eff}}^2$, the measurement of the absorption coefficient would have to be in error by a factor 100.

As an instance of the difficulty of making accurate absolute, as distinct from relative, intensity measurements, we may cite the inability to deduce reliable values of the electric moment from the absolute intensities of 'pure rotation' absorption lines in the far infra-red (not to be confused with the vibration lines

[6] C. and M. Cuthbertson, *Phil. Trans. Roy. Soc.* **213**A, 1 (1913).

[7] D. G. Bourgin, *Phys. Rev.* **29**, 794 (1927). Dennison deduces from Bourgin's absorption data the effective charge $0 \cdot 949 \times 10^{-10}$ e.s.u. (*Phys. Rev.* **31**, 501, 1928). He claims this to be more accurate than Bourgin's original value $0 \cdot 828 \times 10^{-10}$. Still later Bourgin raised slightly his own estimate to $0 \cdot 86 \times 10^{-10}$ (*Phys. Rev.* **32**, 237, 1928). For our purposes it makes no appreciable difference which value is used.

[8] D. M. Dennison, *Phil. Mag.* **1**, 195 (1926).

[9] This quantitative calculation of the contribution of the infra-red vibrations to the dielectric constant by means of the effective charges yielded by absorption measurements was first made by the writer, *Phys. Rev.* **30**, 43 (1927). The difficulty of the negligible contributions thus obtained appears to be too commonly overlooked in the literature.

in the nearer infra-red). The amount of absorption or emission in the pure rotational spectrum is proportional to the square of the electric moment $\mu$, (rather than of $e_{eff}$) and so should yield the numerical value of $\mu$ if absolute absorption measurements can be made. An attempt to determine $\mu$ in this fashion was first made by Tolman and Badger,[10] using Czerny's absorption data on HCl.[11] (Explicitly they calculated the intensity from the moment rather than the moment from the intensity, but the two calculations are simple converses.) The value thus found for the electrical moment of the HCl molecule is less than one-third the standard value $1 \cdot 03 \times 10^{-18}$ obtained from Zahn's measurements of the temperature variation of the dielectric constant. Subsequently Badger[12] repeated Czerny's experiments in the hope of removing this discrepancy, but instead increased it, as he found an absorption only one-half as great as Czerny's. Thus the absolute measurements of absorption intensities in the pure rotation spectrum are apparently in error by a factor about 10 to 20. The determinations of absorption in the vibration spectrum which are used in calculating the effective charge are presumably much more reliable, as they are in a much easier spectral region less far out in the infra-red. Even the vibration intensities, however, are difficult to measure as exemplified by the fact that Bahrs' and Burmeister's early intensity data on HCl yielded according to Dennison's calculations[8] an absorption coefficient only one-sixth as great as that furnished by Bourgin's recent work. The latter is presumably much more accurate, and Bourgin himself explicitly states[13] that he does not think that there can be anything like enough error to permit an appreciable vibrational contribution to the dielectric constant in HCl.

Thus the measurements on absorption intensities, if at all accurate, show that in molecules such as the hydrogen halides, the polarization due to infra-red vibration is too small to have any bearing on the discrepancy between the extrapolated square of the refractive index and the part of the dielectric constant due to induced polarization.

*Determination of $e_{eff}$ from Infra-Red Dispersion.* A series of dispersion measurements in the infra-red should definitely settle whether the atomic polarization does really give an appreciable contribution to the dielectric constants. That is to say, such measurements would enable one to calculate the 'effective charge' by means of formula (4) and the values of $e_{eff}$ thus obtained would presumably be much more reliable than those deduced from absorption coefficients. Unfortunately the available determinations of refraction sufficiently far in the infra-red are rather limited in number. Koch[14] measured the refractive indices of $O_2$, $H_2$, CO, $CO_2$, and $CH_4$ at $6 \cdot 709\mu$ and at $8 \cdot 678\mu$, while Statescu[15]

[10] Tolman and Badger, *Phys. Rev.* **27**, 383 (1926). In reading this paper, also ref. 12, the electrical moment should be calculated by means of Eq. (1), Chapter II, rather than by a formula of the old quantum theory which they give.

[11] Czerny, *Zeits. f. Physik*, **34**, 227 (1926).

[12] Badger, *Proc. Nat. Acad.* **13**, 408 (1926).

[13] D. G. Bourgin, *Phys. Rev.* **32**, 249 (1928).

[14] J. Koch, *Nova Acta Soc. Upsala*, **2**, No. 5 (1909).

[15] J. Statescu, *Phil. Mag.* **30**, 737 (1915).

even succeeded in measuring $CO_2$ at a wave-length as long as $13.19\mu$, and in addition supplemented Koch's data for $CO_2$ by various measurements between 1 and $11\mu$. The data are thus much more complete for $CO_2$ than for any other gas.

Koch's work on $H_2$ and $O_2$ failed to reveal any anomalies in the infra-red, as was undoubtedly to be expected since non-polar diatomic molecules have no pure vibration spectra. The value $1.000332$ which he found for the index of refraction $n$ of CO at both $6.7\mu$ and $8.7\mu$ was slightly lower than that in the optical region (e.g. $1.000335$ at $0.589\mu$) and agreed quite well with the value $1.000327$ which would be obtained by extrapolation of optical data with neglect of vibrational resonance points. This is particularly significant since the fundamental band of CO is at $4.65\mu$, so that Koch's measurements extended beyond the vibrational singularity. The slight discrepancy between $1.000332$ and $1.000327$ may be merely experimental error or perhaps indicate that there is a very small contribution $0.000005$ of the atomic polarization to $n-1$ or $0.00001$ to $n^2-1$. Such a contribution is of no consequence for our studies of dipole moments, as it is smaller than the precision with which dielectric constants can be measured experimentally. Even such a very small contribution, if real, would demand an effective charge of the order $0.9e$, whereas Dennison[8] estimated $0.13e$ from the absorption data of Burmeister[16] and of Coblentz.[17]

A more striking result is obtained in carbon dioxide. The following values of the index of refraction are found by Koch or by Statescu at various wave-lengths:

| $\lambda =$ | $1.0$ | $2.0$ | $3.0$ | $4.0$ | $5.0$ | $6.7$ | $8.7$ | $11$ | $13.19\,\mu$ |
|---|---|---|---|---|---|---|---|---|---|
| $(n-1)\times 10^4 =$ | $4.41$ | $4.34$ | $4.18$ | $2.89$ | $5.32$ | $4.84$ | $4.58$ | $4.47$ | $4.00$ |

The behaviour is thus different from that given by an ordinary optical dispersion formula which takes no cognizance of infra-red resonance points, and which predicts a steady and very gradual decrease of $n$ from its value $1.000449$ at optical wave-lengths (Na D lines) to a value $1.000441$ at infinite wave-lengths.[18] The anomalies shown by the table at $4.0$ and $5.0\mu$ are due to the influence of the vibration band at $4.3\mu$. The abnormally low value $1.000400$ of $n$ at the longest wave-length

[16] B. Burmeister, *Verh. d. D. Phys. Ges.* **15**, 589 (1913).

[17] W. W. Coblentz, *Investigations of Infra-red Spectra*, Part I, Carnegie Institute of Washington, 1905.

[18] Here, and also in the preceding discussion of CO, we make the extrapolations by means of the dispersion formulae given for $CO_2$ and for CO by C. and M. Cuthbertson, *Proc. Roy. Soc.* **97**A, 152 (1920). These formulae are typical of those based only on measurements in the visible and ultra-violet regions.

$13\cdot19\,\mu$ is undoubtedly because of another known vibration band at $14\cdot9\mu$. Reference to curve III, p. 44, shows that the index of refraction should be abnormally low on the short wave-length or high-frequency side of a resonance point, but high on the long wave-length side. Hence if measurements were available beyond $14\cdot9\mu$, they would record a value of $n$ considerably larger than the value $1\cdot00044$ given by an ordinary optical dispersion formula. Fuchs[19] has made a very careful comparison of the existing dispersion data for $CO_2$, and has proposed a dispersion formula which represents the experimental points in the infra-red as well as optical region. The characteristic feature of his formula is that, besides the ordinary terms due to resonance with visible or ultra-violet frequencies, it contains two terms of the form (4) in which the resonance wave-lengths are taken as respectively $4\cdot31\mu$ and $14\cdot91\mu$, and in which the effective charges are taken to be $2\cdot28e$ and $0\cdot61e$, where $e = 4\cdot77\times10^{-10}$ e.s.u. Dennison[8] deduced an effective charge of only $0\cdot09e$ for the $14\cdot9\mu$ vibration from the measurements of absorption intensities by Coblentz[17] and by Rubens and Aschkinass.[20] Since determinations of absorption coefficients are probably much more difficult to put on a quantitative basis than those on dispersion, and since the absorption coefficient varies as the square of the effective charge it thus appears that existing measurements on absorption coefficients for the $14\cdot9$ band in $CO_2$ are too small by a factor no less than $(0\cdot61/0\cdot09)^2$ or almost fifty, despite the fact that the data of Coblentz[17] and of Rubens and Aschkinass,[20] according to Dennison,[8] agree with each other to within 20 per cent. Evidence that Fuchs's larger values of the effective charge are correct is furnished by the behaviour of the dispersion formulae at infinite wave-lengths. An ordinary dispersion formula such as that of Cuthbertson, which includes no atomic polarization, yields $n_\infty^2 - 1 = 1\cdot000882$, whereas Fuchs's formula with the two infra-red resonance points yields $n_\infty^2 - 1 = 1\cdot000975$. The value which Zahn[21] finds for the dielectric constant of $CO_2$ under standard conditions is $1\cdot000968$, while Stuart[22] finds $1\cdot000987$. Hence, according to the Cuthbertson formula, the expression (3) is appreciably different from zero,

[19] O. Fuchs, *Zeits. f. Physik*, **46**, 519 (1927). We interpret Fuchs's formula in terms of an effective charge different from $e$ rather than in terms of an 'effective number of dispersion electrons' $p_i$ per vibration, which has no real physical significance, as $p_i$ is not an integer. Our effective charge is connected with his number $p_i$ according to the relation $(e_{\mathrm{eff}}/e)^2 = 3p_i$. The factor 3 appears in this relation because he assumed the vibrations have three degrees of freedom rather than one.

[20] Rubens and Aschkinass, *Ann. der Physik u. Chem.* **64**, 584 (1898).

[21] C. T. Zahn, *Phys. Rev.* **27**, 455 (1926).

[22] H. A. Stuart, *Zeits. f. Physik*, **47**, 457 (1928).

and yields an electric moment $0.18 \times 10^{-18}$ e.s.u. for the $CO_2$ molecule, whereas, according to the Fuchs formula, the expression (3) is zero within the experimental error and then $CO_2$ has no electric moment. This point was first noted by Wolf.[23] It is the consensus of opinion that the carbon dioxide molecule is without an electric moment, as this is shown, for one thing, by Stuart's[22] investigation of the temperature variation of the dielectric constant. The large effective charge assumed by Fuchs is, as we have seen, in nice quantitative agreement with this view.

It may be noted that the Fuchs's dispersion formula has only two infra-red resonance points. It is well known that the $CO_2$ molecule has numerous other infra-red vibration bands besides those at $4.3\mu$ and $14.9\mu$.[24] The fact that the dispersion measurements can be fitted quite well with only two resonance points must mean that these other vibrations have very low effective charges, or, much more probably, have low amplitudes on account of being 'combinations' or 'harmonics' rather than fundamentals. It is particularly noteworthy that the measurements at $2\mu$ and $3\mu$ can be fitted without including any term due to resonance with the quite pronounced absorption band at $2.72\mu$.

In his dissertation (Upsala, 1924), not available to the writer, Torsten Wetterblatt is reported to have explored the dispersion in the vicinity of $2.72\mu$, and to find only a very slight anomaly when very close to this band, thus indicating pretty clearly that it is a harmonic or combination rather than a fundamental. In general a triatomic molecule has three fundamental modes of vibration, but the third fundamental may not show up in dispersion because it is an 'inactive' or 'symmetrical' mode of vibration which gives rise to no oscillating electric moment. As mentioned by Wolf, the absence of a third intense resonance point in the infra-red dispersion lends considerable weight to Eucken's suggestion[24] that $CO_2$ has an 'inactive' fundamental vibration at about $8\mu$. Inactive fundamentals are still allowed as Raman lines, and this $8\mu$ vibration does indeed play a leading part in the Raman effect of $CO_2$, although the behaviour is irregular because of a complicated 'perturbation' by the harmonic of another vibration.[25]

The tremendous discrepancy between the effective charges deduced from absorption and from dispersion measurements for the $14.9$ band of $CO_2$ makes one sceptical whether any information about the order of magnitude of the atomic polarization can be deduced from existing absorption data. Perhaps the best appraisal is that the effect of the atomic polarization on the dielectric constant is negligible in stable diatomic molecules, but not necessarily in molecules with more than two atoms. Our grounds for suggesting a smaller atomic polarization for diatomic than for polyatomic molecules are that: (a) there are no

[23] K. L. Wolf, *Zeits. f. Phys. Chem.* **131**, 90 (1927).

[24] See, for instance, the analysis by A. Eucken, *Zeits. f. Physik*, **37**, 714 (1926); based on absorption curves by Schaefer and Phillips, *ibid.* **36**, 641 (1926).

[25] See E. Fermi, *Zeits. f. Physik*, **71**, 250 (1931).

very glaring discrepancies for diatomic molecules between the electric moments deduced from (3) and from the temperature variation of the dielectric constant (see table, § 19); (b) Bourgin's recent determinations of absorption intensities in HCl are probably more accurate than the early work of other investigators on $CO_2$; (c) the dispersion measurements reveal a considerably smaller effective charge for CO than for the $4 \cdot 3\mu$ vibration of $CO_2$; (d) one of the various fundamental vibrations in a polyatomic molecule usually has a longer wave-length and hence gives a smaller denominator in (5) than the sole vibration in a diatomic molecule. For the latter reason the $14 \cdot 9\mu$ vibration makes almost as large a contribution to the atomic polarization of $CO_2$ in the Fuchs formula at infinite wave-lengths as does the $4 \cdot 3\mu$ vibration, despite the fact that the latter has a considerably larger effective charge.

Evidence that the atomic polarization is appreciable in polyatomic molecules is not confined to $CO_2$, but is also revealed by the limited number of infra-red dispersion measurements available for methane $(CH_4)$, viz. $n = 1 \cdot 000419$ at $6 \cdot 557\mu$ and $n = 1 \cdot 000450$ at $8 \cdot 678\mu$. These measurements are, of course, insufficient to disclose the proper dispersion formula, but if the anomalies which they exhibit are attributed to the influence of the vibration band at $7 \cdot 7\mu$, the effective charge must be roughly $0 \cdot 20e$,[26] again larger than the effective charge $0 \cdot 095e$ deduced by Dennison[8] from the absorption measurements by Coblentz. An effective charge $0 \cdot 20e$ for this vibration, will remove about one-tenth of the discrepancy between Sänger's value[27] $0 \cdot 00096$ for $\epsilon - 1$ and the value $0 \cdot 00086$ for $(n^2 - 1)_\infty$ obtained by extrapolation of optical dispersion data without considering the atomic polarization. As Sänger's investigation of the temperature variation of the dielectric constant of $CH_4$ shows that it has no electric moment, the discrepancy should disappear completely when proper corrections are made, and the other nine-tenths of the discrepancy may be either experimental error or due to additional infra-red resonance points besides that at $7 \cdot 7\mu$.

It may be noted that in diatomic molecules such as HCl, often the discrepancy between $n_\infty^2 - 1$ and $4\pi N\alpha$ is only a fraction of $4\pi N\alpha$ and that $\alpha$ itself is often small compared to $\mu^2/3kT$. Then either a small experimental error in the absolute value of the total dielectric constant or else in the electric moment, i.e. in the temperature coefficient of $\epsilon$, will suffice to explain away the discrepancy between $4\pi N\alpha$ and $n_\infty^2 - 1$. In HCl, for instance, an increase in the moment from Zahn's value[5] $1 \cdot 034$ to $1 \cdot 06 \times 10^{-18}$ e.s.u. (which corresponds to an error of 6 per cent. in the temperature coefficient of $\epsilon/N$) will increase the contribution of the permanent dipoles to the dielectric constant enough so that the remainder $4\pi N\alpha$ to be ascribed to the induced polarization is decreased to a value $0 \cdot 000871$ in accord with optical data. The discrepancy is also removed if, instead of changing $\mu$, we assume that the correct value of $\epsilon$ at $273°$, 76 cm. is $1 \cdot 00399$ rather than $1 \cdot 00416$. In ammonia the polarization due to the permanent moments so far overshadows the induced

[26] To generalize the vibration formula (4) to molecules with more than two atoms, in particular $CH_4$, it is necessary to replace $m_i$ by $m_i(g_0/g_i)/F_i^2$, where $F_i$ and $g_0/g_i$ are dissymmetry and statistical weight factors explained in Dennison's paper.[8]

[27] R. Sänger, *Phys. Zeits.* **27**, 556 (1926).

polarization that an increase of only 0·3 per cent. in the moment, a change clearly within the experimental error, will diminish Zahn's[21] value 0·000768 for $4\pi N\alpha$ to a value 0·000729 in accord with the Cuthbertson[6] dispersion data.

Often improvement in experimental technique in the temperature variation method has increased the values of the electrical moment and hence decreased the apparent excess of $4\pi N\alpha$ over $n_\infty^2 - 1$. A rather extreme example is the case of ethyl ether. From a study of old data by various experimenters on the temperature variation of its dielectric constant, Debye concluded in the *Handbuch der Radiologie* (vi, p. 625) that its electric moment was $\mu = 0·84 \times 10^{-18}$, and that its value of $4\pi L\alpha/3$ was 38 cm⁻³. In order to make closer connexion with the usage in the literature, we here give the value of $4\pi L\alpha/3$ where $L$ is the Avogadro number, instead of $4\pi N\alpha$. The expression $4\pi L\alpha/3$ is called by Debye the induced molar polarization, or better, polarizability, and will be denoted by the letter $\kappa_0$.[28] It differs from $4\pi N\alpha$ only by a factor $L/3N$ depending solely on density, and has the advantage of being a molar quantity not requiring the specification of pressure or temperature. The value of $(n_\infty^2 - 1)L/3N$ obtained by extrapolation of dispersion data is about 22. (Debye originally gave 22·8, but Stuart suggests that a more accurate value is 22·0.[29]) The discrepancy between 22 and 38 was so great that elsewhere the writer considered it too great to attribute to experimental error.[9] The possibility of sufficient experimental error seemed particularly unlikely because in ethyl ether the polarization by orientation is only a little over half the total polarization, so that $\alpha$ should be relatively insensitive to an error in the electric moment $\mu$. However, careful recent experiments on the temperature variation of the dielectric constant of ethyl ether have recently been made by Stuart[30] and by Sänger and Steiger.[31] Stuart finds $\mu = 1·14 \pm 0·03 \times 10^{-18}$, $\kappa_0 = 25·9$, while Sänger finds $\mu = 1·15 \pm 0·01 \times 10^{-18}$, $\kappa_0 = 26·1$ in close agreement with him. If one uses these results the discrepancy between the values of $\kappa$ obtained from dielectric constants and from extrapolation of dispersion data is only 3·9 or 4·1 as compared to 16 with the old data. Both Sänger and Stuart consider that even a discrepancy 3·9 is larger than the experimental error in $\kappa_0$, which they consider to be about 1·5. They therefore make the traditional suggestion that the refractive extrapolation is in error because of infra-red absorption bands. One cannot, nevertheless, help but wonder whether still further improvements in experimental refinement might remove all the discrepancy between the static and optical values of $\kappa_0$. This is unlikely in view of the excellent agreement between Stuart and Sänger, especially as their apparatus represents a high degree of experimental refinement, in marked contrast to the earlier work.

[28] We use the letters $\kappa$, $\kappa_0$ in place of Debye's $P$, $P_0$ to denote respectively the total and induced molar polarizabilities, as we reserve the letter $P$ for the electrodynamical polarization vector defined by the relation $\mathbf{D} = \mathbf{E} + 4\pi\mathbf{P}$. We shall refer to $\kappa$, $\kappa_0$ as 'molar polarizabilities' rather than 'molar polarizations'. This change from Debye's usage seems advisable since these quantities measure the specific ability of the material to acquire polarization, rather than the total polarization, which depends on field strength.

[29] Recent measurements of the dispersion of ethyl ether by H. Lowery (*Proc. Lond. Phys. Soc.* **40**, 23, 1928) give a value of $n_\infty^2 - 1$ about 1 per cent. lower even than that used by Stuart.

[30] H. A. Stuart, *Zeits. f. Physik*, **51**, 490 (1928).

[31] R. Sänger and O. Steiger, *Helv. Phys. Acta* **2**, 136 (1929); also especially revision given by Sänger in *Phys. Zeits.* **31**, 306 (1930).

## 16. Independence of Temperature of the Index of Refraction

Since we have seen that at visible frequencies the refraction results practically entirely from induced rather than permanent molecular moments, the optical index of refraction should not vary with the temperature except through the density. Such invariance is demanded by Eq. (2) and is also obviously to be expected by analogy to the temperature behaviour of the static dielectric constants of molecules devoid of permanent dipole moments, as in the optical region the permanent polarity of a molecule is ineffective. The most thorough examination of the temperature variation of the index of refraction appears to have been made by Cheney.[32] He measured the refractive indices of air, $N_2$, $NH_3$, $CO_2$, and $SO_2$ over a temperature range 0–300° C. and found that over this range the temperature coefficient of $n^2-1$ (or of $n-1$, as $n^2-1$ is approximately $2(n-1)$) did not differ from the temperature coefficient of the density within the experimental error of 1 or 2 per cent. in $n-1$. In other words, if $v$ denotes the specific volume, the product $v(n-1)$ remained constant with respect to temperature. The constancy of this product is sometimes spoken of as the Dale-Gladstone law.

Slight departures from the Dale-Gladstone law are to be expected if the structure of the molecule changes somewhat with temperature, as, for instance, due to dissociation, centrifugal expansion, &c. Meggers and Peters[33] find, for instance, that in the wave-length region 7500–8700 Å, the temperature coefficient of $n-1$ for air is exactly the same as that $-0.000367$ of the density, but that the former coefficient increases in numerical magnitude to $-0.000387$ when the wave-length is diminished to 2500 Å. These measurements are probably very accurate, though made over the very limited temperature range 0–30° C. The departures from the Dale-Gladstone law which they find at 2500 Å are perhaps because air has an absorption band in the ultra-violet. Changes in temperature will alter the distribution of molecules among different quantized rotational speeds, and hence shift slightly the position of the maximum intensity in an absorption band, as the small molecular rotation frequencies are superposed on the electronic frequencies. A very small change in the location of such a maximum will, of course, materially affect the dispersion near resonance. On this view anomalies such as found by Meggers and Peters would have been absent if they had worked on monatomic vapours, devoid of the molecular rotation.

## 17. Dispersion at Radio Frequencies

We have treated only the two limiting cases of fields which are either static or else too rapid for orientation effects, without considering the gradual transition between the two cases. As already mentioned, the

[32] E. W. Cheney, *Phys. Rev.* **29**, 292 (1927).
[33] Meggers and Peters, *Bulletin of the Bureau of Standards*, **14**, 735 (1917).

transition takes place in gases in the region of the natural molecular rotation frequencies, located in the far infra-red. Formulae for dispersion in this region, based on the Kramers theory (§ 82) and quantum mechanics, have been given by Debye,[34] but unfortunately there is not yet any experimental data adequate to test them. The most interesting feature is that the refractive index should display abrupt discontinuities when the incident frequency is resonant to any of the molecular rotation frequencies, which, because of the quantization, assume a discrete rather than continuous range of values. These discontinuities have, for simplicity, been ironed out in drawing curve III of Fig. 2.

More stimulating and fruitful in experimental confirmation is the dispersion of liquids and solids at low frequencies. A classic theory of this has been developed by Debye [35] (not to be confused with his work on gases just mentioned). He assumes that the resistance to the orientation of molecules by impressed fields arises primarily from a viscous force which, it is to be especially noted, is taken proportional to the angular velocity rather than angular acceleration, and which is probably a convenient approximate mathematical embodiment of the resisting effect of collisions. This viscous force is supposed more important than the inertial or acceleration reactions of the individual molecules, such as centrifugal force, which would be present even without collision phenomena. Because of this viscous retarding force, there is a definite upper limit to the rate at which a field can orient a molecule, just as in mobility theory there is a maximum velocity of migration of ions, since the resistance is proportional to velocity rather than acceleration. Because of the large amount of viscous resistance, Debye finds that an incident field would not have an appreciable orienting influence on molecules in a liquid unless the incident wave-length were so very long as to be in the short radio rather than far infra-red region. His theory is very elegant, but would take us too far afield into liquids for the present volume, and also would require us to enter into the statistical theory of the Brownian movement, or its equivalent. Debye's theory accounts nicely for the critical maxima of the absorption and of the dispersion $dn/d\lambda$ in a certain frequency region, and especially for the variation of the maxima with temperature. These phenomena permit the calculation of the 'relaxation time' in which the molecules would de-orient themselves if a static field were suddenly removed. Debye

---

[34] P. Debye, *Polar Molecules*, Chap. X; also further unpublished work by Manneback.
[35] P. Debye, *Verh. d. D. Phys. Ges.* **15**, 777 (1913), *Polar Molecules*, Chap. V; J. H. Tummers, *Dissertation*, Utrecht, 1914.

also has extended his frictional theory to apply to solids, thereby explaining some of Errera's [36] interesting experiments on the anomalous dispersion of solids for waves of very long radio frequencies. Although many of the dielectric phenomena are explicable by treating the solid as a liquid of very high inner friction and viscosity, such a picture of a solid does not seem consonant with modern views of crystalline structure, and so Debye [37] modifies his frictional theory to allow the molecules to take up only certain particular orientations in solids. On the latter view the electric polarization of ice, for instance, is due to the fact that one $H_2O$ molecule in five million in the ice crystal 'turns over' when an electric field of one volt/cm. is applied.

It is rather striking to compare the orders of magnitude of the regions of anomalous dispersion due to interaction with molecular rotations in gases, liquids, and solids. The critical wave-lengths in the three cases are measured respectively in microns, centimetres, and kilometres. The corresponding values of the relaxation times for the liquids and solids are of the order $10^{-10}$ and $10^{-5}$ sec. respectively. It is clearly to be understood that we are here discussing only the effect of the molecular rotation. The anomalies in dispersion due to resonance with nuclear vibrations and electronic motions are, of course, in the near infra-red and ultra-violet.

## 18. The Dielectric Constants of Solutions

A pure polar liquid cannot in general be treated by the standard Langevin-Debye theory. One reason for this is that in such a liquid the local field $\mathbf{e}_{local}$ is not at all the same as the macroscopic field $\mathbf{E}$ or even the Clausius-Mossotti expression $\mathbf{E}+4\pi\mathbf{P}/3$. Liquids have such high densities that the polarization $\mathbf{P}$ may be much larger than $\mathbf{E}$, and hence the difference between $\mathbf{e}_{local}$ and $\mathbf{E}$ is very great. Thus, until an adequate theoretical expression is available for the local field in dense media in which the inter-molecular distances are comparable with the molecular diameters, any attempts to determine quantitatively the intrinsic molecular polarity by measurements on pure liquids will be deceptive. An attempt, to be sure, to derive a theoretical expression for the local field in liquids has been made by Gans,[38] somewhat by analogy with the Weiss-Gans theory of magnetization. The faultiness of the underlying assumptions is evidenced by the fact that the electric

---

[36] J. Errera, *J. de Physique*, **5**, 304 (1924); *Polarisation Diélectrique*, pp. 127–30.

[37] P. Debye, *Polar Molecules*, p. 102.

[38] R. Gans, *Ann. der Physik*, **50**, 163 (1916); R. Gans and H. Isnardi, *Phys. Zeits.* **22**, 230 (1921); H. Isnardi, *Zeits. f. Physik*, **9**, 153 (1922).

moments deduced by various experiments from pure liquids with the aid of the Gans theory are very frequently at variance with the values deduced by other more reliable methods, and hence should be guarded against in appraising the literature.[39] A particular complication in polar liquids is the probable existence of association or clustering, whereby several molecules combine to form a temporary unit very likely having a resultant moment quite different from that of a single molecule.

Much valuable information on electric moments can, however, be derived by studying dilute solutions of polar molecules in non-polar solvents, as first suggested by Debye. Such a solvent is assumed not to contribute to aggregation effects, and to influence the local field only by adding a term $4\pi\mathbf{P}_1/3$, in accordance with the Clausius-Mossotti relation (Eq. (34), Chap. I). We shall suppose the solute so dilutely dissolved that its contribution to the local field is also given by this relation. The total local field is then

$$\mathbf{e}_{\text{local}} = \mathbf{E} + \frac{4\pi\mathbf{P}_1 + 4\pi\mathbf{P}_2}{3}. \tag{6}$$

Here the subscripts 1 and 2 refer to the solvent and solute respectively. Since the solvent is supposed non-polar and the solute polar, the Langevin-Debye theory gives for the total polarization

$$\mathbf{P} = \mathbf{P}_1 + \mathbf{P}_2 = \left\{ N_1\alpha_1 + N_2\left(\alpha_2 + \frac{\mu_2^2}{3kT}\right) \right\} \mathbf{e}_{\text{local}}, \tag{7}$$

provided we neglect saturation terms. If we introduce the 'mol fractions' $f_1 = N_1/(N_1 + N_2)$, $f_2 = N_2/(N_1 + N_2)$, then

$$N_1 = \frac{f_1 L\rho}{f_1 M_1 + f_2 M_2}, \qquad N_2 = \frac{f_2 L\rho}{f_1 M_1 + f_2 M_2}, \tag{8}$$

where $L$ is the Avogadro number, $\rho$ is the density, and $M_1$, $M_2$ are the molecular weights of the two constituents. On using (6), (8) and the definitive relation $\mathbf{P}/\mathbf{E} = (\epsilon - 1)/4\pi$, we find that (7) becomes

$$\frac{\epsilon - 1}{\epsilon + 2} \frac{f_1 M_1 + f_2 M_2}{\rho} = f_1\kappa_1 + f_2\kappa_2, \tag{9}$$

with the abbreviations

$$\kappa_1 = \frac{4\pi L\alpha_1}{3}, \qquad \kappa_2 = \frac{4\pi L}{3}\left(\alpha_2 + \frac{\mu_2^2}{3kT}\right) = 2\!\cdot\!54 \times 10^{24}\alpha_2 + 6\!\cdot\!18 \times 10^{39}\frac{\mu_2^2}{T}. \tag{10}$$

[39] For instance, the very full compendium on electric moments given by O. Blüh in *Phys. Zeits.* **27**, 226 (1926) does not emphasize which values of the moments tabulated therein are unreliable on account of being deduced from measurements on pure liquids.

The left side of (9) is termed the molar polarizability of the mixture, and will be denoted by $\kappa_{1,2}$. As $f_1 = 1-f_2$, Eq. (9) demands that $\kappa_{1,2}$ be a linear function of the concentration of the solute when the latter is varied. Actually this is usually not the case, as shown, for instance, by the following graphs taken from Debye's *Polar Molecules*.[40] In each instance benzene is utilized as the non-polar solvent. In only one of the three cases, viz. ethyl ether, is the experimental curve the straight line demanded by (9). The reason for the departures from linearity is, of course, simply because with high concentrations of the polar solute

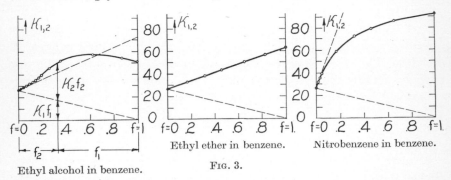

Ethyl alcohol in benzene.      Ethyl ether in benzene.      Nitrobenzene in benzene.

FIG. 3.

the contribution of the latter to the local field cannot be calculated by the Clausius-Mossotti relation.

From the various polarizability-concentration curves for the different materials valuable information can be obtained on the processes of association present in a polar liquid.[41] Any discussion of this subject is clearly beyond the scope of the present volume. The cases in which the curves are concave upwards and concave downwards evidently indicate quite different types of association. If one imputes all the curvature to the solute rather than the solvent, then the graphs will enable one to determine the molar susceptibility of the solute as a function of the concentration. Instead of being independent of the concentration, as the simple theory would demand, it is found in some cases to increase, some to decrease, and in some instances to increase and then decrease as the concentration of the solute is gradually increased from zero to unity. The theoretical interpretation of such differences is at present a little obscure, but they should be valuable clues to future theoretical investigation.

It is interesting to note that for non-polar substances the molar

[40] P. Debye, *Polar Molecules*, pp. 46–7.
[41] Cf., for further details, P. Debye in Marx's *Handbuch der Radiologie*, vi. 663; L. Ebert, *Zeits. f. Phys. Chem.* **113**, 1; **114**, 430 (1924).

polarizability $(\epsilon-1)M/(\epsilon+2)\rho$ is almost identical in the liquid and vapour states, whereas for polar materials it has widely different values in the two states, presumably because of association in the liquid. Zahn, for instance, finds that it equals 3·869 and 4·395 respectively for $O_2$ and $N_2$ gas, while the corresponding values in the liquid state are 3·878 and 4·396, respectively determined by Werner and Keesom and by Gerold.[42] As an example of the great difference between the molar polarizabilities in the two states in the case of polar materials, we may cite that $(\epsilon-1)M/(\epsilon+2)\rho$ equals 4 and 18 respectively for water in the vapour and liquid states. The discrepancy between the values of $(n^2-1)M/(n^2+2)\rho$ for water in the two states is, nevertheless, only about 10 per cent. at sodium wave-lengths, as already mentioned in § 5, which clearly shows that association effects are unimportant at optical frequencies.

If the departures from linearity in Fig. 3 are attributed solely to characteristic polarity effects, the curves should be straight lines in two cases: (a) binary mixtures of two non-polar materials, (b) binary mixtures of either polar or non-polar materials in which the optical refractivity rather than static dielectric constant is investigated, and at sufficiently short wave-lengths to suppress orientation effects. In this latter case a formula analogous to (9) should be applicable, except that $\epsilon$ is replaced by $n^2$, and that the theoretical expressions for the $\kappa$'s are no longer (10) but are instead proportional to the expressions (2). The predicted linearity for case (a) is well confirmed experimentally, as, for instance, in Krchma and Williams's [43] work on mixtures of benzene and carbon tetrachloride. As regards case (b), refractive data for various binary mixtures show that the experimental values of $(n^2-1)M/(n^2+2)\rho$ for these mixtures usually do not differ by more than a few parts in a thousand from the values calculated on the basis of linearity.[44]

Reverting now to the dielectric constants of polar solutes in non-polar solvents, it is only at very low concentrations of the polar material, i.e. the extreme left portions of the graphs in Fig. 3, that there is any approach to gas-like conditions and that formulae such as (9) should be applicable. However, the asymptotic behaviour at zero concentra-

[42] For references see Zahn and Miles, *Phys. Rev.* **32**, 502 (1928). The good agreement in the two states was apparently first noted by Ebert and Keesom, *Proc. Amsterdam Acad.* **29**, 1888 (1926). The value quoted for liquid $N_2$ is determined from refractive data rather than from the static dielectric constant.

[43] Krchma and Williams, *J. Amer. Chem. Soc.* **49**, 2408 (1927); cf. also Grutzmacher, *Zeits. f. Physik*, **28**, 342 (1924).

[44] Cf. for instance, Schutt, *Zeits. f. Phys. Chem.* **9**, 349; Hubbard, *ibid.* **74**, 207 (1910); also especially Höjendahl, Dissertation (Copenhagen, 1928), p. 27.

tion should agree with (9). Hence, if a straight line is drawn tangent to the experimental curve at the origin, its equation should be

$$\kappa_{1,\,2} = (1-f_2)\kappa_1 + f_2\kappa_2.$$

The intercept of the extrapolated tangent line with the right-hand axis $f_1 = 0$, $f_2 = 1$ gives the value of $\kappa_2$. Hence, by determining the rate of change of the dielectric constant when small amounts of a polar material are dissolved in a non-polar solvent, one can find the molar polarizability of this material. To determine the electric moment one must isolate the two terms of $\kappa_2$ representing the induced and dipole polarization. This can be done in either of two ways: either by measuring the temperature coefficient of the dielectric constant of the weak solution, or else by extrapolation of refractive data for the polar material, which, as explained in § 14, enables one to determine the induced molar polarizability $4\pi L\alpha_2/3$. Because aggregation effects are not important at optical wave-lengths, the refractive measurements need not be made in solution, but instead can be made on the pure polar liquid or, better still, on its vapour.

In some cases it may happen that no refractive data are available for the material in question. In such cases the contribution $4\pi N\alpha$ of the induced polarization is sometimes determined by one of the two following approximate methods: (1) calculation of the refraction of the material from that of its constituent atoms or radicals by the additivity method, highly elaborated to allow for the different kinds of chemical bonds (see § 21); or (2) assumption that the dielectric constant $\epsilon_{\text{solid}}$ in the solid state, if available, is the same as $n_\infty^2$. The theoretical work of Debye[35] and the experiments of Errera and Wintsch[36] show that in a truly static field $\epsilon_{\text{solid}}$ is much larger than $n_\infty^2$ unless the temperature is much lower than the melting-point. In the case of ice, for instance, the dielectric constant is near the melting-point about the same as that of water, or about 80, so that the molar polarizability $(\epsilon_{\text{solid}}-1)M/\rho(\epsilon_{\text{solid}}+2)$ is about 18, whereas $(n^2-1)_\infty M/\rho(n_\infty^2+2) \doteq 4$. This difficulty can, however, be at least partially overcome by measuring the dielectric constant of the solid well below the freezing-point and at radio frequencies, which are large compared to the 'relaxation frequency' of the solid, and hence too great to permit alinement of the dipoles in the solid. The dielectric constant of ice, for instance, is only 4·6 at $-2°$ C. when the wave-length is 8 kilometres. The corresponding molar polarizability nevertheless still has an excessively high value 10, as $-2°$ C. is too near the melting-point to freeze in the dipoles completely.

## 19. Numerical Values of the Electric Moments of Various Molecules. Comparison of the Different Methods

The material thus far presented has revealed four methods, $I_{\text{gas}}$, $II_{\text{gas}}$, $I_{\text{sol}}$, $II_{\text{sol}}$, for the quantitative determination of a molecule's electric moment. These methods are:

$I_{\text{gas}}$. This consists in measurement of the dielectric constant of a gas or vapour over a range of temperatures. If the measurements of the dielectric constant at various temperatures, when reduced to a standard density, say that at 76 cm., $273°$ K., can be represented by a formula of the form

$$\epsilon - 1 = A + \frac{B}{T}, \tag{11}$$

then it follows immediately from the Langevin-Debye formula (1), Chap. II, that the electric moment is given by

$$\mu = \left(\frac{3kB}{4\pi N}\right)^{\frac{1}{2}} = 1 \cdot 10 \times 10^{-18} \times B^{\frac{1}{2}}.$$

$II_{gas}$. In the second method the dielectric constant need be measured at only one temperature. The electric moment is then deduced from comparison with extrapolated refractive data, through the aid of Eq. (3). This method is precise only if the 'atomic polarization' due to the infra-red bands is negligible, or in the rare event that dispersion measurements are available which include the effect of these infra-red vibrations.

$I_{sol}$, $II_{sol}$. The third and fourth methods are similar to the methods $I_{gas}$, $II_{gas}$ except that the measurements are made in the fashion explained in § 18 on *dilute* solutions of the material in a non-polar solvent instead of in the pure gaseous or vapour state.

All these methods were originally suggested and stimulated by Debye. The method $I_{gas}$ has recently been used extensively by Zahn,[45] Sänger,[46, 47, 48, 49] Stuart,[50, 51, 52] Braunmühl,[53] and others. Method $II_{gas}$ has been most comprehensively applied by Höjendahl,[54] using measurements of dielectric constants of various gases made by Pohrt in 1913.[55] In the table we have tried to supplement Höjendahl's calculations by applying the method to some of the more recent determinations of dielectric constants. Method $I_{sol}$ has been employed by Miss Lange [56]

[45] C. T. Zahn, *Phys. Rev.* **24**, 400 (1924) (HCl, HBr, HI, $H_2$, $O_2$); **27**, 455 (1926) ($CO_2$, $NH_3$, $SO_2$, $N_2$); Zahn and Miles, *ibid.*, **32**, 497 (1928) (CO, COS, $CS_2$, $H_2S$); Zahn, *ibid.* **35**, 1047 (acetic acid); **35**, 848 (1930) (revision for $CS_2$).

[46] R. Sänger, *Phys. Zeits.* **27**, 556 (1926).

[47] R. Sänger and O. Steiger, *Helv. Phys. Acta* **1**, 369 (1928); **2**, 136 (1929).

[48] R. Sänger, *Dipolmoment und chemische Struktur* (Leipziger Vorträge, 1929), p. 1.

[49] R. Sänger, *Phys. Zeits.* **31**, 306 (1930).

[50] H. A. Stuart, *Zeits. f. Physik*, **47**, 457 (1928).

[51] H. A. Stuart, *Zeits. f. Physik*, **51**, 490 (1928).

[52] H. A. Stuart, *Phys. Zeits.* **31**, 80 (1930). This article quotes unpublished measurements by Fuchs.

[53] H. v. Braunmühl, *Phys. Zeits.* **28**, 141 (1927).

[54] K. Höjendahl, *Studies of Dipole-Moment*, Copenhagen, 1929; brief summaries in *Phys. Zeits.* **30**, 391 (1929); *Nature*, **117**, 892 (1926).

[55] G. Pohrt, *Ann. der Physik*, **42**, 569 (1913).

[56] L. Lange, *Zeits. f. Physik*, **33**, 169 (1925). Most of Miss Lange's determinations are really a hybrid of methods I and II.

and especially by Smyth[57] and associates, while $II_{sol}$ has been utilized for a very large number of substances by Williams[58, 59, 60] and co-workers.

It is not the purpose of the present volume to discuss the technique of experimental methods, but we may nevertheless mention that practically all the recent observations of dielectric constants are made by a 'heterodyne' method, in which the periods of two oscillating circuits are adjusted to be virtually identical. One circuit contains only known resistances, inductances, and capacities, while one unit in the other circuit is a condenser containing the gas or solution whose dielectric constant is desired. The beat phenomenon enables one to determine when the periods of the two circuits approach equality. The period of the first circuit can be calculated from its known constants, while conversely from the thus determined period, the hitherto unknown capacity of the condenser in the second circuit, and hence the desired dielectric constant, may be found. The use of the vacuum tube is the cornerstone to the successful application of the heterodyne method. Most measurements of dielectric constants, and especially their temperature variations, made prior to 1920, before perfection of the technique of the vacuum-tube circuits, are not as a rule very reliable.[61] Hence in our table we have not included the results of Bädeker,[62] Jona,[63] and others, although the importance of their pioneer work must not be overlooked. Pohrt's[55] measurements of the dielectric constants of gases at mainly one temperature are possibly somewhat more accurate than usual for early work, although the resulting moments are very often somewhat high, perhaps because method II neglects the 'atomic polarization'.

The four methods described above are at present the most dependable ways of determining quantitatively the dipole moments of molecules.

[57] C. P. Smyth and S. O. Morgan, *J. Amer. Chem. Soc.* 49, 1030; 50, 1547 (1928); C. P. Smyth and W. N. Stoops, *ibid.* 50, 1883; C. P. Smyth, S. O. Morgan and J. C. Boyce, *ibid.* 50, 1536 (1928).

[58] J. W. Williams and Krchma, *J. Amer. Chem. Soc.* 49, 1676, 2408 (1927); *Phys. Zeits.* 29, 204 (1928); Williams and Allgeier, *J. Amer. Chem. Soc.* 49, 2416 (1927); Williams and Ogg, *ibid.* 50, 94 (1928); Williams and Schwingel, *ibid.* 50, 362 (1928); summary and references to the appropriate individual papers for each mixture in *Phys. Zeits.* 29, 174, 683 (1928), or the following reference[59].

[59] J. W. Williams, *Molekulare Dipolmomente und ihre Bedeutung für die chemische Forschung*. This is Band 20, Heft 5 of the series *Fortschritte der Chemie, Physik, und physikalischen Chemie*.

[60] C. H. Schwingel and J. W. Williams, *Phys. Rev.* 35, 855 (1930).

[61] For a description of typical experimental arrangements, see, for instance, Williams, *l.c.* [59] or Estermann's and Sack's articles in *Ergebnisse der exakten Naturwissenschaften*, VIII.

[62] K. Bädeker, *Zeits. f. Phys. Chem.* 36, 305 (1901).

[63] M. Jona, *Phys. Zeits.* 20, 14 (1919).

It must not, however, be inferred that there are not other experiments which should in principle permit the numerical determination of these moments. We have already mentioned on pp. 47–8 that the electric moment can be directly calculated from absorption coefficients for the pure rotation spectra in the far infra-red if these coefficients can be measured with quantitative precision, but there is apparently some enormous unknown systematic error which has as yet prevented this. Raman and Krishnan [64] have met with some success in deducing dipole moments from a combination of data on the Kerr effect and on the depolarization of light, but the complete theory of these effects is extremely complicated (cf. § 83), and it is hard to say whether the moment can accurately be deduced from the experimental measurements in as simple a manner as implied by their formulae, although the latter are doubtless approximately correct. In some cases the electric moments have been deduced from the amount of electrostriction.[65] Determinations of electrostriction are, in fact, merely one way of measuring the dielectric constant. Saturation effects have been used to calculate the dipole moment (see § 22), but they are far too small to measure with precision, and furthermore they yield the moment only if one assumes that the induced polarization is a strictly linear function of field strength so that saturation is evidenced only in the orientation term. Attempts [66] have been made to calculate the molecular moments from the potential differences at interfaces between two materials, on the assumption that this difference is due entirely to a surface-layer of dipoles. The results thus obtained are not quantitatively reliable, and this is not surprising, as the molecules may not be 100 per cent. oriented as assumed in the simple theory, and especially there may well be at the interfaces a tremendous amount of molecular distortion and induced polarization.[67] Accurate measurement and analysis of the Stark effect or, what is more or less equivalent, of the electrical Stern-Gerlach effect, should in principle permit the calculation of the electric moment provided one can resolve the contributions of the induced and per-

[64] Raman and Krishnan, *Phil. Mag.* **3**, 713 (1927). They deduce the moments $1 \cdot 04 \times 10^{-18}$ and $1 \cdot 66 \times 10^{-18}$ for HCl and $CH_3Cl$ respectively. Reference to the table shows that the agreement with values obtained by the standard methods is much better for HCl than for $CH_3Cl$.

[65] O. E. Frivold, *Phys. Zeits.* **22**, 603 (1921); O. E. Frivold and O. Hassel, *ibid.* **24**, 82 (1923); Kliefoth, *Zeits. f. Physik*, **39**, 402 (1926). Kliefoth finds no electric moment for $O_2$ and $N_2$, and the values $1 \cdot 7 \times 10^{-18}$ and $0 \cdot 20 \times 10^{-18}$ for $SO_2$ and $CO_2$ respectively.

[66] Rideal, *Surface Chemistry*, pp. 236–7, Cambridge University Press, 1926.

[67] Frumkin and Williams, *Proc. Nat. Acad.* **15**, 400 (1929).

manent polarizations.[68] The Born-Lertes rotation effect has also been used to calculate the electric moment, but the results have not been particularly successful.[69]

It would clearly be an unnecessary duplication to tabulate all the molecular electric moments which have been determined by any of the four main methods, as very complete tables, up to date at the time of this writing, have been given by Debye in the German edition of his *Polar Molecules* with a subsequent supplement published in 1930,[70] by Höjendahl in his dissertation,[54] by Williams in his monograph *Dipolmomente und ihre Bedeutung für die chemische Forschung*,[59] and by Estermann and by Sack in Band VIII of *Ergebnisse der exakten Naturwissenschaften* (1929).[71] In the accompanying table we have attempted to include only the common inorganic molecules which have been measured and a selected group of organic ones. In making the selection for the latter we have aimed to list the molecules whose moments have been determined by the greatest number of different observers, and especially by as many of the four methods as possible. It is hoped that our placing in juxtaposition the results of the various methods in a single table rather than in separate ones will enable the reader to estimate more quickly the accuracy and consistency of the different types of observations. Attempts have sometimes been made to give the moments to one more significant figure than given in the table, but the light of experience, especially as revealed in the continual inconsistencies between the different observations, seems to show that very often the experimenters underestimate their errors, and a determination of the moment to within 5 per cent. must be regarded as quite satisfactory. We have appended question-marks to some of the values which

[68] For further discussion of the Stark effect in relation to molecular structure see the end of § 37. The attempt of R. J. Clark (*Proc. Roy. Soc.* **124**A, 689 (1929)) to deduce electric moments quantitatively from his measurements on the electric Stern-Gerlach effect appears erroneous to the writer, as he assumes the dipoles are alined either parallel or antiparallel with respect to the field. Actually the theory of the Stark effect for non-monatomic molecules shows that at any ordinary field strength the orienting effect of the field is very small because of the molecular rotation; this is evidenced by the fact that (71), Chap. VI has $j$ in the denominator.

[69] P. Lertes, *Zeits. f. Physik*, **6**, 56 (1921).

[70] The very complete table of moments prepared by Sänger for the German translation (*Polare Molekeln*, pp. 191–8) was unfortunately not ready for the original English edition. The two 'Nachtrags' to the table are sold separately. A full table of moments has just appeared in Smyth's new book, *Dielectric Constant and Molecular Structure*.

[71] Besides these references we may mention that recent measurements on the dipole moments of certain organic molecules and interesting discussions of the relation of dipole moment to chemical and physical properties are given by various writers in *Dipolmoment und chemische Struktur* (Leipziger Vorträge, 1929).

seem particularly doubtful, and asterisks to values which are probably zero within the experimental error. The various investigators differ considerably in their usage in giving explicitly numerical moments which are virtually zero, and in some cases the observations which we have listed as exactly zero would yield moments about as large as those with asterisks if an attempt is made to calculate small moments literally from their data. In such instances the molecules are in all likelihood non-polar.

Let us turn now to some of the specific items in the table. The vanishing electric moments reported for A, $H_2$, $N_2$, $O_2$ are to be expected, since monatomic molecules and diatomic molecules composed of two identical atoms are theoretically non-polar. For this reason the finite moments recorded for $Br_2$ and $I_2$ are hard to believe. The moment $0 \cdot 40 \times 10^{-18}$ found by Miss Anderson [72] for bromine is based on measurements in the pure liquid rather than gaseous state, and readings were taken only over the very limited temperature interval 0°–30°. For these reasons her results do not seem very conclusive. Even if the temperature variation of the susceptibility per molecule for $Br_2$ is real, it need not imply an electric moment if the induced polarization changes with temperature.[73] Such a change is not allowed for in the usual simple theory, but in relatively unstable molecules such as the halogens it is not inconceivable that there be a change due to the centrifugal expansion with increasing temperature, to say nothing of the possibility of a small amount of dissociation. It is significant that Müller and Sack [74] find that the moment of the iodine molecule becomes zero when hexane is used as a solvent, so that the apparent non-vanishing moment found with benzene as the solvent is doubtless due to some sort of spurious association effect. The true moment of the $I_2$ molecule is thus zero in all probability, and this is hence also presumably true of $F_2$, $Cl_2$, $Br_2$.

Except for the figures given in bold-face, no attempt is made to include the atomic polarization in using the methods $II_{gas}$ and $II_{sol}$. It is seen that on the whole the figures in the second and fourth columns agree quite well with those in the first and third, sometimes about as well as the different observations by the same method. Thus the calculation of the electric polarization does not seem ordinarily to be very

---

[72] Annie I. Anderson, *Proc. Lon. Phys. Soc.* **40**, 62 (1928).

[73] The possibility of temperature variations due to other causes than a permanent dipole moment is discussed at length by L. Ebert in *Dipolmoment und chemische Struktur* (Leipziger Vorträge, 1929), although primarily for large, complicated molecules.

[74] H. Müller and H. Sack, *Phys. Zeits.* **31**, 815 (1930).

### Electric Moments of Some Representative Molecules in E.S.U.

#### (All values to be multiplied by $10^{-18}$)

[Superscripts give footnote reference to the observer]

| Molecule | Method $I_{gas}$ | Method $II_{gas}$ | Method $I_{sol}$ | Method $II_{sol}$ | Solvent used in solution methods |
|---|---|---|---|---|---|
| Argon | 0 [53] | .. | .. | .. | .. |
| Hydrogen ($H_2$) | 0 [53] | 0 [76] | .. | .. | .. |
| Nitrogen ($N_2$) | 0 [45,75] | 0 [76] | .. | 0 [77] | Pure $N_2$ |
| Oxygen ($O_2$) | 0 [75] | 0 [76] | .. | 0 [77] | Pure $O_2$ |
| Bromine ($Br_2$) | .. | .. | 0.40 [72] | 1·0? [78] | Pure $Br_2$ |
| Iodine ($I_2$) | .. | .. | .. | 1·2? [58] | Benzene |
| ,, | .. | .. | .. | 1·0? [74] | ,, |
| ,, | .. | .. | .. | 0 [74] | Hexane |
| Hydrochloric acid (HCl) | 1·03 [45] | 1·06 [78] | .. | .. | .. |
| Hydrobromic acid (HBr) | 0·79 [45] | 0·80 [78] | .. | .. | .. |
| Hydriodic acid (HI) | 0·38 [45] | 0·41 [78] | .. | .. | .. |
| Carbon monoxide (CO) | 0·12 [53] | 0·14 [78] | .. | .. | .. |
|  |  | **(0·12)** |  |  |  |
| ,, | 0·12 [75] | ? [79] | .. | .. | .. |
| ,, | 0·10 [45] | 0·13 [78] | .. | .. | .. |
|  |  | **(0·11)** |  |  |  |
| Carbon dioxide ($CO_2$) | 0·14? [53] | .. | .. | .. | .. |
| ,, | 0·06* [45] | 0·17 [78](0) | .. | .. | .. |
| ,, | 0·00 [50] | 0·18 [78](0) | .. | .. | .. |
| Nitrous oxide ($N_2O$) | 0 [80] | 0·13 [78] | .. | .. | .. |
| ,, | 0 [60] | 0·17 [78] | .. | .. | .. |
| Carbon disulphide ($CS_2$) | 0 [80,45] | .. | .. | 0·06* [58] | Benzene |
| ,, | 0 [60] | 0·28 [78] | .. | 0·08* [58] | Hexane |
| Sulphur dioxide ($SO_2$) | 1·61 [45] | 1·63 [78] | .. | .. | .. |
| Water ($H_2O$) | 1·84 [49] | 1·81 [81] | .. | 1·81 [82] | Benzene |
| Hydrogen sulphide ($H_2S$) | 1·10 [53] | 0·92 [78] | .. | .. | .. |
| ,, | 0·93 [45] | 0·94 [78] | .. | .. | .. |
| Ammonia ($NH_3$) | 1·48 [83] | 1·47 [78] | .. | .. | .. |
| ,, | 1·44 [45] | 1·44 [78] | .. | .. | .. |
| Acetylene ($C_2H_2$) | 0 [84] | .. | .. | .. | .. |
| Ethylene ($C_2H_4$) | 0 [84] | .. | .. | .. | .. |
| Ethane ($C_2H_6$) | 0 [84] | .. | .. | .. | .. |
| Methane ($CH_4$) | 0 [46] | 0·18 [78] | .. | .. | .. |
| Methylchloride ($CH_3Cl$) | 1·69 [85] ? | 1·89 [86] | .. | .. | .. |
| ,, | 1·86 [48] | 1·90 [78] | .. | .. | .. |
| ,, | 1·89 [52] | .. | .. | .. | .. |
| Methylene chloride ($CH_2Cl_2$) | 1·59 [46] | .. | .. | 1·55 [74] | Benzene |
| ,, | 1·61 [87] | .. | .. | .. | .. |
| Chloroform ($CHCl_3$) | 0·95 [46] | 1·1 [78] | 1·05 [57] | .. | Hexane |
| ,, | 1·05 [85] | .. | .. | 1·10 [58] | Benzene |
| ,, | .. | .. | .. | 1·15 [58] | $CCl_4$ |
| Carbon tetrachloride ($CCl_4$) | 0 [46] | .. | .. | 0 [58] | Benzene |
| Tin iodide ($SnI_4$) | .. | .. | .. | 0 [58] | ,, |
| Ethyl ether ($C_2H_5)_2O$ | .. | .. | .. | 1·22 [88] | Benzene |
| ,, | 1·14 [51] | 1·21 [78] | 1·15 [90] | 1·22 [56,58] | ,, |
| ,, | 1·15 [49] | .. | .. | 1·24 [58] | $CCl_4$ |
| ,, | 1·12 [60] | .. | .. | .. | .. |

| Molecule | Method $I_{gas}$ | Method $II_{gas}$ | Method $I_{sol}$ | Method $II_{sol}$ | Solvent used in solution methods |
|---|---|---|---|---|---|
| Methyl ether $(CH_3)_2O$ | 1·29 [51] | 1·33 [78] | .. | .. | .. |
| ,, | 1·32 [47] | 1·37 [78] | .. | .. | .. |
| ,, | .. | 1·23 [86] | .. | .. | .. |
| Propyl ether $(C_3H_7)_2O$ | 0·86 [47] | 1·24 [86] | .. | .. | .. |
| Acetone $(CH_3COCH_3)$ | 2·94 [51] | 2·88 [51] | .. | 2·70 [58] | $CCl_4$ |
| ,, | .. | 2·97 [86] | .. | 2·72 [89] | .. |
| Benzene $(C_6H_6)$ | .. | 0·33 ? [86] | .. | 0·06 [58] | $CCl_4$ |
| ,, | .. | .. | 0 [91] | .. | Pure benzene |
| ,, | .. | .. | .. | 0·10 [58] | $CS_2$ |
| ,, | .. | .. | .. | 0·08 [58] | Hexane |
| Fluorbenzene $(C_6H_5F)$ | .. | .. | .. | 1·39 [92] | Benzene |
| ,, | .. | .. | .. | 1·45 [93] | ,, |
| Chlorobenzene $(C_6H_5Cl)$ | .. | .. | 1·52 [57] | 1·55 [58] | Hexane |
| ,, | .. | .. | .. | 1·52 [58] | $CS_2$ |
| ,, | .. | .. | .. | 1·55 [58] | Benzene |
| ,, | .. | .. | .. | 1·56 [93] | ,, |
| ,, | .. | .. | .. | 1·57 [74] | ,, |
| ,, | .. | .. | .. | 1·61 [57] | ,, Hexane |
| Bromobenzene $(C_6H_5Br)$ | .. | .. | .. | 1·56 [54] | Benzene |
| ,, | .. | .. | .. | 1·51 [59] | ,, |
| ,, | .. | .. | .. | 1·52 [74] | ,, |
| ,, | .. | .. | .. | 1·49 [93] | ,, |
| Iodobenzene $(C_6H_5I)$ | .. | .. | .. | 1·30 [93] | ,, |
| ,, | .. | .. | .. | 1·25 [92] | ,, |
| Nitrobenzene $(C_6H_5NO_2)$ | .. | .. | .. | 3·89 [58] | Hexane |
| ,, | .. | .. | .. | 3·89 [58] | $CS_2$ |
| ,, | .. | .. | .. | 3·90 [58] | Benzene |
| ,, | .. | .. | .. | 3·84 [56] | ,, |
| Hexane $(C_6H_{14})$ | .. | .. | .. | 0·10 [94] | ,, |
| ,, | .. | .. | .. | 0·08 [94] | $CCl_4$ |
| ,, | .. | .. | 0 [57] | .. | Pure Hexane |
| Ethyl alcohol $(C_2H_5OH)$ | 1·70 [95] | 1·72 [86] | .. | 1·74 [96] | Benzene |
| ,, | .. | .. | .. | 1·63 [58] | $CCl_4$ |
| Methyl alcohol $(CH_3OH)$ | 1·68 [95] | 1·73 [86] | .. | 1·64 [96] | Benzene |
| ,, | .. | .. | .. | 1·67 [96] | $CCl_4$ |
| n-Propyl alcohol $(C_3H_7OH)$ | 1·66 [95] | .. | .. | 1·53 [56] | Benzene |
| iso-Propyl alcohol | .. | .. | .. | 1·75 [96] | Benzene |
| iso-Amyl alcohol $(C_5H_{11}OH)$ | .. | .. | .. | 1·85 [58] | $CCl_4$ |
| ,, | .. | .. | .. | 1·62 [96] | Benzene |

[75] Magdalena Forro, *Zeits. f. Physik*, **47**, 430 (1928).

[76] To show how exactly $\epsilon$ and $n_\infty^2$ agree for $H_2$, $O_2$, $N_2$, and hence how precisely method $II_{gas}$ shows that these gases must be non-polar, we can here give some of the measurements of $n_\infty^2$ and $\epsilon$. For hydrogen the value of $n_\infty^2$ yielded by various dispersion measurements, including the infra-red data of Koch, is 1·000273; the corresponding values of the dielectric constant are 1·000273 (Tangl, *Ann. der Physik*, **23**, 559, **26**, 59 (1907–8), 1·000263 (Fritts, *Phys. Rev.* **23**, 345, 1924), 1·000259 (Braunmühl),[53] 1·000265 (Zahn).[45] For nitrogen, the value of $n_\infty^2$ ranges from 1·000580 to 1·000589 according to the observer, while Fritts finds $\epsilon = 1·000555$, and Zahn obtains $\epsilon = 1·000581$. For oxygen $n_\infty^2$ is very approximately 1·000530 (Lowery[29]), while $\epsilon = 1·000507$ (Fritts), 1·000518 (Zahn).[45]

[77] That method $II_{sol}$ gives zero moment for $N_2$ and $O_2$ just as well as method $II_{gas}$ is

greatly impaired by the omission of the atomic polarization in method II, except when a high degree of accuracy is desired. In particular in the halogen hydrides and ammonia, the good agreement between the two methods shows that in these molecules the atomic polarization must be small, as also indicated by absorption measurements (§ 15). In the case of propyl ether, on the other hand, the atomic polarization must be enormous if the observations in both columns are dependable, which is doubtful. In a few instances, the moments recorded by method II are actually smaller than those given by method I, and in such cases the discrepancy cannot be blamed on the atomic polarization. More often, however, method II seems to give slightly larger moments than method I, thus furnishing evidence for a certain amount of real 'atomic

shown by the fact that $N_2$ and $O_2$ have almost exactly the same molar polarizabilities in the liquid and gaseous states. See p. 59.

[78] Calculated by the writer from comparison of extrapolated dispersion data with the measurements of the dielectric constant made by the observer listed in the column directly to the left in the same row. These calculated values are very often only approximate. The values of $n_\infty^2$ have usually been obtained from dispersion formulae given by C. and M. Cuthbertson (*Proc. Roy. Soc.* **83**, 171 (1909) ($SO_2$, $H_2S$); **97**, 152 (CO, $CO_2$, $CH_4$), *Phil. Trans. Roy. Soc.* **213**, 1 (1914) ($Br_2$, HCl, HBr, HI, $N_2O$, $NH_3$). As long as infra-red resonance points are not included, it would make little difference if we used the visible dispersion data of other observers (e.g. the more modern data for $CHCl_3$, ethyl ether, methyl ether, and acetone given by Lowery[29]) as the discrepancy between the different refractive measurements is usually small compared to the error in the measurements of dielectric constants. More refined calculations appear useless as long as the amount of atomic polarization is uncertain, but the results which are tabulated suffice to show that in any case this polarization cannot be very large (except perhaps in propyl ether).

[79] Forro finds a value of $\epsilon$ for CO smaller than $n_\infty^2$. This must be experimental error, as it would yield an imaginary moment in method II. Similar remarks apply to the data of Ghosh, Mahanti, and Mukherjee[80] on $CS_2$.

[80] P. N. Ghosh, P. C. Mahanti, and B. C. Mukherjee, *Zeits. f. Physik*, **58**, 200 (1929).

[81] Calculated from Zahn's[45] data by Stuart[51].

[82] J. W. Williams, *Phys. Zeits.* **29**, 204 (1928); but with the revisions we describe on p. 69.

[83] H. E. Watson, *Proc. Roy. Soc.* **117**A, 43 (1927).

[84] C. P. Smyth and C. T. Zahn, *J. Amer. Chem. Soc.* **47**, 2501 (1925).

[85] S. C. Sircar, *Ind. J. Phys.* **3**, 197 (1928).

[86] Calculated from Pohrt's data[55] by Höjendahl[54].

[87] P. C. Mahanti and R. N. Das Gupta, *J. Ind. Chem. Soc.* **6**, 411 (1929).

[88] J. Rolinski, *Phys. Zeits.* **29**, 658 (1928).

[89] O. Hassel and E. Naeshagen, *Zeits. f. Phys. Chem.* **4**B, 217 (1929).

[90] L. Meyer, *Zeits f. Phys. Chem.* **8**B, 27 (1930).

[91] A. Parts, *Zeits. f. Phys. Chem.* **4**B, 227 (1929).

[92] P. Walden and O. Werner, *Zeits. f. Phys. Chem.* **2**, 10 (1929).

[93] Bergmann, Engel, and Sandor, *Zeits. f. Phys. Chem.* **10**B, 106 (1930).

[94] L. Ebert and H. Hartel, *Naturwissenschaften*, **15**, 669 (1927).

[95] J. B. Miles, *Phys. Rev.* **34**, 964 (1929).

[96] J. D. Stranathan, *Phys. Rev.* **31**, 653 (1928).

polarization'. Especially convincing evidence is furnished by the figures in bold-face type, which are calculated with the dispersion data of Koch,[14] Statescu,[15] and Fuchs,[19] and thus, unlike the other values by method II, include the effect of the infra-red vibrations. Their data have been fully discussed in § 15, and modify the results with method II sufficiently to remove all the discrepancy with method I in the case of CO and $CO_2$.

It is noteworthy that when different solvents have been tried in the solution methods, the values of the electric moment are, as shown in the table, virtually independent of the type of solvent which is employed. This gives assurance that the moments obtained by using solutions have a real physical significance. When the same material has been measured both in the gaseous state and in solution, the moments obtained are seen to be the same within an experimental error no greater than the discrepancies among the different measurements for one kind of state. There is thus little evidence that molecules have a different 'effective moment' in solutions than in the gaseous state, a suggestion which has sometimes been made. If it were necessary to assume such an 'effective moment', its value would presumably depend on the nature of the solvent, whereas actually the moments found for a given molecule are seen from the table to be virtually independent of the solvent, except perhaps in the case of $I_2$ mentioned above. The variations with the type of solvent are remarkably small, and clearly less than the experimental error. The determination of the moment of the water molecule by the solution method requires special mention. It is hard to achieve with precision, as an exact knowledge of the rather low solubility of water in benzene is necessary. Williams formerly used the value of the solubility given by Hill, Jr., which was in substantial agreement with earlier work by Groschuff and by Richards, Carver, and Schumb.[97] He thereby originally reported an electric moment $1 \cdot 7 \times 10^{-18}$ e.s.u. for the water molecule.[82] However, he informs the writer that when new, as yet unpublished, solubility determinations made by Cohen and Weyling at Utrecht and also by Rosenbaum at Wisconsin are utilized, he obtains the higher value $1 \cdot 81 \pm 0 \cdot 05 \times 10^{-18}$. The agreement of the latter with Sänger's value $1 \cdot 84 \times 10^{-18}$ measured in the vapour state is closer than one has any right to anticipate in view of experimental uncertainties, especially neglect of the atomic polarization in method II.

[97] Groschuff, *Zeits. f. Elektrochem.* **17**, 348 (1911); Richards, Carver and Schumb, *J. Amer. Chem. Soc.* **41**, 2019 (1919); Hill, Jr., *ibid.* **45**, 1143 (1923).

## 20. Dielectric Constants and Molecular Structure

By revealing the electric moments of molecules, measurements of the dielectric constants of chemical compounds often shed considerable light on the configurations in which the constituent atoms are grouped to form the molecule. Of course, the value of the electric moment alone does not enable one to determine the exact dimensions and geometry of the molecule, but it does disclose whether or not the atoms are arranged in a symmetrical way. The absence of an electric moment, of course, means a high degree of symmetry. The classic example of this is the once much-mooted subject of the model for the $CO_2$ molecule. Although early dielectric work on $CO_2$ seemed to demand an electric moment, the recent experiments of Zahn[45] and especially Stuart,[50] as well as use of method II with Fuchs's[19] dispersion formula explained in § 15, shows quite definitely that the $CO_2$ molecule has no electric moment. Hence this molecule must be collinear, with the carbon atom at the centre and equidistant from the two oxygen atoms. The triangular and the unsymmetrical collinear models which have sometimes been proposed would clearly lead to an electric moment. A symmetrical collinear model for $CO_2$ is also demanded by other evidence than that on dielectrics. This other evidence has been nicely summarized by Wolf,[23] and includes (a) X-ray analysis of the structure of solid $CO_2$,[98] (b) the rotational specific heat of $CO_2$, which has[24] the value approximately $R$ rather than $3R/2$ calorics per mol, thus showing that there are only two moments of inertia appreciably different from zero, (c) absence of a third intense resonance point in the infra-red dispersion (p. 51), showing that one of the fundamental modes of vibration must be symmetrical.

As sulphur and oxygen are in the same column of the periodic table, one would expect the $CS_2$ molecule to be symmetrical and collinear if this is true of $CO_2$. Williams's measurements[58] on $CS_2$ in solution, also more recently those of Ghosh, Mahanti, and Mukherjee,[80] of Zahn,[45] and of Schwingel and Williams[60] on $CS_2$ in the vapour state, do indeed yield a zero moment for the $CS_2$ molecule. In some of these papers[80, 60] determinations are also made for $N_2O$, and here also the moment proves to be zero, so that the nitrous oxide molecule is collinear. The perceptible, though small, moments reported for $CS_2$ and $N_2O$ respectively in earlier work of Zahn and Miles[45] and of Braunmühl[53] doubtless arose through experimental error.

[98] J. de Smedt and W. H. Keesom, *Proc. Amsterdam Acad.* **27**, 839 (1924); H. Mark, *Zeits. f. Elektrochemie*, **31**, 523 (1925); H. Mark and E. Pohland, *Zeits. f. Krist.* **61**, 293 (1925).

The table shows that $H_2O$ and $SO_2$ have quite large moments. The polarity of water is also well known from other phenomena, such as association in the liquid state. The models of the $H_2O$ and $SO_2$ molecules must therefore be either triangular or unsymmetrical if collinear. The unsymmetrical collinear model encounters serious dynamical difficulties,[99] at least in the case of $H_2O$, and the triangular model for this molecule is the generally accepted one.

Band-spectrum analysis,[100] also perhaps chemical evidence,[101] reveals that the correct model for the ammonia molecule is a pyramidal one, with the N atom at the vertex, and the H atoms at the corners of the base. Such a model would have a moment along the axis of the pyramid, in agreement with the polarity of $NH_3$ revealed by the observations on dielectric constants.

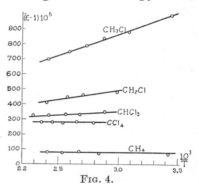

FIG. 4.

The sequence $CH_4$, $CH_3Cl$, $CH_2Cl_2$, $CHCl_3$, $CCl_4$ is one of the standard illustrations of the valuable information on molecular structure revealed by dielectric constants. Fig. 4 shows Sänger's observations of the dielectric constants of these materials as a function of temperature at constant density. The horizontal character of the curves for $CH_4$ and $CCl_4$ shows clearly that these gases are non-polar. The methane and carbon tetrachloride molecules are thus highly symmetrical. The necessary symmetry can be secured by supposing that the four hydrogen or four chlorine atoms are at the corners of a regular tetrahedron, with the carbon atom at the centre. The valencies of the carbon atom thus have the tetrahedral geometry so dear to the organic chemists. A pyramidal model analogous to that for ammonia, which has sometimes been suggested[102], is clearly out of the question, as it would be unsymmetrical. A coplanar model with the carbon atom at the centre of a square would

[99] See Debye, *Polar Molecules*, p. 63 ff.

[100] G. A. Stinchcomb and E. F. Barker, *Phys. Rev.* **33**, 305 (1929); Barker, *ibid.* **33**, 684; R. M. Badger and C. W. Cartwright, *ibid.* **33**, 692 (1929).

[101] A. Hantzsch and A. Werner, *Ber. d. D. Chem. Ges.* **23**, 11 (1890); cf. A. W. Stewart, *Stereochemistry*, p. 197. This stereochemical evidence does not perhaps uniquely demand a pyramidal model, but at least shows that all three nitrogen valencies cannot be in the same plane.

[102] K. Weissenberg, *Phys. Zeits.* **28**, 829 (1927); *Ber. d. D. Chem. Ges.* **59**, 1526 (1926); *Naturwissenschaften*, **15**, 662 (1927); also Ebert, *Naturwissenschaften*, **15**, 669 (1927) and ref. 104; Henri, *Chem. Rev.* **4**, 189 (1927).

be non-polar as well as the tetrahedron, but is very unplausible from chemical and other grounds.[103]  Also it would not explain the polarity of $CH_2Cl_2$ if one makes the natural assumption that alternate corners are filled by Cl and H atoms respectively.  As one passes through the sequence $CH_4$, $CH_3Cl$, $CH_2Cl_2$, $CHCl_3$, $CCl_4$ by replacing one H atom by one Cl at some corner of the tetrahedron, it is clear that with the tetrahedral model perfect symmetry is not secured except at the starting-point $CH_4$ or except when all the H atoms have been replaced by Cl in $CCl_4$.  This is in agreement with the finite electric moments found by Sänger for $CH_3Cl$, $CH_2Cl_2$, and $CHCl_3$.

It may be mentioned that whereas molecules of the type $C\alpha_4$ are non-polar if $\alpha$ is an atom, polar molecules of the structure $C\alpha_4$ are known when $\alpha$ is a complicated radical rather than a simple atom.  The molecules

$$C(CH_2O(O)CCH_3)_4, \; C(COOCH_3)_4, \; C(COOC_2H_5)_4, \; C(OCH_3)_4, \; C(OC_2H_5)_4$$

are, for instance, revealed by their dielectric constant data[104] to be polar, having respectively the moments $1 \cdot 9$, $2 \cdot 8$, $3 \cdot 0$, $0 \cdot 8$, $1 \cdot 1 \times 10^{-18}$.  On the other hand, the moments of $C(CH_2Br)_4$, $C(CH_2Cl)_4$, $C(CH_2I)_4$, $C(N_2O)_4$ are found to be zero, showing that $C\alpha_4$ can sometimes be non-polar even when $\alpha$ is not an atom.  The existence of electric moments for any molecules of the type $C\alpha_4$ at first sight seems quite paradoxical in view of the non-polarity of methane.  A pyramidal model for polar molecules of this form has been suggested[102] as a solution of the paradox, but it seems highly improbable that the carbon valences can have a tetrahedral geometry in some instances and pyramidal in others.  A much more plausible solution, proposed by Höjendahl[105] and by Williams,[106] is that in molecules of the form $C\alpha_4$ the axis of electric moment of $\alpha$ need not coincide with its axis of valency if $\alpha$ is a complicated radical.  Let us suppose that the angle between these two axes is $\theta$, and that the axes of valency coincide with the axes of symmetry drawn from the centre of the carbon tetrahedron to its four vertices.  The dipole axes are then free to rotate around the axes of valency subject only to the constraint that the angle between each corresponding pair of axes have

[103] Band spectrum evidence has been claimed to disqualify the tetrahedral model of methane (V. Guillemin, *Ann. der Physik*, **81**, 173 (1926)), but Dennison finds band spectra consistent with the tetrahedral model (*Astrophys. J.* **62**, 84 (1925); also de Boer and van Arkel, *Zeits. f. Physik*, **41**, 27 (1927)).

[104] L. Ebert, R. Eisenschitz, and H. v. Hartel, *Naturwissenschaften*, **15**, 668 (1927); *Zeits. f. Phys. Chem.* **1B**, 94 (1928). Cf. also J. W. Williams, *Phys. Zeits.* **29**, 686 (1928).

[105] K. Höjendahl, Dissertation (Copenhagen, 1928), p. 60.

[106] J. W. Williams, *Phys. Zeits.* **29**, 271, 683 (1928); *J. Amer. Chem. Soc.* **50**, 2350 (1928); *Dipolmomente und ihre Bedeutung*, p. 46.

the given value $\theta$. In other words, we have what is sometimes called a 'pliable' bond, which is a sort of socket in which the radical is free to turn. The dipole axes tend to set themselves in the position of minimum total energy subject to this constraint, and it is altogether probable, especially in view of the mutual interaction between the various dipoles, that in such a position the four $\alpha$ dipole axes are not arranged with sufficient symmetry to mutually compensate one another, and hence to yield zero resultant moment for the complete molecule. It is interesting to note that in all the polar molecules yet found of the type $C\alpha_4$ the radical $\alpha$ contains an oxygen atom, so perhaps the presence of the oxygen atom is responsible for the non-coincidence of the dipole and valency axes of $\alpha$.

Instances in which polar radicals compensate each other very completely and which are thus the exact reverse of the examples cited in the previous paragraph are furnished by the group of ketones, of the form $\alpha$—CO—$\alpha'$. The following of these ketones,

$$CH_3\text{—}CO\text{—}C_2H_5, \qquad CH_3\text{—}CO\text{—}C_3H_7,$$
$$CH_3\text{—}CO\text{—}C_4H_9, \qquad CH_3\text{—}CO\text{—}C_6H_{13},$$
$$CH_3\text{ }CO\text{—}C_9H_{19}, \qquad C_2H_5\text{—}CO\text{—}C_2H_5,$$
$$C_3H_7\text{—}CO\text{—}C_3H_7, \qquad (CH_3)_3\text{—}CO\text{—}C(CH_3)_3,$$

have been found by Wolf[107] to have electric moments not differing by more than 2 or 3 per cent. from that $2 \cdot 71 \times 10^{-18}$ of acetone

$$(CH_3\text{—}CO\text{—}CH_3).$$

The obvious inference is that the electric moment is due entirely to the CO radical, and that the dipole moments of the other radicals compensate each other completely. It may be noted, however, that here the CO radical has a very much larger moment $2 \cdot 7 \times 10^{-18}$ e.s.u. than that of a free CO atom $(0 \cdot 1 \times 10^{-18})$, so that the CO radical in the ketones presumably borrows or loans electrons to or from the attached radicals in order to have a different structure from the free CO atom. According to Estermann,[108] benzophenol $(C_6H_5\text{—}CO\text{—}C_6H_5)$ has an electric moment $2 \cdot 5 \times 10^{-18}$, about 10 per cent. lower than Wolf's values for the ketones. The difference is perhaps due to distortion of the CO structure by the polarization forces from the radicals, or may be experimental error, as Estermann measured the pure liquid. All the alcohols have approximately (within 20 per cent.) the same moment, $1 \cdot 6 \times 10^{-18}$, which is probably due to the OH radical.

[107] K. L. Wolf, *Zeits. f. Phys. Chem.* **2B**, 39 (1929).
[108] J. Estermann, *Zeits. f. Phys. Chem.* **1B**, 134 (1928).

It is interesting to note that Smyth and Stoops[109] find all nine isomers of heptane ($C_7H_{16}$) to be non-polar.[110] Errera[111] has investigated the various isomers of acetylene dichloride and finds that the cis and so-called asymmetrical forms have moments 1·89 and $1·18 \times 10^{-18}$ respectively, while the trans form has no moment. More recently Müller and Sack[74] find $1·74 \times 10^{-18}$ for the cis form. This is in nice qualitative agreement with the structural formulae

$$
\begin{array}{ccc}
\mathrm{H \quad H} & \mathrm{Cl \quad H} & \mathrm{H \quad Cl} \\
\mathrm{C\!=\!C}, & \mathrm{C\!=\!C}, & \mathrm{C\!=\!C} \\
\mathrm{Cl \quad Cl} & \mathrm{Cl \quad H} & \mathrm{Cl \quad H} \\
\text{(cis)} & \text{(asymmetrical)} & \text{(trans)}
\end{array}
$$

which have been sometimes assumed by the organic chemists. If one measures the dielectric constants of these isomers in the solid state well below the melting-point and with a sufficiently high radio (heterodyne) frequency, the same polarization is found with all three isomers.[112] The reason is, of course, that under these conditions the relaxation time is too large to permit the dipoles to orient themselves in the field, so that there remains only the induced polarization which is independent, or very nearly so, of the symmetry of the atomic grouping in the molecule.

The molecules obtained by substitutions in the benzene ring have had their geometry very thoroughly studied with the aid of dielectric constants, probably more than any other class of chemical compounds. The benzene molecule itself is non-polar, as one expects from the conventional coplanar hexagonal model which the chemists have for the benzene ring. 'Mono-substituted' benzene molecules, of the type-form $C_6H_5\alpha$, which are formed from the benzene molecule by substitution of an atom or radical $\alpha$ for one hydrogen atom are found to be invariably polar, as one might expect. 'Di-substituted' molecules, of the form $C_6H_4\alpha_2$, are found to be polar if the two $\alpha$'s are substituted in the ortho or meta configurations, but not if substituted in the para configuration as long as $\alpha$ is an atom or one of certain types of simple radicals.[113]

[109] C. P. Smyth N. and W. Stoops, *J. Amer. Chem. Soc.* **50**, 1883 (1928).

[110] For structural diagrams and an account of the rather complicated geometrical symmetries which must be assumed to explain this non-polarity see Debye, *Polare Molekeln*, pp. 59–60 (not in Engl. ed.).

[111] J. Errera, *Phys. Zeits.* **27**, 764 (1926); also the discussion by Estermann in *Dipolmoment und chemische Struktur* (Leipziger Vorträge, 1929), p. 36.

[112] J. Errera, *Polarisation Diélectrique* (Paris, 1928), p. 106.

[113] For brevity we do not give, even in our table, the values of the electric moments of all the numerous benzene derivatives. For these see various tables by other writers cited on p. 64; some new determinations when the substituents are halides have been made by Bergmann, Engel, and Sandor, *Zeits. f. Phys. Chem.* **10B**, 106 (1930).

The meaning of these various configurations is explained by the following structural diagrams:

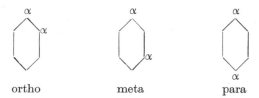

ortho            meta            para

The results on the electric moments are exactly what one should expect, as the ortho and meta arrangements are unsymmetrical, while in the para arrangement the two $\alpha$ atoms are diametrically opposite and there is perfect symmetry.  On the other hand, the dielectric constant data reveal that molecules of the para form can be polar if the $\alpha$'s are certain complicated types of radicals.  Williams, in fact, finds that p-hydroquinone diethyl ether and p-hydroquinone diacetate have electric moments $1 \cdot 7 \times 10^{-18}$ and $2 \cdot 2 \times 10^{-18}$ e.s.u. respectively.[114]  The ordinary structural formulae, viz.

$$H_5C_2O\!\!\left<\underline{\phantom{mmm}}\right>\!\!OC_2H_5 \qquad\qquad H_3CC(O)O\!\!\left<\underline{\phantom{mmm}}\right>\!\!O(O)CCH_3$$

which are given to represent the para configurations of these molecules, would at first thought lead one to expect a zero moment, as the two sides of the substituted benzene ring appear equal and opposite in character.  The solution of the paradox is probably similar to that of the polarity of certain molecules of the type $C\alpha_4$, viz. that the axis of polarity of a radical need not necessarily coincide with its axis of valency.  Hence, in a polar molecule of the form $p\text{-}C_6H_4\alpha_2$, such as the two hydroquinone compounds mentioned above, the dipole axes of the radicals $\alpha$ need not necessarily fall in the plane of the benzene ring. Attempts have even been made to calculate from the observed moments the angles of inclination of the dipole axes to the benzene ring, and especially the angle between the dipole axes of the two like radicals present in the polar para compounds, but as yet the only sure conclusion is that these two axes do not make an angle of 180° with each other, for otherwise there would be complete compensation of the moments and no polarity.  The fact that some other angle than 180° is the most stable appears somewhat startling from a dynamical standpoint, as dipoles tend to set themselves antiparallel.  Very likely there is no angle of static equilibrium, but instead a continual internal pre-

[114] J. W. Williams, *Phys. Zeits.* **29**, 683 (1928); A. Weissberger and J. W. Williams, *Zeits. f. Phys. Chem.* **3B**, 367 (1929).

cession or oscillation of the molecule which makes the angle between the two dipoles a periodic function of the time.

The question of the existence of such internal precessions has been the subject of considerable discussion in the literature. The assumption of a chemical bond which is merely a socket in which the radical can turn freely is usually termed the hypothesis of free rotation (*freie Drehbarkeit*). The most extensive examination appears to have been made in the case of ethylene dichloride ($ClH_2C$—$CH_2Cl$). As pointed out by Williams[115] and by Eucken and Meyer,[116] the observed moment is intermediate between the value zero, characteristic of the antiparallel alinement, and the value calculated under the assumption of free rotation. Hence it would appear that here the radicals $ClH_2$ are not entirely free to turn and exhibit a preference for the antiparallel configuration, although also rotating (or perhaps vibrating) through other configurations. Also X-ray and electron diffraction data[117] show that the molecule spends most of its time in certain particular configurations, perhaps favouring antiparallel alinement. If the potential energy resisting the free turning is comparable with $kT$, the dielectric constant should no longer be a linear function of $1/T$. This is shown by the general quantum-mechanical analysis of dielectric constants to be given in Chapter VII, in which the Debye formula is obtained only if the separation of energy levels is very small or very large compared to $kT$. An analogous discussion of the departures from linearity on the basis of classical mechanics has been given by Meyer.[118] Until recently existing experimental data[119] did not seem adequate to test whether the dielectric constant of ethylene dichloride, and other molecules where partial rotations are suspected, are really accurate linear functions of $1/T$. Some curvature is apparently exhibited in the measurements of Meyer, but not in those of Ghosh, Mahanti, and Gupta. Very recent measurements by Smyth and Walls[119] seem to show quite conclusively that there are pronounced departures from linearity in the case of ethylene dichloride. Sänger reports strict linearity, but perhaps this is because he did not use as low temperatures as Smyth.

Unlike ethylene dichloride, acetylene dichloride ($HClC = CClH$) shows distinct isomers (cf. diagrams, p. 74), and this is direct experimental evidence that in the latter there is no appreciable internal rotation. To explain this, it has commonly been suggested that a carbon double bond is much more rigid as regards turning than a single bond. A theoretical basis for this rigidity has been given by Hückel[120] by means of quantum mechanics.

Considerable work has been done on developing a quantitative 'vector' theory of the electric moments of the disubstituted benzenes.

[115] J. W. Williams, *Zeits. f. Phys. Chem.* **138**, 75 (1928).

[116] A. Eucken and L. Meyer, *Phys. Zeits.* **30**, 397 (1929).

[117] P. Debye, *Phys. Zeits.* **31**, 142 (1930) (report of experiments by Bewilogua and Ehrhardt; R. Wierl, *ibid.* **31**, 366 (1930). Wierl's data seem to indicate two equilibrium positions, whereas the X-ray measurements apparently reveal only one. Sänger[119] claims that none of these diffraction measurements are really precise enough to decide whether or not there is free rotation.

[118] L. Meyer, *Zeits. f. Phys. Chem.* **8**B, 27 (1930).

[119] Meyer, *l.c.*; Sänger, *Phys. Zeits.* **32**, 21 (1931); Smyth and Walls, *J. Amer. Chem. Soc.* **53**, 534 (1931); P. N. Ghosh, P. C. Mahanti, and Sen Gupta, *Zeits. f. Physik*, **54**, 711 (1929).

[120] E. Hückel, *Zeits. f. Physik*, **60**, 423 (1930).

Let us suppose that the electric moment $I$ due to the substitution of an atom or simple radical $\alpha$ in the benzene ring is directed from the centre of this ring to the position of the hydrogen atom replaced by $\alpha$. An analogous assumption will be made about the moment $I'$ due to substitution of another atom or simple radical $\alpha'$. If, then, the two substituents $\alpha$, $\alpha'$ be inserted simultaneously, thus forming a disubstituted benzene, and if the dipole moments due to these two substituents be supposed not to distort each other, then clearly the resultant moment of the molecule is, by the law of vector addition,

$$\mu = [I^2 + I'^2 + 2II' \cos \phi]^{\frac{1}{2}}, \qquad (12)$$

where $\phi$, the angle between the two constituent dipoles, is respectively 60°, 120°, and 180° for the ortho, meta, and para positions respectively. Eq. (12) was first proposed by J. J. Thomson[121] in 1923, but it remained for other investigators to make a proper examination of the experimental validity of his suggestion (12), as unfortunately proper data were not available at the time of his paper. The first adequate experimental tests were made by Errera[122] and by Smyth and Morgan,[123] while only slightly more recently a very great number of benzene compounds have been examined in the light of (12) by Höjendahl[54] and by Williams[58] and co-workers. Some typical results for the dichlorobenzenes are shown in the following table:

|  | o-$C_6H_4Cl_2$ | m-$C_6H_4Cl_2$ | p-$C_6H_4Cl_2$ |
|---|---|---|---|
| $\mu_{obs}$ | $2 \cdot 25 \times 10^{-18}$ | $1 \cdot 48 \times 10^{-18}$ | $0$ $(0 \cdot 4 \times 10^{-18}$ e.s.u.$)$ |
| $\mu_{calc}$ (Eq. 12) | $2 \cdot 65$ | $1 \cdot 53$ | $0$ |
| $\mu_{calc}$ (S. & H.) | $2 \cdot 13$ | $1 \cdot 42$ | $0$ |

The prefixes o-, m-, p-, of course, refer to the ortho, meta, and para states respectively. The first row gives the experimental moments obtained by Smyth and Morgan by the method $II_{sol}$ (see p. 61), while the second row gives the values computed from Eq. (12). As the two atoms which are substituted in the benzene ring are both chlorine atoms, $I$ equals $I'$ in Eq. (12), and the moments given by (12) reduce to the simple expressions $\sqrt{3}I$, $I$, and 0 for the o-, m-, and p-states. The value employed for $I$ is $1 \cdot 53 \times 10^{-18}$, which is a mean of experimental values found by Williams and others for monochlorobenzene (see table, p. 67). The agreement between the calculated and observed values, while by no means perfect, shows that (12) has at least approximate validity for the compounds in question. The agreement between

[121] J. J. Thomson, *Phil. Mag.* **46**, 513 (1923).
[122] J. Errera, *Comptes Rendus*, **182**, 1623 (1926); *Phys. Zeits.* **27**, 764 (1926).
[123] Smyth and Morgan, *J. Amer. Chem. Soc.* **49**, 1030 (1927).

the two sets of values would be perfect if the angle $\theta$ in (12) were taken as 85° and 122° for the ortho and meta states instead of 60° and 120°. These alterations in angle are in the direction one would expect, as two dipoles tend to set themselves antiparallel, but do seem excessively large as regards the ortho state.

Apparently a more probable explanation of the departures of the angles from 60° and 120° is the induced polarization created by the forces between the different parts of the molecule. In other words, the field from one part polarizes the remainder of the molecule. This mutual induced polarization has been studied quantitatively by Smallwood and Herzfeld.[124] They endeavour to calculate quantitatively the resulting correction to Eq. (12) in the case of halogen-substituted benzenes under the assumption that the angles are 60°, 120°, &c. They find that the agreement with experiment is usually considerably improved. This is illustrated in the above table for dichlorobenzene, where the values given in the last row are inclusive of Smallwood and Herzfeld's correction for induced polarization. These are seen to agree with experiment much better than those without this correction.

Numerous applications of (12) to other disubstituted benzenes could also be cited, notably those containing the $NO_2$ radical or other halogens than Cl as the substituents. As an example of a benzene derivative containing two unlike atoms we may consider Höjendahl's observations and calculations [54] on the chloronitrobenzenes, viz.

|  | o-$ClC_6H_4NO_2$ | m-$ClC_6H_4NO_2$ | p-$ClC_6H_4NO_2$ |
|---|---|---|---|
| $\mu_{obs}$ | $4 \cdot 25 \times 10^{-18}$ | $3 \cdot 38 \times 10^{-18}$ | $2 \cdot 55 \times 10^{-18}$ e.s.u. |
| $\mu_{calc}$ | $4 \cdot 78$ | $3 \cdot 26$ | $2 \cdot 11$ |
| $\mu_{w.w.}$ | $3 \cdot 78$ | $3 \cdot 18$ | $2 \cdot 36$ |

The values taken for $I$ and $I'$ in (12) are the moments 1·64 and $3 \cdot 75 \times 10^{-18}$ which Höjendahl found for monochlorobenzene and nitrobenzene respectively.[125] In the last line we have listed the experimental values observed independently by Walden and Werner.[126]

[124] H. M. Smallwood and K. F. Herzfeld, *J. Amer. Chem. Soc.* **52**, 2654 (1930). See also Bergmann, Engel, and Sandor, *l.c.*[93]

[125] The calculated values would be subject to slight revision if one used for $I$ and $I'$ the values of the moments of the $C_6H_5Cl$ and $C_6H_5NO_2$ molecules as determined by other investigators than Höjendahl. These other determinations are listed in the table on p. 67. The newer measurements are presumably more accurate, but the resulting changes are not large enough to throw much additional light on the validity of (12). For instance, Sack, due to different assumed $I$, $I'$, gives 4·76, 3·30 and $2 \cdot 25 \times 10^{-18}$ for the calculated values for the three isomers of chloronitrobenzene, and 3·61, 4·10 and 4·20 for those of nitrotoluene (*Ergebnisse der exakten Naturwissenschaften*, viii. 345 (1929).

[126] P. Walden and O. Werner, *Zeits. f. Phys. Chem.* **2**B, 10 (1929).

The case of nitrotoluene is particularly interesting, as it is necessary to suppose that here $I$ and $I'$ have opposite signs. Höjendahl finds the moments $0.43 \times 10^{-18}$ and $3.75 \times 10^{-18}$ for toluene and nitrobenzene respectively, but these measurements fix only the absolute values and not the signs of the moments for the toluene and $NO_2$ radicals, and to obtain any kind of agreement with his observations for the nitrotoluenes it is necessary to take $I = +0.43 \times 10^{-18}$, $I' = -3.75 \times 10^{-18}$ (or else $I = -0.43 \times 10^{-18}$, $I' = +3.75 \times 10^{-18}$, as only relative signs are of interest). The agreement with experiment is then quite good, as shown by the following table. The experimental values on the last line are those of Williams and Schwingel.[58]

|  | o-$CH_3C_6H_4NO_2$ | m-$CH_3C_6H_4NO_2$ | p-$CH_3C_6H_4NO_2$ |
|---|---|---|---|
| $\mu_{obs(Höj)}$ | $3.64 \times 10^{-18}$ | — | $4.31 \times 10^{-18}$ e.s.u. |
| $\mu_{calc}$ | $3.56$ | $3.98$ | $4.18$ |
| $\mu_{w.s.}$ | $3.75$ | $4.20$ | $4.50$ |

By way of summary we may give a table taken from Williams of the atoms whose effect on the moment in benzene substitutions has been found capable of approximate calculation by means of (12), at least in some cases. The table gives the values of the contributory moments $I$ which according to Williams[127] must be used for each of them. For purposes of comparison the electric moments which are obtained when these various atoms or radicals are substituted for a hydrogen atom in $CH_4$ and $H_2$ are also given when available:

| | $NO_2$ | $C\begin{smallmatrix}H\\\\O\end{smallmatrix}$ | OH | Cl | Br | I | $OCH_3$ | $C\begin{smallmatrix}O\\\\OH\end{smallmatrix}$ | $CH_3$ | $NH_2$ |
|---|---|---|---|---|---|---|---|---|---|---|
| $I \times 10^{18}$ | $-3.9$ | $-2.8$ | $-1.7$ | $-1.5$ | $-1.5$ | $-1.3$ | $-1.2$ | $-0.9$ | $+0.4$ | $+1.5$ |
| $\mu \times 10^{18}(CH_3\alpha)$ | $3.1$ | | $1.6$ | $2.0$ | $1.9$ | $1.6$ | | | | |
| $\mu \times 10^{18}(H\alpha)$ | | | $1.8$ | $1.0$ | $0.8$ | $0.4$ | | | | $1.5$ |

Questions of sign have no significance in the last two lines, as only one constituent dipole is involved in $CH_3\alpha$ or $H\alpha$. The agreement between the various lines in the table is surprisingly good, and shows that each substitution does often have approximately a characteristic dipole moment. The deviations in the hydrogen halides are to be expected, as here merely an atom, non-polar by itself, is substituted, and the moments in such cases must be due entirely to distortion of the electronic distributions.

The discussion in the preceding paragraphs has undoubtedly conveyed an impression of excessive optimism regarding the universal approximate validity of Eq. (12). The numerical examples which we

---

[127] J. W. Williams, *Dipolmomente und ihre Bedeutung*, Tables X and XI. We have added the value of $I$ for iodine given by Walden and Werner.

have given are some of the most favourable ones, and in some cases the agreement is very poor. For p-nitraniline ($O_2N—C_6H_4—NH_2$), for instance, use of (12) with the values of $I$, $I'$ given in the table yields $1 \cdot 5 — (—3 \cdot 9) = 5 \cdot 4 \times 10^{-18}$, whereas the observed value[54] is $7 \cdot 1 \times 10^{-18}$, showing that the mutual distortion between the two constituent radicals must be very great. A much more flagrant example of the inadequacy of (12) is furnished by the fact that the dipole moment of OH must be assumed to have different signs in different cases. In both the cresols ($CH_3—C_6H_4—OH$)[128] and chlorophenols[129] ($Cl—C_6H_4—OH$) the dipole moment is found to be distinctly greater in the para than in the meta or the ortho configuration. Hence the OH radical must make contributions of the opposite signs to those of $CH_3$ and of Cl. But reference to the table shows that $CH_3$ makes a positive contribution and Cl a negative one. Hence OH behaves negatively in one case and positively in the other. As regards the example we have given, the anomaly in sign might be blamed on $CH_3$ or on Cl, but comparison with a number of other examples shows that it is in all probability to be attributed to OH. Fogelberg and Williams[130] have recently found that similar anomalies also are unavoidable for $NH_2$. When such anomalies in sign arise, Eq. (12) ceases to have much meaning. It is probable that the escape from the dilemma is that the electric moment of the OH radical does not fall in the plane of the benzene ring. This has already been mentioned in connexion with the finite moment found for certain hydroquinone compounds where (12) would demand zero. A radical of this type Höjendahl in his dissertation calls an 'inclined group', in distinction to the 'positive' and 'negative' groups to which (12) is applicable. In the case of inclined groups, the geometric addition of the dipole moments of the various radicals to obtain the resultant moment of the entire molecule must be made in three rather than two dimensions, and then the usual so-called 'vector models' of the polarity of the benzene substituents based on vector addition entirely in the plane of the benzene ring of course lose all meaning. In short, the approximate applicability of (12) to benzene substituents is for a limited class of compounds rather than a universal property, and doubtless this will be increasingly revealed by the continual extension of the experimental measurements to include more and more of these substituents.

[128] Smyth and Morgan, *J. Amer. Chem. Soc.* **49**, 1036 (1927) (their calculations utilized earlier experimental measurements by Philip and Haynes, *J. Chem. Soc.* **87**, 998 (1905)); cf. also Williams and Fogelberg, *J. Amer. Chem. Soc.* **52**, 1356 (1930).

[129] J. W. Williams, *Phys. Zeits.* **29**, 683 (1928).

[130] Fogelberg and Williams, *Phys. Zeits.* **32**, 27 (1931).

The data on the symmetrical trisubstituted benzenes are particularly interesting because of the light they shed on the structure of the benzene ring. It is found that mesitylene,[58] 1,3,5 triethylbenzene,[58] and 1,3,5-tribromobenzene,[54] have zero moments within the experimental error.[131] As implied by the suffixes 1,3,5, the substituent atoms or radicals replace every other hydrogen atom in the benzene ring. If the benzene ring is really a ring, i.e. six atoms evenly spaced in a plane, no electrical moment should result for these compounds. On the other hand, structural formulae proposed by Körner, Baeyer, and Ladenburg [132] would require a three-dimensional instead of coplanar model, and would lead to a finite electric moment for all symmetrical trisubstituted benzenes, contrary to experiment. In particular, the model in which alternate hydrogen atoms are in different planes, and in which the familiar hexagon is thus replaced by two triangles in parallel planes, must be rejected.

A study of the dielectric properties of the derivatives of diphenyl, which contains two benzene rings, has led to interesting information on the coupling between the two rings, but this would take us even farther afield into organic chemistry.[133]

A detailed knowledge of electronic motions and distributions would enable one to calculate directly by pure dynamics the moments of simple molecules and radicals, but so far the attempts made in this direction have been rather unsuccessful. The reader should particularly guard against the idea that the moment of a molecule such as HCl is anything like $er_0$, where $e$ is the charge of an electron and $r_0$ is the distance between the nuclei. The moment $er_0$ is, perhaps, what one would naïvely expect if one used the picture which has sometimes been given of HCl as having a proton at one end and a negatively charged chlorine ion at the other, so that the molecule would be merely $H^+Cl^-$. The value of $r_0$ for the HCl molecule is $1 \cdot 28 \times 10^{-8}$ cm.,[134] and hence $er_0$ is $6 \cdot 11 \times 10^{-18}$ e.s.u., whereas the actual moment is only $1 \cdot 03 \times 10^{-18}$.[135] The reason the actual moment is so small is that

[131] The moments found are of the order $0 \cdot 2 \times 10^{-18}$ or less, which may be considered virtually zero. Sym-trinitrobenzene seems to have a real electric moment of approximately $0 \cdot 8 \times 10^{-18}$ e.s.u.

[132] Körner, *Gazz. Chem. Ital.* **4**, 444 (1874); Baeyer, *Ann. der Chemie*, **245**, 103 (1888); Ladenburg, *Ber. d. D. Chem. Ges.* **2**, 140 (1869).

[133] See J. W. Williams,[59] also Williams and Weissberger, *J. Amer. Chem. Soc.* **50**, 2332 (1928), *Zeits. f. Phys. Chem.* **3B**, 367 (1929); summary in Debye, *Polare Molekeln* (German ed. only), p. 66.

[134] From band spectra; Birge, *International Critical Tables*, v. 414.

[135] C. T. Zahn, *Phys. Rev.* **24**, 400 (1924). It may be noted that the moment $1 \cdot 03 \times 10^{-18}$ e.s.u. found experimentally by Zahn for HCl is almost exactly the product $e_{\text{eff}}r_0 = 1 \times 10^{-18}$ of the inter-nuclear distance $r_0$ and the effective charge $0 \cdot 86 \times 10^{-10}$ found by Bourgin from spectral intensities for the infra-red vibration of HCl. This has sometimes been quoted as proof that Bourgin's value of the effective charge is very approximately correct, but there is no reason why the moment $\mu$ should be identical with $e_{\text{eff}}r_0$. As a matter of fact the two expressions are not even of comparable magnitude in CO if the effective

the hydrogen atom does not lose all its charge to the chlorine atom. Another way of saying more or less the same thing is that a proton at distance $r_0$ from a chlorine ion would attract some of the latter's negative charge and thus polarize the ion greatly. K. T. Compton and Debye[136] have both examined whether perchance the actual moment is approximately $er_0 - \alpha E$, where $\alpha$ is the polarizability of the chlorine ion as deduced from refractive data, and where $E$ is the Coulomb field $e/r_0^2$ which the H nucleus would exert at the geometric centre of the Cl⁻ ion. Actually the value of $\alpha$ is so large that the term $\alpha E$ is greater than $er_0$, and the molecule 'over-polarizes' itself, an obvious absurdity. The absurdity has doubtless arisen because the polarizability deduced from refractive measurements applies only to fields which are sensibly constant over the dimensions of an atom or ion, whereas a proton so close to the Cl⁻ ion as $r_0 = 1 \cdot 28 \times 10^{-8}$ cm. gives rise to a highly divergent Coulomb field which is much larger on the near than on the far side of the chlorine ion. Furthermore, it is questionable whether it is a good approximation to consider HCl as derived from $H^+ + Cl^-$ rather than $H + Cl$, for recent developments in the quantum mechanics seem to show that the valence in HCl is perhaps more non-polar than polar in nature. At any rate Compton's and Debye's calculations show that it is eminently reasonable that the actual moment be very much smaller than $er_0$.

## 21. Optical Refractivities and Molecular Structure

We have seen that a certain degree of success has attended the calculation of the moments of complicated molecules by the vectorial addition of the dipole moments of the constituent radicals or groups. The optical refractivity of a chemical compound, or, what is essentially [137] equivalent, the 'induced' part $4\pi N\alpha$ of its dielectric constant, can be calculated on the whole more accurately and more generally than can the dipole moment from the properties of the constituent atoms or radicals. The greater simplicity in the synthesis of the induced rather than permanent polarization of a molecule is to be expected, as each atom is capable of induced polarization, whereas permanent moments arise only from complicated interactions between atoms. In other words, induced polarization is to a considerable extent a purely atomic property. If this is true, the index of refraction $n$ of a chemical compound should be capable of calculation from the indices $n_i$ of the constituents in the same way as for a mixture without chemical combination, so that by considerations similar to those used in obtaining (9),

$$k = \sum \eta_i k_i, \tag{13}$$

where $\eta_i$ is the number of atoms or radicals of type $i$ contained in

charge $4 \times 10^{-10} = 0 \cdot 9e$ deduced from infra-red dispersion (see § 15) is correct, for then $e_{\text{eff}} r_0 = 5 \times 10^{-18}$, whereas $\mu = 0 \cdot 1 \times 10^{-18}$. Molecules with more than two atoms can have vibration spectra without having a permanent moment, so that in them there is no immediate connexion between the moment and effective charge.

[136] K. T. Compton, *Science*, **63**, 53 (1926); P. Debye, *Polar Molecules*, p. 62.

[137] Provided, as is ordinarily the case, the atomic polarization is comparatively small.

a molecule of the compound, and where $k$ and $k_i$ are the so-called 'molar refractivities',

$$k = \frac{M}{\rho}\frac{n^2-1}{n^2+2}, \qquad k_i = \frac{M_i}{\rho_i}\frac{n_i^2-1}{n_i^2+2},$$

of the compound and of a typical constituent, which have densities and molecular weights $\rho$, $M$ and $\rho_i$, $M_i$ respectively. The scalar nature of the addition in (13) is to be contrasted with the vectorial addition of the dipole moments involved in an equation such as (12). The absence of vector properties simplifies the study of the refractivities of chemical compounds, but at the same time makes it much less illuminating on molecular structure than the study of dipole moments.

The refractivities of various classes of molecules have been extensively analysed in the light of (13), especially in the nineteenth century. To quote from a book-review by C. P. Smyth: [138] 'The polarization induced within the molecule, that is, the molecular refraction, was discussed so often a generation and more ago that it is now commonly regarded as an outworn subject and dismissed with a cursory treatment as a necessary preliminary to the discussion of the dipole polarization.' As a typical illustration of the early work with (13), we shall consider some calculations made by Landolt [139] in 1862–4. Like many other investigators in this field, he defined the molecular refractivity by means of the Gladstone-Dale formula $k' = (n-1)M/\rho$ instead of the Lorenz-Lorentz one $k = (n^2-1)M/\rho(n^2+2)$. If $n-1$ is not too large, the difference between the two formulae is small except for a constant factor $2/3$ which is of no interest in connexion with study of an additivity rule such as (13). The series expansion of $(n^2-1)/(n^2+2)$ in $n-1$ is $\frac{2}{3}[(n-1)-\frac{1}{6}(n-1)^2+...]$. Thus to the first approximation the two formulae are the same except for the constant factor, while the difference in the second approximation is small because of the factor $1/6$. Landolt found that by assuming the following values of $k'$ for the constituent atoms

$$k'_C = 5\cdot00, \qquad k'_H = 1\cdot30, \qquad k'_O = 3\cdot00, \qquad (14)$$

he could account nicely for the refractivities of certain compounds of these elements by using the additivity rule $k' = \sum \eta_i k'_i$. This is shown in the following table:

|  | $CH_4O$ | $C_4H_{10}O$ | $C_2H_4O_2$ | $C_6H_{12}O_2$ | $C_4H_8O_2$ | $C_{10}H_{20}O_2$ | $C_3H_6O$ |
|---|---|---|---|---|---|---|---|
| $k'_{calc}$ | 13·2 | 36·0 | 21·2 | 51·6 | 36·4 | 82·0 | 25·8 |
| $k'_{obs}$ | 13·2 | 36·1 | 21·1 | 51·6 | 36·2 | 82·1 | 26·1 |

[138] C. P. Smyth, *Phys. Rev.* **34**, 166 (1929).

[139] Landolt, *Pogg. Ann.* **117**, 353 (1862); **122**, 545 (1864); **123**, 596 (1864); also especially **123**, 626 (1864) and *Ann. der Chem.* 4 Supp. p. 1. Summary on p. 38 ff. of Eisenlohr's book.[141]

In order to avoid confusion we have added primes to $k$ to designate that the Gladstone-Dale rather than the Lorenz-Lorentz definition of the molar refractivity is used. It is to be emphasized that an equation such as (13) will not account for the refractivities of all compounds containing C, H, O if the values (14) for the constituent refractivities are used. Brühl[140] found in 1880 that the indices of refraction of certain other compounds of these elements could be approximately calculated by assuming that each double carbon bond contributed an amount $K$ to the molecular refractivity. This makes $k' = \sum \eta_i k'_i + \eta K$, where $\eta$ is the number of double bonds. The calculated and observed values are then as follows:

| | $C_3H_6O$ | $C_5H_{10}O$ | $C_4H_6O_2$ | $C_5H_{10}$ | $C_5H_8$ | $C_6H_{10}$ | $C_6H_6$ | $C_7H_8$ | $C_7H_8O$ | $C_9H_{12}O$ |
|---|---|---|---|---|---|---|---|---|---|---|
| $\eta$ | 1 | 1 | 1 | 1 | 2 | 2 | 3 | 3 | 3 | 3 |
| $k'_{calc}$ | 27·2 | 42·1 | 35·0 | 39·2 | 38·6 | 46·1 | 42·9 | 50·3 | 53·2 | 68·2 |
| $k'_{obs}$ | 27·1 | 42·2 | 35·1 | 39·3 | 38·7 | 45·0 | 42·2 | 50·1 | 53·2 | 68·8 |

The compounds with three double bonds are of the so-called aromatic type. The contributions of the various atoms are taken by Brühl to have the following values slightly different from (14):

$$k'_C = 4·86, \qquad k'_H = 1·29, \qquad k'_O = 2·90, \qquad K = 2·0. \qquad (15)$$

It must be mentioned that neither the atomic refractivities given in (14) or (15), nor the data in the tables, are the most recent or highly refined values, but the later work discriminates between many different types of bonds, and would take us too far afield into organic chemistry.[141] Oxygen, for instance, is attributed different refractive equivalents in different types of compounds. The introduction of numberless such complications makes one feel that the highly developed elaborations and ramifications of (13) are to a certain extent numerical juggling. Complicated additivity rules are, of course, extremely useful in enabling one to calculate in advance the approximate value of the refractivity of a chemical compound whose dispersion has not been measured, but do not seem to have any very elemental physical significance. Also, it must be cautioned that such rules apply only to certain particular types of chemical compounds, especially the organic, and that their success is not at all universal. The artificiality of the additivity technique is nicely shown by the fact that the atomic refractivity of approximately 1·3 which must be assumed for hydrogen in applying the rules is not the same as either the actual refractivity 2·5 of the

---

[140] Brühl, *Ann. der Chemie*, **200**, 139 (1880).

[141] For a very comprehensive survey of additivity rules and the refractivities of organic chemical compounds see F. Eisenlohr, 'Spektrochemie organischer Verbindungen' (*Chemie in Einzeldarstellungen*, Band III).

hydrogen atom, calculated by quantum mechanics, or half the refractivity 3·1 of the hydrogen molecule.[142]

The reader should not confuse the atomic refractivities which enter in the application of additivity rules to organic compounds with the 'ionic refractivities' which enter in similar applications to solid salts and ionic solutions. The ionic refractivities have much more physical significance, as they are presumably identical with those of free ionized atoms, whereas we have seen, especially in the case of hydrogen, that there is no necessary immediate connexion between the atomic refractivities utilized in the organic compounds and the true refractivities of free atoms. In order to permit use of the results of quantum theory, estimates and discussion of ionic refractivities will be deferred until § 52.

## 22. Saturation Effects in Electric Polarization

Throughout the chapter we have supposed the field sufficiently small so that the moment is proportional to field strength. This is a condition usually fulfilled except in exceedingly strong fields. If $e_{loc}$ denote the effective local field to which the molecule is subjected, an accurate[143] representation of the polarization as a function of field strength will involve a power series of the form

$$P = Np_E = N[a_0 e_{loc} + a_1 e_{loc}^3 + ...].  \quad (16)$$

The ordinary approximation is obtained by retaining only the first term. Eq. (16) involves exclusively odd powers of $e_{loc}$ since in an isotropic medium the polarization changes sign with the field strength. If only the polarization due to orientation of the permanent dipoles needed to be considered, the values of the coefficients $a_0$, $a_1$,... in the development (16) could be obtained by expanding the Langevin function defined in (4), Chap. II, as a power series in the ratio[144] $x = \mu e_{loc}/kT$. Actually there are also terms resulting from the induced polarization, and

[142] These molar refractivities 2·6, 3·1 are the values of $(n-1)M/\rho$ corresponding to the theoretical dielectric constant 1·000225 for atomic hydrogen (see § 48) and the measured[76] dielectric constant 1·000273 of $H_2$. The first resonance lines of both H and $H_2$ are so far in the ultra-violet that the refractivities in the optical region differ very little from those for infinite wave-lengths.

[143] Even an expression such as (16) seems to the writer to involve some error, as the mean value of the cube of the effective field to which the atom is subjected is not necessarily the cube of the mean effective field, &c. In other words, a different expression for $e_{loc}$ may be necessary for each power in the development. However, the error from this source is negligible, as all the terms but the first in the development (16) are extremely small, and so a small correction to them is insignificant.

[144] In Eq. (4), Chap. II, $x$ was defined as the ratio $\mu E/kT$ instead of $\mu e_{loc}/kT$ because we did not there bother to distinguish between the local and macroscopic fields. The distinction is, however, vital in considering saturation effects.

especially its interaction with the orientation effects. Even in the strongest field obtainable experimentally, it is sufficient to include only the first two terms of (16). The first term $a_0$ is, of course, the expression $\alpha + \mu^2/3kT$ which we have encountered so often, while further calculation, which we omit, shows that the dependence of the second term on the temperature is of the form

$$a_1 = q_0 + \frac{q_1}{kT} + \frac{q_2}{k^2T^2} - \frac{\mu^4}{45k^3T^3}. \tag{17}$$

The constants $q_0$, $q_1$, $q_2$ are expressible in terms of the dynamical characteristics of the model (i.e. matrix amplitudes in quantum mechanics), but are too complicated to be given here. The values of $q_0$, $q_1$, $q_2$ were first calculated by Debye [145] in classical theory, using the conventional model (§ 12) of harmonic oscillators mounted on a rigid rotating framework. Recently Niessen,[146] using the quantum mechanics, has given general formulae for these $q$-coefficients without the necessity of making any special assumptions concerning the nature of the electronic motions. It may be remarked that the coefficient $q_0$ vanishes, in either quantum or classical theory, if one makes the unreal supposition that the electronic motions can be represented by simple harmonic oscillators, and so $q_0$ appears in Niessen's calculations but not in Debye's. If these oscillators be supposed isotropic as well as simple harmonic, the coefficients $q_1$ and $q_2$ also vanish. In an actual molecule all the $q$'s are different from zero if it is polar, while only the terms $q_0$, $q_1$ remain if it is non-polar. The reason for this is that $q_0$ and part of $q_1$ are due entirely to the induced polarization, while the remainder of $q_1$ and all of $q_2$ arise from the interaction between the induced and permanent polarity, provided there is any of the latter. It is clear that the tendency of the permanent dipoles towards alinement parallel to the field destroys the random orientation, and so changes the induced polarizability if the molecule is optically anisotropic. Because even the induced moment tends to aline itself in the field, the term $q_1$ does not vanish even in a non-polar molecule. The 'interaction terms' $q_1$, $q_2$ are closely related to the Kerr effect, as the latter effect is the alteration in optical refractivity due primarily to orientation in a static electric field. The final term $-\mu^4/45k^3T^3$ in (17) is due exclusively to the permanent moment, and is the same as obtained by series expansion of the Langevin function.

In order to measure the effect of electrical saturation, it is usual to

[145] P. Debye, *Handbuch der Radiologie*, vol. vi, p. 754.
[146] K. F. Niessen, *Phys. Rev.* **34**, 253 (1929).

measure the change in the moment $P$ or in the dielectric displacement $D = E + 4\pi P$ when an already large field $E$ is changed to $E + dE$ without altering its direction. It is therefore convenient and customary to define the dielectric constant in a strong field as the slope $dD/dE$ of the $D$–$E$ curve rather than as the ratio $D/E$ of its ordinate and abscissa. If we assume that the local field has the Clausius-Mossotti value $E + 4\pi P/3$, then

$$\frac{dD}{dE} = \epsilon_0 + 12\pi \left( \frac{\epsilon_0 + 2}{3} \right)^4 Na_1 E^2, \tag{18}$$

where $\epsilon_0$ is the ordinary dielectric constant for small field intensities, i.e. the value of $dD/dE$ at the origin $E = 0$. To obtain (18) we substitute $e_{\text{loc}} = E + 4\pi P/3$ in the first right-hand term of (16), and the approximate value $e_{\text{loc}} = E(\epsilon_0 + 2)/3$ in the second term; we then solve the resulting equation for $P$ and calculate $d(E + 4\pi P)/dE$, noting that $3(\epsilon_0 - 1)/(\epsilon_0 + 2) = 4\pi Na_0$.

The effect of the correction or 'saturation' term in (18) which is proportional to $E^2$ is very hard to measure, as it is exceedingly small, and appreciable only in such strong fields that it is difficult to eliminate error due to the effect of electrostriction on the size of the apparatus. As a numerical illustration let us, following Debye,[147] consider the case of ethyl ether; here $\epsilon_0 = 4\cdot30$, $N = 5\cdot83 \times 10^{21}$, $\mu = 1\cdot14 \times 10^{-18}$, and (18) reduces at $T = 293$ to $dD/dE = 4\cdot30 - 0\cdot25 \times 10^{-8} E^2$ provided we neglect all but the last term of (17). In this formula the field strength must be expressed in electrostatic units, and hence in a field of 10,000 volts/cm. $= 33$ e.s.u. the correction term is only of the order $10^{-6}$ as large as the main term $4\cdot30$. The reality of the saturation effect appears to have been first demonstrated by Herweg.[148] He even attempted to evaluate the constant $a_1$ in (18) from the amount of saturation observed experimentally, and hence determine the electric moment $\mu$, assuming that the last term in (17) is predominant. He thus obtained a moment $1\cdot20 \times 10^{-18}$ e.s.u. for ethyl ether, in exceedingly good agreement with the value $1\cdot14 \times 10^{-18}$ obtained by other, more standard, methods (see table, p. 66). It is hard to believe that this agreement is anything but accidental, for the derivation of moments from the amount of saturation is very difficult, not merely because the small saturation effects are very hard to measure with precision, but also because the first three terms of (17) are in reality not negligible, and further it is necessary to work

---

[147] P. Debye, *Polar Molecules*, p. 111.

[148] J. Herweg, *Zeits. f. Physik*, **3**, 36 (1920); J. Herweg and W. Potzsch, *ibid.* **8**, 1 (1922); An earlier attempt at measuring the saturation effect was made by S. Ratnowsky, *Verh. d. D. Phys. Ges.* **15**, 497 (1913).

with pure liquids, where the Clausius-Mossotti expression for the local field is probably a poor approximation. Hence it appears undue optimism to expect quantitative rather than qualitative results from existing saturation experiments. The saturation effect has recently been measured for a number of materials by Kautsch,[149] and by Gundermann.[150] Kautsch finds that for ethyl ether, chloroform, and monochlorobenzene, all polar molecules, the saturation term in (18) proves to be negative. In hexane and benzene, Kautsch and Gundermann respectively find this term too small to detect, and in carbon disulphide, which, like hexane, is non-polar, Kautsch finds it has a small positive value. This is in nice agreement with theory, as in highly polar molecules, the last term in (17), which is invariably negative, probably predominates, while in non-polar molecules only the first two terms of (17) remain, and these terms are probably small and usually positive.

It has commonly been supposed that an elegant indirect way of observing saturation is furnished by the lowering of the dielectric constant of a liquid when a readily ionized salt is dissolved therein. Such a lowering is attributed by Debye and Sack[151] to the saturation of the molecules of the liquid by the intense fields arising from the dissolved ions. Clearly the effective susceptibility is not that appropriate to the applied field alone, but rather the much lower susceptibility appropriate to the resultant field obtained by compounding vectorially the applied field and the much larger ionic field. However, the experimental results have never been very consistent. The most recent experimental work, that by Wien,[152] seems to show that the dissolved ions raise rather than lower the dielectric constant. This, if true, is contrary to the earlier results of Sack, who found a lowering proportional to the 3/2 power of the valence of the dissolved salt, in accord with his saturation theory. If the results of Wien are accepted, the saturation effect is presumably still present, but masked by an increase of the susceptibility due to some other cause.

[149] F. Kautzsch, *Phys. Zeits.* **29,** 105 (1928); measurements on water, glycerine, and ethyl ether have been made by F. Malsch, *Ann. der Physik,* **84,** 841 (1927).

[150] H. Gundermann, *Ann. der Physik,* **6,** 545 (1930).

[151] P. Debye, *Polar Molecules,* Chap. VI (includes references to other literature); H. Sack, *Phys. Zeits.* **27,** 206 (1926); **28,** 199 (1927).

[152] Unpublished work of Max Wien, communicated to the author by Professor Falkenhagen.

# THE CLASSICAL THEORY OF MAGNETIC SUSCEPTIBILITIES

## 23. Conventional Derivation of the Langevin Formulae for Para- and Diamagnetism

In Chapter II it was seen that if the molecule has a permanent electrical moment of magnitude $\mu$, and if further the molecule is supposed rigid and hence incapable of induced polarization, the electric susceptibility is given by the expression

$$\chi = \frac{N\mu^2}{3kT}. \tag{1}$$

Let us now suppose that the molecule has a magnetic instead of electric moment, or, in other words, is a tiny permanent magnet. These molecular magnets will tend to aline themselves parallel to an applied magnetic field $H$, but are resisted by the 'temperature agitation' mentioned in § 10. By applying exactly the same physical reasoning and mathematical calculations as in Chapter II, except that the polarization is magnetic rather than electric, one concludes that the magnetic susceptibility is also given by an expression of the form (1), which is the Langevin formula for paramagnetism. According to Eq. (1) the paramagnetic susceptibility should be inversely proportional to the temperature, provided the density is kept constant. This relation is known as Curie's law, as it was discovered experimentally and enunciated by Curie[1] before it was obtained theoretically by Langevin.[2] Of course this law is not without numerous exceptions and refinements, which unfortunately tend to increase in number with improvements in experimental technique, but nevertheless Curie's law represents on the whole pretty well the gist of a large mass of experimental data for not merely gases, but many liquids and solids.[1] Of the two common paramagnetic gases, oxygen obeys Curie's law quite accurately right down to the temperature of liquifaction,[3] whereas nitric oxide shows appreciable departures for reasons to be given in § 67. From the magnitude of the temperature coefficient of the susceptibility it is possible to deduce the magnitude of the permanent magnetic moment of the molecule, in the same fashion as in the electrical case. A discussion of the numerical values so obtained experimentally for $\mu$ will be deferred until

---

[1] P. Curie, *Ann. de Chim. et Phys.* (7) **5**, 289 (1895); *Œuvres*, Paris 1908, p. 232.

[2] P. Langevin, *J. de Physique*, (4) **4**, 678 (1905); *Ann. Chim. Phys.* (8) **5**, 70 (1905).

[3] P. Curie, *l.c.*[1] and more recent other work to be cited and discussed in § 66.

Chapters IX–XI as the theoretical estimates of $\mu$ with which they are to be compared are very intimately connected with the quantization of angular momentum. Just as in the electrical case, Eq. (1) holds only in fields inadequate for saturation effects, and in very strong fields the right side of (1) should be replaced by $N\mu H^{-1}L(\mu H/kT)$, where $L(x)$ is the complete Langevin function $\coth x - (1/x)$, which has already been discussed and graphed on p. 32. The saturation effects are easier to detect experimentally in the magnetic than in the electric case, and for gadolinium sulphate, in particular, Woltjer and Onnes[4] have, by using very low temperatures and high fields (1·31° K. and 22,000 gauss), succeeded in making the magnetic polarization reach over 80 per cent. of the saturation value $N\mu$ corresponding to perfect alinement of all the molecular magnets parallel to the field. These measurements will be discussed more completely in § 61 after we have developed the quantum theory of magnetism.

Eq. (1) always makes $\chi > 0$ and hence accounts only for paramagnetism. How can we explain the existence of diamagnetic media, which have susceptibilities $\chi < 0$? In his celebrated paper Langevin answered this by showing that one indeed obtains diamagnetism if one considers the induced rather than permanent magnetic moment of the molecule. Such a result was also intimated, though less precisely, at considerably earlier dates by Weber and others. In Chapter I, especially Eq. (11), we saw that the magnetic moment of an orbit is proportional to its angular momentum. Suppose now that the molecule is 'non-gyroscopic', i.e. has no electronic angular momentum in the absence of external fields (except the feeble electronic part of the angular momentum due to 'end over end' rotation of the molecule as a whole). If now a magnetic field is applied, the electronic motions are modified, and an 'induced' angular momentum is created. The electronic orbits around the nuclei in many respects resemble a current undamped by resistance, and Lenz's well-known law states that currents induced by a magnetic field have such a sense that their magnetic fields tend to oppose the original field. The induced angular momentum thus has such a sign that the total microscopic magnetic field is less than the applied macroscopic field $H$, and hence by Eq. (6), Chap. I, the magnetic induction $B$ is less than $H$, making the material diamagnetic. These qualitative arguments may easily be made more precise if the molecule is monatomic, so that we can utilize Larmor's theorem (§ 8). The more general

[4] H. R. Woltjer and H. Kamerlingh-Onnes, *Leiden Communications*, 167c (or *Versl. Amsterdam Akad.* **32**, 772, 1923).

non-monatomic case will be treated in § 69. If $\rho_i$, $z_i$, $\phi_i$ be cylindrical coordinates of the electrons with the $z$ axis coincident with the direction of $H$, then Larmor's theorem tells us that $\rho_i$, $z_i$ are the same functions $\rho_i(t)$, $z_i(t)$ of the time as for a motion characteristic of $H = 0$, while the angular velocities $\dot{\phi}_i$ about the axis are of the form $\dot{\phi}_i^0(t) + He/2mc$, the extra term $He/2mc$ representing the Larmor precession. The angular momentum $\sum m\rho_i^2\dot{\phi}_i$ of the atom thus becomes $(He/2c)\sum \rho_i^2$ if we suppose that $\sum m\rho_i^2\dot{\phi}_i = 0$ when $H = 0$, or, in other words, that the atom has no permanent angular momentum. The summations, of course, extend over all the electrons in the atom. As the ratio of electronic magnetic moment to angular momentum is $-e/2mc$ (Eq. (11), Chap. I), the field thus creates a magnetic moment $-He^2 \sum \rho_i^2/4mc$. The susceptibility is hence $-Ne^2 \overline{\overline{\sum \rho_i^2}}/4mc$, where the double bar indicates a statistical average over a very large number of molecules. If the orientations of an assembly of atoms are random,[5] then clearly the statistical mean of $\rho_i^2 = x_i^2 + y_i^2$ is two-thirds that of $r_i^2 = x_i^2 + y_i^2 + z_i^2$. If the molecules are all alike in size, there is no difference between the statistical mean $\overline{\overline{\sum r_i^2}}$ over a large number of molecules, and the time-average $\overline{\sum r_i^2}$ for a single molecule. Thus we find

$$\chi = -\frac{Ne^2}{6mc^2} \sum \overline{r_i^2}, \qquad (2)$$

which is Langevin's formula for the diamagnetic susceptibility in the form given by Pauli.[6]

One may also obtain Eq. (2) very simply by using Eqs. (48) and (49) of Chap. I. If one assumes that there is no paramagnetism, so that Eq. (48) contains no linear term in $H$, then it is a direct consequence of these equations that the susceptibility $\chi = N\overline{m}_z/H$ is

$$\chi = -N \sum \frac{e^2}{6m_ic^2} \overline{r^2} \qquad (2\,a)$$

since the average of $x^2 + y^2$ is $\frac{2}{3}r^2$. The particles involved in the summation consist of the nuclei and electrons. The nuclei have such large masses compared to the electrons that their contributions to (2 a) may be neglected, inasmuch as (2 a) involves the masses in the denominator. In the case of electrons we can set $e_i = -e$, $m_i = m$, and (2 a) thus becomes identical with (2).

This second method of proof is short and does not explicitly use Larmor's theorem. We have nevertheless first given the proof based on his theorem because such a proof is the usual one and gives more physical insight into the diamagnetic effect. Also the shorter proof is perhaps a little misleading because it gives the

[5] The random orientations will be slightly upset by the applied field, but the correction to the diamagnetism on this account would only give a very small term.

[6] W. Pauli, Jr., *Zeits. f. Physik*, **2**, 201 (1920). Langevin's original paper gave the correct basic formula priori to the spacial averaging, but in performing this average Langevin inadvertently took the mean value of $x^2 + y^2$ as $\frac{1}{3}r^2$ rather than $\frac{2}{3}r^2$, thus giving an expression half as great as (2).

impression that (2) is valid even without Larmor's theorem. This, however, is not the case, as when his theorem is inapplicable, the linear terms in $H$ in (48), Chap. I, cannot be disregarded. For this reason Eq. (2) cannot be applied to molecules, as will be discussed more fully in § 69.

Instead of the volume susceptibility $\chi$ it is common practice to use a 'molar susceptibility' $\chi_{mol}$ similar to the molar electric suscepti-bilities mentioned in Chapter II. The molar susceptibility may be defined as the quotient obtained by dividing by the field strength the polarization of one gramme mol of the material rather than that of one c.c. Clearly $\chi_{mol}$ is given by an expression identical with (2) except that $N$ is replaced by the Avogadro number $L$. Whenever the material is monatomic, the molar susceptibility is also sometimes termed the atomic susceptibility.

There are two things particularly to be noted about Eq. (2): first, that it predicts that the diamagnetism per molecule be independent of the temperature provided the molecules always retain the same sizes, and, second, that the amount of diamagnetism should be propor-tional to $\sum r_i^2$, or approximately to the combined areas of the various orbits. The invariance of the diamagnetic susceptibility with respect to temperature was observed experimentally by Curie even before the Langevin theory. The molar susceptibilities of phosphorus, sulphur, and bromine, for instance, are independent of the temperature within the experimental error. For a great many elements, however, the independence of temperature is only approximate,[7] and in a few instances there are very marked alterations in the diamagnetism at certain critical temperatures. Perhaps the worst offender is bismuth. Above its melting-point its atomic susceptibility has the constant value $-7\cdot3\times10^{-6}$, but at this point the susceptibility changes abruptly to about $-200\times10^{-6}$ and becomes even more highly diamagnetic as the temperature is lowered still further. De Haas and van Alphen have just found[8] a most remarkable periodic variation of the susceptibility of bismuth with field strength at the temperature of liquid hydrogen. These departures from the simple invariance of temperature and field strength predicted by the Langevin formula need not worry us too

---

[7] Stoner, *Magnetism and Atomic Structure*, p. 265, gives a comprehensive table of the sign of the temperature coefficients and amounts of diamagnetism for the different chemi-cal elements. The temperature variation of diamagnetism at low temperatures has recently been measured for $N_2$ and $H_2$ by Bitter, *Phys. Rev.* **36**, 1648 (1930). He finds a very large variation in the case of hydrogen, which is hard to understand from a theoretical standpoint, and he suggests that his measurement on this gas ought to be repeated.

[8] W. J. de Haas and P. M. van Alphen, *Leiden Communications*, 212 a (1931).

much. In the first place small variations with temperature can be understood on the ground that the sizes of the orbits are not invariants, so that $\sum r_i^2$ changes somewhat with $T$. Of course the tremendous anomalies found in bismuth cannot be interpreted on the basis of any ordinary orbital contraction or expansion, but then bismuth has always been a black sheep because of its anomalous behaviour as regards electrical and other properties in the solid state. Ehrenfest and Raman [9] have stressed that perhaps its large diamagnetism when solidified is due to the orbits extending around several atomic nuclei and hence having large diameters. The variations with field strength at low temperatures are presumably due to some sort of resonance between the radius of curvature of the electron's path in the magnetic field and inter-atomic distances. It is to be particularly emphasized that the large variations of diamagnetism with temperature are all found in the liquid or especially the solid state. The simple Langevin theory should be applicable primarily to gases, and their molar diamagnetic susceptibilities are indeed invariant of the temperature, or at least very nearly so.

From the absolute magnitude of the susceptibility it is possible to deduce an estimate of the sizes of the orbits. When numerical values are substituted for $e$, $c$, $m$, $L$, the formula for the molar susceptibility following from (2) is
$$\chi_{\text{mol}} = -2 \cdot 832 \times 10^{10} \sum r_i^2. \tag{3}$$
Now the diamagnetic susceptibilities observed experimentally are usually of the order of magnitude $10^{-6}Z$, where $Z$ is the atomic number. As there are $Z$ electrons that contribute to the sum in (3), the expression (3) becomes of this order of magnitude if the electronic orbits have on the average radii of the order $10^{-8}$ cm. This is in nice agreement with the estimates of molecular radii obtained by kinetic theory and other methods. It is to be clearly understood that the value of the orbital radius which we have deduced is only a crude average over all classes of orbits. The valence orbits may be somewhat larger than the estimate, while the innermost ones will usually be considerably smaller. Quantitative calculations of susceptibilities by means of (3) will be considered more fully in Chapter VIII.

In case the molecule has a permanent magnetic moment, the diamagnetic term (2) ought really to be added to the right side of (1) to obtain a complete expression for the susceptibility. It is always to be remembered that diamagnetic induction is a universal characteristic of all atoms and molecules, although the diamagnetic terms are usually

[9] P. Ehrenfest, *Physica*, **5**, 388 (1925); *Zeits. f. Physik*, **58**, 719 (1929); C. V. Raman, *Nature*, **123**, 945; **124**, 412 (1929).

overshadowed by the paramagnetic ones if the molecule has a permanent moment. Thus in rough determinations of paramagnetism it is not necessary to add (2) to (1) unless the paramagnetism happens to be quite feeble, for strongly paramagnetic substances have molar susceptibilities of the order $10^{-4}$ or greater, whereas diamagnetic susceptibilities are ordinarily of the order $10^{-6}$ to $10^{-5}$. In accurate measurements or calculations, the correction for the diamagnetic part of the susceptibility should always be made if one wishes to deduce the purely paramagnetic susceptibility from the observed susceptibility. The diamagnetic susceptibility cannot, of course, be measured separately, but can be estimated theoretically with accuracy sufficient for the correction, as it is a small one. When the diamagnetic term is added, Eq. (1) of the present chapter becomes of the same form as (1), Chap. II, if now $N\alpha$ denotes the right side of (2). The diamagnetic correction term thus resembles the second term of (1), Chap. II, arising from the induced polarization in the electrical case, inasmuch as both are independent of the temperature, and are due to distortion of the electronic motions by the applied field. The analogy is, however, a very incomplete one, for in the electrical case $\alpha$ is positive rather than negative and not generally small in magnitude compared to the term $\mu^2/3kT$ arising from the permanent dipoles. Also somewhat different models have been used in the electric and magnetic cases, as in Chapter II we assumed the electrons had positions of static equilibrium, whereas we now picture them as circulating in orbits to endow the molecule with angular momentum. This inconsistency is an inherent classical one, and will be removed only in the quantum mechanical treatments given in later chapters.

## 24. Absence of Magnetism with Pure Classical Statistics

If we could stop at this point, we should feel exceedingly happy, for the simple Langevin theory has been shown to explain nicely many of the experimental phenomena, especially the difference between the temperature effects in para- and diamagnetism. However, in 1919 Miss van Leeuwen [10] demonstrated the remarkable and rather disconcerting

[10] J. H. van Leeuwen, Dissertation, Leiden, 1919. A comprehensive summary is given in *J. de Physique*, (6) **2**, 361 (1921). The work which we quote is especially that given on pp. 372–4 of the summary. Besides the study of the magnetism for the general atomic dynamical system, Miss van Leeuwen also examines special models in which the electrons are replaced by continuous currents. These models seem much less satisfactory than the general dynamical method which we have reproduced. She mentions and discusses at some length the fact that a susceptibility different from zero can be obtained if in statistical mechanics there is imposed some auxiliary condition (*Nebenbedingung*) which restricts to a definite numerical value some other function of the dynamical

fact that when classical Boltzmann statistics are applied completely to any dynamical system, the magnetic susceptibility is zero. We shall refer to this result as 'Miss van Leeuwen's theorem', but we must mention that other investigators [11] had previously predicted zero magnetic susceptibilities under certain conditions, but it remained for Miss van Leeuwen to review critically the whole subject of susceptibilities in classical theory. There is no analogous theorem on null susceptibilities in the electrical case. One immediately wonders how Miss van Leeuwen's theorem can be reconciled with the fact that the simple Langevin theory predicts a susceptibility which can be either positive or negative, but not in general zero. The answer is that the conventional Langevin theory is open to the objection that it assumes *a priori* that the molecule has a definite 'permanent' magnetic moment which is the same for all molecules of similar chemical composition. As magnetic moment is proportional to angular momentum (if all the circulating particles are identical), we are thus supposing that the electronic angular momentum of the molecule has one definite value. Actually this cannot be the case with pure unadulterated classical statistics, as they always give a continuous range of permissible values to all coordinates, and hence to the angular momentum. Thus the electronic angular momentum should have all values ranging from $-\infty$ to $+\infty$. Similarly in the diamagnetic term, the radius of a given orbit can have a continuous range of values rather than the one particular size presupposed in the Langevin theory. In other words, it was not legitimate just before Eq. (2) to replace the double bars denoting the statistical average by the single bars denoting the time average for an individual atom. The relative prevalence of the different values of the angular momentum and radius should, of course, be determined by the Boltzmann probability factor $e^{-\mathcal{H}/kT}$. In the conventional derivation given in § 23, we have thus frozen ('ankylosed', as Jeans terms it) the electronic motions to one particular size and shape, rather than admitted the infinite number of possibilities allowed by

variables of the assembly of molecules besides its total energy. There is, however, no known justification for the imposition of such an extra condition in assemblies such as are encountered in the theory of magnetism.

[11] W. Voigt, *Ann. der Physik*, **9**, 115 (1902); J. J. Thomson, *Phil. Mag.* (6) **6**, 673 (1903). The mathematics of the theory of magnetic susceptibilities have been extensively developed by R. Gans in a number of papers: *Gött. Nachr.*, 1910, p. 197; 1911, p. 118, *Verh. d. D. Phys. Ges.* **16**, 780, 964 (1914); *Ann. der Physik*, **49**, 149 (1916), summary by Wills in *Theories of Magnetism* (Bulletin 18 of the Nat. Res. Counc.) Gans's work contains stimulating features, but the type of magneton which he assumes can scarcely be reconciled with modern knowledge of atomic structure. Many of Miss van Leeuwen's results were previously obtained in Bohr's dissertation (Copenhagen, 1911), but this unfortunately is probably rather inaccessible to most readers.

real classical statistics. One thus has to modify, or rather supplement, the classical statistics by an auxiliary condition (*Nebenbedingung*) that the angular momentum of the molecule be restricted to a particular value, and such a restriction appears highly artificial, to say the least. Of course the fact that the electronic motions do not contribute to the specific heat shows that real classical statistics cannot be applied to them, but it is nevertheless, from a logical standpoint, not at all satisfying to apply, as the Langevin theory does, the classical distributions to the 'external' degrees of freedom specifying the rotation of the molecule as a whole, but not to the 'internal' or 'electronic' degrees of freedom. When one tries to be consistent and apply the classical Boltzmann distribution to all coordinates necessary to specify the configuration of the system (assuming this to be possible—actually it is not in real atoms, as we shall see in § 27), the paramagnetic and diamagnetic parts of the susceptibility exactly compensate each other.

The proof of Miss van Leeuwen's theorem is very simple. The magnetic moment of the molecule in any direction, say $z$, may be taken to be a linear function

$$m_z = \sum_{k=1}^{f} a_k \dot{q}_k \tag{4}$$

of the generalized velocities $\dot{q}_1,..., \dot{q}_f$ corresponding to any set of Lagrangian positional coordinates adequate to specify the configuration of the molecule. The coefficients will in general be functions of the $q$'s. These remarks are obvious in Cartesian coordinates, as here

$$m_z = \frac{1}{2c} \sum e_i(x_i \dot{y}_i - y_i \dot{x}_i)$$

(Eq. (11), Chap. I), and the linearity in the velocities is preserved under any 'point' transformation to another set of generalized coordinates. The magnetic moment per unit volume in the direction $z$ of the applied field is (Eq. (57), Chap. I)

$$M_z = CN \int ... \int \sum a_k \dot{q}_k e^{-\mathcal{H}/kT} \, dq_1...dq_f dp_1...dp_f. \tag{5}$$

Let us consider any particular term $a_j \dot{q}_j$ in the summation. By Hamilton's equations $\dot{q}_j = \partial \mathcal{H}/\partial p_j$, and hence it is clear that of the $2f$ integrations, the one over $p_j$ can immediately be performed for this particular term, as the integrand is merely $-kT\partial(a_j e^{-\mathcal{H}/kT})/\partial p_j$. If $a$ and $b$ denote the two limits of integration for $p_j$, the contribution of the term under consideration to (5) becomes

$$-CNkT \int ... \int \left[ a_j e^{-\mathcal{H}/kT} \right]_{p_j=a}^{p_j=b} dq_1...dq_f dp_1...dp_{j-1} dp_{j+1}...dp_f. \tag{6}$$

We now suppose that the energy becomes infinite when the momentum

$p_j$ assumes its extreme values $a$ or $b$. The fulfilment of this condition is the essential requirement in Miss van Leeuwen's proof, and is obviously realized in a Cartesian system, as Cartesian momenta can range from $-\infty$ to $+\infty$, and when the momentum is infinite the kinetic energy is, of course, also infinite. Thus we appear quite warranted in assuming that $\left[a_j e^{-\mathcal{H}/kT}\right]_a^b = 0$ regardless of the values of the remaining variables $q_1..., p_1..., p_{j-1}, p_{j+1}...$. Hence the contribution (6) of a typical term of the summation in (5) is zero, and as this demonstration is applicable to all terms, we see that (5) does indeed vanish. This null result holds quite irrespective of the presence of an applied magnetic field, as nothing in the proof requires that $\mathcal{H}$ be independent of $H$.

## 25. Alternative proof of Miss van Leeuwen's Theorem

It has occurred to the writer that the null susceptibility with pure classical theory can also be demonstrated by the following method as an alternative to Miss van Leeuwen's own one given above.[12] Let us, for simplicity, use a Cartesian system. The magnetic moment is

$$M_z = \frac{N \int ... \int \sum \frac{e_i}{2m_i c} (x_i p^0_{y_i} - y_i p^0_{x_i}) e^{-\mathcal{H}/kT} \, dxdydzdp_x dp_y dp_z}{\int ... \int e^{-\mathcal{H}/kT} \, dxdydzdp_x dp_y dp_z}, \qquad (7)$$

where $dxdydz$ means $dx_1 dx_2...dy_1 dy_2...dz_1 dz_2...$, with an analogous interpretation of $dp_x dp_y dp_z$. We have here used $p^0_{x_i}$ as an abbreviation for the expression $m_i \dot{x}_i$, which is not the same as the canonical momentum $p_{x_i} = m_i \dot{x}_i + e_i A_{x_i}/c$, as already explained in §§ 7–8. The $p^0$ are essentially the velocity coordinates, as they differ from the velocities only by the constant mass factors $m_i$. Now when expressed in terms of the canonical variables $x$, $y$, $z$, $p_x$, $p_y$, $p_z$ the Hamiltonian function $\mathcal{H}$ involves the magnetic field $H$ as a parameter, whereas when expressed in terms of the $x$, $y$, $z$, $p^0_x$, $p^0_y$, $p^0_z$ it does not involve $H$ explicitly, as it is exactly the same function of its arguments as for $H = 0$. This has been seen in § 7, especially Eq. (51), and is associated with the fact that magnetic forces do no work, making the energy the same function of position and velocity as in the absence of the field. This expression $\mathcal{H}^*$ cannot be regarded as a true Hamiltonian function, as the variables $x,..., p^0_x,...$, unlike $x,..., p_x,...$, do not satisfy Hamilton's equations. For

---

[12] Since writing the present section, the author has learned that this alternative proof somewhat resembles one in Bohr's dissertation (Copenhagen, 1911) as Bohr also notes that absence of magnetism is a consequence of the fact that the functional determinant (8) is unity.

clarity we attach an asterisk to $\mathcal{H}$ when it is expressed in terms of the $p^0$ rather than $p$. In view of the foregoing,

$$\mathcal{H} = \mathcal{H}^*(x, y, z, p_x^0, p_y^0, p_z^0) \qquad \text{whereas} \qquad \mathcal{H} = \mathcal{H}(x, y, z, p_x, p_y, p_z, H).$$

Because of the independence of $\mathcal{H}^*$ of $H$, it is convenient to change the variables of integration in (7) from the $p_x$, $p_y$, $p_z$ to the $p_x^0$, $p_y^0$, $p_z^0$. Because the transformation equations are of the form

$$p_{x_i}^0 = p_{x_i} + f(x, y, z), \qquad x_i = x_i, \qquad (i = 1, ..., f)$$

the functional determinant

$$\frac{\partial(p_x, p_y, p_z, x, y, z)}{\partial(p_x^0, p_y^0, p_z^0, x, y, z)} \tag{8}$$

of the transformation is unity.[13] Hence

$$dp_x dp_y dp_z dx dy dz = dp_x^0 dp_y^0 dp_z^0 dx dy dz,$$

or in other words, the 'weight' is the same in the $p_x^0...x...$ as in the $p_x...x...$ space. This is the crux of the whole proof, and enables us to calculate simply distributions in the $p_x^0...x...$ space. We could not have done this at the outset, as the theorems of statistical mechanics relate fundamentally to the 'phase space' of the canonical variables $p_x...x...$ rather than to the space of the position and velocity ones. We now see that Eq. (7) retains its validity if we write $\mathcal{H}^*$ in place of $\mathcal{H}$ and $dp_x^0 dp_y^0 dp_z^0$ in place of $dp_x dp_y dp_z$. Because of the kinematical significance of the $p^0$ as proportional to velocities, the limits of integration for the $p^0$ are independent of $H$. From this and the fact that $\partial \mathcal{H}^*/\partial H = 0$, it thus follows that by changing the variables to the $p^0$, we have made the right side of (7) completely independent of $H$. This means that the moment is the same as in the absence of the magnetic field, and hence is zero, since an isotropic, non-ferromagnetic body supports no outstanding moment when $H = 0$.

As a corollary of the above, it follows that the probability that the system be in a configuration corresponding to the element

$$dp_x^0 dp_y^0 dp_z^0 dx dy dz,$$

in which $p_{x_1}^0$ falls between $p_{x_1}^0$ and $p_{x_1}^0 + dp_{x_1}^0$, &c., is

$$Ce^{-\mathcal{H}^*/kT} \, dp_x^0 dp_y^0 dp_z^0 dx dy dz.$$

The distribution of values of the coordinates and velocities is thus the same as in the absence of the magnetic field, since $\mathcal{H}^*$ is independent of $H$. (The distribution of the canonical variables $p_x, ..., x, ...,$ on the

---

[13] Because the coordinates $x$, $y$, $z$ are the same in the old and new system of variables, this determinant is equal to the smaller determinant $\partial(p_x, p_y, p_z)/\partial(p_x^0, p_y^0, p_z^0)$, which is obviously unity. The identity of the large and small determinants is similar to that mentioned in footnote 7 of Chap. II.

other hand, given by Eq. (55), Chap. I, involves the magnetic field through $\mathcal{H}$.) The Maxwell distribution of translational velocities for free particles is, for instance, unmodified by a magnetic field. It is clear that the statistical mean of any function of the variables $p_x^0$, $p_y^0$, $p_z^0$, $x$, $y$, $z$ which does not involve $H$ explicitly is unaltered by application of a magnetic field. This may be regarded as a generalization of Miss van Leeuwen's theorem, and her null result on susceptibilities is merely the special case that the function is $\sum (e_i/2m_i c)(x_i p_{y_i}^0 - y_i p_{x_i}^0)$.

We have already mentioned that the reason that Langevin obtained a non-vanishing susceptibility is because he did not apply the Boltzmann distribution to the internal or electronic degrees of freedom of the molecule. We may now amplify this point a little farther. Of the $f$ generalized coordinates in Eq. (5), three, say $q_1$, $q_2$, $q_3$, will, in the general polyatomic molecule, be what we may term 'external' coordinates, which specify the orientation of the molecule as a whole, as, for instance, the Eulerian angles in § 12. The remaining coordinates $q_4$, $q_5$,... will be internal coordinates. (We do not need to include coordinates specifying the translational motion of the molecule as a whole, as in Chapter I we agreed to consider the centre of gravity of the molecule to be at rest.) Now in the usual derivations of the Langevin formula, the Boltzmann distribution is applied to the canonical variables $q_1$, $q_2$, $q_3$, $p_1$, $p_2$, $p_3$ but not to $q_4,..., p_4,....$ Consequently the usual results (1) and (2) so obtained ought therefore for consistency to be integrated over these remaining variables. When we combine the paramagnetic and diamagnetic parts, the complete susceptibility should thus be given by the formula [14]

$$\chi = \frac{N \int ... \int \left(\dfrac{\mu^2}{3kT} - \sum \dfrac{e_i^2}{6m_i c^2} r_i^2\right) e^{-\mathcal{H}/kT} p_f dq_4 ... dq_f dp_4 ... dp}{\int ... \int e^{-\mathcal{H}/kT} p_f dq_4 ... dq_f dp_4 ... dp_f}. \tag{9}$$

Here $\mu$ and the $r_i$ are to be regarded as functions of $q_4,..., p_4,...$ rather than as molecular constants as in the ordinary Langevin treatment. Miss van Leeuwen's theorem tells us that when the integration is performed the para- and diamagnetic parts of (9) always cancel. Eq. (9) is not general enough to show the full sweep of Miss van Leeuwen's theorem, since the latter assures that the para- and diamagnetic effects always compensate to all powers of $H$, whereas (9) does not aim to

---

[14] In writing Eq. (9) we use the slightly modified form (2a) of (2) which was given on p. 91. Eq. (2a) includes the feeble contribution of the nuclei to the diamagnetism, without which the cancellation of the two parts of (9) would be very approximate rather than exact.

include saturation effects and gives only the part of the susceptibility which is independent of field strength.

It is perhaps illuminating to verify explicitly for a very simple dynamical system that the two parts of (9) cancel, without appealing to the general proof. Let us suppose that we have a particle of charge $e$ and mass $m$ constrained to always remain at a distance $l$ from a fixed centre. Let us further assume that the particle is subject to no other force except that of constraint, so that it will move in a circle with a constant angular velocity $\Omega$. The radius $r$ of the orbit will have the constant value $l$, and our example is thus not illustrative of the most general case in which $r$ is a statistical variable. The magnetic moment $el^2\Omega/2c$ is, on the other hand, such a variable, as a molecule can acquire any amount of angular velocity $\Omega$. By the equipartition theorem, the statistical average of the kinetic energy $\frac{1}{2}ml^2\Omega^2$ is $kT$, since the particle has two degrees of freedom. Now in this example the square of the magnetic moment differs from the kinetic energy only by a constant factor $e^2l^2/2mc^2$. Hence the statistical mean square of the magnetic moment, such as results from the integration in (9), is $\overline{\overline{\mu^2}} = kTe^2l^2/2mc^2$. The proportionality of this expression to $T$ cancels the $T$ in the denominator of the Langevin formula, and we have indeed

$$\overline{\overline{\mu^2}}/3kT - e^2l^2/6mc^2 = 0.$$

## 26. Absence of Diamagnetism from Free Electrons in Classical Theory

In § 25 we have shown that a magnetic field does not influence the Maxwellian distribution of translational velocities. This result is of particular interest when applied to free electrons, e.g. either stray electrons in a gas or conduction electrons in a solid. Of course when a magnetic field is applied, free electrons no longer move in rectilinear paths, but instead describe circular orbits about the direction of the field. One usually associates Maxwell's distribution with rectilinear motions, but it is not at all incompatible with the existence of such circular trajectories. Now since the Maxwellian velocity distribution is unaltered, the mean moment of the free electrons is uninfluenced by a magnetic field, and hence they cannot give either a paramagnetic or diamagnetic effect. Numerous attempts,[15] to be sure, have been made in the literature to show that free electrons behave diamagnetically, but if classical statistics are applied in their simplest and most direct manner

[15] J. J. Thomson, *Rapports du Congrès de Physique*, Paris 1900, p. 149; E. Schrödinger, *Wien. Ber.* **121**, 1305 (1912); J. N. Kroo, Dissertation, Göttingen, 1913, *Ann. der Physik*, **42**, 1354 (1913); H. A. Wilson, *Proc. Roy. Soc.* **97**A, 321 (1920).

given above, their contribution to the magnetic moment is nil. This appears to have been first shown by Bohr,[16] and has also been observed by Lorentz and Miss van Leeuwen.

This absence of a diamagnetic susceptibility from free electrons at first thought appears quite paradoxical. If each electron describes a circle about the field, it certainly possesses angular momentum about the centre of the orbit, and the sense of the rotation is such that the attendant magnetic moment is opposite to the field, apparently giving diamagnetism. However, the magnetic moment involved in the susceptibility is not the magnetic moment of each electron with respect to the centre of its particular orbit, but instead the combined magnetic moment of all the electrons with reference to some one common point chosen as the origin for measuring angular momentum. In the schematic figure on p. 102, in which the magnetic field is supposed perpendicular to the plane of the paper, electron 2 clearly gives a diamagnetic moment with respect to point $A$, electron 3 with respect to point $B$, &c., but what we need is the combined moment of electrons 1, 2, 3..., with respect to some one point, say $B$. Now when electron 2 passes through the small element enclosed by the dotted square, its angular momentum relative to $B$ is just equal and opposite to that of electron 1 when it passes through this element. Since actually electrons are distributed on the average continuously through space rather than with their orbits end to end as in the figure, it is clear that to every given electron passing through a given point in space with a velocity in a given direction, there is another electron describing another circle and passing through the point with an equal velocity in an exactly opposite direction. In case the body containing the electrons is bounded in extent, the electrons near the boundary cannot describe complete circles but are reflected from the boundary (indicated by the heavy line). Instead, they describe cuspidal paths, such as are illustrated for electrons numbered 1 in the diagram. These boundary electrons are very vital, as without them there would be diamagnetism. An electron 1, for instance, is needed to compensate electron 2 at the point where their orbits touch. Fig. 5 is, of course, entirely too naïve, but perhaps does afford some sort of a physical illustration of the general null result derived in § 25. It may be noted that in § 25 we did not need to use specifically the fact that the orbits are circles. This illustrates the beautiful freedom of the

[16] N. Bohr, Dissertation, Copenhagen, 1911. H. A. Lorentz, *Göttinger Vorträge über die kinetische Theorie der Materie und der Elektrizität* (Leipzig, 1914), p. 188; J. H. van Leeuwen, Dissertation, Leiden, 1919, p. 49; *J. de Phys.* (6) **2**, 361 (1921).

statistical method from the necessity of inquiry into the details of the motion of a dynamical system; only the Hamiltonian function is required. It might seem as if the characteristics of the bounding surface might make a difference in the proof. In Fig. 5, for instance, we assumed specular reflection at a cylindrical boundary of radius $R$. However,

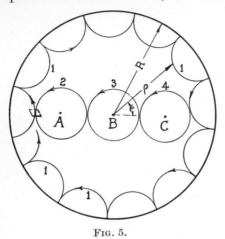

FIG. 5.

the boundaries for the spacial co-ordinates did not enter in the demonstration, and the medium could, in fact, be infinite in extent, or of a different shape or degree of smoothness than in Fig. 5. Also the electrons can suffer collisions.[17] The molecules move so slowly relative to the electrons that the former may be considered fixed scattering centres, and no harm is done in the proof if it is supposed that the potential energy of the electrons becomes very large

at certain points, which consequently act as such scattering centres. A potential barrier is also required at the boundary to reflect the electrons.

Of course in a true theory, quantum modifications must be taken into account, and it will be shown in § 81 that in quantum mechanics there is a diamagnetic effect from free electrons, not to mention the spin paramagnetism (§ 80). Thus the theorem on the absence of diamagnetism is valid only in classical theory.

## 27. Inapplicability of Classical Statistics to any Real Atomic System

Let us now revert to atoms and molecules rather than free electrons. Needless to say, the zero susceptibilities predicted in §§ 24–5 are not the rule experimentally. In the theory the only escape from zero moment is not to apply the Maxwell-Boltzmann distribution to all coordinates and momenta, but instead to restrict their ranges of permissible values. Such restrictions are effectively 'quantization', and we now anticipate the inevitable need of a quantum theory. Even in the electrical case the complete application of classical statistics to all

[17] Miss van Leeuwen notes that the collisions might conceivably cause the free electrons to contribute to the susceptibility, provided some other function of the assembly's dynamical variables besides the total energy remains constant during the collisions. Cf. note 10.

degrees of freedom gives rather absurd results, though nothing as striking as a null susceptibility. For if we assume a statistical distribution of electrons among orbits of various sizes, some molecules of a given chemical composition would be large, others small. Such a concept as the familiar atomic diameter in kinetic theory would be impossible, and also, more especially for our purposes, that of the permanent molecular moment. Instead we could speak only of the distributions of values for the diameters and moments, and we could employ only the statistical mean square moment (somewhat as in Eq. (22), Chap. II), which would in general vary with temperature and cease to be useful.

All these things, along with the specific heat difficulty, force the conclusion that classical statistics give only nonsense when applied to the internal or electronic degrees of freedom of the molecule. Another consideration which shows this even more urgently is the following. In the classical Boltzmann distribution formula it is ordinarily supposed that the numerical value of the energy or Hamiltonian function $\mathcal{H}$ can range from 0 to $\infty$, as the total integrated probability $C \int ... \int e^{-\mathcal{H}/kT} \, dq_1...dp_f$ can then be made to converge to unity by proper normalization of the amplitude constant $C$. However, for real motions of the electrons, the energy approaches $-\infty$ when an electron is close to the nucleus, and 0 when it is removed to infinity. The energy thus ranges from $-\infty$ to 0 rather than from 0 to $\infty$. When $\mathcal{H}$ approaches $-\infty$ the Boltzmann probability factor increases without limit. In a hydrogenic atom, for instance, the probability becomes infinite in the fashion $e^{Ze^2/rkT}$ as one approaches the nucleus, which we suppose located at the origin $r = 0$. It is thus infinitely more probable that the electron be infinitely close to the nucleus than anywhere else. The total integrated probability can clearly be finite only if we nonsensically take the amplitude $C$ to be zero, and suppose the probability is infinitesimal of the electron being anywhere but right at the nucleus. In other words, we have a collision catastrophe, which is a little reminiscent of the 'ultra-violet catastrophe' in the classical theory of black body radiation, whereby the Rayleigh-Jeans formula $u_\nu = 8\pi\nu^2 kT/c^3$ demands that the energy density $u_\nu$ increase without limit as we go to higher and higher frequencies. Modern physics shows a good deal of parallelism between matter and radiation, and they both have their catastrophes in classical statistics. The absurdities arising from non-convergence are frequently emphasized in connexion with the radiation problem, but, as the writer has mentioned elsewhere,[18] do not seem commonly enough appreciated as

---

[18] Cf. J. H. Van Vleck, *Quantum Principles and Line Spectra*, p. 14.

regards the application of classical statistics to the Rutherford atom. It is because of this inherent limitation in classical theory that it has always been necessary in the classical theory of induced polarization to use not a real Rutherford atom but instead, as in Chapter II, an unplausible model consisting of electrons oscillating harmonically about positions of static equilibrium. The limited range of molecular models which can be used in classical statistics makes Miss van Leeuwen's theorem rather academic, but nevertheless it is occasionally useful for other problems besides proving the absence of diamagnetism from classical free electrons.

To summarize, the success of the Langevin and Debye theories shows that classical statistics give good results when applied to the external (i.e. rotational) degrees of freedom of the molecule. On the other hand, when one attempts to apply classical statistics to electronic motions within the atom, the less said the better. Hence, in the following chapters we must seek a quantum mechanics which constrains the electrons to move in certain discrete stationary states instead of giving a classical continuous distribution of orbits near the nucleus, but which when applied to rotational degrees of freedom gives nearly the same statistical results as classical theory except perhaps at very low temperatures.

# SUSCEPTIBILITIES IN THE OLD QUANTUM THEORY CONTRASTED WITH THE NEW

## 28. Historical Survey

To some readers it may seem like unburying the dead to devote a chapter to the old quantum theory. Every one knows that the original quantum theory developed by Bohr in 1913 has been refined and in a certain sense replaced by the new quantum mechanics of Heisenberg, Schrödinger, Born, and Dirac. However, there is perhaps no better field than that of electric and magnetic susceptibilities to illustrate the inadequacies of the old quantum theory and how they have been removed by the new mechanics. We shall merely summarize the results of applying the old theory, without giving any mathematical analysis. Also, we shall contrast descriptively with these results some of the outstanding features of the new quantum mechanics of susceptibilities, thereby giving a qualitative account of some of the new improvements which may perhaps satisfy some readers who do not wish to read the mathematics in the two following chapters.

The old quantum theory was probably more successful as applied to magnetic than to electric susceptibilities. In the first place, inasmuch as it substituted discrete for continuous distributions, it clearly removed the difficulty found in the classical theory (§ 27) of the overwhelming probability of orbits infinitesimally close to the nucleus. The smallest allowed quantum orbit had instead a finite radius. Also consistency no longer demanded zero susceptibility, as Miss van Leeuwen's theorem was no longer applicable. Furthermore, the old quantum theory (supplemented by the spin anomaly) was not very far from predicting quantitatively the magnetic moments $\mu$ of atoms. To do this correctly it would have to yield the formula for the anomalous Zeeman effect. Landé[1] indeed gave a semi-theoretical derivation of his celebrated formula for this effect, but besides introducing the anomalous factor two in the magnetic moment of what he called the atom-core (but which we now know is electron spin), he found it necessary to give certain quantum numbers half-integral instead of integral values, and also even then to insert an extra term $-\frac{1}{4}$ in order to get agreement with experiment.[2] The old quantum theory was thus patched almost beyond

---

[1] A. Landé, *Zeits. f. Physik*, **15**, 189 (1924).

[2] This was because the expression $J(J+1)$ characteristic of the true quantum mechanics was interpreted as $J^{\dagger 2} - \frac{1}{4}$, where $J^{\dagger}$ is a half quantum number $J + \frac{1}{2}$.

recognition, but Landé's work nevertheless distinctly showed that he was hot on the track of a true theory of the anomalous Zeeman effect, since supplied (§ 42) by the new mechanics. There were other difficulties in the old quantum theory of magnetic susceptibilities, especially the troubles with weak and strong spacial quantization. These troubles will be discussed more specifically in connexion with dielectric constants, but the difficulties found in the electric case are usually also reflected in the magnetic one.

One of the best-known and most characteristic features of the quantum theory is the phenomenon of spacial quantization. By this is meant the fact that according to the quantum conditions the molecule can only assume certain particular orientations in space. The particular condition responsible for the spacial quantization is usually the requirement that the angular momentum of the molecule along some direction fixed in space be an integral or half-integral multiple $M$ of $h/2\pi$. Here $M$ is called the 'equatorial', 'axial', or (even in the electric case!) the 'magnetic' quantum number. A direct experimental confirmation of spacial quantization is furnished by the well-known experiments of Gerlach and Stern [3] on the deflexion of atoms in a non-homogeneous magnetic field. (The field must be non-homogeneous to give a translational force on a magnetic dipole.) The discovery of a discrete rather than continuous set of deflexions in these experiments is conclusive evidence that the atoms can only orient themselves in particular directions under the influence of an applied field.

Because of the spacial quantization, one immediately expects the dielectric constant to be given by a different formula than in classical theory, where random orientations are assumed. This, indeed, proved to be so in the old quantum theory. Pauli,[4] treating polar molecules as rigid non-gyroscopic rotating dipoles (the so-called 'dumb-bell' model for molecules such as HCl), found that the electric susceptibility was still given by a formula of the form

$$\chi = N\left(\frac{C\mu^2}{kT} + \alpha\right) \tag{1}$$

as in classical theory, with $\mu$ the moment of the molecule, and $C$ a pure

[3] Gerlach and Stern, *Zeits. f. Physik*, **9**, 349 (1922) and numerous subsequent papers by Gerlach and others. The ordinary Stern-Gerlach experiment is performed with magnetic fields. The analogous experiment with electric fields is more difficult, but has recently been performed by E. Wrede, *Zeits. f. Physik*, **44**, 261 (1927) and by J. Estermann, *Zeits. f. Phys. Chem.* **1**, 161 (1928), *Dipolmoment und chemische Struktur* (Leipziger Vorträge 1929), p. 17; *Ergebnisse der exakten Naturwissenschaften*, viii. 279.

[4] W. Pauli, Jr., *Zeits. f. Physik*, **6**, 319 (1921).

number. However, the numerical factor $C$ no longer had the value 1/3 found in classical theory, but was instead 1·54. Later, progress in the analysis of band spectra made it increasingly apparent that the quantum numbers involved in the theory of the rotating dipole should be given half-integral instead of integral values to agree with experiment. Pauling[5] therefore revised Pauli's calculations by introducing half-quantum numbers. The result was still another value of $C$. These vicissitudes in $C$ are listed in the following table, together with the corresponding values of the electrical moment $\mu$ of the HCl molecule deduced by applying the formulae to Zahn's[6] measurements on the temperature variation of the dielectric constant of HCl. The changes in $C$, of course, profoundly affect the value of $\mu$ deduced from such experimental data.

| Value of Constant C. | Form and Year of Theory. | Corresponding Value of Electrical Moment $\mu$ of HCl Molecule. |
|---|---|---|
| $\frac{1}{3}$ | Classical, 1912 | $1·034 \times 10^{-18}$ e.s.u. |
| 1·54 | Whole quanta, 1921 | $0·481 \times 10^{-18}$ |
| 4·57 | Half quanta, 1925 | $0·332 \times 10^{-18}$ |
| $\frac{1}{3}$ | New mechanics, 1926 | $1·034 \times 10^{-18}$ |

The last line gives the results obtained with the new quantum mechanics, which will be derived in detail in the following chapters. It is seen that this new dynamics restores the factor $\frac{1}{3}$ characteristic of the classical Langevin formula. After quite a history, the computed electrical moment of the HCl molecule thus reverts to its original value. In general, the susceptibilities obtained with the new quantum mechanics are more closely akin to those of the classical theory than are those obtained with the old quantum theory. For this reason we were able in Chapter III to discuss fairly completely the theoretical interpretation of experimental material on dielectric constants without deferring the discussion to the quantum chapters. It will be noted that in the old quantum theory, the discrepancy with the classical value of $C$ persisted regardless of the temperature. Such a discrepancy did not seem plausible even before the discovery of the new mechanics, as the correspondence principle led us to expect usually an asymptotic connexion of the classical and quantum results at high temperatures. In the old quantum theory the value of the numerical factor $C$ was not a universal constant, as it was very sensitive to the nature of the model employed;

[5] L. Pauling, *Phys. Rev.* **27**, 568 (1926).
[6] C. T. Zahn, *Phys. Rev.* **24**, 400 (1924).

a gyroscopic [7] rather than a dumb-bell model would, for instance, furnish a different $C$ than 1·54 or 4·57. On the other hand, we shall see that the new mechanics always yield $C = \frac{1}{3}$ without the necessity of specifying the details of the model, and the generality of this value of $C$ is one of the most satisfying features of the new theory.

## 29. Weak and Strong Spacial Quantization

A difficulty particularly characteristic of the old quantum theory is found in what is sometimes termed 'weak' and 'strong' quantization. Spacial quantization cannot be effective unless it has some axis of reference. In the calculations of Pauli and Pauling cited above, the direction of the electric field is taken as such an axis. If the electric field is the only external one, this choice for the axis of quantization has a good dynamical justification, for then the angular momentum about this particular axis, and no other, remains constant after application of the electric field. On the other hand, in the absence of all external fields, the components of angular momentum in all directions remain constant, and there is no reason for choosing one direction in space rather than another for the axis of spacial quantization. The only escape from this ambiguity is to assume that in the absence of external fields the orientations of the atoms are random instead of quantized. Suppose now a field is gradually applied. As there are no impulsive forces to suddenly change the orientations of atoms, their spacial distribution should presumably remain random for exceedingly weak fields. The constant $C$ would then have [8] a value different from either of those calculated by Pauling or Pauli, and it is only when the field becomes strong enough for spacial quantization that their computations become applicable. If the spacial quantization is supposed achieved gradually, the term 'weak quantization' has sometimes been used to designate the case in which the quantization has only been acquired to a slight extent,

---

[7] By a gyroscopic molecule we mean one with an angular momentum about the axis of symmetry. In the 'symmetrical top' gyroscopic model which has often been used to represent the behaviour of symmetrical polyatomic molecules, Manneback showed that the constant $C$ has the asymptotic value $\frac{1}{3}$ even in the old quantum theory, but that considerably higher temperatures are required than in the new mechanics in order to make this asymptotic value a valid approximation; *Phys. Zeits.* **28**, 72 (1927).

[8] One's first guess by classical analogy would be that the constant $C$ would be $\frac{1}{3}$ with random orientations (weak quantization) in the old quantum theory. Pauling showed that instead $C$ would be zero under these circumstances if the non-gyroscopic dumb-bell model is used. The reason for this is that with such a model the classical polarization by orientation is due entirely to contributions from very slowly rotating molecules, and with a minimum of a half-quantum unit of rotational angular momentum, there are no molecules sufficiently slow to contribute. This difficulty is overcome in the new mechanics; for details and references see § 45.

and 'strong quantization' the case in which the quantization is nearly perfect.[9] There should thus be a change of susceptibility with field strength due to the transition from weak to strong spacial quantization. This is not to be confused with the variation of susceptibility with field strength due to saturation effects, i.e. the effect of terms beyond the first power in the series development of the moment in terms of the field strength. The transition from weak to strong spacial quantization would involve the passage from one such series development to another one with totally different coefficients, and in either series only the coefficient of the linear term in $E$ is ordinarily of interest. Saturation effects are found only in exceedingly large fields, whereas any changes in susceptibility attendant to passage from weak to strong quantization would be found in considerably smaller fields, at least at low pressures, for reasons given below. As far as the writer is aware, there is no experimental evidence for a variation of susceptibility with field strength in the peculiar fashion which would be characteristic of the change in quantization in the old quantum theory.

It is apparent that at least in the old quantum theory one needed some sort of a quantitative estimate of how large a field is required for spacial quantization. Such an estimate was usually made by assuming that a quantum condition is 'completely' or 'strongly' fulfilled if the frequency with which it is associated by the correspondence principle is large compared to the frequencies of any disturbances which upset the regular motion of the molecule in a stationary state. Such disturbances were deemed due to the transitions of the molecule to other stationary states and to interruptions by collisions. In the 'dumb-bell' model of a dipole gas, the collision disturbances are the important ones, and the probability of transitions due to the absorption or emission of radiation is relatively slight. According to these ideas, the spacial quantization should be achieved when the frequency of precession about the field, which is the frequency associated with the 'equatorial quantum number', is so large that the atom can persist through several periods of precession without molestation by collision. As the mean free time between collisions is of the order $10^{-10}$ sec. under standard conditions, and as the Larmor precession frequency is $1\cdot40\times10^6 H$ sec.$^{-1}$, a field of the order 10,000 gauss should on this view be required to establish spacial quantization at atmospheric pressure, while at low pressures,

[9] For papers on the old theory of weak and strong quantization see Ehrenfest and Breit, *Proc. Amsterdam Acad.* **25**, 2 (1922); *Zeits. f. Physik,* **9**, 207 (1922); Ehrenfest and Tolman, *Phys. Rev.* **24**, 287 (1924); Slater, *ibid.* **26**, 419 (1925).

where collisions are less frequent, a considerably smaller field would be required. The sharpness of Zeeman patterns at comparatively high pressures indicates that these estimates are perhaps too high. Just how large an electric field is required for spacial quantization is not quite clear, due to the complication that non-gyroscopic molecules exhibit only a quadratic Stark effect (§ 37). At any rate, either in the magnetic or electric case there should be certain critical pressures at which there is a pronounced pressure variation of the susceptibility per molecule due to the passage from 'weak' to 'strong' spacial quantization attendant on changes in the collision intervals. At one time it was thought that there was evidence for such a variation in the diamagnetic susceptibility of $H_2$, $N_2$, CO, and $CO_2$. This result was named the 'Glaser effect' in honour of its discoverer. He found [10] the molar diamagnetic suscepti- bility for these gases to be approximately three times larger at low than at high pressures. Theoretical physicists [11] interpreted this as meaning that with spacial quantization the average value of $x^2+y^2$ was greater than $\frac{2}{3}r^2$, its mean with random orientation. When one particular axis is chosen as that of spacial quantization the different coordinate axes are not on a parity in the old quantum theory, and so there was no apparent reason why $x^2$, $y^2$, $z^2$ could not have mutually different values, thus making $\overline{x^2+y^2}$ different from the value $\frac{2}{3}r^2$ supposed in the classical equation (2), Chap. IV. On the other hand, it is hard to see how the effect could be as large as found by Glaser, because the average of $x^2+y^2$ cannot possibly exceed $r^2$, and so even with spacial quantization the molar susceptibility should not be more than 1·5 times the classical or high-pressure value, whereas Glaser found a value 3 times as great.[12]

The reader may well feel that such changes of susceptibility are very 'unphysical', as they have no analogue in classical theory, contrary to the usual expectations from the correspondence principle. Now for- tunately it is found that the new quantum mechanics removes com- pletely this bugbear of weak and strong spacial quantization. It is a very remarkable fact that in the new mechanics the susceptibility is invariant of the choice of the axis of quantization, as we shall see in § 46. As random orientations are equivalent to a haphazard distribution of the axes of quantization, the susceptibility is the same with and

---

[10] A. Glaser, *Phys. Zeits.* **26**, 212 (1925); *Ann. der Physik,* **75**, 459 (1924); **78**, 641 (1925); **1**, 814; **2**, 233 (1929).

[11] Mathematical theories of the Glaser effect in the old quantum theory have been attempted by Debye, *Phys. Rev.* **25**, 586 (1925) (abstract) and by Breit, *J. Washington Acad. Sci.* **15**, 429 (1925).

[12] This difficulty is also noticed by Stoner, *Magnetism and Atomic Structure,* p. 276.

without spacial quantization. If the reader has felt that our presentation of weak and strong quantization in the old quantum theory was somewhat mystifying (as indeed it had to be, as physicists themselves were hazy on the details of the passage from one type of quantization to another), he need now no longer feel alarmed, as the new mechanics gives no susceptibility effects without some analogue in classical theory.

## 30. Spectroscopic Stability in the New Quantum Mechanics

The theorem of the new quantum mechanics in virtue of which the question of weak versus strong spacial quantization becomes of no consequence for susceptibilities is termed the 'principle of spectroscopic stability' and will be proved in § 35. The term is not a particularly happy one. It was originally introduced by Bohr[13] to designate the concept that a magnetic field should not influence the polarization of secondary radiation excited by temperature radiation or some other isotropic source. Later Born, Heisenberg, and Jordan[14] used the term to denote the invariance of a certain sum of matrix elements of the system of quantization, as this sum entered in the polarization problem studied by Bohr. Precisely this sum enters in the theory of susceptibilities, and for a mathematical formulation of the principle as a 'sum-rule' the reader will have to wait until § 35, as we have not yet developed sufficient mathematical background. If a physical rather than mathematical definition of the principle of spectroscopic stability is desired, it can for our purposes be considered identical with the idea that the susceptibility is invariant of the type of quantization, or in the special case of spacial quantization, that summing over the various quantized orientations is equivalent, as far as results are concerned, to a classical integration over a random orientation of orbits. It is indeed remarkable that a discrete quantum summation gives exactly the same answers as a continuous integration. This was not at all true in the old quantum theory. In virtue of the principle, we can feel sure that in the new quantum mechanics the average of $x^2+y^2$ over the various allowed spacial orientations is $\frac{2}{3}r^2$, just as though the orbits could have random directions. Another example is that the average of the square of a

[13] N. Bohr, *The Quantum Theory of Line Spectra*, p. 85. It is clearly to be understood that when the excitation is by a directed beam of light rather than by primary radiation coming simultaneously from all directions, the secondary radiation may exhibit an outstanding polarization materially influenced by magnetic fields. The subject of spectroscopic stability is intimately connected with the polarization of resonance radiation in magnetic fields; for discussion and references see J. H. Van Vleck, *Quantum Principles and Line Spectra*, pp. 177 ff.

[14] Born, Heisenberg, and Jordan, *Zeits. f. Physik*, **35**, 590 (1926).

direction cosine is $\frac{1}{3}$, even though the angle can only take on particular values.

The reader should not form the impression that the principle of spectroscopic stability applies only to spacial in distinction from other types of quantization. It assures equally well the invariance of the susceptibility of all questions concerning the choice of the system of quantization. Or, in more precise technical language, if the dynamical system is initially 'degenerate', the spectroscopic stability shows that the susceptibility is invariant of the manner in which the degeneracy is removed. As an example, the hydrogen atom should have the same dielectric constant in weak fields, in which polar coordinates are needed to separate the variables in the relativistic Schrödinger equation, as in strong fields, in which parabolic coordinates are required even without the relativity corrections. Another example of spectroscopic stability is the invariance of magnetic susceptibilities of the Paschen-Back effect. In a very powerful magnetic field the orbital and spin angular momenta are quantized separately rather than only collectively relative to the axis of the field, and corresponding to this there is a complete re-organization of the Zeeman patterns, known as the Paschen-Back effect, but no change in the susceptibility. A big alteration in the Zeeman effect without any attendant change in the susceptibility may at first thought seem almost an impossibility, but it must be remembered that the position of any given Zeeman component of a spectral term involves only one value of the magnetic quantum number, whereas the calculation of a magnetic susceptibility always requires a summation over all the stationary states corresponding to all possible values of the magnetic quantum number. The sum thus encountered is invariant of the Paschen-Back reorganization, even though the individual energy-levels of which the sum is composed are altered. Similarly even in the new quantum mechanics the matter of spacial quantization still enters in the Stern-Gerlach effect, for this effect relates to the properties of individual Zeeman states, in contrast to the statistical nature of susceptibilities.

What now becomes of the Glaser effect, which if real would contradict the principle of spectroscopic stability ? Glaser's experiments were repeated by Lehrer [15] and by Hammar,[16] who found the molar dia-magnetic susceptibility invariant of the pressure, and the effect hence non-existent. In other words, the susceptibility per unit-volume, which

[15] E. Lehrer, *Ann. der Physik*, **81**, 229 (1926).
[16] C. W. Hammar, *Proc. Nat. Acad. Sci.* **12**, 597 (1926).

is proportional to the density, is a strictly linear function of the pressure. We must, however, remark that Glaser, despite the criticisms that have been made of his work, still claims that his effect is real.[17] The experiments of Lehrer and Hammar were performed at almost exactly the same time as the new mechanics was developed far enough to show the theoretical non-existence of the Glaser effect. It must have saved physicists a great deal of time and worry that the new results in theory and experiment came practically hand in hand.

As emphasized by Ebert,[18] the fact that the same electric moments are obtained by the vapour and by the solution methods, also the fact that non-polar materials have the same molar polarizabilities in the gaseous and pure liquid states (see p. 59), is a nice confirmation of the spectroscopic stability characteristic of the new mechanics. In the old quantum theory, on the other hand, one might expect different results in the liquid and vapour states, because in the liquid the collisions are more frequent and the quantization hence 'weaker'.

Before closing this section we must caution the reader not to attach too much physical reality to the spacial quantization discussed above, as the new mechanics does not endow orbits with as much geometrical reality as previously. Since in the new theory there is no detectable difference between weak and strong quantization as far as susceptibilities are concerned, the question of the mechanism by which spacial quantization is acquired loses much of its former interest.

## 31. Effect of a Magnetic Field on the Dielectric Constant

The influence of a magnetic field on the dielectric constant (or of an electric field on the magnetic susceptibility) was ludicrously large in the old quantum theory because of the spacial quantization. Ordinarily in studying dielectric constants, the quantization can be taken with respect to the axis of the applied electric field. Suppose, however, a powerful magnetic field is applied simultaneously, and at right angles to the electric one. If the former is made sufficiently large, it will make a stronger bid for the axis of spacial quantization than the latter. This axis then becomes perpendicular to the electric field, and under such

[17] Hammar[16] suggests that Glaser's anomalous results may be due to absorption of water as an impurity on the test body, while H. Buchner (*Ann. der Physik*, **1**, 40, 1929) attributes them to systematic variations in the temperature of this body. He shows that an undetected temperature alteration of the order 0·01° to 0·1° C. might explain the anomaly. These contentions are answered at length by Glaser in *Ann. der Physik*, **3**, 1119 (1929). Recently Bitter finds very convincing evidence in support of Hammar's claim that the anomaly is due to water (*Phys. Rev.* **35**, 1572, 1930).

[18] L. Ebert, *Naturwissenschaften*, **14**, 919 (1926).

circumstances the old quantum theory yielded a dielectric constant radically different from that when the axis of quantization is parallel to the electric field. This has been shown by Pauling.[19] He demonstrated that a crossed magnetic field would make the constant $C$ in Eq. (1) negative, an absurdity. Only a comparatively feeble magnetic field would be required. If the electric field were 100 volts/cm., the magnetic one would only have to be 1 gauss. The smallness of the necessary magnetic field relative to the electric one is a consequence of the fact that molecules such as HCl[20] have a first-order Zeeman effect but only a second-order Stark effect. An innocent little magnetic field of only a few gauss should thus in the old quantum theory change the sign of the temperature coefficient of the dielectric constant, and make the electric susceptibility negative in so far as the orientation rather than induced polarization is concerned. This is what one might term extreme spectroscopic instability. Needless to say, such a cataclysmic influence of a magnetic field on the dielectric constant is not found experimentally. Mott-Smith and Daily[21] showed that a field of 4,800 gauss did not alter the electric susceptibilities of NO or HCl within the experimental error (8 per cent. in NO and 1 per cent. in HCl). Also a few months previously Weatherby and Wolf[22] found an analogous lack of effect of a magnetic field of 8,000 gauss on the electric susceptibilities of He, $O_2$, and air (within 10 per cent. in He and 0·4 per cent. in $O_2$ and air). The results for HCl and NO are perhaps a little more directly significant because they relate to polar substances, such as were assumed in Pauling's theory.

As a matter of fact, even the complication of a crossed magnetic field is not really required to yield the absurdity of a negative $C$ in Eq. (1), provided one uses half-quantum numbers in the old theory. Pauling, to be sure, found the positive

[19] L. Pauling, *Phys. Rev.* **29**, 145 (1927).

[20] The magnetic moment of a diamagnetic molecule such as HCl is developed solely in virtue of rotation of the molecule as a whole, and so the corresponding Zeeman effect, though of the first order, is only $m/M$ times the ordinary atomic Zeeman effect. Here $m/M$ is the ratio of the electronic to effective nuclear mass. Even though minute, this first order Zeeman effect is larger than the second order Stark effect. The first order Stark effect disappears as long as the molecule is non-gyroscopic, as will be seen in Eq. (64) of § 37.

[21] L. M. Mott-Smith and C. R. Daily, *Phys. Rev.* **28**, 976 (1926). We give the percentage error in the electric susceptibility rather than in the dielectric constant. The error in the susceptibility is the more significant because the dielectric constants of gases are nearly unity. Consequently a high precision in measuring the dielectric constant (1 part in 100,000 for NO, HCl; 1 in 500,000 for He, $O_2$) is necessary to determine the susceptibilities as accurately as mentioned above. The absence of the converse effect, the alteration of magnetic susceptibilities by an electric field, has been proved by Mott-Smith for HCl and NO (*Phys. Rev.* **32**, 817, 1928).

[22] B. B. Weatherby and A. Wolf, *Phys. Rev.* **27**, 769 (1926).

value $C = 4 \cdot 57$ already tabulated on p. 107 by assuming half-quantum numbers and no magnetic field. However, he took the *a priori* probability of a rotational state $J$ to be $p_J = 2J + 2$. Here $J$ denotes the integral rotational quantum number of the new mechanics; i.e. $J + \frac{1}{2}$ is the half integral effective rotational quantum number of the old theory. Modern experimental knowledge of band intensities and the Zeeman effect, as well as the theoretical dictums of the new mechanics, demand that instead the *a priori* probability should be $p_J = 2J + 1$. When the calculations are made with $p_J = 2J + 1$, the constant $C$ turns out to be negative instead of $+4 \cdot 57$ when $H = 0$. It is for this reason that Pauling preferred to use $p_J = 2J + 2$. With either choice of $p_J$ the application of a crossed magnetic field alters the sign of $C$. Thus if Pauling's theory is modified by taking $p_J = 2J + 1$, a magnetic field of a few gauss abruptly makes $C$ positive.

In the new quantum mechanics the choice of the axis of spacial quantization is no longer of importance, and so a magnetic field should be almost without effect on the dielectric constant, in agreement with the experiments reported above. We say 'almost' rather than 'completely' without effect because a tremendously large magnetic field may still slightly distort the dielectric constant. This distortion is closely akin to a saturation effect, as it is proportional to the square of the magnetic field. It is thus negligible in any field of ordinary magnitude, and increases very gradually when the magnetic field is increased to a tremendous value, quite unlike the abrupt alterations reported in the old quantum theory. The order of magnitude of this distortion effect in the new quantum mechanics is precisely the same as in the classical theory. Consequently, if we are interested in seeing qualitatively about how large should be the influence of a magnetic field on the dielectric constant, we may make a classical calculation. This will be given in the next paragraphs. Such a classical digression may appear out of place in a chapter on old quantum theory, but it seems advisable to discuss magnetic distortion of the dielectric constant once for all.

We shall use the same model and substantially the same notation as in § 12, except of course for the addition of a magnetic moment. Let $\mu_1$, $\mu_2$, $\mu_3$ and $\mu_1^*$, $\mu_2^*$, $\mu_3^*$ be respectively the components of permanent electric and permanent magnetic moment along the principal axes $x'$, $y'$, $z'$ of the molecule. To facilitate printing, we here and henceforth use subscripts $_{1,2,3}$ in place of the previous $_{x',y',z'}$. The small induced diamagnetic moment will be neglected, and the various coefficients connected with the induced electric polarization will be taken as in § 12. The angle between the applied electric and magnetic fields will be denoted by $\Omega$. The direction cosines of the angles which the principal axes of the molecule make with the field $E$ will, as in § 12, be denoted by $\lambda_1$, $\lambda_2$, $\lambda_3$, while those of the angles which these axes make with $H$

will be denoted by $\Lambda_1$, $\Lambda_2$, $\Lambda_3$. Because of the potential energy of the permanent magnetic moment in the field $H$, we must add to the Hamiltonian function (9), Chap. II, the extra term

$$-H(\Lambda_1\mu_1^* + \Lambda_2\mu_2^* + \Lambda_3\mu_3^*). \tag{2}$$

We must now develop the partition function (12), Chap. II, as a power series in the two variables $E$ and $H$, instead of in the single variable $E$. This development will take the form

$$Z = Z_0(1 + A_{20}E^2 + A_{02}H^2 + A_{40}E^4 + A_{22}E^2H^2 + A_{04}H^4 + \cdots), \tag{3}$$

where $Z_0$ is the partition function in the absence of external fields. The factor $Z_0$ is of no importance for us as it is independent of $E$ and $H$. If we did not want the distortion or saturation effects it would have sufficed to stop with the second rather than fourth order terms. The omission of all odd powers of $E$ and $H$ from (3) requires some comment. It is obvious that there can be no terms proportional to $E^sH^t$ when $s+t$ is an odd integer, for on physical grounds the susceptibility, and hence $Z$, must be unaffected if we reverse simultaneously both $E$ and $H$. The disappearance of such terms can also be verified by performing the integration over the Eulerian angles. Terms for which $s$ and $t$ are both odd are omitted on the ground that it is equally probable that the electrons rotate in either a left- or right-handed sense about the direction of the electric moment. This idea of the equal probability of both senses of rotation is easily seen to imply that $Z$ must be unaltered if the sign of $H$ is reversed, and will be discussed more fully in § 70 on the non-existence of a magneto-electric directive effect.

The first two coefficients in (3) have the values

$$A_{20} = \frac{1}{6k^2T^2}[\mu_1^2 + \mu_2^2 + \mu_3^2 + kT(\alpha_{11} + \alpha_{22} + \alpha_{33})],$$

$$A_{02} = \frac{1}{6k^2T^2}[\mu_1^{*2} + \mu_2^{*2} + \mu_3^{*2}]. \tag{4}$$

The first of these formulae has already been included in (17), Chap. II, and the derivation of the second is entirely analogous except that the polarization is magnetic rather than electric. In (4) and subsequent equations we use the abbreviations $\alpha_{ij}$ for the 'polarization coefficients':

$$\alpha_{11} = \sum \frac{c_{x'i}^2}{a_i}, \qquad \alpha_{22} = \sum \frac{c_{y'i}^2}{a_i}, \qquad \alpha_{12} = \sum \frac{c_{x'i}c_{y'i}}{a_i}, \qquad \&c. \tag{4a}$$

By adding the magnetic term (2) to the Hamiltonian function, and carrying the development of the exponent farther than in (15), Chap. II, the coefficient $A_{22}$ in (3) is found to be

$$A_{22} = \frac{Z_1}{4Z_0 k^4 T'^4} \int \cdots \int [p_1\lambda_1 + p_2\lambda_2 + p_3\lambda_3]^2 \times$$

$$\times [\mu_1^*\Lambda_1 + \mu_2^*\Lambda_2 + \mu_3^*\Lambda_3]^2 e^{-\Sigma\, a_i\xi_i^2/2kT} \sin\theta\, d\theta d\phi d\psi d\xi_1 \cdots \quad (5)$$

where $Z_1$ is a constant independent of $E$, introduced just before Eq. (14) in Chapter II, and where the $p_i$ are the components of combined permanent and induced moment, as given in Eq. (5), Chap. II. By (14), Chap. II, and (3) the electric susceptibility is

$$\chi_{el} = NkT \frac{2A_{20} + 2A_{22}H^2 + 4A_{40}E^2}{1 + A_{20}E^2 + A_{02}H^2 + \cdots} = N[a_{el} + bH^2 + \cdots (+ c_{el}E^2 + \cdots)]. \quad (6)$$

where

$$a_{el} = 2kTA_{20} = \frac{\mu_1^2 + \mu_2^2 + \mu_3^2}{3kT} + \frac{\alpha_{11} + \alpha_{22} + \alpha_{33}}{3},$$

$$b = 2kT(A_{22} - A_{02}A_{20}), \qquad c_{el} = 2kT(2A_{40} - A_{20}^2).$$

We are not at present interested in the purely electrical saturation term $c_{el}E^2$, and we have hence not made the rather laborious calculation of $A_{40}$.[23] On use of (4) and evaluation of the integrals in (5) it proves that the explicit formula for $b$ may be written

$$b = \frac{1}{90k^2T^2}[3\cos^2\Omega - 1] \sum_{i>j} \left[ (\mu_i^{*2} - \mu_j^{*2})\left(\frac{\mu_i^2 - \mu_j^2}{kT} + \alpha_{ii} - \alpha_{jj}\right) + \right.$$

$$\left. + 6\mu_i^*\mu_j^*\left(\frac{\mu_i\mu_j}{kT} + \alpha_{ij}\right)\right]. \quad (7)$$

In a similar fashion we find that the magnetic susceptibility is

$$\chi_{mag} = N[a_{mag} + bE^2 + \cdots (+ c_{mag}H^2 + \cdots)], \quad (8)$$

where $b$ is defined as previously and

$$a_{mag} = 2kTA_{02} = \frac{\mu_1^{*2} + \mu_2^{*2} + \mu_3^{*2}}{3kT}, \qquad c_{mag} = 2kT(2A_{04} - A_{02}^2).$$

Comparison of (6) and (8) shows that the correction for magnetic distortion of the electric susceptibility has the same coefficient $b$ as the corresponding term for electric distortion of the magnetic susceptibility. This identity of the coefficients would be true even with quantum-mechanical refinements. It may be noted that by (7) the coefficient $b$ has opposite signs for parallel and crossed fields (given by $\Omega = 0$ and $\Omega = \pi/2$ respectively) and vanishes at the critical angle[24]

$$\Omega = \cos^{-1}\sqrt{\tfrac{1}{3}} = 54\cdot1°.$$

[23] The saturation coefficient $c_{el}$ has been calculated with this model by Debye, in *Handbuch der Radiologie*, vi, p. 779.

[24] In the old quantum theory Pauling found because of the spacial quantization a factor $3\cos^2\Omega - 1$ even in the main term $a_{el}$ of (6), and this is why his calculations gave such a tremendous anisotropy of the dielectric constant in a magnetic field.

Coefficients of the form $\alpha_{ij}$ $(i \neq j)$ in (8) can be made zero by proper choice of axes as (4a) shows that such coefficients are constructed of cross-product terms like the familiar 'products of inertia'; or, in other words, the axes $x'$, $y'$, $z'$ can be made to coincide with the principal axes of Debye's polarization ellipsoid.[25] There is only one common paramagnetic gas which is polar, viz. nitric oxide, and its electric moment is very small. Consequently the interplay between the permanent magnetic moment and the induced electric one probably gives the most likelihood of experimental detection, and in the following numerical estimates we shall assume the molecule non-polar, making $\mu_1 = \mu_2 = \mu_3 = 0$. The distortion coefficient $b$ is then inversely proportional to the square of the temperature and vanishes for all values of the angle $\Omega$ if the molecule is optically isotropic ($\alpha_{11} = \alpha_{22} = \alpha_{33}$, $\alpha_{ij} = 0$, $i \neq j$). Use of low temperatures would thus greatly favour the detection of the distortion, which is of course small. Most molecules have an electric polarizability $a_{el}$ of the order $10^{-23}$, while a molecule with a Bohr magneton of permanent magnetic moment has $\mu^* = 0 \cdot 9 \times 10^{-20}$. Hence if the molecular dissymmetry is so large that ratios such as $(\mu_1^{*2} - \mu_2^{*2})/\mu_1^{*2}$, $(\alpha_1 - \alpha_2)/\alpha_1$, &c., are comparable with unity, the coefficient $b$ is of the order $a_{el}\mu^{*2}/90k^2T^2$ or $10^{-33}/T^2$, as $k = 1 \cdot 37 \times 10^{-16}$. The percentage alteration in the electric susceptibility by a magnetic field is then of the order $10^{-10}H^2/T^2$, while that in the magnetic susceptibility by an electric field is of the order $10^{-9}E^2/T$, where $E$ is measured in electrostatic units. These alterations are too small to have yet been detected, although it seems probable that with the recent technique of powerful magnetic fields, the magnetic distortion of dielectric constants will be observed before long. Also it is much easier than the converse effect of an electric field on magnetic susceptibilities, due primarily to the low rating of volts in electrostatic units. According to the above estimates, a magnetic field of 10,000 gauss would change the electric susceptibility by about one part in $10^7$ at ordinary temperatures, while an electric field of 10,000 volts/cm. (= 33 e.s.u.) would alter the magnetic susceptibility only by about one part in $10^8$. The purely electrical saturation effects for such a field strength are also of the order one part in $10^5$, as already mentioned in § 22. A comparable distortion by a magnetic field certainly does not seem beyond the possibility of future detection, but on the other hand our estimates of this distortion may be a little

---

[25] Cf. Debye, l.c., pp. 760 ff. In Chap. II we took the $x'$ $y'$, $z'$ axes to be the principal axes of inertia, but as the kinetic part of the problem has been eliminated (cf. § 12), we are now at liberty to take them as the principal axes of the Debye ellipsoid.

too high because the molecular dissymmetry is not as great as we assumed.

We shall now mention qualitatively what modifications of the above results (6), (7), (8) are to be expected in the new quantum mechanics. The calculation of the distortion coefficient $b$ has not yet been made in the new theory, but careful perusal of Niessen's [26] quantum-mechanical calculation of the somewhat related saturation coefficient $c_{el}$ reveals the general type of result to be expected. If we still were to assume that the electrons vibrate harmonically about positions of static equilibrium, formulae of exactly the type (6), (7), (8) would doubtless still remain valid, as the quantum and classical theories almost always give identical results for the harmonic oscillator. The quantum mechanics, however, frees us from the need of such an unreal assumption, and enables us to represent the electronic motions in their full dynamical generality. In the general case the dependence of the distortion coefficient $b$ on the temperature would be of the form $q_0 + q_1/T + q_2/T^2 + q_3/T^3$ rather than $q_2/T^2 + q_3/T^3$ as in (7). Here the expressions $q_0$, $q_1$, $q_2$, $q_3$ would be functions of the matrix elements and characteristic spectroscopic frequencies of the molecule, and would resemble Niessen's expressions, $q_0$, $q_1$, $q_2$, $q_3$ in their general type of structure, though numerically different as he calculated the expansion of $c_{el}$ rather than $b$ in $1/T$.[27] The dependence of the coefficient $b$ on angle through a factor of the form $3\cos^2\Omega - 1$ can be shown to remain valid only as long as we assume the molecule has the same moments $\mu_1^*$, $\mu_2^*$, $\mu_3^*$ in its normal and excited states. Actually this will not be the case, so that we cannot expect $b$ to vanish at $\Omega = 54\cdot1°$, although it may well be small at this angle. These diversities between the classical and quantum results in the dependence on temperature and on angle are not so much due to inherent differences

---

[26] K. F. Niessen, *Phys. Rev.* **34**, 253 (1929).

[27] The calculation of the magnetic distortion is more difficult than that of the electric saturation effects in quantum mechanics because of the fact that the various components of magnetic moment do not commute with each other in matrix multiplication, or with the various components of electric moment. In a second paper (*Zeits. f. Physik*, **58**, 63 (1929) Niessen has purported to give a computation of the magnetic distortion of the part of the dielectric constant resulting from the permanent dipoles. He assumes that the same commutation (*Vertauschung*) relations apply to the low frequency or 'permanent' part of the magnetic moment as to the total magnetic moment. This need not be the case, as these relations apply in general to complete matrices rather than to a portion thereof (*Teilmatrixen*). Niessen's calculations are correct from a formal mathematical standpoint once his initial assumption is granted, but it is hard to imagine any molecular model to which this is applicable. Instead it is quite conceivable that in a polyatomic molecule the permanent magnetic moment consists entirely of diagonal elements when measured in the $x'$, $y'$, $z'$ system, in which case the peculiar quantum terms found by Niessen would be completely wanting.

of the two types of theories as to the more general model which can be utilized in the quantum theory. Because of the fact that the matrix calculations involve (in a sense 'scramble together') all the states of the molecule even though one is interested only in the normal state, it is not necessary to choose a molecule which has $\mu^*$ different from zero in the normal state in order to obtain the paramagnetic distortion of electric susceptibilities or the converse effect. Instead one could employ a normally diamagnetic molecule, as such molecules are usually paramagnetic in excited states. For this reason nitric oxide should no longer be the sole polar molecule capable of a distortion of the dielectric constant by a magnetic field. The general order of magnitude of the distortion coefficient $b$ is probably about the same as calculated above classically, and hence it still remains too small to be detected in experiments of the same precision as those of Wolf and Weatherby or Mott-Smith and Daily.

Although we have especially emphasized the null results of these investigators, it must not be inferred that the dielectric constants of no substances whatsoever have yet been influenced by magnetic fields. The experiments of Friedel, Jezewski, and especially Kast [28] show that the dielectric constants of certain 'mesomorphic' substances (anisotropic liquids) are perceptibly altered by magnetic fields, to a greater extent than we would expect from the above calculations. In fact some of these substances thus distorted are merely diamagnetic rather than paramagnetic! This does not necessarily contradict the theory; for, as noted by Ornstein, [29] liquid crystals are probably built out of large complexes ('elementary crystals') rather than out of ordinary free molecules such as assumed in the theory intended primarily for gases. If each elementary crystal has a large moment and is oriented as a unit by external fields, it is clear that abnormally large effects may be expected. Particularly convincing evidence on this point is furnished by the scattering of X-rays. Investigations of Professor G. W. Stewart, which are to be published shortly, show that in mesomorphic liquids the interference pattern is greatly changed by a magnetic field, whereas that in ordinary liquids or solids is not. This is only comprehensible if large groups of molecules, perhaps entire elementary crystals, are oriented *en bloc* by the field in the mesomorphic materials.

Closely akin to the influence of a magnetic field on the static dielectric

[28] E. Friedel, *Comptes Rendus*, **180**, 269 (1925); Jezewski, *J. de Physique* **5**, 59 (1924); W. Kast, *Ann. der Physik*, **73**, 145 (1924); also see discussion by E. Bauer, *Comptes Rendus*, **182**, 1541 (1926) and Errera, *Polarisation diélectrique* (Paris, 1928), pp. 150–1.

[29] L. S. Ornstein, *Zeits. f. Physik*, **35**, 394 (1926); *Ann. der Physik*, **74**, 445 (1924).

constant is the influence of such a field on the optical refractivity. The latter has been observed by Cotton and Mouton and others,[30] who find different refractive indices when the magnetic field is parallel and perpendicular to the electric vector of the light wave. The difference in the two cases is found to be proportional to the square of the field, as one should expect by analogy with the result (6) for static fields. This 'Cotton-Mouton effect' is the magnetic analogue of the Kerr effect, and is not to be confused with the familiar Faraday rotation of the plane of polarization (§ 84) which is linear in $H$ and hence much easier to measure.

[30] A. Cotton and H. Mouton, *J. de Physique*, **1**, 5 (1911); *Ann. Chim. Phys.* **19**, 153; **20**, 194 (1910); Raman and Krishman, *Comptes Rendus*, **184**, 449 (1927); *Proc. Roy. Soc.* **117**A, 1 (1927); M. Ramanadham, *Indian J. of Physics*, **4**, 15, 109 (1929); Cotton and Dupouy, *Comptes Rendus*, **190**, 630 (1930); Cotton and Scherer, *ibid.* **190**, 700; Salceaunu, *ibid.* **190**, 737; **191**, 486; Zadoc-Kahn, *ibid.* **190**, 672; general survey by Cotton in the proceedings of the 1930 Solvay Congress.

## QUANTUM-MECHANICAL FOUNDATIONS

### 32. The Schrödinger Wave Equation

Schrödinger's equation [1]

$$\mathcal{H}\left(\frac{h}{2\pi i}\frac{\partial}{\partial q_1},\ldots; q_1,\ldots\right)\psi_n - W_n\psi_n = 0 \qquad (1)$$

is to-day so celebrated that we introduce it without further ado. Here $\mathcal{H}$ is the operator which is obtained by replacing each momentum $p_k$ by $\frac{h}{2\pi i}\frac{\partial}{\partial q_k}$ in the classical Hamiltonian function $\mathcal{H}(p_1,\ldots; q_1,\ldots)$. In case generalized coordinates are used, it is advisable to make the substitution of operators for momenta before rather than after transforming from Cartesian to generalized coordinates, as the direct formulation of the wave equation in generalized coordinates by extrapolation from classical theory encounters serious difficulties and ambiguities resulting from the non-commutativeness of multiplication by $q$ and $\partial.../\partial q$.[2] For an ordinary atomic or molecular system, subject to external electric and magnetic fields $E$, $H$ directed along the $z$ axis, the expression for the operator $\mathcal{H}$ in Cartesian coordinates is

$$\mathcal{H} = \sum_{i=1}^{\eta}\left\{-\frac{h^2}{8\pi^2 m_i}\left(\frac{\partial^2}{\partial x_i^2}+\frac{\partial^2}{\partial y_i^2}+\frac{\partial^2}{\partial z_i^2}\right) - Ee_iz_i - \right.$$
$$\left. -\frac{He_ih}{4\pi im_ic}\left(x_i\frac{\partial}{\partial y_i}-y_i\frac{\partial}{\partial x_i}\right)+\frac{H^2e_i^2}{8m_ic^2}(x_i^2+y_i^2)\right\}+V. \quad (2)$$

This can be seen by comparison with the classical Hamiltonian for a similar system given in Eq. (48), Chap. I. Here $e_i$, $m_i$ are the charge and mass of a typical particle (nucleus or electron), and $V$ is the ordinary internal electrostatic potential energy $\sum_{j>i} e_ie_j/r_{ij}$ (cf. Eq. (39), Chap. I).

Unless otherwise stated, relativity corrections and, until § 38, internal magnetic forces are always neglected.

Solutions of (1) are required which are single-valued, vanish at infinity,

---

[1] For a full discussion of the properties of the Schrödinger wave equation, see, for instance, Schrödinger's original papers assembled in *Abhandlungen zur Wellenmechanik*, or its English translation, *Wave Mechanics*; also Condon and Morse, *Quantum Mechanics*; Frenkel, *Wellenmechanik*; Sommerfeld, *Wellenmechanischer Ergänzungsband*; Ruark and Urey, *Atoms, Molecules, and Quanta*.

[2] For a good critical exposition of this difficulty see B. Podolsky, *Phys. Rev.* **32**, 812 (1928).

and are finite and twice differentiable over the whole of coordinate space, except perhaps for a few isolated points at which the solution becomes infinite in such a way that the integral $\int...\int |\psi_n|^2\,dv$ converges to a finite value even when these points are included. Solutions $\psi_n$ which meet these demands are called 'characteristic functions' (*Eigenfunktionen*) of (1), and constitute the 'wave functions' of conservative systems in quantum mechanics. In the interest of simplicity we throughout the chapter consider only conservative systems, rather than the more general case in which $t$ appears explicitly and the energy-constant $W_n$ is replaced by the operator $-\dfrac{h}{2\pi i}\dfrac{\partial}{\partial t}$. Eq. (1) will in general admit solutions which are characteristic functions only if the energy-constant $W_n$ has certain particular 'characteristic values', which furnish the quantized energies to be used in the Bohr frequency condition $h\nu = W' - W''$.

Two wave functions $\psi_n$, $\psi_{n'}$ representing states of different energy are orthogonal, i.e. possess the property that

$$\int...\int \psi_{n'}^* \psi_n\,dv = 0, \qquad (n' \neq n) \qquad (dv = dx_1 dx_2...dz_\eta), \qquad (3)$$

where the integration is to be extended throughout the coordinate space. Here and throughout the rest of the volume the asterisk * denotes the conjugate imaginary; thus $\psi_{n'}^*$ denotes the conjugate of $\psi_{n'}$. To establish (3) we first observe that $\psi_n$ and $\psi_{n'}^*$ satisfy respectively the equations

$$\mathcal{H}.\psi_n - W_n\psi_n = 0, \qquad \mathcal{H}^*.\psi_{n'}^* - W_{n'}\psi_{n'}^* = 0. \qquad (4)$$

The second of these equations is equivalent to $\mathcal{H}.\psi_{n'} - W_{n'}\psi_{n'} = 0$ since a complex expression and its conjugate vanish together; it is unnecessary to attach an asterisk to $W$ in passing to the conjugate as $W$ is a real number.

In order to distinguish clearly between operator functions and ordinary algebraic functions we shall insert a period between the operator and the subject of the operation except when the operator is written in full in terms of differentiations. Such a period is, of course, not to be confused with the dot involved in the scalar product of two vectors printed in bold-face type.

To continue the proof of (3) we multiply the first equation of (4) by $\psi_{n'}^*$, the second by $\psi_n$, subtract the resulting expressions, and integrate over the coordinate space. This yields

$$(W_n - W_{n'})\int...\int \psi_{n'}^*\psi_n\,dv = \int...\int (\psi_{n'}^*\mathcal{H}.\psi_n - \psi_n\mathcal{H}^*.\psi_{n'}^*)\,dv. \qquad (5)$$

The right side of (5) is most readily proved zero by specializing[3] $\mathcal{H}$ to be the operator (2), as this side then becomes

$$-\sum_i \int \cdots \int \left\{ \frac{h^2}{8\pi^2 m_i} (\psi_n^* \nabla_i^2 \psi_n - \psi_n \nabla_i^2 \psi_{n'}^*) + \right.$$
$$\left. + \frac{He_i h}{4\pi i m_i c} \left[ x_i \left( \psi_{n'}^* \frac{\partial \psi_n}{\partial y_i} - \psi_n \frac{\partial \psi_{n'}^*}{\partial y_i} \right) - y_i \left( \psi_{n'}^* \frac{\partial \psi_n}{\partial x_i} - \psi_n \frac{\partial \psi_{n'}^*}{\partial x_i} \right) \right] \right\} dv, \quad (6)$$

and partial integration, as in Green's theorem, shows that an expression such as (6) vanishes, assuming that $\psi_n$, $\psi_{n'}^*$ vanish in the usual way at infinity. Thus the right-hand member of (5) equals zero, and hence the validity of Eq. (3) is demanded as long as the energies $W_n$, $W_{n'}$ are different so that the factor $(W_n - W_{n'})$ does not vanish in (5). Even wave functions belonging to states of coincident energy, as in a degenerate system, can be made orthogonal by taking proper linear combinations (see Eq. (32) below). That it is possible to choose wave functions for degenerate systems in such a way that they are orthogonal is also obvious from the fact that degenerate systems are limiting cases of non-degenerate systems in which the difficulty of coincident energies is not encountered. Thus we may henceforth without loss of generality suppose that the wave functions belonging to different states are orthogonal regardless of whether or not these states all have different energies.

Because Eq. (1) is linear, the $\psi$'s all have arbitrary constant amplitude factors, which are, however, conveniently normalized by imposing the requirement that

$$\int \cdots \int |\psi_n|^2 \, dv = 1, \qquad (|\psi_n|^2 = \psi_n^* \psi_n). \quad (7)$$

## 33. Construction of the Heisenberg Matrix Elements by Use of the Wave Functions

Many readers will recall that before Schrödinger developed his wave equation, the quantum mechanics were first formulated in a matrix language by Born, Heisenberg, and Jordan.[4] The so-called Heisenberg matrix elements are readily constructed if we know all the characteristic functions of the given dynamical system. Suppose we desire these elements for an arbitrary matrix function $f(q_1,...; p_1,...)$ of the co-

---

[3] More generally, it can be shown that the wave functions are orthogonal whenever the Hamiltonian operator is 'Hermitian' or 'self-adjoint'. See P. Jordan, *Zeits. f. Physik*, **40**, 818 (1927).

[4] Heisenberg, *Zeits. f. Physik*, **33**, 879 (1925); Born and Jordan, *ibid.* **34**, 858 (1925); Born, Heisenberg, and Jordan, *ibid.* **35**, 557 (1926); Born and Jordan, *Elementare Quantenmechanik*.

ordinates and momenta. The procedure is as follows. Construct from $f$ the operator $f\left(q_1, \ldots; \dfrac{h}{2\pi i} \dfrac{\partial}{\partial q_1}, \ldots\right)$ by substitution of $\dfrac{h}{2\pi i} \dfrac{\partial}{\partial q_k}$ for each $p_k$. If we let this operator operate on a typical wave function, we thereby generate a function $f.\psi_n$. It is to be clearly understood that while $f$ is an operator, $f.\psi_n$ is an ordinary algebraic function of the coordinates $q_1, \ldots$. It can be shown that the complete set of wave functions corresponding to all possible stationary states constitutes a 'complete' (*vollständig*) orthogonal set, such that any arbitrary function may be expanded as a series in these functions.[5] Hence we may expand $f.\psi_n$ as a series in the $\psi_{n'}$, so that

$$f.\psi_n = \sum_{n'} f(n'; n)\psi_{n'}. \tag{8}$$

It will be proved, and this is the fundamental theorem of the present section, that the coefficients $f(n'; n)$ in this expansion are the Heisenberg matrix elements[6] (exclusive of the time factor). That is, $f(n'; n)$ is the element associated with a transition between a state characterized by a set of quantum numbers $n'$ to one characterized by a set of quantum numbers $n$. Here the letters $n'$, $n$ in general each signify more than one quantum number since a dynamical system with several degrees of freedom requires several quantum numbers to specify a stationary state.

*Proof.* To show that the $f(n'; n)$ defined by (8) are really the Heisenberg matrix elements we must show that they possess all the characteristic properties of the latter. This means that we must show that they: (*a*) obey the matrix algebra, (*b*) obey the quantum conditions, (*c*) make the energy a diagonal matrix, (*d*) are Hermitian if $f$ is a function only of the $q$'s but not the $p$'s. The meaning of these terms will be explained when we shortly discuss the individual items (*a*), (*b*), (*c*), and (*d*). Born, Heisenberg, and Jordan[7] show that all the characteristic features of the matrix theory, including the validity of the canonical Eqs. (46), Chap. I, as matrix equations, follow uniquely from (*a*), (*b*), (*c*), and (*d*) if one impose the additional requirement that the time factor $e^{2\pi i \nu(n'; n)t}$ of a matrix element have its frequency determined by the Bohr frequency condition $h\nu(n'; n) = W_{n'} - W_n$, where the $W$'s are the diagonal elements $H(n; n)$ of the energy matrix. As we use (8) to define merely the amplitude part of the Heisenberg matrix elements, it will clearly be

---

[5] The proof of the 'complete' property in case the wave equation is of the so-called Sturm-Liouville type is given in Courant-Hilbert, *Methoden der Mathematischen Physik*, pp. 278, 284, 291, 336, 337.

[6] This correlation between the wave and matrix theories was first established by Schrödinger, *Ann. der Physik*, **79**, 734 (1926) and by Ekhart, *Phys. Rev.* **28**, 711 (1926).

[7] Born, Heisenberg, and Jordan, *Zeits. f. Physik*, **35**, 564 (1926).

permissible to insert a time factor $e^{2\pi i \nu(n';n)t}$ of the above type. Hence it only remains to show that $(a)$, $(b)$, $(c)$, and $(d)$ follow from (8).

$(a)$ The proof of the addition law $(f+g)(n';n)=f(n';n)+g(n';n)$ is trivial, as the coefficients in the expansion of $(f+g)\cdot\psi_n$ in the fashion (8) are clearly the sums of the coefficients in the expansions of $f\cdot\psi_n$ and $g\cdot\psi_n$. The proof of the matrix multiplication law

$$(fg)(n'';n)=\sum_{n'}f(n'';n')g(n';n) \tag{9}$$

is only a trifle more difficult. We note that the function $f\cdot g\cdot\psi_n$ may be expressed equally well as

$$(fg)\cdot\psi_n=\sum_{n''}(fg)(n'';n)\psi_{n''}, \tag{10}$$

or as

$$f\cdot(g\cdot\psi_n)=f\cdot\sum_{n'}g(n';n)\psi_{n'}=\sum_{n'}\{g(n';n)\sum_{n''}f(n'';n')\psi_{n''}\}$$
$$=\sum_{n''}\{\sum_{n'}f(n'';n')g(n';n)\}\psi_{n''}. \tag{11}$$

The result (9) follows on comparison of coefficients in (10) and (11). The matrix multiplication is non-commutative, as in general

$$(fg)(n';n)\neq(gf)(n';n).$$

$(b)$ The quantum conditions on the coordinate and momentum matrices $q_k$, $p_k$ are

$$p_kq_k-q_kp_k=\frac{h}{2\pi i}1, \qquad p_kq_l-q_lp_k=0 \qquad (l\neq k), \qquad \langle 12\rangle$$

$$p_kp_l-p_lp_k=0, \qquad q_kq_l-q_lq_k=0, \qquad \langle 13\rangle$$

where the elements of the unit matrix 1 are given by $1(n;n)=1$; $1(n';n)=0$ $(n\neq n')$.

*Notation.* If an equation is assigned a number, this number will throughout the rest of the volume be enclosed in angular rather than in round parentheses, e.g. $\langle 12\rangle$ rather than (12), in case the equation is an equation between entire matrices rather than ordinary algebraic quantities. Not all expressions appearing in such a matrix equation need necessarily themselves be matrices, as some of the constants of proportionality may be ordinary numbers, like $h/2\pi i$, for instance, in $\langle 12\rangle$. An equality between matrix elements, as distinct from entire matrices, will not be given the distinctive numbering, as the occurrence of indices such as $(n;n')$, &c., indicates clearly that we are dealing with matrix elements.

To prove the first relation of $\langle 12\rangle$ from (8) we observe that

$$\left(\frac{\partial}{\partial q_k}q_k-q_k\frac{\partial}{\partial q_k}\right)\psi_n=\frac{\partial}{\partial q_k}(q_k\psi_n)-q_k\frac{\partial\psi_n}{\partial q_k}=\psi_n.$$

The operator $\left(\dfrac{\partial}{\partial q_k} q_k - q_k \dfrac{\partial}{\partial q_k}\right)$ is thus equivalent to multiplication by unity, and for the particular case $f = p_k q_k - q_k p_k$, the right side of (8) reduces to the single term $(h/2\pi i)\psi_n$, whence

$$f(n;n) = h/2\pi i, \qquad f(n';n) = 0 \qquad (n' \neq n),$$

The remainder of the conditions given in $\langle 12\text{--}13 \rangle$ are obviously fulfilled since

$$\frac{\partial}{\partial q_k}(q_l\psi_n) - q_l\frac{\partial\psi_n}{\partial q_k} = 0 \quad (k \neq l), \qquad \frac{\partial^2\psi_n}{\partial q_k \partial q_l} = \frac{\partial^2\psi_n}{\partial q_l \partial q_k}, \qquad (q_k q_l - q_l q_k)\psi_n = 0.$$

(c) By a diagonal matrix is meant one whose elements vanish except when $n' = n$. If the energy or Hamiltonian function $\mathcal{H}$ is to be a diagonal matrix, then the expansion (8) must reduce for the special case $f = \mathcal{H}$ to $\mathcal{H} \cdot \psi_n = \mathcal{H}(n;n)\psi_n$, the right side thus consisting of but a single term. Comparison with (1) shows that this is merely the Schrödinger wave equation, as $W_n$ is simply another notation for $\mathcal{H}(n;n)$. Thus his wave equation is equivalent to the requirement that the energy be a diagonal matrix.

(d) A matrix $f$ is termed Hermitian if $f(n;n')$ is the conjugate $f^*(n';n)$ of $f(n';n)$. Before discussing the Hermitian property it is convenient to derive a formula for the coefficients in the expansion (8). To do this we multiply Eq. (8) by some $\psi^*$, say $\psi_{n''}^*$, and integrate over the entire coordinate space. In virtue of the orthogonality (3), only the particular term $n' = n''$ remains on the right side after performing the integration, and this term becomes $f(n'';n)$ in virtue of the normalization (7). Hence

$$f(n'';n) = \int \dots \int \psi_{n''}^* \cdot f \cdot \psi_n \, dv. \tag{14}$$

If we use the expansion for $f \cdot \psi_{n'}$ analogous to (8), multiply by $\psi_n^*$, integrate, and take the conjugate, we find that

$$f^*(n;n'') = \int \dots \int \psi_n f^* \cdot \psi_{n''}^* \, dv, \tag{14a}$$

as $\psi_n^{**} = \psi_n$. If the operator $f$ is a function only of the generalized coordinates $q_k$ and not of the momentum operators $\dfrac{h}{2\pi i}\dfrac{\partial}{\partial q_k}$, then $f^*$ is identical with $f$ since we may ordinarily suppose that $i$ does not occur in any $f$ explicitly, but only through the momentum operators. Also, with this restriction on $f$, the operator $f$ degenerates into an ordinary algebraic function $f$, so that $\psi_n f \cdot \psi_{n''}^* = \psi_{n''}^* f \cdot \psi_n$. The expressions (14a) and (14) are then identical, demonstrating the Hermitian property for the particular function $f = q_k$, or, more generally, for any function of the $q_k$'s alone. It will be noticed that the normalization (7) has been used in proving (d) though not in (a), (b), and (c). It is clear that the normalization must be involved somewhere, for otherwise the matrix elements defined by (8) would not be unique, as each wave function would have an arbitrary constant factor $C_n$ corresponding to the fact that $C_n \psi_n$ is a solution of (1) if $\psi_n$ is one.

In case $p_k$ is a *Cartesian* momentum $m_i \dot{x}_i + e_i A_{xi}/c$, it is readily shown to be Hermitian, merely by using (14), and making a partial integration with respect to $q_k$, as follows:

$$p_k(n''; n) = \int \cdots \int \psi_{n''}^* \frac{h}{2\pi i} \frac{\partial \psi_n}{\partial q_k} dq_1 \cdots dq_f = \int \cdots \int \psi_n \left(-\frac{h}{2\pi i}\right) \frac{\partial \psi_{n''}^*}{\partial q_k} dq_1 \cdots dq_f = p_k^*(n; n'').$$

If, however, $p_k$ be a canonical momentum in an *arbitrary* system of generalized coordinates, it need not necessarily be Hermitian. In such a system the volume element will take the form $\Delta dq_1 \cdots dq_f$ instead of the Cartesian form $dq_1 \cdots dq_f$ used above, where $\Delta$ is the functional determinant of the transformation from the Cartesian to the generalized system. Partial integration with respect to $q_k$ will lead to an integrand $-\frac{h}{2\pi i} \psi_n \left[\frac{\partial \psi_{n''}^*}{\partial q_k} \Delta + \psi_{n''}^* \frac{\partial \Delta}{\partial q_k}\right]$, and the Hermitian property is secured only in the special case that $\partial \Delta / \partial q_k = 0$. As a matter of fact, the generalized momenta can always be made Hermitian by taking the wave function to be $\psi^\dagger = \psi \Delta^{\frac{1}{2}}$ rather than $\psi$, and the wave equation to be that satisfied by $\psi^\dagger$ rather than $\psi$. One then takes the generalized volume element as $dq_1 \cdots dq_f$ rather than $\Delta dq_1 \cdots dq_f$. Jordan[8] has shown that this amounts to introducing a normalization in the definition of the canonical momenta which are otherwise ambiguous as regards an arbitrary additive function of the coordinates.

Even if we use a Cartesian system, so that the $p$'s as well as $q$'s are Hermitian, an arbitrary function $f(p_k, q_k)$ will still not in general be Hermitian. To see that this is true, we need only note that if $f$ and $g$ be any two Hermitian matrices which do not commute in multiplication, such as $f = q_k$, $g = p_k$, their product will not be Hermitian. In fact the matrix law of multiplication (9) shows that if $f, g$ be any two Hermitian matrices

$$(fg)^*(n''; n) = \sum_{n'} f^*(n''; n') g^*(n'; n) = \sum_{n'} g(n; n') f(n'; n'') = (gf)(n; n'')$$

so that the necessary and sufficient condition that their product be Hermitian is that these matrices satisfy the relation $fg = gf$. One sees, however, that the product $fg + gf$ which involves what we shall call 'symmetrical' multiplication of $f$ and $g$, is indeed Hermitian. Thus matrix functions constructed from a Hermitian set of coordinates and momenta, such as Cartesian ones, by repeated applications of addition and symmetrical multiplication will always be Hermitian. It is in general such symmetrical or 'Hermitianized' matrices which should be used in quantum mechanics. The related operators are termed 'self-adjoint' or 'real'. The quantum conditions ⟨12⟩–⟨13⟩ can be made to appear Hermitian by multiplication through by $i$, as $i(fg - gf)$ is Hermitian if $f, g$ are. The electrical and magnetic moments are necessarily Hermitian, since

$$\mathbf{p} = \Sigma e_i \mathbf{r}_i, \qquad m_x = \sum \frac{e_i}{2m_i c} \left[y_i \left(p_{z_i} - \frac{e_i}{c} A_{z_i}\right) - z_i \left(p_{y_i} - \frac{e_i}{c} A_{y_i}\right)\right],$$

[8] P. Jordan, *Zeits. f. Physik*, **37**, 383 (1926); cf. also Podolsky, *l.c.*[2]

with analogous formulae for $m_y$, $m_z$ and since therefore no non-commutative multiplications are involved in constructing these moments from the Cartesian $p_k$'s and $q_k$'s. We suppose throughout the remainder of the volume that the Hamiltonian operator is always taken of a self-adjoint form, permitting us to set $H(n; n') = H^*(n'; n)$.

Eq. (14) is exceedingly useful, as it yields the Heisenberg matrix elements by a simple quadrature when the wave functions are known. We shall refer to it so frequently that it is convenient to give it a special name, and we shall therefore call it the 'fundamental quadrature'. If the reader is more fond of or familiar with the 'wave' than with the matrix formulation of quantum mechanics, he can take (14) to be definition of matrix elements without knowing anything more about them, and we have then proved the attributes ($a$, $b$, $c$, $d$) for these elements. Even if one tries to avoid explicit use of the matrix language and employ a purely wave picture, the wave functions inevitably appear in quadratures of the form (14), or equivalent expansions (8), especially in perturbation theory, so that the introduction of the matrix elements, even though not explicitly so called, is unavoidable. For our purposes it would really suffice to define matrix elements by means of (8) or (14) without bothering to show that they are the same as Heisenberg's matrix elements, but the proof of the identity of Heisenberg's definition and the definition (8) or (14) in terms of wave functions, is so often omitted in texts on quantum mechanics, despite its simplicity and fundamental significance, that its incorporation in the present chapter is, we hope, not too much out of the way. If, as in this chapter, the wave functions are used primarily in connexion with the expansion (8) or quadratures (14), these functions become primarily tools for calculating the matrix elements, and are not given as much physical interpretation as they deserve, but this formal procedure seems better than going to the other extreme and constructing, as is sometimes done, hydrodynamical models of the molecule which localize and distribute the electronic charge with a definiteness contrary to the Heisenberg uncertainty principle. A diagonal Heisenberg matrix element $f(n; n)$ has the physical significance of being the average value of $f$ over all phases of the motion in a given stationary state. Only such an average, and not instantaneous values in a stationary state, are accessible to measurement. The well-known significance of $|\psi_n|^2$ as proportional to the statistical charge density in a system with only one electron, can be obtained from the fundamental quadrature (14) by taking $f$ to be unity in a small volume element $dv$ and zero everywhere else. Non-diagonal elements are important only as intermediaries to the calculation of the

3595.3

diagonal elements of other functions, or of the same function under different conditions. It is not the purpose of the present volume to inquire further into the broad questions of interpretation in quantum mechanics, which would take us too far afield into transformation theory, but instead to find the procedure for calculating energy-levels such as are involved in the study of electric and magnetic suscepti-bilities.[9] This requires primarily the development of two things: per-turbation theory and the theorem of spectroscopic stability. The aspects of the quantum mechanics which we present are perhaps rather formal, but in the last analysis a theory is most 'physical' when it permits the calculation of a large number of experimentally observable quantities in terms of a few fundamental postulates. The triumph of the quantum mechanics is probably due more than in any one thing to its success and utility in making possible the formal numerical cal-culation of energy-levels and spectral intensities.

In the hydrodynamical formulation of the quantum theory, the expressions for the charge and current densities for a system with a single electron are taken to be respectively[10]

$$\rho' = -e\Phi\Phi^* \quad \text{and} \quad \rho'\mathbf{v} = -\frac{eh}{4\pi im}(\Phi^*\operatorname{grad}\Phi - \Phi\operatorname{grad}\Phi^*) - \frac{e^2}{mc}\mathbf{A}\Phi\Phi^*, \qquad \text{(A)}$$

where $\mathbf{A}$ is the vector potential, and $\Phi$ is a normalized solution of the generalized wave equation obtained by replacing $W$ by the operator $-\dfrac{h}{2\pi i}\dfrac{\partial}{\partial t}$ in (1). The hydro-dynamical theory is not without its attractions. For instance, the charge and current thus defined satisfy the equation of continuity. However, difficulties are encountered in the generalization to systems with more than one electron, as with $\eta$ particles it is necessary to use a $3\eta$-dimensional geometry, which has no direct physical significance. Also the spontaneous radiation in the hydrodynamical theory, while in nice accord with the Bohr frequency condition, turns out to be proportional to the concentrations of electrons in both the final and initial states rather than to that in the initial state alone.[11]

Eq. (10), Chap. I, shows that in any hydrodynamical theory, the electric and magnetic moments of a stationary state containing only one electron are respectively

$$\iiint \rho'\mathbf{r}\,dv \quad \text{and} \quad \frac{1}{2c}\iiint [\mathbf{r}\times\rho'\mathbf{v}]\,dv. \qquad \text{(B)}$$

The moments yielded by substitution of (A) in (B) are the same as those obtained by our own standpoint, in which we take the average moment of a stationary state to be one of the diagonal elements of the appropriate Heisenberg matrix, and which we shall later prove equivalent to defining the moment by means of

[9] For the postulational foundations of quantum mechanics, see Dirac's book, *The Principles of Quantum Mechanics*, in this series.

[10] Cf., for instance, Schrödinger, *Ann. der Physik*, **81**, 137, **82**, 265 (1927); Gordon, *Zeits. f. Physik*, **40**, 117 (1927).

[11] For exposition of this difficulty see, for instance, Sommerfeld, *Wellenmechanischer Ergänzungsband*, p. 56; Condon and Morse, *Quantum Mechanics*, p. 90.

Eq. (46) to be given subsequently. It is obvious in the electric case that (B) furnishes the same electric moment as that which we use, for if the atom is in a definite stationary state, then $\Phi = \psi_n e^{-2\pi i W_n t/h}$ and with this restriction the first integral of (B) becomes identical with the fundamental quadrature (14) when in (14) we set $f = -\mathbf{e}\mathbf{r}$. The proof of the identity of the two standpoints in the magnetic case is similar,[12] except that a partial integration of one term in the integral is necessary. In this case we take in (14) for the $x$ component

$$f = -\frac{e}{2mc}\left[y\left(\frac{h}{2\pi i}\frac{\partial}{\partial z}+\frac{e}{c}A_z\right)-z\left(\frac{h}{2\pi i}\frac{\partial}{\partial y}+\frac{e}{c}A_y\right)\right]$$

since in a magnetic field $m\dot{x} = p_x + \dfrac{e}{c}A_x$, &c. and since $m_x = -e(y\dot{z}-z\dot{y})/2c$.

It may be cautioned that in general the hydrodynamical theory yields correctly only expressions which are linear in the charge or current. The reason for this is that it really gives only the average charge and current distributions of a stationary state, since by the uncertainty principle the instantaneous distributions at a given point of space cannot be specified once the energy has a definite value. Unless one remembers this, the hydrodynamical theory can be quite misleading. For example, in the hydrogen atom one easily verifies that in the hydrodynamical theory the angular momentum is directed *entirely* along the $z$ direction, if this is the 'axis of quantization' along which the angular momentum is given the quantized value $m_l h/2\pi$. One can, however, verify by matrix methods (cf. Eqs. (75)–(7)) that the squares of the $x$ and $y$ components of angular momentum are then really not zero (except in $S$ states). The explanation is, of course, that the square of the mean and the mean of the square are not the same. The mean of the first power, such as is yielded correctly by the hydrodynamical theory, is indeed zero for the $x$ and $y$ components, but the mean square is not. As another example, the hydrodynamical theory yields zero current whenever the wave functions are real except for the time factor, provided there is no magnetic field $H$. This is seen by setting $\Phi = \psi_n e^{-2\pi i W_n t/h}$, $\psi_n = \psi_n^*$, $\mathbf{A} = 0$ in (A). This does not mean that the electron is stationary, but only that it is as likely to be moving in any given direction as in its opposite.

## 34. Perturbation Theory [13]

Let us suppose that the Hamiltonian function consists of two parts: a main part $\mathscr{H}^0$ which is characteristic of the 'unperturbed problem', and a small 'perturbative potential' (*Störungsfunktion*) $\lambda\mathscr{H}^{(1)}+\lambda^2\mathscr{H}^{(2)}+\dots$. Here $\lambda$ is some small numerical parameter in which we suppose a series development can be effected. For our particular purposes the perturbative potential will usually be the terms added to the Hamiltonian function by application of a constant external electric or magnetic field, and $\lambda$ will be proportional to the field strength. As usual in perturbation

---

[12] The identity of the hydrodynamical with the matrix viewpoint as regards magnetic moments has also been noted by Bitter, *Phys. Zeits.* **30**, 497 (1929), and previously for the special case of hydrogen atoms by Fermi, *Nature*, **118**, 876 (1926).

[13] The perturbation theory of quantum mechanics was first given by Born, Heisenberg, and Jordan, *Zeits. f. Physik*, **35**, 565 (1926) and by Schrödinger, *Ann. der Physik*, **80**, 437 (1926).

theory, we shall assume that the complete set of normalized characteristic functions and characteristic values $\psi^0$, $W^0$ are known for the
unperturbed problem. As the $\psi^0$ for the unperturbed problem constitute
a complete orthogonal set, the wave functions $\psi$ for the perturbed
problem may be expanded in terms of the unperturbed ones, so that

$$\psi_n = \sum_{n'} S(n';n)\psi^0_{n'}. \tag{15}$$

We now substitute the expansion (15) in the complete wave equation

$$(\mathcal{H}^0 + \lambda\mathcal{H}^{(1)} + \lambda^2\mathcal{H}^{(2)} + \ldots) \cdot \psi_n - W_n\psi_n = 0 \tag{16}$$

which we wish to solve. We may utilize the fact that the $\psi^0_{n'}$ are solutions of the wave equation

$$\mathcal{H}^0 \cdot \psi^0_{n'} - W^0_{n'}\psi^0_{n'} = 0 \tag{17}$$

for the unperturbed problem, and that by (8)

$$\mathcal{H}^{(1)} \cdot \psi^0_{n'} = \sum_{n''} \mathcal{H}^{(1)}(n'';n')\psi^0_{n''}, \tag{18}$$

where the $\mathcal{H}^{(1)}(n'';n')$ are the matrix elements of the part $\mathcal{H}^{(1)}$ of the
perturbative potential calculated in the system of quantization of (i.e.
with the wave functions of) the original unperturbed system. When we
utilize (15), (17) and (18), Eq. (16) reduces to an expansion

$$\sum_{n'',n'} \{W^0_{n''}\delta(n'';n') + \lambda\mathcal{H}^{(1)}(n'';n') + \lambda^2\mathcal{H}^{(2)}(n'';n') - \delta(n';n'')W_n\}S(n';n)\psi^0_{n''} = 0$$

in terms of the unperturbed wave functions, with constant coefficients.
Now if such an expansion is identically equal to zero, the coefficient of
each $\psi$ in this expansion must vanish separately. Hence

$$\sum_{n'} [W^0_{n''}\delta(n'';n') + \lambda\mathcal{H}^{(1)}(n'';n') + \lambda^2\mathcal{H}^{(2)}(n'';n') - \delta(n'';n')W_n]S(n';n) = 0. \tag{19}$$

Here, as customary, $\delta(n'';n')$ means that $\delta(n';n') = 1$, $\delta(n'';n') = 0$,
$n'' \neq n'$. In the short-hand of matrix notation, the totality of homogeneous linear equations (19) for determining the $S(n';n)$ are equivalent
to the single-matrix equation $(\mathcal{H}^0 + \lambda\mathcal{H}^{(1)} + \lambda^2\mathcal{H}^{(2)} + \ldots)S - SW = 0$,
where $S$ denotes the whole matrix whose elements are the $S(n';n)$.
Since there are an infinite number of states $n$ or $n'$, the simultaneous
equations (19) for determining the $S(n';n)$ are infinite in number and
so clearly can be solved only by successive approximations.

*Non-degenerate Systems.* A dynamical system in quantum mechanics
is termed degenerate if two or more energy-levels coincide. If the
original system is non-degenerate we may develop the coefficients

$S(n'; n)$ and energy $W$ as power series in $\lambda$ in the following fashion:

$$S(n'; n) = \delta(n'; n) + \lambda S^{(1)}(n'; n) + \lambda^2 S^{(2)}(n'; n) + ..., \tag{20}$$

$$W_n = W_n^0 + \lambda W_n^{(1)} + \lambda^2 W_n^{(2)} + .... \tag{21}$$

The fact that $S^0(n'; n) = \delta(n'; n)$ is a consequence of the circumstance that $\psi_n$ reduces to $\psi_n^0$ for $\lambda = 0$. We now substitute (20) and (21) in (19) and equate to zero the coefficients of successive powers of $\lambda$. We shall carry the calculation only through terms of the second order in $\lambda$. The equations obtained by equating to zero the first and second powers of $\lambda$ are respectively

$$(W_{n''}^0 - W_n^0) S^{(1)}(n''; n) + \mathcal{H}^{(1)}(n''; n) - \delta(n''; n) W_n^{(1)} = 0. \tag{22}$$

$$(W_{n''}^0 - W_n^0) S^{(2)}(n''; n) + \mathcal{H}^{(2)}(n''; n) + $$
$$+ \sum_{n'} [\mathcal{H}^{(1)}(n''; n') - \delta(n''; n') W_n^{(1)}] S^{(1)}(n'; n) - \delta(n''; n) W_n^{(2)} = 0. \tag{23}$$

The solution of (22) is clearly

$$W_n^{(1)} = \mathcal{H}^{(1)}(n; n), \qquad S^{(1)}(n''; n) = \frac{\mathcal{H}^{(1)}(n''; n)}{h\nu(n; n'')} \qquad (n'' \neq n), \tag{24}$$

where $\nu(n; n'')$ denotes a frequency of the unperturbed problem, which is, of course, given by the Bohr frequency condition

$$h\nu(n; n'') = W_n^0 - W_{n''}^0 = -h\nu(n''; n). \tag{25}$$

Thus $\nu$ is really $\nu^0$, but omission of the superscript simplifies the printing and is not likely to cause confusion in this particular case. The first relation of (24) is the expression in the new quantum mechanics of the well-known theorem, also true in the old quantum theory,[14] that the perturbed energy is to a first approximation the original energy $W^0$ plus the perturbative potential averaged over an unperturbed orbit. We have already mentioned that diagonal matrix elements such as $\mathcal{H}^{(1)}(n; n)$ are to be interpreted as average values. When we substitute (24) in (23) we obtain the second-order results:

$$W_n^{(2)} = \sum_{n'}' \frac{\mathcal{H}^{(1)}(n; n') \mathcal{H}^{(1)}(n'; n)}{h\nu(n; n')} + \mathcal{H}^{(2)}(n; n), \tag{26}$$

$$S^{(2)}(n''; n) = \sum_{n'}' \frac{\mathcal{H}^{(1)}(n''; n') \mathcal{H}^{(1)}(n'; n)}{h\nu(n''; n) h\nu(n'; n)} - \frac{\mathcal{H}^{(1)}(n''; n) \mathcal{H}^{(1)}(n; n)}{\{h\nu(n''; n)\}^2} +$$
$$+ \frac{\mathcal{H}^{(2)}(n''; n) + \mathcal{H}^{(1)}(n''; n) S^{(1)}(n; n)}{h\nu(n; n'')} \qquad (n'' \neq n). \tag{27}$$

The primes over the summation signs mean that the states $n' = n$ and $n'' = n$ are to be excluded from the summation.

[14] For exposition of this theorem in the old theory, and references, see J. H. Van Vleck, *Quantum Principles and Line Spectra*, p. 203.

The equations (22) and (23) do not suffice to determine the diagonal elements $S^{(1)}(n;n)$ or $S^{(2)}(n;n)$ of the matrix $S$. These diagonal elements are, in fact, arbitrary unless one requires that the wave functions be normalized. Let us suppose that the wave functions for the unperturbed problem are normalized, i.e.

$$\int \ldots \int |\psi_{n'}^0|^2 \, dv = 1. \tag{28}$$

Let us seek to make the perturbed wave functions also normalized, so that they satisfy equation (7). If we substitute the expansion (15) in (7) and utilize (28), (3) (with $\psi^0$'s), the normalizing condition (7) becomes

$$\sum_{n'} S^*(n';n)S(n';n) = 1. \tag{29}$$

On substituting the development (20), Eq. (29) becomes

$$1 + 2\lambda S^{(1)}(n;n) + \lambda^2[2S^{(2)}(n;n) + \sum_{n'} S^{(1)*}(n';n)S^{(1)}(n';n)] + \ldots = 1,$$

whence $\quad S^{(1)}(n;n) = 0, \qquad S^{(2)}(n;n) = -\tfrac{1}{2}\sum_{n'} S^{(1)*}(n';n)S^{(1)}(n';n).$

Both the perturbed and unperturbed wave functions are orthogonal, as our proof of Eq. (3) by means of (4), (5), (6) is general. If one substitutes (15) in (3) and utilizes at the same time the orthogonality property (3) applied to the unperturbed wave functions, one obtains

$$\sum_{n'} S^*(n';n'')S(n';n) = 0, \qquad (n'' \neq n) \tag{30}$$

a result which may also, of course, be verified explicitly to terms of the second order in $\lambda$ by use of (24) and (27). Eqs. (29) and (30) are equivalent to the single matrix equation

$$\tilde{S}^*S = 1,$$

where $\tilde{S}$ is the 'transposed' matrix [15] formed from $S$ by interchanging initial and final indices, so that $\tilde{S}(n';n) = S(n;n')$. Since the product of $\tilde{S}^*$ and $S$ is a unit matrix, the matrix $\tilde{S}^*$ is the reciprocal of the matrix $S$, i.e.

$$\tilde{S}^* = S^{-1}. \tag{31}$$

A matrix possessing the property $\langle 31 \rangle$ is termed 'unitary'. It does not in general have the Hermitian property $S = \tilde{S}^*$ as this would require $S^{-1} = S$.

*Degenerate Systems.* The preceding calculation fails in case the unperturbed system is degenerate, as there will be states of coincident unperturbed energy, so that some of the denominators in equations such as (26) or (27) will be zero. To avoid confusion, we shall henceforth use a double index $n$, $m$ rather than a single index $n$ to specify a sta-

---

[15] In the literature $\tilde{S}^*$ is often called the matrix 'adjoint' to $S$, and denoted by $S\dagger$.

tionary state. The letter $m$ will signify the totality of quantum numbers which are without effect on the unperturbed energy. Such quantum numbers are, of course, found only in degenerate systems. The letter $n$ will designate the remaining quantum numbers. Thus two stationary states having the same $n$ but different $m$'s will possess the same original energy, so that frequencies of the type $\nu(nm';nm)$ will be zero. In a degenerate system an arbitrary linear combination

$$\psi'^0_{nm} = \sum_{m'=1}^{r} S^0(nm';nm)\psi^0_{nm'} \tag{32}$$

of the wave functions of all the states having the same energy is still a solution of the original wave equation, as all the $\psi^0_{nm}$ having the same $n$ satisfy the same unperturbed wave equation $(\mathcal{H}^0 - W_n^0)\psi^0_{nm} = 0$. We suppose for concreteness that there are $r$ states of coincident unperturbed energy, which will be represented symbolically by giving the index $m$ or $m'$ the values 1, 2,..., $r$. The number $r$ will in general be a function of $n$. It is to be especially noted that whereas the summation in (15) was over an infinite number of stationary states, that in (32) is over a finite, restricted number, as in any ordinary degenerate system only a finite number of states coincide in energy and so $r$ is a finite number. Because of the arbitrariness (32) in the unperturbed wave functions we are not in general justified in supposing that

$$S^0(nm';nm) = \delta(nm';nm)$$

by analogy with Eq. (20) for degenerate systems. Instead $S^0$ will possess terms which are non-diagonal in $m$ (i.e. of the form $m' \neq m$). To determine these terms we substitute (32) in (16), use (18), and equate to zero the coefficient of the first power of $\lambda$, remembering that then the coefficient of each $\psi$ must vanish separately. This is tantamount to adapting (19) to the case $(nm;nm')$ and yields

$$\sum_{m'=1}^{r} [\mathcal{H}^{(1)}(nm'';nm') - \delta(m'';m')W_{nm}^{(1)}]S^0(nm';nm) = 0, \ (m''=1,...,r). \tag{33}$$

Although the original system of equations (19) was infinite, (33) is a finite set of $r$ simultaneous homogeneous linear equations for determining $S^0(n1;nm)$, $S^0(n2;nm)$,..., $S^0(nr;nm)$. The various equations belonging to a set are obtained by setting in turn $m''=1$, 2,..., $r$. In other words, we have a finite number $r$ rather than infinite number of simultaneous equations. Each value of $n$, i.e. each family of originally coincident levels, has its own characteristic set of such simultaneous equations. Now a set of homogeneous linear equations admits a nontrivial solution only if the determinant of the coefficients is zero. This requirement gives the determinantal or 'secular' equation

$$\begin{vmatrix} \mathscr{H}^{(1)}(n1;n1)-W_{nm}^{(1)} & \mathscr{H}^{(1)}(n2;n1) & \mathscr{H}^{(1)}(n3;n1) & . & \mathscr{H}^{(1)}(nr;n1) \\ \mathscr{H}^{(1)}(n1;n2) & \mathscr{H}^{(1)}(n2;n2)-W_{nm}^{(1)} & \mathscr{H}^{(1)}(n3;n2) & . & \mathscr{H}^{(1)}(nr;n2) \\ \mathscr{H}^{(1)}(n1;n3) & \mathscr{H}^{(1)}(n2;n3) & \mathscr{H}^{(1)}(n3;n3)-W_{nm}^{(1)} & . & \mathscr{H}^{(1)}(nr;n3) \\ . & . & . & & \\ \mathscr{H}^{(1)}(n1;nr) & \mathscr{H}^{(1)}(n2;nr) & \mathscr{H}^{(1)}(n3;nr) & . & \mathscr{H}^{(1)}(nr;nr)-W_{nm}^{(1)} \end{vmatrix}=0 \quad (34)$$

or in briefer notation

$$|\mathscr{H}^{(1)}(nm'';nm')-\delta(m'',m')W_{nm}^{(1)}|=0 \qquad (m',m''=1,2,...,r). \quad (34\,a)$$

Eq. (34) or (34a) is an algebraic equation of degree $r$ and so has $r$ roots for the unknown $W_{nm}^{(1)}$. The resulting values of $W_n^0+\lambda W_{nm}^{(1)}$ are the first approximations to the perturbed energy values of the family of states in question. If these roots are all distinct, the perturbation has completely removed the degeneracy, otherwise not. In case the roots are not all distinct, difficulty due to degeneracy may be encountered in higher order approximations, but discussion of this is beyond the scope of the present chapter, and the treatment of degeneracy which is removed only in higher-order terms is a fairly obvious extension of the method we have given for the first order.[16]

Having found the values of $W_{nm}^{(1)}$ we may substitute any one of them in (33) and then determine the $S^0(nm';nm)$ by solving these equations, which will be consistent with each other because (34) is satisfied. Eqs. (33), to be sure, determine only the ratios of the $S^0(nm';nm)$, but their absolute values may be found by invoking the aid of the normalization (29).

Even after solving Eqs. (33), and thus finding the $W_{mn}^{(1)}$ and $S^0(nm';nm)$, the complete solution of the wave equation has not been obtained, as in substituting (33) for (19) we have considered only the interaction between states of the same $n$ but different $m$. Actually one must include also the effect of the matrix elements in the Hamiltonian function of the form $\mathscr{H}^{(1)}(n'm';nm)$, where $n' \neq n$ (also the effect of all of $\mathscr{H}^{(2)}$ and higher-order terms). To obtain the complete solution we choose the sums (32) as new unperturbed wave functions $\psi'^0_{nm}$. We may then proceed as in a non-degenerate system, and build up a power-series solution of the form (20), with of course the understanding that the $\psi'^0$'s rather than $\psi^0$'s are to be used in equations such as (18) or (15). When we employ the $\psi'^0$'s rather than $\psi^0$'s, the difficulties characteristic of degenerate systems no longer appear, at least in low-order approxima-

---

[16] The procedure when the degeneracy is removed only in the higher orders is given by the writer in *Phys. Rev.* **33**, 467 (1929), and more fully by Born and Jordan, *Elementare Quantenmechanik*, pp. 209 ff.

tions, for use of the linear combinations (32) with coefficients $S^0(nm'; nm)$ determined by (33) makes diagonal in $m$ the portion of the energy matrix for which $n = n'$; in other words,

$$\mathcal{H}^{(1)} \cdot \psi'^0_{nm} = W^{(1)}_{nm} \psi'^0_{nm} + \sum_{n', m'(n' \neq n)} \mathcal{H}^{(1)}(n'm'; nm) \psi'^0_{n'm'}.$$

The energy is affected only in the second approximation (26) by the portion of $\mathcal{H}^{(1)}$ for which $n' \neq n$. Hence to a first approximation the energy is given by solution of (34), and the effect of the 'high frequency elements' $n' \neq n$ is only secondary.

*Nearly Degenerate Systems.* A case which commonly arises, and of which we shall give a specific example in Eq. (101), is that in which some of the unperturbed energy-levels, while not coincident, nevertheless lie so close together that their separations are comparable in magnitude with the perturbative potential. A series of the usual type (20) for non-degenerate systems cannot then be used at the outset, as some of the denominators $h\nu(nm; nm')$ in (26) would be nearly zero. We here use the notation $nm; nm'$ to denote states of nearly the same energy. The procedure is quite similar to that in degenerate systems, and consists in finding a linear combination (32) of a finite number of unperturbed wave functions which will dispose of the troublesome 'low frequency elements' $n = n'$, $m \neq m'$ in the Hamiltonian function. It is readily seen that the secular equation now becomes

$$|W^0_{nm'} \delta(m'; m'') + \lambda H^{(1)}(nm''; nm') - \delta(m'; m'') W_{nm}| = 0$$

$$(m', m'' = 1, ..., r) \quad (35)$$

instead of (34) or (34a). Here the $W^0_{nm'}$ are the unperturbed energy-levels, and $W_{nm}$ is the approximate energy inclusive of the perturbations, which cannot here be conveniently expressed as a power series in $\lambda$. Such a development is useful only if there is little tendency towards degeneracy, or else complete degeneracy. (We must, however, mention that even in the intermediate case of near degeneracy, the secondary influence of the high frequency elements $n' \neq n$ can still be handled by the series method.)

## 35. Matrix Elements of a Perturbed System. Proof of Spectroscopic Stability

The matrix elements of any function $f$ in the perturbed system are given by the fundamental quadrature (14) if we use in (14) the normalized functions appropriate to the perturbed system. If we substitute in (14) the expansions

$$\psi^*_{n''m''} = \sum_{n'''m'''} S^*(n'''m'''; n''m'') \psi^{0*}_{n'''m'''}, \qquad \psi_{nm} = \sum_{n'm'} S(n'm'; nm) \psi^0_{n'm'}$$

similar to (15) for the perturbed in terms of the unperturbed wave functions, then (14) yields

$$f(n''m''; nm) = \sum_{n'''m''',n'm'} S^*(n'''m'''; n''m'')f^0(n'''m'''; n'm')S(n'm'; nm), \quad \textbf{(36)}$$

where the $f^0(n'''m'''; n'm')$ are the matrix elements evaluated for the unperturbed system, given by

$$f^0(n'''m'''; n'm') = \int ... \int \psi^{0*}_{n'''m'''} f \cdot \psi^0_{n'm'} \, dv.$$

In the brief matrix language (cf. Eq. $\langle 31 \rangle$), Eq. (36) may be written

$$f = \tilde{S}^* f^0 S = S^{-1} f^0 S. \quad \langle 37 \rangle$$

The matrix $S$ formed by the coefficients of the expansion of the perturbed in terms of the unperturbed wave functions is called the transformation matrix. Thus we can evaluate the matrix elements of any function for the perturbed system if we know all the elements of the same function for the unperturbed state, and if in addition we know the transformation matrix. The formula (36) or $\langle 37 \rangle$ will be entirely accurate if we know the transformation matrix accurately, and approximate if we know it only approximately by confining ourselves to low powers in the development (20).

The transformation matrix $S$ need not necessarily be used in connexion with the effect of a perturbation exerted upon a system. Another common use is in transforming from one system of quantization to another in a degenerate system not subject to perturbations that remove the degeneracy. We have already mentioned that in such a system any linear combination (32) of the wave functions of the states of identical energy is still a solution of the wave equation. When we pass from one set of wave functions $\psi^0_{nm}$ to another set $\psi^{0'}_{nm}$ by constructing arbitrarily such linear combinations, we make what is called a 'canonical' transformation.[17] Such a transformation amounts to changing the system of quantization, as the latter is not unique because of the ambiguity arising from the degeneracy. A familiar specific illustration is change in the direction of spacial quantization, which is arbitrary in the absence of external fields. Because we are now using instead of the infinite series (15) only the restricted sums (32) over the states of identical energy, the transformation matrix will now be diagonal in $n$, i.e. will have no

---

[17] Dirac notes (*Quantum Mechanics*, p. 82), that one must be careful in dealing with transformations to note whether one is making a change of variables or a change in the representation, i.e. in what we call the system of quantization. He proposes the names 'contact' and 'canonical' to designate the former and the latter types of transformation. In the earlier literature both types of transformation were indiscriminately termed canonical transformations.

'high frequency' elements in which $n' \neq n$. Hence (36) may be written, on readjusting the prime notation,

$$f(nm; n'm') = \sum_{m'',m'''} S^*(nm''; nm) f^0(nm''; n'm''') S(n'm'''; n'm'). \quad (38)$$

From (38) it is seen that

$$\sum_{m,m'} f(nm; n'm') f^*(nm; n'm') = \sum_{m,m',m'',m''',m^{\mathrm{IV}},m^{\mathrm{V}}} \{f^0(nm''; n'm''') \times$$

$$\times f^{0*}(nm^{\mathrm{IV}}; n'm^{\mathrm{V}}) S^*(nm''; nm) S(n'm'''; n'm') S(nm^{\mathrm{IV}}; nm) S^*(n'm^{\mathrm{V}}; n'm')\}, \quad (39)$$

where we write $m^{\mathrm{IV}}$ for $m''''$, &c. Now in the present case the normalization and orthogonality relations (29), (30) yield

$$\sum_m S^*(nm''; nm) S(nm^{\mathrm{IV}}; nm) = \delta(m''; m^{\mathrm{IV}}). \quad (40)$$

The inversion of initial and final indices as compared with (29)–(30) is legitimate since $\tilde{S}^* = S^{-1}$ and since we have $SS^{-1} = 1$ as well as $S^{-1}S = 1$. There are, of course, equations similar to (40) in which $n, m, m'', m^{\mathrm{IV}}$ are replaced by $n', m', m^{\mathrm{V}}, m'''$ respectively. Thus (39) reduces to

$$\sum_{m,m'} f(nm; n'm') f^*(nm; n'm') = \sum_{m'',m'''} f^0(nm''; n'm''') f^{0*}(nm''; n'm'''). \quad (41)$$

Now on the right-hand side we may replace $m'', m'''$ by $m, m'$, for this is only a change in the notation for the variable of summation. Also the product of a complex number and its conjugate equals the square of its absolute magnitude. Hence (41) may be written

$$\sum_{m,m'} |f(nm; n'm')|^2 = \sum_{m,m'} |f^0(nm; n'm')|^2. \quad (42)$$

This rather formal identity of the sums in the two systems of quantization is the mathematical expression and formulation of the theorem of spectroscopic stability, whose far-reaching physical significance has already been discussed in § 30. It doubtless seems to most readers a far cry from the abstract mathematical result (42) to its superficially not at all related physical interpretation given in § 30. To bridge the gap one must examine its application to spacial degeneracy, which will be discussed in the next few paragraphs, and also especially the specific use of the theorem in the proof of the Langevin-Debye formula, which will not be given until § 46. Before proceeding to the discussion of spacial degeneracy we may note that the theorem (42) applies to all types of degeneracy, not merely to the particular type involved when the direction of spacial quantization is ambiguous. Also, we may further note that the expression (42) is invariant even when $n = n'$, for there is nothing in the above demonstration which requires $n \neq n'$. With $n = n'$

the summation in (42) extends over the various transitions within a multiple level rather than over those between two multiple levels.

*Application to Spacial Degeneracy.* The most important application of (42) in calculating susceptibilities is to the case where the degeneracy arises from the absence of an external field, so that one direction in space is as good as another. Then the various values of the indices $m$ and $m'$ correspond to different values of the axial (often called 'equatorial' or 'magnetic') quantum number belonging to a system of multiple levels whose components differ from each other only in that they represent different 'quantum-allowed' orientations relative to the axis of quantization. Ordinarily $m$ then measures the component angular momentum of the entire molecule in the direction of this axis, in multiples of the quantum unit $h/2\pi$ of angular momentum. The canonical transformation of the type considered above now simply involves a rotation of the coordinate axes, and means that the direction of spacial quantization is shifted from one direction in space to another. Clearly, if $\mathbf{A}$ is any vector, the double sum (42) has by symmetry the same value whether we take $f$ equal to any one of the three components $A_x$, $A_y$, $A_z$ provided we average (42) over all possible directions for the axis of quantization, for after the average there is no preference between the $x$, $y$, and $z$ directions in the absence of external fields. But we have proved an expression of the form (42) invariant of the axis of quantization, and hence the average over all directions for this axis is unnecessary. Thus (42) always has the same value with $f$ equal to $A_x$, $A_y$, or $A_z$. Hence it follows that

$$\sum_{m,m'} |A_x(nm;n'm')|^2 = \tfrac{1}{3} \sum_{m,m'} |A(nm;n'm')|^2, \tag{43}$$

where

$$|A(nm;n'm')|^2 = |A_x(nm;n'm')|^2 + |A_y(nm;n'm')|^2 + |A_z(nm;n'm')|^2. \tag{44}$$

The expression (44), and hence (43), is clearly invariant of the choice of axis of quantization. There are, of course, equations analogous to (43) for the $y$ and $z$ components. Eq. (43) shows that summing over the axial quantum number has the same effect as a classical integration over random orientations, inasmuch as each Cartesian component contributes one-third of the total. Thus a quantum average over a discrete series of 'allowed' orientations is equivalent to a classical average over a continuous distribution of orientations.

An example or two will perhaps make these results more concrete. If $\mathbf{A}$ be a unit-vector matrix, then $A_x$ may be regarded as the cosine of the angle between this vector and some fixed direction in space chosen as the $x$ axis. In other words, $A_x$ is then a matrix representing a direc-tion cosine. Eq. (43) shows that *the mean value of the square of a direction cosine is one-third* when we average over the various allowed orienta-tions relative to the axis of quantization. This is the same mean value as classically.

Another simple illustration of (42) is furnished by the theory of diamagnetism. It can be shown (see p. 91) that the diamagnetic susceptibility of an atom is proportional to $\overline{x^2+y^2}$ if the magnetic field is applied in the $z$ direction. Now the average value of $x^2$ for the state $n$ is

$$\frac{1}{g_n} \sum_m x^2(nm;nm) = \frac{1}{g_n} \sum_{m,n',m'} |x(nm;n'm')|^2. \tag{45}$$

Here we have utilized the matrix multiplication law (9). Hence $n'$ is to be summed over all possible states, including $n' = n$. The 'a priori probability' $g_n$ is the number of different values of $m$ belonging to the multiple state $n$. The multiplicity is, of course, due to the fact that the axial quantum number $m$ may in general assume a variety of values for a given assignment of $n$. A diagonal matrix element $x^2(nm;nm)$ is the time average of $x^2$ for a component state having a particular value of $m$. Summation over $m$ followed by division by $g_n$ is necessary in order to yield the mean taken over the various components. Now (45) is an expression of the form (43) summed over $n'$, and there are, of course, similar expressions for the $y$ and $z$ components. Hence by (43) the average values of $x^2$, $y^2$, $z^2$ are equal, and since $r^2 = x^2+y^2+z^2$, we can take $\overline{\overline{x^2}}+\overline{\overline{y^2}} = \frac{2}{3}\overline{r^2}$, just as in classical theory. This has an important experimental application, as it shows that $x^2+y^2$ has the same mean value as $\frac{2}{3}r^2$, with or without spacial quantization, so that it is immaterial whether or not there are frequent collisions to upset the spacial quantization. Thus there should be no variation of the diamagnetic susceptibility per molecule with pressure due to change in the collision frequency, and hence no basis for the Glaser effect (§ 29) on the ground of change in quantization.

*Application to the Intensities of Spectral Lines.* Eq. (42) has an important application to the intensities of spectral lines. Let us suppose that the initial and final levels involved in the emission of a spectral line are both multiple, but that the spectral instruments do not have sufficient resolving power to reveal the multiplet structure. The ob-served intensity is then the sum of the multiplet components and is thus proportional to the sum of the squares of the matrix elements for the electric moment over all values of the subordinate indices $m$, $m'$

consistent with given $n$, $n'$. In other words, the intensity is proportional to an expression such as (42). If the multiplet structure is very narrow, it is very easily distorted (as in the Paschen-Back effect), and its pattern completely changed. By Eq. (42), however, the intensity in the entire pattern is the same as without the distortion. A magnetic field, for instance, should not affect the intensity of spectral lines unless we care to isolate the intensities of individual Zeeman components.[18]

*Invariance of the Spur.* If we take $n' = n$, $m' = m$ in (38), sum over $m$, and then use (40), we have the very useful relation

$$\sum_m f(nm; nm) = \sum_m f^0(nm; nm).$$

The sum involved in this equation is called the 'diagonal sum' or 'spur' of the sub-matrix (*Teilmatrix*) formed from $f$ by considering only the elements connecting the family of states of given $n$ but variable $m$. The spur of any finite matrix is thus an invariant of a canonical transformation. The infinite matrices formed by varying $n$ as well as $m$ do not in general have bounded diagonal sums, as the sum is now an infinite one over both $n$, $m$. Hence the spur relation cannot be employed when the transformation matrix is not diagonal in $n$, unless perchance it involves only a finite number of states.

The invariance of the spur requires that the sum of the roots of the secular equation equals the sum of the diagonal elements of the Hamiltonian function calculated in the original system of representation, i.e. in the unperturbed system of quantization. This is true inasmuch as (33) takes the form $W^{(1)} = S^{0-1}\mathcal{H}^{(1)}S^0$ in matrix language, so that the roots of the secular equation are merely the diagonal elements of the energy matrix when transformed into diagonal form. Thus the sum of the roots of (34) is $\sum_m \mathcal{H}^{(1)}(nm; nm)$, and of (35) is $\sum_m [W_{nm}^0 + \lambda\mathcal{H}^{(1)}(nm; nm)]$. Without using the invariance of the spur, these values can also be verified by expanding the determinants in (34) or (35) so as to yield an explicit algebraic equation $W^r + a_1 W^{r-1} + ... + a_r$ of degree $r$. The sum of the roots is, of course, $-a_1$, which is found to have the values given.

*Notation for Diagonal Matrices.* A special symbolism will be convenient for diagonal matrices, i.e. matrices whose only non-vanishing elements are the diagonal elements. A dot over the equality sign will

[18] If the multiplet width is at all different from zero, the case is, to be sure, that of near rather than complete degeneracy, and the transformation matrix will usually contain elements not diagonal in $n$, so that (42) is not rigorously applicable, but these 'high frequency elements' are usually small, since the corresponding denominators in (24) are relatively small, and so (42) is a good approximation.

mean that the left-hand side is a diagonal matrix and that the right side gives the diagonal elements of this matrix. Thus $p_\phi \doteq m_l h/2\pi$, for instance, is an abbreviated way of saying that $p_\phi(nm; nm) = m_l h/2\pi$, $p_\phi(nm; n'm') = 0$ ($n' \neq n, m' \neq m$). A symbol resembling an equality sign as much as possible has been desirable because the physicist likes to picture the diagonal elements of a physical quantity represented by a diagonal matrix as the values which it can assume in the stationary states. Thus one speaks of the axial component $p_\phi$ of angular momentum as *being* $m_l h/2\pi$ in a stationary state. On the other hand, the equality sign without the modification of the dot over the equality sign would not be mathematically correct as one cannot equate an entire matrix (the left side) to a diagonal element thereof (the right side). A bar is unnecessary to designate the time average of a function capable of representation by a dotted equality, as its matrix consists solely of diagonal elements and hence it is constant with respect to time.

The diagonal elements of a diagonal matrix are called its characteristic values. We tacitly consider throughout the volume only matrices in what is called the 'Heisenberg scheme of representation' in the parlance of the transformation theory of quantum mechanics. We do not need to occupy ourselves with the theorem of transformation theory [9] that any matrix can be brought into diagonal form if we are willing to sacrifice the diagonal form of the Hamiltonian function. When we say an expression is a diagonal matrix we mean that the diagonal form can be achieved without impairing the diagonal form of the energy. This restriction is necessary because we are dealing with conservative systems; otherwise every matrix would be potentially a diagonal matrix.

## 36. Formulae for the Electric and Magnetic Moments of a Stationary State

The average electric and magnetic moments in any given stationary state are obtainable from the formulae for the energy by a simple differentiation, viz.

$$\bar{p}_{Enm} = p_E(nm; nm) = -\frac{\partial W_{nm}}{\partial E}, \qquad \bar{m}_{Hnm} = m_H(nm; nm) = -\frac{\partial W_{nm}}{\partial H}. \quad (46)$$

The bar denotes the time average for a given stationary state, and is, of course, the same as a diagonal element of the Heisenberg matrix for the electric or magnetic moment. Thus if the series development of the energy in the field strength is $W = W^0 + E W^{(1)} + E^2 W^{(2)} + ...$, then

$$p_E(nm; nm) = -W_{nm}^{(1)} - 2E W_{nm}^{(2)} + .... \quad (47)$$

To obtain specific formulae for $W^{(1)}$, $W^{(2)}$... we use (24) and (26). We assume that the system is non-degenerate or, if degenerate, that it has had the troublesome 'degenerate elements' $n = n'$, $m \neq m'$ eliminated from the Hamiltonian function by finding a new set of wave functions by a proper linear transformation (32). In case the only external field is the given electric or magnetic field, the degeneracy difficulty due to the arbitrariness of spacial orientation in the absence of the field is avoided by taking the direction of the axis of quantization as identical with the direction of the applied field. The matrices representing the components of electric and magnetic moment in this direction are readily shown to be diagonal in the axial quantum number $m$.

We shall first derive formulae for $W^{(1)}$ and $W^{(2)}$ in the electric case. As usual, we suppose the applied field along the $z$ axis. Here we may take the parameter $\lambda$ to be the field strength $E$, and comparison with Eq. (2) shows that

$$\mathcal{H}^{(1)} = - \sum e_i z_i = - p_E, \qquad \mathcal{H}^{(2)} = 0. \qquad \langle 48 \rangle$$

Except for sign, the matrix elements $\mathcal{H}^{(1)}(nm; n'm')$ involved in the perturbative potential $E\mathcal{H}^{(1)}$ are thus identical with those $p_E^0(nm; n'm')$ of the electric moment, provided the latter are calculated in the absence of the field, as indicated by the superscript $^0$. This proviso is necessary since the unperturbed wave functions are used in the definition (18) of the elements $\mathcal{H}^{(1)}(nm; n'm')$. These elements may be calculated by means of the fundamental quadrature (14) taking $f = \sum e_i z_i$, and the wave functions to be those of the unperturbed state. By (24), (26), and (48)

$$W_{nm}^{(1)} = - p_E^0 (nm; nm), \qquad W_{nm}^{(2)} = \sum_{n'm'}{}' \frac{|p_E^0(nm; n'm')|^2}{h\nu(nm; n'm')}, \qquad (49)$$

and hence by (47) and (49)

$$p_E(nm; nm) = p_E(nm; nm) + 2E \sum_{n'm'}{}' \frac{|p_E^0(nm; n'm')|^2}{h\nu(n'm'; nm)}, \qquad (50)$$

since

$$p_E^0(nm; n'm')p_E^0(n'm'; nm) = p_E^0(nm; n'm')p_E^{0*}(nm; n'm') = |p_E^0(nm; n'm')|^2$$

in virtue of the Hermitian property of the electric moment matrices, and since by (25) $\nu(n'm'; nm) = -\nu(nm; n'm')$. The presence of the second right-hand member of (50) means that the average electrical moment $p_E(nm; nm)$ of an atom or molecule in the presence of the field is not the same as the average $p_E^0(nm; nm)$ for the same stationary state in the absence of the field. This is, naturally, because the presence of the electric field distorts the electronic (and nuclear) motions, and polarizes the atom so that there is an induced moment, given by the second term of (50).

In the magnetic case we have $\lambda = H$, and Eq. (2) of the present chapter or Eq. (48), Chap. I, shows that

$$\mathcal{H}^{(1)}(nm; n'm') = -m_H^0(nm; n'm'),$$

$$\mathcal{H}^{(2)}(nm; n'm') = \sum \frac{e_i^2}{8m_i c^2}(x_i^2 + y_i^2)(nm; n'm'), \qquad (51)$$

where $m_H^0(nm; n'm')$ denotes a matrix element of $\sum \dfrac{e_i}{2m_i c}(x_i p_{y_i} - y_i p_{x_i})$ evaluated in the unperturbed state, i.e. an element of the magnetic moment in the absence of the magnetic field. The presence of the second-order term $\mathcal{H}^{(2)}$ in (51) is because (2) contains a non-vanishing quadratic term in $H$, which has no analogue in the electric case. Proceeding as before, we find from (24), (26), (46), and (51) that

$$m_H(nm; nm)$$

$$= m_H^0(nm; nm) + 2H \sum_{n'm'}{}' \frac{|m_H^0(nm; n'm')|^2}{h\nu(n'm'; nm)} - H \sum_i \frac{e_i^2(x_i^2 + y_i^2)}{4m_i c^2}(nm; nm). \qquad (52)$$

The last term of (52), which is not paralleled in (50), is a diamagnetic one, as can, for instance, be seen by comparison with the classical theory of magnetism previously given on p. 91. As we have mentioned on pp. 22–4, this third term is essentially a correction for the fact that in a magnetic field the 'canonical angular momentum' $P_{z_i} = x_i p_{y_i} - y_i p_{x_i}$ is not the same as the true angular momentum $m_i(x_i \dot{y}_i - y_i \dot{x}_i)$. Hence in the field a matrix element $m_H(nm; n'm')$ of the true magnetic moment is not the same as $\sum_i (e_i/2m_i c)P_{z_i}(nm; n'm')$. This distinction disappears when the field is absent, so that $m_H^0(nm; n'm') = \sum_i (e_i/2m_i c)P_{z_i}^0(nm; n'm')$.

*Proof of Eqs.* (46). Having shown at some length how Eqs. (46) may be used to calculate the moment of a stationary state, it remains to give the proof of these equations. To do this, we note that Eqs. (49), Chap. I, viz.

$$p_E = -\frac{\partial \mathcal{H}}{\partial E}, \qquad m_H = -\frac{\partial \mathcal{H}}{\partial H}, \qquad \langle 53 \rangle$$

are valid in quantum mechanics provided $p_E$, $m_H$, $\mathcal{H}$ are interpreted now as matrices, indicated by the angular parentheses around the equation number, and provided in the differentiation the matrix elements of $\mathcal{H}$ are calculated for the system of representation appropriate to a particular field strength, say $E_0$ (or $H_0$), rather than the variable one

$E_0 + \Delta E$ (or $H_0 + \Delta H$). The reason that these equations are still valid
is that the derivation of (49), Chap. I, from (48), Chap. I, involved no
operations (such as the multiplication $q_k p_k$) which are non-commutative
in quantum mechanics, and so the various steps in going from (48) to
(49) in Chapter I retain their validity in matrix as well as ordinary
algebra. Let now the electric field be changed from $E_0$ to $E_0 + \Delta E$.
The term added to the Hamiltonian function is then $(\partial \mathcal{H}/\partial E)\Delta E$,
neglecting squares of $\Delta E$. Further, if now we take $\lambda = \Delta E$, instead of
$\lambda = E$ as previously, the change $\Delta W$ in the quantized energy is to a first
approximation in $\Delta E$ by (21) and by (24) the average or diagonal
value of the term added to the perturbative potential. Thus to this
approximation we see, using $\langle 48 \rangle$, that

$$\Delta W_{nm} = \Delta E \frac{\partial \mathcal{H}}{\partial E}(nm; nm) = -\Delta E p_E(nm; nm),$$

and passing to the limit $\Delta E = 0$ we obtain the first relation of (46).
The proof of the second relation is similar.[19]

Eqs. (46) and $\langle 53 \rangle$ are not to be confused, as $W$ is the energy appropriate to any given field strength, and is always a diagonal matrix,
whereas $\mathcal{H}$ is the Hamiltonian function expressed in the system of
quantization appropriate to one particular field strength $E_0$, and is not
a diagonal matrix when $E \neq E_0$. Eq. $\langle 53 \rangle$ gives the matrix representing
the instantaneous value of the moment, whereas (46) gives the time
average. Because the distinction between (46) and $\langle 53 \rangle$ is a little subtle,
some readers may prefer to take (46) to be the definition of the average
moment, rather than falling back upon the definition of moment given
in Eq. (11), Chap. I. This alternative is not without its advantages,
and is sometimes used in the literature. However, if we regard (46) as
a definition of the average moment, rather than as a consequence of
(11), Chap. I, it is not at all obvious that the average moment per
molecule, when multiplied by the number of molecules per c.c., is
identical with the macroscopic polarization vector $\mathbf{P}$ given by the
familiar macroscopic relation $\mathbf{D} = \mathbf{E} + 4\pi\mathbf{P}$. In other words, we have

[19] In performing the differentiation in $\langle 53 \rangle$ it is essential that the system of representation, i.e. of quantization, for $\mathcal{H}$ be held fast to that appropriate to a particular field
strength $E_0$. Similarly Eqs. (49) of Chap. I are valid only in systems of coordinates
obtained from Cartesian ones by transformations which are independent of the field
strength $E$, but which can nevertheless involve the constant parameter $E_0$. Relations
similar to (46) are readily proved valid in the classical or old quantum theory by essentially the same method as that which we use in the new. Then $W_{nm}$ denotes the energy
expressed as a function of the angle and action variables $w_k$, $J_k$ appropriate to the variable field strength, and so $W_{nm}$ is independent of the $w_k$ corresponding to the fact that the
energy is a diagonal matrix in (46) but not in $\langle 53 \rangle$.

proved Eqs. (12), Chap. I, viz.

$$\mathbf{P} = N\overline{\overline{\mathbf{p}}}, \qquad \mathbf{M} = N\overline{\overline{\mathbf{m}}}, \qquad (12, \text{I})$$

from the definition (11), Chap. I, rather than from (46) of the present chapter. Even so, some readers may object that there is still a lack of rigour in our proof of the fundamental theorem (12, I) from (11), Chap. I, in the quantum mechanical case, as our proof of (12, I) in § 3, which was inevitably rather long, was an entirely classical one, so that we are now reasoning only by analogy with classical theory. Apparently a completely rigorous justification of (12), Chap. I, would require a quantum theory of the electromagnetic field,[20] which is a very intricate subject beyond the scope of the present volume. However, one can always be almost certain that classical averages are replaced by diagonal matrix elements in quantum mechanics, and this is all we have used. As a matter of fact, considerable of the work in Chapter I can be repeated in the matrix language, at least when the fields are constant in time, taking $\mathbf{E}$, $\mathbf{H}$, $\mathbf{D}$, $\mathbf{B}$, &c., to be now matrices, and in this way one can see that the validity of the relations (12, I), with $\mathbf{p}$, $\mathbf{m}$ defined by (11), Chap. I, is virtually unavoidable even in quantum mechanics.

## 37. The Rotating Dipole in an Electric Field [21]

It is customary to treat the 'end-over-end' rotation of a diatomic molecule by using a simplified, idealized model, sometimes called the 'rigid rotator' or 'dumb-bell model'. The behaviour of this model in an electric field furnishes a simple illustration [22] of the perturbation

---

[20] A tentative form of such a theory has been given by Heisenberg and Pauli, *Zeits. f. Physik*, **56**, 1, **59**, 168 (1929), but is not without objections; (cf. Oppenheimer, *Phys. Rev.* **35**, 461 (1930).

[21] This problem was treated more or less simultaneously by Mensing and Pauli, *Phys. Zeits.* **27**, 509 (1926); R. de L. Kronig, *Proc. Nat. Acad. Sci.* **12**, 488 (1926); C. Manneback, *Phys. Zeits.* **27**, 563 (1926); and J. H. Van Vleck, *Nature*, **118**, 226 (1926) (abstract only). The wave equation for the rotating dipole in the absence of fields was first formulated and solved by Schrödinger, *Ann. der Physik*, **79**, 520 (1926). The behaviour in fields so powerful as to prevent the use of the usual perturbation theory has been considered by Brouwer, Dissertation, Amsterdam, 1930; cf. also Lennard-Jones, *Proc. Roy. Soc.* **129**A, 598 (1930).

[22] If the reader desires a still simpler example of perturbation theory, he may consider the rotating dipole in two dimensions subject to an electric field in the plane of motion. The unperturbed wave functions are then simple sines or cosines, and the development (15) of the perturbed wave function takes the form of a Fourier series, consisting exclusively of sine or cosine terms. The wave equation for the perturbed problem is of the form known as Mathieu's equation, and is similar to the wave equation for the two-dimensional simple pendulum, which has been discussed qualitatively by Condon, *Phys. Rev.* **31**, 891 (1928). Our three-dimensional wave equation (54) is, of course, like that of the spherical pendulum. Despite the very simple form of the two-dimensiona lequation, its characteristic functions cannot be expressed except in series, as there are no closed

theory given in § 34. If we neglect the molecular vibrations, the nuclei of a diatomic molecule remain at a constant distance $r_0$ from each other, and so the end-over-end rotation may be expected to resemble that of a dumb-bell of length $r_0$ with masses $M_1$, $M_2$ at the two ends, equal to the masses of the nuclei. The moment of inertia is then

$$I = \frac{M_1 M_2}{M_1 + M_2}\, r_0^2.$$

If the molecule is polar, we may suppose that there is a constant dipole moment $\mu$ along the axis of the dumb-bell. Let $\theta$, $\phi$ be the usual polar coordinates specifying the position of the axis of the dumb-bell relative to a fixed direction in space, which we shall suppose to be the direction of an applied electric field $E$. The Schrödinger wave equation is then

$$-\frac{h^2}{8\pi^2 I}\left[\frac{1}{\sin\theta}\frac{\partial}{\partial\theta}\left(\sin\theta\frac{\partial\psi}{\partial\theta}\right) + \frac{1}{\sin^2\theta}\frac{\partial^2\psi}{\partial\phi^2} + \frac{8\pi^2 I}{h^2}(W + \mu E\cos\theta)\psi\right] = 0. \quad (54)$$

Eq. (54) is the specialization of the general wave equation (1) appropriate to our particular model.

The term $-\mu E\cos\theta$ is clearly the potential energy $V$ of the dipole in the applied field $E$. The derivation of the first two terms of (54) is somewhat more complicated. The classical Hamiltonian function for the kinetic energy of a rotating dipole is

$$\frac{1}{2I}\left[p_\theta^2 + \frac{p_\phi^2}{\sin^2\theta}\right], \quad (55)$$

and if we replace $p_\theta$, $p_\phi$ by $h\partial.../2\pi i\partial\theta$, $h\partial.../2\pi i\partial\phi$ the first term of (54) would be $(-h^2/8\pi^2 I)\partial^2\psi/\partial\theta^2$. The difficulty is the one mentioned at the beginning of § 32, namely, that the transcription into the operator language is ambiguous because $\partial.../\partial\theta$ does not commute in multiplication with $f(\theta)$. The classical Hamiltonian can be written equally well as

$$\frac{1}{2I}\left[\frac{1}{\sin\theta}p_\theta\sin\theta\, p_\theta + \frac{p_\phi^2}{\sin^2\theta}\right], \quad (56)$$

since in any ordinary algebra $p_\theta\sin\theta = \sin\theta\, p_\theta$. Eq. (56) yields (54) on replacing momenta by operators in the fashion described above. That we should use (56) rather than (55) can be seen from a rule given by Schrödinger[23] for setting up his wave equation in generalized coordinates. Schrödinger first derived his rule by a variational method, but it is tantamount to throwing the Laplacian into generalized coordinates. In spherical coordinates the Laplacian operator is

$$\nabla^2 = \frac{1}{r^2}\frac{\partial}{\partial r}\left(r^2\frac{\partial}{\partial r}...\right) + \frac{1}{r^2\sin\theta}\frac{\partial}{\partial\theta}\left(\sin\theta\frac{\partial}{\partial\theta}...\right) + \frac{1}{r^2\sin^2\theta}\frac{\partial^2}{\partial\phi^2}...,$$

formulae for these 'Mathieu functions'. The problem which we are treating may be regarded as the generalization of the Mathieu problem to three dimensions. In the hypothetical two-dimensional problem the factor in the Langevin Debye formula is $\frac{1}{2}$ rather than $\frac{1}{3}$, and the states for which $j\neq 0$ make a negative rather than positive contribution to the susceptibility, whereas in § 45 we shall see that they do not contribute at all with the three-dimensional dumb-bell model.

[23] E. Schrödinger, *Ann. der Physik*, **79**, 748 (1926).

and we obtain the first two terms of (54) on assuming that $\partial\psi/\partial r = 0$, suggested by the fact that the inter-nuclear distance $r$ is constrained to the constant value $r_0$. This way of treating the constraint is more heuristic than rigorous, as (1) was intended for free particles. A better way of deriving (54) is to use the complete quantum-mechanical representation of molecular motions, taking into account the electronic and vibrational as well as rotational degrees of freedom. An elaborate theory has been developed by Born and Oppenheimer[24] for treating these different degrees of freedom by methods of successive approximations, beginning with the motions of largest energy, viz. the 'electronic' motions relative to fixed nuclei. It finally turns out that the end-over-end motion is given approximately by (54), provided that the molecule is in what band spectroscopists call a Σ state, and provided even then that we neglect 'wobbles' due to nuclear vibrations, to departures of the instantaneous forces exerted on the nuclei by the electrons from the average of these forces, &c. These wobbles are important in the precise spectroscopy of rotational fine structure, but are unimportant for us. By a Σ state we mean a state with no electronic angular momentum about the axis of figure (see § 63 for further details). All common diatomic molecules except NO have Σ states for their normal or 'ground levels'.

*Unperturbed System.* The unperturbed system we can take to be that in the absence of the electric field. When we set $E = 0$ the differential equation (54) becomes that of surface harmonics, and can be shown to have a solution having the necessary properties of single-valuedness, &c., outlined in § 32 only if the constant $8\pi^2 I W/h^2$ has the value $j(j+1)$, where $j$ is an integer, so that [25]

$$W_j = \frac{j(j+1)h^2}{8\pi^2 I}. \tag{57}$$

The corresponding solutions are

$$\psi_{jm}^0 = \sqrt{\frac{(2j+1)(j-m)!}{4\pi(j+m)!}}\, P_j^m(\cos\theta)e^{im\phi}, \tag{58}$$

where

$$P_j^m(x) = \frac{1}{2^j j!}(1-x^2)^{m/2}\frac{d^{m+j}}{dx^{m+j}}(x^2-1)^j. \tag{59}$$

The integer $m$ can take on any integral value in the interval

$$-j \leqslant m \leqslant +j.$$

The functions (59) are called associated Legendre functions, and the ordinary Legendre polynomials are comprised as the special case $m = 0$. The radical is included as a constant factor in (58) to make the solutions

---

[24] Born and Oppenheimer, *Ann. der Physik*, **84**, 457 (1927), or Condon and Morse, *Quantum Mechanics*, p. 153.

[25] We use small letters for the quantum numbers in the present section despite the fact that the latest usage in molecular spectroscopy demands capitals. We do this for two reasons: first, because the recursion formulae, &c. would be rather awkward with capital subscripts and second, because the present 'rotating dumb-bell' is not necessarily to be taken as representing accurately an actual molecule.

normalized to unity. If we use the usual δ-symbol, the normalization
and orthogonality properties can be expressed in the single equation

$$\iint \psi_{jm}^{0*}\psi_{j'm'}^{0}\, d\omega = \delta(jm; j'm').\qquad(60)$$

Here the element $d\omega = \sin\theta\, d\theta\, d\phi$ of solid angle replaces the volume
element $dv$ in equations such as (3). It is not our purpose to show that
(57) and (58) are the characteristic values and characteristic functions
of (54) when $E = 0$, or that they fulfil (60). In fact, it is not our aim
to discuss how accurate solutions are found in the rather limited number
of cases in which the wave equation is exactly soluble, but rather how
approximate solutions are obtained for a perturbed system if the unperturbed one has been solved precisely. The necessary proofs connected
with (57)–(59) will be found in all standard treatises on spherical harmonics, not to mention many recent texts on quantum mechanics,[26]
although it may be mentioned that often the treatments side-step the
task of showing that (57) and (58) (or linear combinations thereof of
the form (61)) are the *only* characteristic values and functions. However, thorough investigation shows that the most general surface harmonic of degree $j$, i.e. the most general solution of (54) for $E = 0$, is
obtained by taking an arbitrary linear combination

$$\psi_j'^0 = \sum_{m=-j}^{+j} a_m \psi_{jm}^0\qquad(61)$$

of the 'tesseral harmonics' (58) over all values of $m$ consistent with
given $j$. Eq. (61) is an illustration of the general theorem (32), and the
arbitrariness (61) is thus to be expected since $m$ is a 'degenerate'
quantum number not appearing in the energy formula (57). The non-
appearance of $m$ in (57) expresses the fact that the spacial orientation
of the axis of rotation is immaterial in the absence of external fields.

The quantum numbers $j$, $m$ have the following physical interpretation. The square of the total angular momentum $P$ of the molecule is
$P^2 \doteq j(j+1)h^2/4\pi^2$. The component angular momentum $p_\phi$ about the
axis of the polar coordinate system is $p_\phi \doteq mh/2\pi$. To prove the first
of these statements we have only to use (57) and to note that the
energy $W$ has the value $P^2/2I$ in terms of angular momentum. To
prove the second statement, take $\hat{f}$ in the fundamental quadrature
(14) to be the operator $h\partial.../2\pi i\partial\phi$ corresponding to $p_\phi$. As by (58),
$\partial\psi_{jm}^0/\partial\phi = im\psi_{jm}^0$, the integral (14) then differs from the normalizing
relation (60) only by a factor $mh/2\pi$, and hence $p_\phi$ is a diagonal matrix
whose elements are $p_\phi(jm; j'm') = \delta(jm; j'm')mh/2\pi$. The energy, of

[26] Cf., for instance, Sommerfeld, *Wellenmechanischer Ergänzungsband*, § 2A.

course, depends on the total angular momentum rather than on its component in a particular direction. The latter component merely determines the spacial orientation. The energy formula (57) is a very familiar one in band-spectroscopy. As $j(j+1) = (j+\frac{1}{2})^2 - \frac{1}{4}$ the energy is, apart from an unimportant additive constant, the same as though we used half-quantum numbers in the energy expression $j^2 h^2 / 8\pi^2 I$ of the old quantum theory.

*Perturbed System.* When $E \neq 0$, it has not been found possible to obtain accurate solutions of (54), and it is necessary to resort to the methods of perturbation theory, which yield the first few degrees of approximation very easily, if we take $\lambda = E$. The first step is to calculate the elements of the perturbative potential $\lambda \mathcal{H}^{(1)} = -\mu E \cos \theta$. In virtue of (14) these are given by

$$\mathcal{H}^{(1)}(jm; j'm') = -\mu \cos \theta(jm; j'm') = -\mu \int \ldots \int \psi_{jm}^{0*} \cos \theta \, \psi_{j'm'}^{0} \, d\omega. \quad (62)$$

Now the associated Legendre functions obey the recursion formula

$$(2j+1)\cos \theta \, P_j^m(\cos \theta) = (j+m)P_{j-1}^m(\cos \theta) + (j-m+1)P_{j+1}^m(\cos \theta),$$

which by (58) is equivalent to the following relation between our normalized wave functions:

$$\cos \theta \, \psi_{jm}^0 = \sqrt{\frac{(j-m)(j+m)}{(2j+1)(2j-1)}} \, \psi_{j-1m}^0 + \sqrt{\frac{(j-m+1)(j+m+1)}{(2j+3)(2j+1)}} \, \psi_{j+1m}^0.$$

The integral (62) is thus reducible to two integrals of the form (60), and so one finds that

$$\cos \theta(jm; j-1\,m) = \cos \theta(j-1\,m; jm) = \sqrt{\frac{j^2 - m^2}{(2j+1)(2j-1)}}$$

$$\cos \theta(jm; j+1\,m) = \cos \theta(j+1\,m; jm) = \sqrt{\frac{(j+1)^2 - m^2}{(2j+3)(2j+1)}} \quad (63)$$

and that all other elements vanish.

The fact that the non-vanishing elements are all diagonal in $m$ shows that the degeneracy difficulty (i.e. appearance of elements diagonal in $j$ but not in $m$) is avoided by taking the axis of quantization identical with that of the applied field. It has thus been allowable to use (58) for our initial wave functions instead of the more general linear combinations (61). As by (62) and (63) $\mathcal{H}^{(1)}$ contains no diagonal elements in our problem, Eq. (24) shows that

$$W^{(1)} = 0. \quad (64)$$

The summation in (26) reduces to but two terms, whose associated frequencies are by (25) and (57) $\nu(j;j\pm1)=h(\mp2j\mp1-1)/8\pi^2I$. By (62) and (63), Eq. (26) yields

$$W_{jm}^{(2)}=\mu^2\sum_{j'=j-1,j+1}\frac{[\cos\theta(jm;j'm)]^2}{h\nu(j;j')}=\frac{4\pi^2I\mu^2}{h^2}\left[\frac{j(j+1)-3m^2}{j(j+1)(2j-1)(2j+3)}\right].$$
(65)

The case $j=0$ requires special consideration. Here the summation reduces to a single term $j'=j+1=1$. There is no term $j'=j-1=-1$ as states of negative $j$ are non-existent, and as one can also verify from (63). Thus

$$W_{00}^{(2)}=\frac{\mu^2[\cos\theta(00;10)]^2}{h\nu(0;1)}=-\frac{4\pi^2I\mu^2}{3h^2}.$$
(66)

*Spectroscopic Stability.* From (63) and the rule (9) for matrix multiplication it follows that the diagonal elements of $\cos^2\theta$ are

$$\cos^2\theta(jm;jm)=\sum_{j'=j-1,j+1}[\cos\theta(jm;j'm)]^2=\frac{2j^2+2j-1-2m^2}{(2j-1)(2j+3)}.$$
(67)

This gives the time average of $\cos^2\theta$ for one particular stationary state. To obtain the average of $\cos^2\theta$ over all the different allowed spacial orientations one must take the mean over the $2j+1$ different allowed values of $m$ ranging from $-j$ to $+j$. Now

$$3\sum_{m=-j}^{+j}m^2=(2j+1)j(j+1).$$
(68)

This formula for the sum of squares of integers is one we shall have frequent occasion to use. It is readily proved inductively as follows. Assume it holds for a given $j$. Then it also holds for $j+1$ as

$$6(j+1)^2+(2j+1)j(j+1)=(2j+3)(j+1)(j+2).$$

To complete the proof we need merely note that (68) is obviously correct for $j=0$ or $j=1$. From (66) and (68) it follows that

$$\overline{\cos^2\theta}=\frac{1}{2j+1}\sum_{m=-j}^{+j}\cos^2\theta(jm;jm)=\tfrac{1}{3},$$
(69)

in agreement with the statements made in § 30 and § 35 that the square of a direction cosine has the same mean value 1/3 in quantum mechanics as in classical theory.

*The Symmetrical Top.*[27] Another, somewhat more general model

---

[27] The unperturbed wave equation for the symmetrical top was first solved by Reiche and Rademacher (*Zeits. f. Physik*, **39**, 444; **41**, 453 (1926)), by Manneback (*Phys. Zeits.* **28**, 72, 1927), and by Kronig and Rabi (*Phys. Rev.* **29**, 262 (1927)), although Dennison had previously obtained formula (70) by matrix methods (*Phys. Rev.* **28**, 318 (1926)). The perturbed levels (72) in an electric field were obtained by R. de L. Kronig (*Proc. Nat. Acad. Sci.* **12**, 608 (1926)), and more especially by C. Manneback, *l.c.*, and Debye and

which has been used to represent molecular rotations is that of the so-called symmetrical top, which is a rigid body having two equal moments of inertia $I$ and a third moment of inertia $C$. As compared to the rigid dumb-bell, the symmetrical top has an extra degree of freedom and moment of inertia, connected with rotation about the axis of symmetry and hence with the moment of inertia $C$. In the absence of external fields the wave equation for this model proves to be rigorously solvable, and has the energy

$$W_j^0 = \frac{h^2}{8\pi^2}\left[\frac{j(j+1)-\Lambda^2}{I}+\frac{\Lambda^2}{C}\right], \tag{70}$$

where $\Lambda$ is a quantum number specifying the angular momentum about the axis of symmetry. Perturbation calculations, which we omit, show that the change in energy produced by a field $E$ is given by

$$EW^{(1)}+E^2W^{(2)}+\ldots$$

with

$$W_{jm}^{(1)} = -\frac{\mu m\Lambda}{j(j+1)}, \tag{71}$$

$$W_{jm}^{(2)'} = \frac{4\pi^2 I\mu^2}{h^2}\left[\frac{(j^2-m^2)(j^2-\Lambda^2)}{j^3(2j-1)(2j+1)} - \frac{[(j+1)^2-m^2][(j+1)^2-\Lambda^2]}{(j+1)^3(2j+1)(2j+3)}\right], \tag{72}$$

under the supposition, of course, that the dipole moment coincides in direction with the axis of symmetry of the top.

The symmetrical top model has two applications to actual molecules. It can be shown [24] to represent (apart from an unimportant additive constant independent of $j$, $m$) the rotational energy of a diatomic molecule in $\Pi, \Delta, \Phi, \ldots$ electronic states corresponding to $\Lambda = 1, 2, 3,\ldots$ . The $\Sigma$ states which can be represented by the dumb-bell model are comprised as the special case $\Lambda = 0$, where (70), (71), (72) reduce to (57), (64), (65). In applying the symmetrical top to diatomic molecules, the term $\Lambda^2/C$ of (70) must be dropped, as it is included in the internal or electronic energy of the molecule. This term would, in fact, be meaningless, as the moment of inertia of a diatomic molecule about its axis of figure is virtually nil, being due entirely to the small electronic masses, and is not constant in time, as the electrons are continually moving. A second and simpler application of the symmetrical top model is to represent the rotational motion of a non-collinear polyatomic molecule with two equal moments of inertia, i.e. molecules such as $NH_3$, &c. In this case the quantum number $\Lambda$ is associated with a rotation of the whole molecule about the axis of symmetry, whereas in the previous

Manneback (*Nature*, **119**, 83 (1927)), who considered Eqs. (71)–(72) explicitly in connexion with the Stark effect as well as implicitly in connexion with dielectric constants.

application it was only an 'electronic quantum number' which determined the electronic level rather than the position within the band.
A polyatomic molecule has two rotational quantum numbers $j$, $\Lambda$ which
can take on arbitrary integral values subject only to the restriction
$|\Lambda| < j$, and hence it possesses exceedingly complicated band-spectra.

*Stark Effect.* Eqs. (64) and (71) reveal an important distinction:
namely, that there is no first-order Stark effect for an ordinary un-
excited diatomic molecule in a $\Sigma$ state, but that there is such an effect
for a diatomic molecule not in a $\Sigma$ state, or for a polyatomic molecule.[28]
Unfortunately, adequate measurements on the Stark effect, i.e. displacements of spectral frequencies in electric fields, are wanting in
molecular spectra, but it would be exceedingly gratifying if such
measurements could be made, as we would then be able to verify the
theoretical predictions of equations such as (64), (65), (71), (72) on the
energies of *individual* stationary states in electric fields, not necessarily
the electronic ground-levels, whereas measurements of dielectric constants test only the statistical average of the energies of the various
component rotational states of the ground-level only. In other words,
Stark-effect measurements will isolate individual values of the quantum
numbers $j$, $m$, whereas susceptibility determinations will not. The
technique of Stark-effect observations in molecular spectra is, of course,
a difficult one. The second-order Stark effect, which is the only type
found in $\Sigma$ levels, is so very small in any ordinary field strength that
it would be hard to measure with any precision, and even the first-order
effect in other levels or in polyatomic molecules is very minute except
for the first few lines of a band, inasmuch as the rotational quantum
number $j$ appears in the denominator of (71). Hence, incidentally,
experiments on the electric analogue of the Stern-Gerlach effect[29] will
produce only very small deflexions in molecules. It must be mentioned
that besides the second-order term (65) or (72) due to the permanent
dipoles, there is also another second-order term due to the induced
polarization, not included in our simple models. Experiments on the
quadratic Stark effect would measure only the sum of the two terms.
However, if the molecule should happen to be nearly isotropic optically,

---

[28] The first-order effect in such molecules should, however, appear only when the energy
due to the external electric field is large compared to the so-called '$\Lambda$-type doubling'.
See § 70. This restriction does not appear in Eq. (71), as the model is too simple to take
account of the $\Lambda$-doubling phenomenon. If $h\Delta\nu(j)$ denote the width of the $\Lambda$-doublet,
the true formula is $\pm(\frac{1}{4}h^2\nu\Delta^2 + E^2 W^{(1)2})^{\frac{1}{2}}$ instead of (71), where $W^{(1)}$ is defined by (71);
cf. W. G. Penney, *Phil. Mag.*, **11**, 602 (1931).

[29] For references to such experiments see note 3, Chap. V.

the induced portion would depend but little on $m$, and determinations of the relative in distinction from absolute displacements of the Stark effect components should then furnish a test of (65) or (72).

## 38. The Electron Spin

The writer begins this section with considerable trepidation, as the theory of the spin is neither particularly simple nor particularly rigorous. The concept that an electron has an internal degree of freedom about which it is free to spin has been extraordinarily fruitful in clarifying the analysis of spectra. This idea is due primarily to Uhlenbeck and Goudsmit,[30] although the spin has been proposed in other connexions at earlier dates by Compton, Kennard,[31] and others. The theory of the electron spin may be presented in two ways, viz. by means of what we shall call a semi-mechanical model or by means of Dirac's 'quantum theory of the electron'.

In the semi-mechanical model, matrix expressions for the spin angular momentum are written down by analogy with the orbital angular momentum matrices, with certain postulates regarding the occurrence of a half-quantum of spin per electron which will be explained below. It is further assumed that the ratio of spin magnetic moment $M_s$ to spin angular momentum $P_s$ has twice the classical value $-e/2mc$ for the ratio of orbital magnetic moment to orbital angular momentum, so that

$$\frac{M_s}{P_s} = -\frac{e}{mc}. \tag{73}$$

The assumption (73) is made to explain the fact that in experiments on rotation by magnetization (the Einstein-Richardson-de-Haas effect) as well as on the converse magnetization by rotation (Barnett effect), the ratio of magnetic moment to angular momentum has approximately the value (73) instead of the classical orbital value.[32] The anomalous ratio (73) for the spin is also required by the anomalous Zeeman effect, as will be seen more fully in § 42. Landé[33] found that his celebrated $g$-formula could be explained, except for certain characteristic modifications resulting from the new quantum mechanics not understood

[30] Uhlenbeck and Goudsmit, *Die Naturwissenschaften*, **13**, 953 (1925); *Nature*, **117**, 264 (1926).

[31] A. H. Compton, *J. Franklin Institute*, **192**, 145 (1921); E. H. Kennard, *Phys. Rev.* **19**, 420 (1922) (abstract). Kennard's note is often overlooked; in it the spin was proposed explicitly in connexion with the gyromagnetic anomaly.

[32] For description of these gyromagnetic experiments, and references, see Stoner, *Magnetism and Atomic Structure*, p. 184.

[33] E. Landé, *Zeits. f. Physik*, **15**, 189 (1923) or Back and Landé, *Zeemaneffekt und Multiplettstruktur der Spektrallinien*, pp. 43, 79.

prior to 1926, by assuming that the atom contained a rather mysterious 'atom-core' (*Atomrumpf*) whose ratio of magnetic moment to angular momentum has the value (73). This mystical 'atom-core' now turns out in reality to be the spin.

Besides the arbitrary character of its postulates, the semi-mechanical model has the drawback that it is able to describe only to a first approximation (i.e. through terms of the order $1/c^2$) the internal magnetic forces of the atom. That is to say, it does not furnish an adequate dynamics of the interaction of the spins with each other and with orbital forces. Practically, this is not a serious handicap, as the terms of higher order $1/c^4$ are entirely too small to be of any consequence in the optical region, although they are large enough to be observable in the case of X-ray doublets in heavy atoms. The interaction of the spin with external magnetic fields, which is our particular concern, is handled perfectly well by the semi-mechanical model. However, an approximate theory of internal magnetic forces is never as satisfying logically as an exact theory, and because these forces are only approximately described, the Hamiltonian function used in the semi-mechanical model does not behave properly under a Lorentz transformation, and so does not meet the requirements of the special theory of relativity.

It is this need of relativity invariance which led Dirac to the discovery of his brilliant 'quantum theory of the electron'.[34] In the case of a system with one electron, he boldly replaced the single second-order Schrödinger wave equation by four simultaneous first-order wave equations, involving the use of four wave functions. In a system with $f$ electrons there would be $4f$ wave functions, but the extension of Dirac's theory to many electron systems is at present in a rather unsettled state, and this is one reason we do not incorporate it in the present volume. Previously to Dirac, Pauli had shown that the existence of two wave functions per electron, and of two corresponding simultaneous second-order equations, was necessary in order to interpret in wave language the spin matrices of the semi-mechanical model. One wave function corresponds in a certain sense to the alinement of spin parallel to the axis of quantization, and the other to it anti-parallel. Four wave functions are twice too many, and in order to vest them with a physical interpretation it seems necessary to interpret certain states as repre-

[34] P. A. M. Dirac, *Proc. Roy. Soc.* **117**A, 610; **118**A, 351 (1928); or *The Principles of Quantum Mechanics*, Chap. XIII. The explicit calculation of the susceptibility of an atom with one valence electron by means of Dirac's four simultaneous equations is given by Sommerfeld in the report of the 1930 Solvay Congress. The results are the same as with the semi-mechanical model except for terms too small to be observable.

senting an electron of negative mass. If Dirac's quartet of wave functions were separable into two non-combining pairs, i.e. into pairs such that integrals of the form (14) always vanish if the two wave functions belong to different pairs, the difficulty would not be so serious. Actually the two pairs of wave functions do 'combine', so that in the ordinary quantum-mechanical interpretation of wave functions there is a non-vanishing probability of the mass of the electron changing sign, an obvious absurdity. This difficulty is probably the most serious flaw in the logical framework of present-day quantum mechanics,[35] and very likely will not be cleared up until the long-awaited theory is evolved which explains the differences in mass of the electron and proton. However, Dirac's theory is marvellously successful in explaining all spin phenomena. After setting up his four first-order equations, Dirac magically extracts all the properties of the spin, such as the anomalous ratio (73). His equations have the necessary relativity invariance, and give the internal magnetic interactions exactly rather than approximately. They yield spin doublets of exactly the same width as Sommerfeld's relativity doublets in the old quantum theory, thus yielding one of the most amazing fortuitous coincidences in the history of physics. The previous semi-mechanical model gave this coincidence only to terms of the order $1/c^2$ inclusive.

To many readers it will doubtless appear a step backwards that we shall dismiss Dirac's theory after this cursory qualitative discussion, and present the quantitative aspects of the spin entirely with the aid of the older semi-mechanical model. However, besides the difficulty of the physical interpretation of the superfluous pair of wave functions, Dirac's theory, with its four simultaneous equations, has necessarily a certain amount of mathematical complexity, and the semi-mechanical model is easier to visualize—more 'anschaulich' as the Germans say. This property makes results on susceptibilities easier to remember and interpret, and perhaps less liable to computational errors if the semi-mechanical model is used. There is no loss of rigour, as it can be shown that Dirac's theory yields the same matrices for the spin energy in an external magnetic field as the previous Uhlenbeck-Goudsmit model. We can thus regard Dirac's theory as the most refined way of deriving the

---

[35] Dirac (*Proc. Roy. Soc.* **126**A, 360 (1930)) has made the bold but interesting suggestion that the states with negative mass may be nearly 'all full', as the Pauli exclusion principle allows each state to occur only once. What we interpret as ordinary electric neutrality is then really a maximum, infinite charge density of electrons with negative mass. and a proton is a vacancy or 'hole' in the infinity of negative states. This idea, however, encounters many serious difficulties, and its ultimate significance is uncertain.

matrix elements of the spin, which in the semi-mechanical model are taken as sheer postulates. Our omission of derivation of the spin matrix elements by Dirac's method is in accord with our policy of not attempting to solve dynamical problems exactly, but only to show how the perturbed energy can be approximately found once the matrix elements of the perturbative potential are known. One reason that we use the semi-mechanical model is that while Dirac's quantum theory of the electron is discussed in most recent texts on quantum mechanics, Heisenberg and Jordan's very compact and elegant treatment of the anomalous Zeeman effect by means of the pure-matrix theory is too generally ignored.

We shall present the semi-mechanical model in the pure matrix language, without giving the allied wave functions, as the latter do not help in setting up the appropriate secular equations (35). The first attempt at finding wave functions associated with the spin was made by Darwin.[36] In natural analogy with orbital motions he supposed that there was an azimuthal rotational coordinate $\phi_s$ associated with precession of the spin axis. The wave function would then contain a factor $e^{im_s\phi_s}$, where $m_s$ is a quantum number specifying the axial component of spin angular momentum. Unfortunately this function then does not have the necessary property of single-valuedness, as for a single electron $m_s$ has the values $\pm\frac{1}{2}$ instead of being an integer, and $e^{\frac{1}{2}i(\phi_s+2\pi)} \neq e^{\frac{1}{2}i\phi_s}$. Because of this difficulty we speak of the Uhlenbeck-Goudsmit model as 'semi-mechanical' rather than 'mechanical'. As a matter of fact Darwin ingeniously found that spin matrix elements could be calculated by means of the fundamental quadrature (14) even with multiple-valued wave functions, but this appears a little fortuitous. Pauli[37] later showed that the difficulty of multiple-valuedness could be overcome by taking the arguments of the wave functions to be the axial component $s_z$ of spin angular momentum instead of a rotational coordinate. The Dirac-Jordan transformation theory indeed permits us to use any set of coordinates and momenta as arguments of the wave function, which is a special case of a 'probability amplitude'. Now $s_z$ has only the two discrete characteristic values $\pm\frac{1}{2}(h/2\pi)$, whereas $\phi_s$ assumes a continuous range of values. A function whose argument only assumes two values is equivalent to a pair of functions, so Pauli's scheme involves two wave functions per electron. For definition of the operators corresponding to spin angular momenta, which cannot be expressed as

[36] C. G. Darwin, *Proc. Roy. Soc.* **115**A, 1 (1927).
[37] W. Pauli, Jr., *Zeits. f. Physik*, **43**, 601 (1927).

differentiations, and for modification of the fundamental quadrature (14) to include summation over the discrete spin characteristic values as well as integration over the continuous orbital coordinates, the reader is referred to Pauli's paper [37] and closely allied work by Darwin.[38] The treatment of the anomalous Zeeman effect either by the Pauli operators or by Darwin's multiple-valued wave functions is, of course, only superficially different from that with matrices (§ 42). All methods inevitably lead to the same secular equation.

## 39. Orbital and Spin Angular Momentum Matrices

First let us consider the matrix elements of the orbital angular momentum of a single electron in a central field. Although we are now aiming to study the spin, these orbital elements will be useful for purposes of comparison. It is well known that in a central field the wave functions of a single electron, neglecting spin, are

$$\psi_{nlm} = R_{nl}(r) . \sqrt{\frac{(2l+1)(l-m_l)!}{4\pi(l+m_l)!}} \, P_l^{m_l}(\cos\theta)e^{im_l\phi}, \tag{74}$$

where $P_l^{m_l}$ is an associated Legendre function (59), and where $R$ is a radial wave function, which we suppose normalized separately to unity, so that $\int_0^\infty |R_{nl}|^2 r^2 \, dr = 1$. The factors involving $\theta$, $\phi$ in (74) are the same as in (58), and the present calculations of angular momentum matrices are similar to those for the rigid rotator of § 37, except that the notation $l, m_l$ rather than $j, m$ is now used because the angular momentum is purely orbital and electronic. The quantum number $l$ is the familiar azimuthal quantum number having the values 0, 1, 2,... for $s$, $p$, $d$,... electronic states. The maximum value of $l$ is $n-1$, where $n$ is the principal quantum number. The non-vanishing matrix elements of the $x$, $y$, and $z$ components of orbital angular momentum are

$$
\begin{aligned}
(l_x\pm il_y)(nlm_l\pm1; nlm_l) &= [l(l+1)-m_l(m_l\pm1)]^{\frac{1}{2}}, \\
l_z(nlm_l; nlm_l) &= m_l.
\end{aligned} \tag{75}
$$

Here and throughout the balance of the volume we measure angular momentum in multiples of the quantum unit $h/2\pi$, as this saves continually writing $h/2\pi$ on the right-hand side of equations such as (75). Also we give the $x$ and $y$ components in the $x\pm iy$ combination, as this makes the formulae more compact and simpler. To prove the relations (75) we take in turn $f$ in the fundamental quadrature (14) to be one of

[38] C. G. Darwin, *Proc. Roy. Soc.* **116A**, 227 (1927).

the following operators:

$$\frac{1}{i}\left[\left(y\frac{\partial}{\partial z}-z\frac{\partial}{\partial y}\right)\pm i\left(z\frac{\partial}{\partial x}-x\frac{\partial}{\partial z}\right)\right]=\frac{1}{i}e^{\pm i\phi}\left[\pm i\frac{\partial}{\partial\theta}-\cot\theta\frac{\partial}{\partial\phi}\right],$$

$$\frac{1}{i}\left[x\frac{\partial}{\partial y}-y\frac{\partial}{\partial x}\right]=\frac{1}{i}\frac{\partial}{\partial\phi}. \tag{76}$$

The operator on the second line is, for instance, that corresponding to the $z$ component of angular momentum, since $l_z$ has the value $xp_y-yp_x$ in terms of the components $p_x$, $p_y$, $p_z$ of linear momentum, and since the operator to be identified with $p_z$ is $h\partial../2\pi i\partial z$, &c. The factor $h/2\pi$ can be dropped because of our choice of units. In (76) we have also stated the form which the operators take when transformed in an elementary way to polar coordinates. The integrals are readily evaluated if we use the relations [39]

$$e^{\pm i\phi}\left[\pm i\frac{\partial}{\partial\theta}-\cot\theta\frac{\partial}{\partial\phi}\right]P_l^{m_l}(\cos\theta)e^{im_l\phi}$$

$$=-\frac{i(l\mp m_l)[l-(m_l\pm 1)]!}{(l-m_l)!}P_l^{m_l\pm 1}(\cos\theta)e^{i(m_l\pm 1)\phi},$$

$$\frac{\partial}{\partial\phi}P_l^{m_l}(\cos\theta)e^{im_l\phi}=im_l P_l^{m_l}(\cos\theta)e^{im_l\phi}$$

obeyed by the associated Legendre functions, as then the integrals are reducible to linear combinations of integrals of the type form (60). From (75) one, of course, finds that

$$l^2(nlm_l;nlm_l)=\sum_{m_l'=m_l\pm 1}\left[|l_x(nlm_l;nlm_l')|^2+|l_y(nlm_l;nlm_l')|^2\right]+[l_z(nlm_l;nlm_l)]^2$$

$$=l(l+1), \tag{77}$$

in agreement with the value of the square of the angular momentum given in § 37.

*Angular Momentum Matrices for Spins Subject to Individual Space Quantization.* Let us hypothetically imagine that the spins are subject to no forces whatsoever from within the atom. If now an external magnetic field is applied, it will exert the only forces on the spin axes, which will hence be quantized individually relative to the direction of this field. By analogy with the orbital case, the matrix for each spin

[39] The second relation is trivial and the first relation with the upper sign is readily seen to be an identity when one makes the substitution (59). The first relation with the lower sign is perhaps most readily established inductively, as by differentiating the relation with respect to $x=\cos\theta$ and using (59), one can verify that if the relation is true for any given $m_l$ it holds also for $m_l$ one unit larger. To complete the proof one has only then to note that the formula is true for the easy case $m_l=-j+1$. Eqs. (75) follow when we express the formulae in terms of the normalized $\psi$'s instead of the $P$'s, as on p. 151.

angular momentum can be assumed to be of the form (75), except that $l$, $m_l$ are replaced by quantum numbers $s$, $m_s$ determining the resultant spin angular momentum of an individual electron and the axial component thereof. It is further supposed that for each individual electron $s = \frac{1}{2}$, so that $m_s$, which can range from $-s$ to $+s$, has only the two values $\pm\frac{1}{2}$. This is demanded by the fact that two deflexions are found experimentally in the Stern-Gerlach effect for hydrogen atoms or alkali atoms,[40] which, of course, resemble hydrogen in having only one valence electron. All such atoms are normally in $S$ states, so that the magnetic moment is entirely due to spin and must have two positions of quantization to give two deflexions. The result $s = \frac{1}{2}$ is also demanded by the fact that the alkalis have a doublet multiplet-structure. The doublet structure requires two orientations of the spin, here relative to internal rather than external fields.

By substituting $s$, $m_s$ for $l$, $m_l$ in (75) and further setting $s = \frac{1}{2}$, $m_s = \pm\frac{1}{2}$ we see that with individual quantization, the spin angular momentum matrices of any electron are [41]

$$(s_x - i s_y)(-\tfrac{1}{2}; \tfrac{1}{2}) = (s_x + i s_y)(\tfrac{1}{2}; -\tfrac{1}{2}) = 1,$$
$$s_z(\tfrac{1}{2}; \tfrac{1}{2}) = -s_z(-\tfrac{1}{2}; -\tfrac{1}{2}) = \tfrac{1}{2}. \tag{78}$$

We here, for brevity, write in only the indices $m_s$, $m_s'$ in which the matrices are not diagonal. It is to be clearly understood that experimentally it is impossible to achieve a magnetic field so extremely powerful that the 'internal forces' exerted on the spin can be neglected in comparison therewith, except for the valence electrons of light atoms in unusually strong fields producing a Paschen-Back effect. Hence the case represented by (78) is an idealized one, but it is nevertheless useful

---

[40] Phipps and Taylor, *Phys. Rev.* **29**, 309 (1927); Wrode, *Zeits. f. Physik*, **41**, 569 (1927), and references to earlier literature. The old quantum theory would give a third, undeflected beam contrary to experiment, unless one ruled out $m_l = 0$ as sometimes proposed. For in the old theory the lowest state of hydrogen had $l = 1$, making $m_l = -1, 0, +1$, as compared to the new $m_l + 2m_s = 2m_s = \pm 1$.

[41] Eqs. (78) are really the starting point of the Pauli operator theory.[37] From Eqs. (78) one can verify the celebrated 'Vertauschung' relations

$$s_x s_y - s_y s_x = i s_z, \; s_y s_z - s_z s_y = i s_x, \; s_z s_x - s_x s_z = i s_y$$

for the matrices representing the various components of spin angular momentum. Analogous formulae for $l$ can be demonstrated from (75) or more elegantly, directly from the quantum conditions (12) (cf. Dirac, *The Principles of Quantum Mechanics*, p. 138). These relations measuring the non-commutativeness of the multiplication of various components of **s** or of **l** are very important for the establishment of general theorems involving angular momentum, but we shall not have particular occasion to use them. Angular momenta of different electrons, also the spin and orbital angular momenta of the same electron are commutative, so that $s_{x_i} s_{y_j} - s_{y_j} s_{x_i} = l_{x_i} l_{y_j} - l_{y_j} l_{x_i} = 0 \, (i \neq j)$, $s_{x_i} l_{y_j} - l_{y_j} s_{x_i} = 0$ including $j = i$.

M

in exhibiting the simplest form of the spin matrices, and permits the most elementary formulation of the Pauli exclusion principle (viz. that no two electrons have the same $n$, $l$, $m_l$, $m_s$). The appearance of half-quantum numbers, of course, shows a fundamental difference as compared to orbital motions, but all the necessary so-called boundary conditions on the matrices (zero probability of transition to non-existent states) are fulfilled quite as well with half as with whole integers. In fact, in the early days of quantum mechanics, Born, Heisenberg, and Jordan [42] could not discriminate between whether half or whole quantum numbers should appear. (Their investigations demanded unit spacing of the values of $m_s$ from $-s$ to $+s$. This is possible if, and only if, $s$ is an integer or half-integer.)

## 40. Russell-Saunders Coupling, Spectroscopic Notation, &c.

In the previous section we have neglected internal forces, but actually there are powerful forces of this character tending to couple together the various angular momentum vectors of the atom. The simplest assumption is that the energy of interaction between any two vectors is proportional to the cosine of the angle included between them or, what is equivalent, to their scalar product. The Hamiltonian function will then contain terms of the form

$$a_{ik}\mathbf{l}_i\cdot\mathbf{s}_k, \qquad b_{ik}\mathbf{l}_i\cdot\mathbf{l}_k, \qquad c_{ik}\mathbf{s}_i\cdot\mathbf{s}_k, \qquad (i,k=1,...,\eta), \qquad \langle 79\rangle$$

where $\eta$ is the number of electrons in the atom. Throughout the rest of the volume all expressions in bold-face type are to be construed as vector matrices, i.e. vectors of which each component is a matrix rather than an ordinary number. The proportionality constants $a_{ik}$, $b_{ik}$, $c_{ik}$ will in general be functions of all quantum numbers (such as, for instance, $n$, $l$) other than those quantizing the relative orientations of the vectors involved. The expression $a_{ik}\mathbf{l}_i\cdot\mathbf{s}_k$, for instance, means the energy associated with the force which the orbital angular momentum of the $i$th exerts on the spin of the $k$th electron. Ordinarily it turns out that $|a_{ii}|\gg|a_{ik}|$, $k\neq i$, meaning that the orbital angular momentum of a given electron interacts more strongly with its own than with other spins. It can be shown that [43]

$$a_{ii}=\frac{h^2 Z_{\text{eff}}e^2}{8\pi^2 m^2 c^2}\overline{\frac{1}{r^3}}, \qquad (80)$$

[42] Born, Heisenberg, and Jordan, *Zeits. f. Physik*, **35**, 600 (1926). They have since been able to prove that the orbital $m_l$ must be a whole integer by matrix methods without using the wave functions (74). See *Elementare Atommechanik*, p. 162.

[43] L. H. Thomas, *Nature*, **117**, 514 (1926); *Phil. Mag.* **3**, 1 (1927); J. Frenkel, *Zeits. f. Physik*, **37**, 243 (1926). Formula (80), which is of course also yielded by Dirac's 'Quan-

where $r$ is the distance of the electron from the nucleus, provided the given electron is not so highly perturbed by other electrons but that it may be regarded as moving in a Coulomb field. Although the validity of the cosine law ⟨79⟩ is only approximate, and can be justified theoretically only with the aid of many simplifying assumptions, the departures from ⟨79⟩ need not cause us concern, as the general different types of quantization which we delineate by means of ⟨79⟩ are significant even when ⟨79⟩ is not strictly applicable. Actually, the coupling of the $l$ vectors often departs widely from the cosine form given in the second term of ⟨79⟩. Also our arguments are not affected by the fact, to be discussed in § 76, that the constants $c_{ik}$ coupling the various spin vectors with each other are due primarily not to magnetic forces but to the Heisenberg exchange effect.

*Russell-Saunders Coupling.*[44] If the constants $a$, $b$, $c$ in ⟨79⟩ are all of the same order of magnitude, the problem of the energy and nature of the atomic motion becomes one of extreme complexity. Very often, however, the factors $a_{ik}$ (including $i = k$) are small compared to the factors $b_{ik}$, or to the factors $c_{ik}$, or both. In other words, often the interaction between spin and orbital angular momenta is small compared to the interaction of orbital angular momenta among themselves, or else of the spins among themselves. Then the spins form a resultant **S**, and similarly the orbital angular momenta form a resultant **L**. If no external field is applied, the vectors **S** and **L** are compounded together to form a resultant **J**. The corresponding quantum number $J$ can assume the range of values

$$J = |L-S|, \qquad |L-S+1|,..., \qquad L+S-1, \qquad L+S. \qquad (81)$$

The number $J$ measures the resultant spin plus orbital angular momentum of the atom. Its projection along the axis of quantization is the 'magnetic quantum number' $M$, which can have the values

$$M = -J, \qquad -J+1,..., \qquad J-1, \qquad J \qquad (82)$$

and which determines the component of total angular momentum in the direction of the axis of quantization, which we take as the $z$ direction. The present case of Russell-Saunders quantization is illustrated in (b) of Fig. 6. All such attempts at geometrical pictures should not,

---

tum Theory of the Electron' with appropriate approximations, differs by a factor 2 from what one would expect from elementary, over-simplified calculations.

[44] For more complete discussion of the various coupling possibilities in this so-called 'vector model of the atom', and comparison with experimental spectroscopy, see Pauling and Goudsmit, *The Structure of Line Spectra*. Russell and Saunders first suggested their type of coupling in *Astrophysical Journal*, **61**, 38 (1925).

however, be taken too seriously, as in quantum mechanics angular momentum vectors are matrices rather than ordinary geometrical magnitudes. We shall frequently use rather loosely geometrical terms which must not be taken too literally, and which aim merely to indicate heuristically the analogues in classical mechanics. Thus we may say in a certain sense that the maximum and minimum values of $J$ in (81) correspond respectively to $S$ and $L$ being mutually parallel and anti-parallel, and the maximum and minimum values of $M$ in (82) to $J$ being parallel and anti-parallel to the axis of quantization. However, the

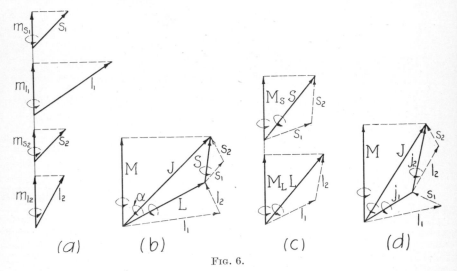

FIG. 6.

inadequacy of this geometrical interpretation is shown by the fact that the matrices for both **L** and **S** always contain non-vanishing components perpendicular to **J**.[45] Also, the matrix elements for $J_x^2$ and $J_y^2$ never vanish for any state, indicating that there are always components of **J** perpendicular to the axis of quantization, so that the alinement is never perfectly parallel or anti-parallel relative to this axis. Whenever we use terms such as '**S** and **L** form a quantized resultant **J**', or that '**J** measures the total angular momentum', this does not mean that the resultant angular momentum is equal numerically to the inner quantum

[45] This is a consequence of the fact that in Eq. (88) the elements $(JM; J+1M)$ and $(JM; J-1M)$ never vanish simultaneously, except in the trivial case that $S$ or $L$ is zero. These elements are seen by the correspondence principle (§ 41) to arise from the part of **S** or **L** which is perpendicular to **J**, inasmuch as non-diagonal elements in $J$ correspond to classical trigonometric terms involving the frequency $\omega_j$ of precession about **J** (cf. Eq. 95). This frequency clearly appears only in the perpendicular in distinction from parallel components. (The first and second terms of (93) or (95) embody respectively the parallel and perpendicular components.)

number $J$. Instead, the square of the total angular momentum is a diagonal matrix of elements $J(J+1)$ rather than $J^2$, with analogous relations for $S$ and $L$, so that

$$L^2 \doteq L(L+1), \qquad S^2 \doteq S(S+1), \qquad J^2 \doteq J(J+1). \qquad (83)$$

On the other hand, the projection of the total angular momentum $\mathbf{J}$ in the direction of the axis of quantization is a diagonal matrix of elements $M$ rather than $[M(M+1)]^{\frac{1}{2}}$. This may seem rather paradoxical, but the reason for the difference as compared with (83) is that we are dealing with a component of angular momentum in a single direction rather than with the sum of squares of three Cartesian components.

The maximum values of $L$, $S$ are, of course, $\sum l_i$ and $\sum s_i = \frac{1}{2}\eta$, where $\eta$ is the number of electrons. The minimum values are the smallest expressions of the form $\sum \pm l_i$ or $\sum \pm s_i$ obtainable with any choice of sign: e.g. $L_{\min} = |l_1 - l_2|$ for a system with only two electrons, while more generally $S_{\min} = 0$ or $\frac{1}{2}$, depending on whether $\eta$ is even or odd.[46] The quantum numbers $S$, $J$, and $M$ are half-integral or integral according as the number of electrons is odd or even, whereas $L$ is always integral. For given $S$ and $L$, the various values of $J$ give the various components of a multiplet level. For example, the two upper levels involved in the $D$ lines of sodium both have $L = 1$, $S = \frac{1}{2}$, but one has $J = \frac{1}{2}$, the other $J = \frac{3}{2}$, and their difference in energy is such as to make the two $D$ lines differ by 6 Ångströms. By (81) the number of multiplet components is $2S+1$ if $L \geqslant S$, or $2L+1$ if $L \leqslant S$. The multiplicity of a spectral system is by definition $2S+1$. The full multiplicity is not developed in levels for which $L < S$. For instance, if $S = 2$, $L = 1$, the multiplet level has only three components, but is still spoken of as a 'quintet level'. In Russell-Saunders coupling the multiplets conform approximately to a cosine law of the form

$$\mathcal{H}^0 = \mathcal{H}^{00} + A\mathbf{L}\cdot\mathbf{S}, \qquad \langle 84 \rangle$$

so that $\qquad W_J^0 = W^{00} + \frac{1}{2}A[J(J+1) - L(L+1) - S(S+1)]. \qquad (84\,\mathrm{a})$

Here $\mathcal{H}^{00}$ denotes the part of the Hamiltonian function which is independent of the coupling between $L$ and $S$ and which hence does not involve $J$. Eq. (84a) has been obtained from $\langle 84 \rangle$ by using the vector addition relation $\qquad \mathbf{J}^2 = (\mathbf{L}+\mathbf{S})^2 = \mathbf{L}^2 + \mathbf{S}^2 + 2\mathbf{L}\cdot\mathbf{S} \qquad \langle 85 \rangle$

---

[46] In case there are 'equivalent' electrons, i.e. electrons with identical $n$, $l$, not all combinations of $L$ and $S$ predicted by this rule are compatible with the Pauli exclusion principle. For instance, with two equivalent $p$ electrons ($l_1 = l_2 = 1$) this rule gives $L = 0, 1, 2$; $S = 0, 1$, i.e. ${}^1S$, ${}^3S$, ${}^1P$, ${}^3P$, ${}^1D$, ${}^3D$, but out of these six terms only the three ${}^1S$, ${}^3P$, ${}^1D$ are in accord with the Pauli principle. For details on which states must be ruled out see Pauling and Goudsmit, *l.c.*,[44] or Hund, *Linienspectra*, p. 118.

together with (83). It can be shown that $\mathbf{S}$ and $\mathbf{L}$ 'commute' in multiplication, so that in $\langle 85 \rangle$ it has been unnecessary to distinguish between $\mathbf{S} \cdot \mathbf{L}$ and $\mathbf{L} \cdot \mathbf{S}$. The constant factor $A$ is not the same as that $a_{ii}$ given in (80) for a single electron, but can often be calculated in terms of the $a_{ii}$ for the individual electrons by methods developed by Goudsmit.[47] A multiplet is called 'regular' or 'inverted' according as $A > 0$ or $A < 0$.

*Spectroscopic Notation.* In the now commonly accepted notation due primarily to Russell and Saunders,[48] a spectral term is indicated by a symbol such as

$$1s^2 \, 2s^2 \, 2p^6 \, 3p \, 6d \; {}^3F_2. \tag{86}$$

The small letters give the azimuthal quantum numbers of the individual electrons, and the numbers preceding them their principal quantum numbers. The superscripts following each small letter give the number of electrons of each type. Thus in (86) there are two electrons having $n = 1, l = 0$, two having $n = 2, l = 0$, six having $n = 2, l = 1$, one having $n = 3, l = 1$, and one having $n = 6, l = 2$. Each electron, of course, has a spin $s = \frac{1}{2}$, which it is unnecessary to record in the notation. The value of the capital letter gives the value of $L$, with the usual understanding that $S, P, D, F, G,...$ mean respectively $L = 0, 1, 2, 3, 4,....$ The subscript attached to the capital letter is the value of $J$, and thus fixes the multiplet component. The superscript preceding this letter is the multiplicity $2S+1$, and has the values $1, 2, 3, 4...$ for singlet, doublet, triplet, quartet... terms. Very often the small letters specifying the quantum numbers of the individual electrons are omitted, in fact almost invariably those of electrons in closed shells. Otherwise the notation would be too cumbersome for a heavy atom such as uranium. Thus in the alkaline earths one gives only the quantum numbers of the two valence electrons. The normal state of magnesium, for instance, may be written as $3s^2 \, {}^1S$, and a singlet state in which one electron is excited to a $3p$ level as $3s \, 3p \, {}^1P$, omitting ten electrons in closed shells which were written out explicitly in (86). Since $L = l$ when the second valence electron remains in its normal $s$ state, it is not really even necessary in these examples to list the individual quantum numbers of the valence electrons, so that the terms given in the preceding sentence are usually written as merely $3 \, {}^1S, \, 3 \, {}^1P$ (also as $1 \, {}^1S, \, 2 \, {}^1P$ or even $1 \, {}^1S, \, 1 \, {}^1P$ as, unfortunately, there is at present considerable diversity in usage in the choice of origin for the so-called ordinal number). When both valence electrons are excited, as in (86), this is sometimes indicated by attaching

[47] S. Goudsmit, *Phys. Rev.* **31**, 946 (1928).

[48] For complete details on approved spectroscopic nomenclature see report of an informal committee on notation in *Phys. Rev.* **33**, 900 (1929).

a prime instead of writing out the quantum numbers of the two individual electrons.

It is to be emphasized that the above notation is intended only for Russell-Saunders coupling. Spectra possessing this type of coupling are sometimes termed 'normal multiplet structures', and fortunately they are characteristic of the simpler types of spectra, as, for instance, the alkalis, alkaline earths, and earths, except perhaps for complicated cases in which more than one electron is excited. Russell-Saunders coupling is also the rule in the iron and rare earth groups, so that it is the only type of quantization which we need consider for our magnetic work. Two commonplace illustrations of Russell-Saunders coupling are atoms with one valence electron, where $L$, $S$ are identical with $l$, $s$; and inert gas atoms in their normal state, as completed shells ($K$, $L$, $M$ shells, &c.) have zero resultant $L$, $S$, making them magnetically dead, so that they are in a sense Russell-Saunders quantized to a null resultant. Excited inert gas atoms have exceedingly complicated spectra and do not conform to any simple system of quantization.

*Angular Momentum Matrices for Russell-Saunders Coupling in Weak Fields* ($b$, Fig. 6). Let us suppose that external fields are either absent or too weak to upset the tendency of $\mathbf{L}$, $\mathbf{S}$ to form a quantized resultant $\mathbf{J}$. Let us as usual take the $z$ axis as the direction of spacial quantization. Then the non-vanishing elements for the $z$ components of orbital and spin angular momentum can be shown to be

$$\left.\begin{aligned}
S_z(JM;JM) &= \frac{1}{2J(J+1)}[J(J+1)+S(S+1)-L(L+1)]M, \\
L_z(JM;JM) &= \frac{1}{2J(J+1)}[J(J+1)+L(L+1)-S(S+1)]M,
\end{aligned}\right\} \quad (87)$$

$$\left.\begin{aligned}
S_z(JM;J+1\,M) &= S_z(J+1\,M;JM) = f, \\
L_z(JM;J+1\,M) &= L_z(J+1\,M;JM) = -f, \\
\text{where} \quad f &= \sqrt{\left[\frac{\begin{array}{c}(J+L+S+2)(-J+S+L)(J+S-L+1)\times \\ \times(J+L-S+1)(J+M+1)(J-M+1)\end{array}}{4(J+1)^2(2J+1)(2J+3)}\right]}.
\end{aligned}\right\} \quad (88)$$

Elements of the form $(J-1\,M;JM)$, &c., are, of course, obtainable from (88) by lowering $J$ one unit. From (87) and (88) it follows that $S_z+L_z \doteq M$, as is to be expected from our previous remarks regarding the significance of the magnetic quantum number $M$. Formulae could also be worked out for the $x$ and $y$ components, but are not needed for our work.[49]

[49] The $x$ and $y$ components differ from the $z$ only as regards their factors depending

*Paschen-Back Effect, and Angular Momentum Matrices for Russell-Saunders Coupling in Strong Fields* (c, Fig. 6). Suppose that a magnetic field is applied which is so strong as to produce a change in energy large compared to the coupling energy $A\mathbf{L} \cdot \mathbf{S}$, but at the same time small compared to the terms $c_{ik}\mathbf{s}_i \cdot \mathbf{s}_k$, $b_{ik}\mathbf{l}_i \cdot \mathbf{l}_k$ in $\langle 79 \rangle$. Then the spin and orbital angular momenta will continue to have quantized resultants $\mathbf{S}$, $\mathbf{L}$ respectively, but $\mathbf{L}$ and $\mathbf{S}$ will no longer form a quantized resultant $\mathbf{J}$, as the field is by hypothesis strong enough to overpower the interactions between $\mathbf{L}$ and $\mathbf{S}$, but not between the $\mathbf{s}_i$ or between the $\mathbf{l}_i$ among themselves. Instead, $\mathbf{L}$ and $\mathbf{S}$ will be separately quantized with reference to the field, as illustrated in (c) of Fig. 6. The projections of $\mathbf{L}$ and $\mathbf{S}$ along the direction $z$ of the applied field are diagonal matrices whose non-vanishing elements are respectively $M_L$ and $M_S$, where $M_L = -L, ..., +L$; $M_S = -S, ..., +S$. The sum $M_L + M_S$ is the magnetic quantum number $M$ previously used. As one might expect, the formulae for the matrix elements of $S_x$, $S_y$, $S_z$ and $L_x$, $L_y$, $L_z$ are similar to (75) except that $l$, $m_l$ are replaced by $L$, $M_L$ or $S$, $M_S$. Thus their non-vanishing elements are

$$(L_x \pm iL_y)(LM_L \pm 1; LM_L) = [L(L+1) - M_L(M_L \pm 1)]^{\frac{1}{2}},$$
$$L_z(LM_L; LM_L) = M_L; \tag{89}$$

$$(S_x \pm iS_y)(SM_S \pm 1; SM_S) = [S(S+1) - M_S(M_S \pm 1)]^{\frac{1}{2}},$$
$$S_z(LM_S; LM_S) = M_S. \tag{90}$$

From (89) and (90) it, of course, follows in a fashion similar to (77) that $\mathbf{L}^2$, $\mathbf{S}^2$ are diagonal matrices as given in (83), but $\mathbf{J} = \mathbf{L} + \mathbf{S}$ is no longer quantized as in (83), and (87) and (88) are replaced by (89) and (90) since now $\mathbf{L}$, $\mathbf{S}$ are not coupled together to give a constant resultant.

The distortion in the spectroscopic multiplet structures and Zeeman pattern when a powerful magnetic field causes a passage from the quantization (b) to (c) in Fig. 6 is called the Paschen-Back effect. A still more powerful field might in principle overpower all the interactions in $\langle 79 \rangle$ and so give space quantization for individual electrons, studied in § 39 and illustrated in (a), Fig. 6, but we have already mentioned that sufficiently powerful fields to do this cannot usually be built experimentally.

*j-j Coupling.* If the terms of the form $a_{ii}\mathbf{l}_i \cdot \mathbf{s}_i$ in $\langle 79 \rangle$ are large compared to the other terms $c_{ik}\mathbf{s}_i \cdot \mathbf{s}_k$, $b_{ik}\mathbf{l}_i \cdot \mathbf{l}_k$, $a_{ik}\mathbf{l}_i \cdot \mathbf{s}_k$ ($i \neq k$) then the spins no longer form a quantized resultant $\mathbf{S}$, or the orbital angular momenta a quantized resultant $L$. Instead

on $M$ and independent of $L$, $S$. Such factors are easier to work out than those independent of $M$, and so are commonly found in text-books (e.g. Born and Jordan, *Elementare Quantenmechanik*, p. 150).

the $l_i$ and $s_i$ of an individual electron form a quantized resultant associated with a quantum number $j_i = l_i \pm \frac{1}{2}$, so that each electron has, so to speak, its own private or individual inner quantum number. The total angular momentum of the whole atom is conserved, and this is expressed by the fact that the various **j** vectors form a quantized resultant **J**, whose projection in the direction of the axis of quantization is $M$. This is illustrated in $(d)$ of Fig. 6. Angular momentum matrices, and various stages of the Paschen-Back effect can be worked out for $j$-$j$ coupling, but we omit them, as this type of coupling is much less common than Russell-Saunders coupling, especially in the case of the 'normal' or 'ground' levels such as are involved in the study of magnetic susceptibilities. The $j$-$j$ coupling is most likely to be realized in heavy atoms or in atoms which are multiply ionized. The reason for this is that the internal magnetic forces responsible for the constants $a_{ii}$ in $\langle 79 \rangle$ increase rapidly with the effective nuclear charge. In order for $j$-$j$ coupling to occur it is usually necessary for there to be more than one 'uncompensated' electron having $l \neq 0$ and so certain atoms may exhibit this type of coupling in excited states even though they do not in the normal level. For instance, high members of the 'primed' series of the alkaline earths, which represent excitation of both electrons, show some tendency towards $j$-$j$ coupling.

## 41. Classical Analogue of the Angular Momentum Matrices, and the Correspondence Principle

We have stated that Eqs. (73) and (78) are the basic spin postulates, and so equations such as (87) and (88) or (89) and (90) should be derivable from (78) and the related orbital formula (75). Eqs. (89) and (90) are considerably easier to deduce than (87) and (88), although we shall not give the derivation of either. Formulae more or less equivalent to (89) and (90) were deduced in the early days of quantum mechanics by Born, Heisenberg, and Jordan, and by Dirac with matrix and '$q$-number' methods respectively, as a consequence of the 'Vertauschung' relations satisfied by angular momentum matrices.[50] Their papers considered explicitly the compounding of orbital rather than spin angular momenta, but their results are readily adaptable to the spin because of the parallelism between (75) and (78). When there are *several* electrons, the proof of (89), which forms a part of what Dirac calls 'the elimination of nodes', is much more complicated by means of the Schrödinger wave functions than by use of non-commutative algebra, and the derivations of (89) and (90) by means of wave functions which have so far been published all involve rather abstruse group-theory considerations.[51]

[50] Born, Heisenberg, and Jordan, *Zeits. f. Physik*, **35**, 603 (1926); Dirac, *Proc. Roy. Soc.* **110**A, 561 (1926).

[51] Weyl, *Gruppentheorie und Quantenmechanik*, p. 156; E. Wigner, *Zeits. f. Physik*, **43**, 624, **45**, 601 (1927); Neumann and Wigner, *ibid.* **47**, 203, **49**, 73 (1928). One must not confuse formula (89) for the resultant of several electrons with the easily proved similar formula (75) for one electron.

Eqs. (88) have seldom [51a] been explicitly given in the literature, but are adaptations of general intensity formulae derived on semi-empirical grounds by Kronig, Russell, and Sommerfeld and Hönl [52] just before the advent of quantum mechanics. The details of the adaptation are explained in an accompanying footnote, and were carried out by E. Hill in work unpublished except in abstract.[53] These semi-empirical formulae have been justified quantum mechanically by Dirac,[54] so that their use implies no loss of rigour.

It is a general characteristic of the Heisenberg matrix elements that they merge asymptotically into the coefficients in classical Fourier expansions when the quantum numbers become very large.[55] It is easy to work out the classical amplitudes for various precessions of the angular momentum vectors, and it is illuminating to verify their asymptotic agreement with our previous quantum-mechanical formulae (87), (88), (89) and (90). This serves as an interesting check, but, of course, not a derivation of these formulae.

First consider case (c), Fig. 6. Here $\mathbf{L}$ has a constant component $M_L$ along the $z$ axis. Hence $L_x^2 + L_y^2$ equals $L^2 - M_L^2$, as in the old or 'classical' quantum theory the square of the total angular momentum

---

[51a] Formulae substantially equivalent to (88) have, however, been given by Rosenfeld in his paper on the Faraday effect, *Zeits. f. Physik*, **57**, 835 (1929), especially his Eq. (75). He derives them by a group method due to Neumann and Wagner, *ibid.* **51**, 844 (1930).

[52] R. de L. Kronig, *Zeits. f. Physik*, **31**, 885; **33**, 261 (1925); H. N. Russell, *Proc. Nat. Acad.* **11**, 314, 322 (1925); Sommerfeld and Hönl, *Sitz. Preuss. Akad.* **9**, 141 (1925).

[53] E. Hill and J. H. Van Vleck, *Phys. Rev.* **31**, 715 (1927). To get the matrix elements or 'amplitudes' for $L$ given in (87) and (88) from Kronig's formulae, one takes the Kronig formulae for Zeeman components relating to transitions of the form $\Delta L = 0$, given on p. 893 of his paper, and normalizes his constant $B$ in such a way that $\mathbf{L}^2 \doteq L(L+1)$. This gives $B = \frac{1}{4}$, as his elements sum to $4BL(L+1)$. Kronig's $K$, $R$, $J$ are the same as $L+\frac{1}{2}$, $S+\frac{1}{2}$, $J+\frac{1}{2}$ in our notation, and his elements are intensity ones, and hence proportional to the square of ours. The Kronig elements for $\Delta L = \pm 1$ do not need to be considered for our purposes, as $\mathbf{L}$ has no component perpendicular to itself. The formulae for $S$ given in (87) and (88) follow on interchanging $\mathbf{L}$ and $\mathbf{S}$, with allowance for phase difference of 180° in the parts of $L$ and $S$ perpendicular to $J$, or more simply, on noting that $\mathbf{L} + \mathbf{S} = \mathbf{J}$.

[54] P. A. M. Dirac, *Proc. Roy. Soc.* **111**A, 281 (1926). Alternative methods of derivation have recently been given by Kramers, *Proc. Amsterdam Acad.* **33**, 953 (1930) and by Güttinger and Pauli, *Zeits. f. Physik*, **67**, 754 (1931). Kramers employs the group theory of invariants, while Güttinger and Pauli use elementary matrix algebra. Their proof unfortunately appeared too late to include in the present volume.

[55] For exposition of Bohr's correspondence principle see N. Bohr, *The Quantum Theory of Line Spectra*, or for a more elementary discussion, Ruark and Urey, *Atoms, Molecules, and Quanta*, Chap. VI. That amplitudes (i.e. matrix elements) in the new mechanics do really merge asymptotically into classical Fourier coefficients has been shown by C. Eckart, *Proc. Nat. Acad.* **12**, 684 (1926) and by J. H. Van Vleck, *ibid.* **14**, 178 (1927); the related questions of convergence have been covered by Jeffreys, *Proc. Lon. Math. Soc.* **23**, 428 (1924); cf. also Eckart, *Zeits. f. Physik*, **48**, 295 (1928).

is $L^2$ rather than $L(L+1)$. If $\phi$ be the angle between the $x$ axis and the projection of $L$ on the $xy$ plane, then $L_x = (L^2 - M_L^2)^{\frac{1}{2}} \cos\phi$, $L_y = (L^2 - M_L^2)^{\frac{1}{2}} \sin\phi$. But we may write $\phi = 2\pi\omega_M t + \epsilon_M$, where $\epsilon_M$ is a trivial epoch constant, and where $\omega_M$ is the frequency of precession of $L$ about the $z$ axis, i.e. the frequency associated with the quantum number $M_L$. Thus

$$L_x \pm i L_y = (L^2 - M_L^2)^{\frac{1}{2}} e^{\pm(2\pi i \omega_M t + i\epsilon_M)}, \qquad L_z = M_L. \qquad (91)$$

Now according to Bohr's correspondence principle, a quantum-mechanical matrix element approaches asymptotically a coefficient in a classical multiple Fourier expansion

$$\sum_{\tau_1, \tau_2 \ldots} A_{\tau_1 \tau_2} \ldots e^{2\pi i(\tau_1 \omega_1 + \tau_2 \omega_2 + \ldots)t + i\epsilon_{\tau_1 \tau_2} \ldots} \qquad (92)$$

provided we select the particular overtone for which each $\tau_i$ $(i = 1, 2, \ldots)$ equals the change (i.e. difference between initial and final index) in the quantum number associated with the frequency $\omega_i$. Comparison of (89) and (91) shows that the requirements of the correspondence principle are indeed fulfilled, as $L(L+1) - M_L(M_L+1)$ is asymptotically the same as $L^2 - M_L^2$ if $L$, $M_L$ are very large. The fact that in (89) all the amplitudes for $L_x$, $L_y$ vanish unless $M_L' = M_L \pm 1$ is an expression of the fact that the first part of (91) is a special case of the general series (92), in which all amplitudes for $L_x$, $L_y$ vanish unless $\tau = \pm 1$. The diagonality of (89) in all quantum numbers other than $M_L$ is because (91) involves a sole frequency $\omega_M$, i.e. is simply rather than multiply periodic. The proof of the asymptotic identity of (90) with classical theory is entirely analogous, as $S$, $M_S$ simply replace $L$, $M_L$.

In case $(b)$, Fig. 6, $S$ and $L$ precess around $J$, and $J$ in turn precesses around the axis $z$ of quantization. Let $\Omega$ be the angle between the plane determined by the vectors $J$, $S$, $L$, and the plane determined by the vector $J$ and the $z$ axis. Then from the geometry

$$S_z = S\cos(S, J)\cos(J, z) + S\sin(S, J)\sin(J, z)\cos\Omega. \qquad (93)$$

But $\Omega = 2\pi\omega_j t + \epsilon_j$, where $\omega_j$ is the frequency with which $S$, $L$ precess about $J$, and further

$$\cos(S, J) = \frac{J^2 + S^2 - L^2}{2SJ}, \qquad \cos(J, z) = \frac{J_z}{J} = \frac{M}{J}. \qquad (94)$$

Thus (93) becomes

$$S_z = \frac{M(J^2 + S^2 - L^2)}{2J^2} + f^{\text{cl}}\big[e^{2\pi i \omega_j t + \epsilon_j} + e^{-2\pi i \omega_j t - \epsilon_j}\big], \qquad (95)$$

where

$$f_{\text{cl}} = \sqrt{\frac{(J+L+S)(-J+L+S)(J+S-L)(J+L-S)(J-M)(J+M)}{16J^4}}$$

and we see that the three non-vanishing amplitudes in (95) do indeed agree asymptotically with the corresponding elements of $S_z$ in (87) and (88). The proof for the elements of $L_z$ instead of $S_z$ is entirely similar.

It is possible, in the following elementary way, to obtain the diagonal elements (87) from the constant term of (95) *exactly* rather than asymptotically, thus achieving what Fowler terms a 'refined' application of the correspondence principle. The constant term of (95) is the classical value of

$$\frac{J_z(\mathbf{J}^2+\mathbf{S}^2-\mathbf{L}^2)}{2\mathbf{J}^2}. \tag{96}$$

Now with the Russell-Saunders coupling presupposed in case (b), Fig. 6, $J_z$, $\mathbf{J}^2$, $\mathbf{L}^2$, and $\mathbf{S}^2$ are all diagonal matrices, i.e. constant in time, and hence (96) is also diagonal. Furthermore,

$$(1/J^2)(JM;JM) = 1/J^2(JM;JM)$$

because $J^2$ is diagonal. Also $J_z \doteq M$. When we interpret (96) as a matrix expression, and substitute the values (83) of the elements, we have indeed the first equation of (87). The proof of the second equation of (87) is similar.

## 42. The Anomalous Zeeman Effect in Atomic Spectra

Once the matrix elements (87) and (88) or (89) and (90) are granted, the formulae for this effect are very easy to deduce by the perturbation theory of § 34. Eq. (48), Chap. I, which corresponds to the wave Eq. (2) of the present chapter, gave the Hamiltonian function exclusive of spin. If we neglect the motion of the nucleus, we may take $e_i/m_i = -e/m$, and then the part of this function which is linear in $H$ may be written $(Heh/4\pi mc)L_z$, where $L_z$ is the component of orbital angular momentum, measured in multiples of $h/2\pi$, in the direction $z$ of the applied field. To incorporate the spin, we add a term $(Heh/2\pi mc)S_z$ due to the action of the external field $H$ on the spin, not to mention new spin terms in the part $\mathcal{H}^0$ of the Hamiltonian function which is independent of $H$. The factor $e/2\pi mc$ rather than $e/4\pi mc$ appears in the spin term proportional to $H$ because of the anomalous ratio (73) of spin magnetic moment to angular momentum. Thus if we neglect the 'diamagnetic' part $H^2e^2 \sum (x_i^2+y_i^2)/8mc^2$, which is quadratic in $H$, the Hamiltonian function is

$$\mathcal{H} = \mathcal{H}^0 + \frac{Heh}{4\pi mc}(L_z+2S_z). \tag{97}$$

For arbitrary couplings of the spin, i.e. arbitrary values of the constants

$a, b, c$ in $\langle 79 \rangle$, the problem is excessively complicated.[56] We shall therefore henceforth assume that the atom has Russell-Saunders coupling.
If we further assume the 'cosine law', then $\mathcal{H}^0$ is of the form $\langle 84 \rangle$, but
this extra restriction is unnecessary. As our unperturbed system let us
take that of the atom in the absence of the external field. Then by (87),
(88), and $\langle 97 \rangle$ the non-vanishing elements of the perturbative potential
are

$$\lambda \mathcal{H}^{(1)}(JM;JM) = \frac{Heh}{4\pi mc}\left[1 + \frac{J(J+1)+S(S+1)-L(L+1)}{2J(J+1)}\right]M,$$

$$\lambda \mathcal{H}^{(1)}(JM;J+1\,M) = \frac{Heh}{4\pi mc}f(J,M),$$

$$\lambda \mathcal{H}^{(1)}(JM;J-1\,M) = \frac{Heh}{4\pi mc}f(J-1,M),$$

(98)

where $f(J,M)$ is defined as in (88).

If there were no spin, i.e. if $S = 0$, $J = L$, as is the case in singlet
spectra, then $f$ would vanish and the perturbing potential would consist
solely of diagonal elements $HehM/4\pi mc$. This can also readily be seen
to have been the case if we had omitted to insert the anomalous factor
2, so that we had $L_z + S_z$ rather than $L_z + 2S_z$ in $\langle 97 \rangle$. The energy would
then be given rigorously (neglecting the small diamagnetic effect to be
discussed in § 43) by the formula

$$W = W^0 + \frac{Heh}{4\pi mc}M.$$

There would then be only a normal Lorentz triplet $\nu = \nu_0$, $\nu_0 \pm He/4\pi mc$,[57]
since the selection principle for the magnetic quantum number allows
only $\Delta M = 0, \pm 1$.

Actually the perturbative potential is not a diagonal matrix except
when $S$ or $L$ vanishes. If the applied field is small enough compared
to the multiplet width to permit a series development (21) in the parameter $\lambda = H$, then Eqs. (24) and (26) show that the energy is

$$W = W_J^0 + \frac{Heh}{4\pi mc}gM + \frac{H^2e^2h^2}{16\pi^2m^2c^2}\left\{\frac{[f(J,M)]^2}{h\nu(J;J+1)} + \frac{[f(J-1,M)]^2}{h\nu(J;J-1)}\right\} + ..., \quad (99)$$

where
$$g = 1 + \frac{J(J+1)+S(S+1)-L(L+1)}{2J(J+1)}. \quad (100)$$

---

[56] The $g$-factors and hence the energy to a first approximation in $H$ have been given
for $j$-$j$ and some limiting forms of coupling other than Russell-Saunders by Goudsmit
and Uhlenbeck, *Zeits. f. Physik*, **35**, 618 (1926).

[57] We suppose the reader at least a little familiar with the theory of the normal
Zeeman effect, and the selection rules. See, for instance, Ruark and Urey, *Atoms,
Molecules and Quanta*, pp. 138, 143, 568.

The frequencies appearing in the denominator of (99) are those separating adjacent levels in a multiplet. If we assume the cosine law expressed in Eq. (84a), then $2h\nu(J; J\pm 1) = -A\mp(2J+1)A$, but this specialization is unnecessary and it is better to substitute the experimental values of the multiplet intervals in (99), as the cosine law seldom holds precisely. In applying the Bohr frequency condition to get the spectroscopic frequencies predicted by (99), one must not forget that the selection principle allows [57] only $\Delta J = 0, \pm 1$; $\Delta M = 0, \pm 1$.

The first-order term in (99) is the familiar Landé $g$-formula.[58] The presence of second- and higher-order terms is too commonly overlooked. The second-order term is, to be sure, ordinarily so small with the values of $H$ used experimentally that it is confirmed by only a very limited amount of spectroscopic evidence, but is often quite important in the study of magnetic susceptibilities (*vide* §§ 56–9). The second-order terms were calculated in the old quantum theory by Landé himself,[59] and the form (99) which they take in the new quantum mechanics was obtained by Hill and Van Vleck.[53, 60] The physical significance of the second-order Zeeman term is that there is a component of magnetic moment perpendicular to the axis **J** of angular momentum, since the moment vector $(-e/2mc)(\mathbf{L}+2\mathbf{S})$ clearly is not in general parallel to $\mathbf{L}+\mathbf{S}$ because of the factor 2. The ordinary first approximation involved in the Landé $g$-formula utilizes only the component of magnetic moment along **J**, since by (24) the perturbed energy is to a first approximation the perturbative potential averaged over an unperturbed orbit, and such an average introduces only the component of moment parallel to **J**. This is most quickly seen by consulting the classical Eqs. (93), (94), (95), as the constant term in (95) involves $S$ only through the projection $S\cos(S, J)$ along $J$, and similarly for the contribution of $L$.

Landé has shown that the second-order term in $H$ is confirmed by a certain amount of direct spectroscopic evidence on the Zeeman effect, despite the smallness of this term in ordinary fields. The agreement with experiment is somewhat improved by using formula (99) instead of Landé's analogous formula with the old theory. This is illustrated by the following table for the Mg triplet, 5184, 5173, 5167 Å at 38,900

---

[58] For the abundant spectroscopic evidence confirming the $g$-formula see, for instance, Back and Landé, *Zeemaneffekt und Multiplettstruktur*.

[59] A. Landé, *Zeits. f. Physik*, **30**, 329 (1924).

[60] Eq. (99) has also been given independently for the special case of triplets by A. Zwann, *Zeits. f. Physik*, **61**, 62 (1928). Extensive calculations of the energy-levels of triplets at intermediate field strengths by numerical solution of the secular equation, here a cubic, have been made by K. Darwin, *Proc. Roy. Soc.* **116A**, 264 (1928).

gauss, which is the most comprehensive example quoted by Landé. The entries in the table are the ratio $q$ of the energy separation between components with the second-order terms to the separation without this term. Experimentally this ratio is determined from the dissymmetry between the two sides of the Zeeman pattern, as the departures of the ratio from unity gauge the distortion from a strictly linear or symmetrical pattern:

| | $\sigma_{15}-\sigma_{14}$ | $\sigma_{11}-\sigma_{10}$ | $\pi_6-\pi_5$ | $\pi_5-\pi_4$ | $\pi_4-\sigma_3$ | $\sigma_3-\sigma_2$ | $\sigma_2-\sigma_1$ |
|---|---|---|---|---|---|---|---|
| $q_{obs}$ | 0·89 | 1·11 | 1·02 | 1·00 | 0·96 | 1·04 | 0·96 |
| $q_{Landé}$ | 0·92 | 1·08 | 1·01 | 0·99 | 0·98 | 1·02 | 1·01 |
| $q_{new}$ | 0·89 | 1·11 | 1·02 | 1·00 | 0·96 | 1·04 | 0·97 |

The notation of the components is explained in Landé's paper.[59] Out of the fifteen ratios recorded in his table, we give only the seven which are changed by the new mechanics. The writer is indebted to E. Hill for his calculation (unpublished elsewhere) of the above $q_{new}$ from Eq. (99).

Eq. (99) ceases to be a good approximation when the field is so powerful, or the multiplets so narrow, that there is an appreciable tendency towards a Paschen-Back effect, i.e. considerable progress in the passage from case (b) to case (c) in Fig. 6. We must then use the perturbation technique for nearly degenerate systems. By Eq. (35) the energy-levels are the roots of the secular equation

$$\left|\lambda\mathcal{H}^{(1)}(JM;J'M)+\delta(J;J')(W^0_J-W)\right|=0, \qquad (101)$$

where $J, J' = Q, Q+1,..., L+S$ with $Q = |L-S|$ if $|L-S| \geqslant |M|$, while $Q = |M|$ if $|M| \geqslant |L-S|$. Each value of $M$ furnishes a different secular equation. Eq. (98) shows that the determinant involved in (101) has zeros everywhere except along the principal diagonal and elements adjacent thereto. Even so, (101) cannot in general be solved explicitly, as it furnishes an algebraic equation of order $L+S-Q+1$. Hence it is solvable in an elementary way for all allowable values of $M$ only for the case of doublet spectra. Then (101) yields a quadratic equation for $W$, whose roots are [61]

$$W = h\Delta\nu_n\left\{M\pm\frac{1}{2}\sqrt{\left[1+\frac{4M\Delta\nu}{(2L+1)\Delta\nu_n}+\left(\frac{\Delta\nu}{\Delta\nu_n}\right)^2\right]}\right\}+\text{const.}, \qquad (102)$$

as can be seen by specializing (98) and (101) by setting $S = \frac{1}{2}$, $J = L\pm\frac{1}{2}$. Here $\Delta\nu$ denotes the doublet separation in the absence of the field and

[61] The case $M = \pm(L+\frac{1}{2})$ requires special consideration, as here the secular equation is linear instead of quadratic, and has the solution $W = \pm(L+1)h\Delta\nu_n+\frac{1}{2}h\Delta\nu+\text{const.}$, the same as (102) only if one makes the proper choice of sign for the radical, which is arbitrary for other values of $M$. The physical significance of this is that only one of the doublet components can have $M = \pm(L+\frac{1}{2})$, as $M$ cannot exceed $J$ in magnitude.

$\Delta\nu_n$ is the normal Lorentz displacement $\Delta\nu_n = He/4\pi mc$. Eq. (102) has, rather fortuitously, the same form as Sommerfeld's adaptation [62] of Voigt's classical formula based on a model not in accord with modern knowledge of atomic structure.

The quantum mechanics of the anomalous Zeeman effect was first given by Heisenberg and Jordan.[63] One slight difference, however, may be noted between their procedure and that just given. They use as the unperturbed system of quantization that appropriate to a magnetic field powerful enough to give a Zeeman effect large compared to the multiplet structure, and hence separate spacial quantization of $\mathbf{S}$ and $\mathbf{L}$, as shown in (c), Fig. 6. The energy due to the external magnetic field is included in the unperturbed system, and the coupling forces between $\mathbf{S}$ and $\mathbf{L}$ treated as a perturbation, just the reverse of what we have done. Thus with the cosine law $\langle 84 \rangle$, the perturbing potential is $A\mathbf{L}\cdot\mathbf{S}$. If the external field is really so strong that (c), Fig. 6, is a good approximation, one may replace $A\mathbf{L}\cdot\mathbf{S}$ by its mean value, which is readily seen[64] to be $AM_LM_S$ with the separate precessions of $\mathbf{S}$ and $\mathbf{L}$. Thus for very strong fields, which produce a complete Paschen-Back effect, the energy-levels are

$$W = W^{00} + \frac{Heh}{4\pi mc}(M_L + 2M_S) + AM_LM_S + \dots. \tag{103}$$

More accurate formulae than (103) can, of course, be obtained by taking into account the non-diagonal terms arising in the Hamiltonian function for case (c) because $\mathbf{L}\cdot\mathbf{S}$ is not identical with $\mathbf{L}\cdot\mathbf{S}$. Eq. (21) then takes the form of a power-series development in a parameter of the order $A/h\Delta\nu_n$ instead of the order $h\Delta\nu_n/A$ as in (99). Here $\Delta\nu_n$ is the 'normal' Zeeman displacement $He/4\pi mc$, and $A$ gauges the magnitude of the multiplet interval. Thus the neglected terms in (103) are of the order of magnitude $A^2/h\Delta\nu_n$. The development (103) in $A/h\Delta\nu_n$ is, of course, a poor approximation if $A/h\Delta\nu_n$ is large, i.e. if the field is not great enough for an almost complete Paschen-Back effect, and one can instead use the perturbation technique for nearly degenerate systems, and set up the proper secular equation. This Heisenberg and Jordan proceed to do. Their secular equation, being figured from (c) rather than (b) in Fig. 6 has a different super-ficial appearance from (101), but must yield the same algebraic equation for $W$ as (101), since the method based on the secular equation is always rigorous regardless of whether or not the assumed initial system of quantization is a close approximation to that appropriate to the actual field strength. A direct general proof has not yet been given that the two secular equations are the same, or what is partially equivalent, that our secular equation has asymptotically the roots (103) for very large $H$, or that Heisenberg and Jordan's secular equation has asymptotically the roots (99) for small $H$.[65] Such a proof would be of interest

[62] Sommerfeld, *Atombau*, 4th ed., p. 672.

[63] Heisenberg and Jordan, *Zeits. f. Physik*, **37**, 263 (1926); see Darwin, *l.c.*[36] for the transcription into wave language.

[64] This can be seen classically by taking the constant term of the multiple Fourier series for $L_xS_x + L_yS_y + L_zS_z$ obtained by multiplying (91) with the corresponding formulae for the components of $S$; or quantum mechanically by the taking diagonal elements of this scalar product when formed by multiplying together the matrices whose elements are given by (89) and (90).

[65] To show rigorously that the two secular equations are the same one would have to

only as mathematical manipulation, since the physical knowledge of the various appropriate quantizations assures the results must be the same with either method. In the particular case of doublets, it is, of course, directly verifiable that either secular equation yields the same quadratic equation (102), which agrees asymptotically with (99) and (103) specialized to $S = \frac{1}{2}$, $J = L \pm \frac{1}{2}$. Heisenberg and Jordan treat weak fields separately, and deduce the first-order terms in (99) by the same quantum-mechanical refinement of the constant term of (95) as that already discussed after (95). The first-order terms in (99), and hence the celebrated Landé $g$-factor, are deducible in this elementary fashion involving only the quantum formulation of the cosine law, whereas, as already mentioned, the derivation of the non-diagonal elements (88) and hence of the second-order terms in (99), which are the only thing of consequence not given in Heisenberg and Jordan's eventful paper, are more difficult. Their use of case (c), Fig. 6, as compared to our use of (b) for the point of departure for deducing the rigorous secular equation has the advantage in that the matrix elements (89) and (90) are easier to deduce from the basic spin postulate (78) than are the non-diagonal elements (88) of (87) and (88), but the disadvantage in that with ordinary field strengths case (c) is a poorer approximation to the true state of quantization than (b), and so furnishes a less natural starting point even though use of (c) entails no loss of rigour or generality. Our use of (b) rather than (c) perhaps frees us a little more readily from the specializations appropriate to the cosine law. We have, for instance, shown that the Voigt formula (102) is valid without the assumption of the cosine law made by Heisenberg and Jordan, but this is not at all surprising when it is remembered that the doublet case inevitably leads to a quadratic secular equation.

We have mentioned that, except when $S = \frac{1}{2}$, it is impossible because of algebraic difficulties, to trace readily the transition of individual roots of the secular determinant from (99) to (103) as the field is made very great. However, it is quite easy to verify that the sum of all the roots of the secular determinant pass properly from one limit to the other. As mentioned on p. 142, this sum is the 'spur' or diagonal-sum of the Hamiltonian matrix. Reference to the diagonal elements of the determinant (101) shows that this sum must be linear in $H$, so that

$$\sum_J W = \alpha_1 + \alpha_2 H, \tag{104}$$

where $\alpha_1$ and $\alpha_2$ are constants independent of $H$. Explicit formulae could be given for $\alpha_1$ and $\alpha_2$, but are rather cumbersome inasmuch as it is necessary to differentiate between different cases depending on the relative magnitudes of $S$, $L$, $M$. Now it is not hard to verify that Eqs. (99) and (103) yield identical values of $\alpha_1$ or of $\alpha_2$. With (103) we of course sum over all values of $M_L$, $M_S$ consistent with given $M$ rather than over $J$. That (104) is linear in $H$ is the so-called principle of permanence of $\Gamma$- and $g$-sums,[66] which was known on semi-empirical grounds before the advent of quantum mechanics. The terms $\Gamma$-sum and $g$-sum are used to designate the parts of (104) which are independent of $H$ and proportional to $H$, i.e. the parts $\alpha_1$ and $\alpha_2 H$ respectively.

prove that their roots when expanded in some parameter, say $h\Delta\nu_n/A$, are the same to all powers in $H$ rather than merely to the second power given in (99). The identity to the first power has been shown by Darwin.[36]

[66] For elaboration of these permanence principles, see Back and Landé, *Zeemaneffekt und Multiplettstruktur*, pp. 62–82. For explicit verification of the invariance of $\alpha_2$ see the writer's *Quantum Principles and Line Spectra*, p. 244. Pauli has shown (*Zeits.*

## 43. The Diamagnetic Second-Order Zeeman Term

Finally, we must not fail to note that besides the term in (99) proportional to $H^2$, there is another kind of quadratic term in $H$ which we have so far neglected, viz. that arising from the term $\sum H^2 e_i^2 (x_i^2 + y_i^2)/8m_i c^2$ in Eq. (48), Chap. I, or Eq. (2) of the present chapter. If we call this term $\lambda^2 \mathcal{H}^{(2)}$, and if we remember that diagonal matrix elements have the physical significance of being time averages, Eq. (26) shows that its effect on the energy is approximately

$$\frac{H^2 e^2}{8mc^2} \sum \overline{(x_i^2 + y_i^2)}, \tag{105}$$

provided degeneracy difficulties are not encountered. We have assumed the nucleus at rest at the origin, so the sum is only over the electrons, for which $e_i = -e$, $m_i = m$. The expression (105) is very small unless one or more of the orbits is very large. Let us suppose for simplicity that there is only one electron not in a closed shell. Then (105) is very small compared to the quadratic term in (99) unless the valence electron has a very large principal quantum number $n$. The magnetic coupling is very small for such an orbit, as the factor $A = a_{11}$ in (84a) can be shown to vary as $n^{-3}$. Thus under the conditions, viz. high field strength and large orbits, under which (105) might be capable of observation spectroscopically, there is certain to be separate spacial quantization of the orbit and spin, and (105) must then be added to the energy expression (103) rather than (99). Thus the two types of quadratic terms are never simultaneously of importance. When the spin is quantized separately, the time average (105) can be calculated as though the spin were entirely absent. By setting $f = x^2 + y^2$ in the fundamental quadrature (14), and taking the $\psi$'s to be of the central form (74), it follows [67] that for an electron moving without spin subject to a central field, one has

$$\overline{x^2 + y^2} = \overline{r^2} \left[ \frac{2l^2 + 2l - 2 + 2m_l^2}{(2l-1)(2l+3)} \right]. \tag{106}$$

f. *Physik*, **16**, 155 (1923)) that the permanence of g-sums permits calculation of the g-factors for weak fields from the strong field formula (103), assuming the linear term in $H$ to be proportional to $M$ in weak fields.

[67] Because the wave functions (74) are products of the form $R(r)S(\theta,\phi)$, it follows from (74) that $\overline{r^2(1 - \cos^2\theta)} = \overline{r^2}(1 - \overline{\cos^2\theta})$. Also the value of $\overline{\cos^2\theta}$ has already been calculated in Eq. (67), as the factor $S(\theta, \phi)$ is identical in form with the wave functions of the 'dumb-bell' used in § 37. Incidently, group theory considerations show that the dependence of $\overline{x_i^2 + y_i^2}$ on $M_L$ is of the form $A + BM_L^2$ whenever there is Russell-Saunders coupling and separate spacial quantization of **S** even though the dynamical problem is that of many electrons rather than one (cf. H. A. Kramers, *Proc. Amsterdam Acad.* **32**, 1179 (1929)).

The mean square radius $\overline{r^2}$ depends on the nature of the central field. It can be shown [68] that if it is Coulomb,

$$\overline{r^2} = \left(\frac{h^2}{4\pi^2 Ze^2 m}\right)^2 n^4 \left[\frac{5}{2} - \frac{3l(l+1)}{2n^2} + \frac{1}{2n^2}\right]. \tag{107}$$

Unfortunately this value is never rigorously applicable to our Zeeman problem, for if the field is Coulomb the system is degenerate in the azimuthal quantum number $l$. Instead of using (106) one must then set up a secular equation, which has been given by Halpern and Sexl [69] and which proves to be not explicitly solvable except for the uninteresting case of small values of $n$. If on the other hand the field is non-Coulomb, (106) is not accurate. It will perhaps be an approximately correct expression for a non-Coulomb central field if one uses in place of $n$ the so-called effective quantum number $n^*$, defined by $n^* = n - \Delta$, where $\Delta$ is the 'quantum defect' in the Rydberg formula $R/(n-\Delta)^2$ for a spectral term. To avoid degeneracy difficulties, the expression (106) must be small compared to the departures from Coulomb character, which decrease rapidly with increasing $n$, as $R/(n-\Delta)^2 - R/n^2 \sim 2\Delta R/n^3$. Fortunately the case of greatest interest, that of small values of $l$ along with great values of $n$ as in e.g. high numbers of the principal series of sodium, is accompanied by comparatively large values of $\Delta$, at least in the alkalis.

We shall not discuss this matter further, as suitable experimental evidence on the Zeeman effect of very large orbits, needed to test the theory, is wanting. The quadratic term (105) is of vital importance for the theory of diamagnetism, but the theory of this does not involve or test experimentally the mathematical problems connected with the degeneracy, as the susceptibility involves only the statistical average over all orientations, permitting us to replace $x^2 + y^2$ by $\frac{2}{3}r^2$, regardless

---

[68] The result (107) is obtained by using a method developed by Waller for evaluating the mean value of any power of $r$ in Keplerian motion (*Zeits. f. Physik*, **38**, 635 (1926)). The result is, of course, the same as evaluation of the fundamental quadrature (14) with $f = r^2$, $n = n'$, which is tedious if done by ordinary methods.

[69] O. Halpern and Th. Sexl, *Ann. der Physik*, **3**, 565 (1929). The analogous problem in the old quantum theory was considered by Burgers, Dissertation, p. 106, also Halpern, *Zeits. f. Physik*, **18**, 352 (1923), and likewise was not soluble in closed form. The order of magnitude of the quadratic effect arising from (105) has been estimated by E. Guth, *Zeits. f. Physik*, **58**, 368 (1929). He finds it cannot give a displacement of more than 0·08 Å. for the 13th Balmer line of hydrogen, in a field of 30,000 gauss, whereas the normal first-order displacement is 0·19 Å. If we went to still higher lines the quadratic term would soon become more important, as it varies as $n^4$. All the writers consider primarily hydrogen, although the alkalis, where the degeneracy difficulties are less bothersome, would appear likewise easier to test experimentally.

of the type of quantization. For the particular case when (106) is applicable, one can verify that the statistical average $\overline{x^2+y^2}$ is $\frac{2}{3}\overline{r^2}$ not only by virtue of the general proof of spectroscopic stability, but also by direct evaluation of the summation over $m_l$ by means of Eq. (68), as already virtually done in Eq. (69).

## QUANTUM-MECHANICAL DERIVATION OF THE LANGEVIN-DEBYE FORMULA

THROUGHOUT the present chapter we shall suppose that we are dealing with electric rather than magnetic polarization. The few modifications necessary to adapt the analysis to the calculation of magnetic instead of electric susceptibilities will be given in § 53.

### 44. First Stages of Calculation

In § 36 we showed that if an atom or molecule is in a given stationary state $n, j, m$, the time average of its electrical moment in the direction of the applied field $E$ is given by the formula

$$p_E(njm; njm) = -\frac{\partial W}{\partial E} = -W_{njm}^{(1)} - 2EW_{njm}^{(2)} - \dots, \tag{1}$$

where the $W_{njm}^{(i)}$ are the coefficients in the development

$$W_{njm} = W_{njm}^0 + W_{njm}^{(1)}E + W_{njm}^{(2)}E^2 + \dots \tag{2}$$

of the energy in terms of the field strength $E$. We now use three indices to specify a stationary state, rather than two as in most of Chapter VI, inasmuch as later in the present chapter it will be necessary to distinguish between three kinds of quantum numbers. Eq. (1) gives only the moment for a single stationary state. The total polarization or moment $P$ per unit volume is the statistical mean over all stationary states, weighted according to the Boltzmann factor $e^{-W_{njm}/kT}$ and multiplied by the number $N$ of molecules per c.c. Thus

$$P = N \frac{\sum\limits_{njm} p_E(njm; njm)e^{-W_{njm}/kT}}{\sum\limits_{njm} e^{-W_{njm}/kT}}. \tag{3}$$

Eq. (3) is, of course, the quantum analogue of (58), Chap. I. We assume here, and elsewhere unless otherwise stated, that the medium is sufficiently rarefied so that one may use the Boltzmann instead of the Fermi statistics. This assumption is fully warranted except for conduction electrons in solids. That the probability of a state is proportional to the factor $e^{-W_{njm}/kT}$ follows from exactly the same sort of statistical premises as in classical theory,[1] discussed on p. 25. The only difference is that there is now a discrete rather than continuous distribution of configurations. It is to be understood that we employ as many quantum numbers as degrees of freedom even though some of them are really

---

[1] See R. H. Fowler, *Statistical Mechanics*, Chap. II.

superfluous in degenerate systems, and we regard states of different quantum numbers as distinct even though they happen to have coincident energies. We adopt this convention to avoid the necessity of introducing an '*a priori* probability' or 'statistical weight'. If instead we treated a family of states of coincident energy as a single state, we would have to take the Boltzmann factor as $g_{nj}e^{-W_{nj}/kT}$ rather than $e^{-W_{njm}/kT}$, where the weight $g_{nj}$ is the number of states so coinciding.

We can immediately substitute (1) and (2) in (3), and by expanding the exponentials as series $e^{-W_{njm}/kT} = e^{-W^0_{njm}/kT}\left(1 - \dfrac{W^{(1)}_{njm}}{kT}E - ...\right)$ in $E$, we can then develop the numerator and denominator as power series in $E$. We shall neglect saturation effects, and so consider only the portion of the susceptibility $\chi = P/E$ which is independent of field strength. This means that we need develop the numerator of (3) only to the first power of $E$ inclusive, and retain only the portion of the denominator which is independent of $E$. With this approximation

$$\chi = N \frac{\sum\limits_{njm}[(W^{(1)}_{njm}{}^2/kT) - 2W^{(2)}_{njm}]e^{-W^0_{njm}/kT}}{\sum\limits_{njm} e^{-W^0_{njm}/kT}}. \tag{4}$$

In deducing Eq. (4) from (3) we have assumed, as is always done in calculations such as the present, that

$$\sum_{njm} p^0_E(njm; njm)e^{-W^0_{njm}/kT} = \sum - W^{(1)}_{njm}e^{-W^0_{njm}} = 0, \tag{5}$$

or, in other words, that the medium does not possess a 'permanent' or 'residual' polarization per c.c. in the absence of the field $E$. This assumption clearly involves no loss of generality, as such residual effects are ordinarily found experimentally only in crystalline dielectrics, which are beyond the scope of the present volume. Also, from a theoretical standpoint, the expression (5) clearly vanishes on symmetry grounds if we neglect inter-molecular forces, for in the absence of all fields there can be no preference between directions parallel and anti-parallel to $E$. In solids there are in reality important inter-molecular fields, but if these directions are random, the sum (5) still vanishes by symmetry on averaging over a tremendous number of molecules. If there is some other applied external field, namely, say, a magnetic field, which remains even in the absence of the given electric field $E$, one might think that (5) could be different from zero due to alinement of molecules in this other field, but in § 70 on the non-existence of a magneto-electric directive effect we shall show that at any rate a magnetic field cannot make (5) appreciably different from zero.

## 45. Derivation of the Langevin-Debye Formula with Special Models

Eq. (4) is the initial stage in the calculations of the susceptibility in quantum theory. Before one can proceed farther it is necessary to examine the structure of the formulae for $W^{(1)}$ and $W^{(2)}$. The completion of the calculation was first achieved simultaneously by Mensing and Pauli, Kronig, Manneback, and Van Vleck [2] for the special model of the 'rigid rotating dipole' or 'dumb-bell', whose characteristics have been explained and energy-levels determined in § 37. As two quantum numbers suffice for this model, we may omit the index $n$ in Eq. (4), and take $j$ and $m$ to be respectively the inner and axial or magnetic quantum numbers, just as in § 37. Now in § 37 we supposed that the electric field $E$ is the only field to which the molecule is subjected, so that the energy in the absence of $E$ is independent of spacial orientation, and hence $W_{jm}^0$ has a value $W_j^0$ independent of $m$ (cf. Eq. (57), Chap. VI). Also we showed that this model had no first-order Stark effect, i.e. $W_{jm}^{(1)} = 0$ (Eq. (64), Chap. VI). For a given value of $j$, there are $2j+1$ possible values of $m$, viz. $-j$, $-(j-1),..., j$. Thus Eq. (4) reduces to

$$\chi = -2N \frac{\sum\limits_{j} \left[\sum\limits_{m} W_{jm}^{(2)}\right] e^{-W_j^0/kT}}{\sum\limits_{j} (2j+1)e^{-W_j^0/kT}}. \tag{6}$$

Now by Eqs. (65) and (68) of Chapter VI,

$$\sum_{m=-j}^{+j} W_{jm}^{(2)} = 0 \qquad (j \neq 0). \tag{7}$$

In other words, even the second-order energy vanishes on averaging over all values of the quantum number $m$ consistent with a given $j$. An exception is the lowest rotational state $j = 0$, in which the summation involved in (7) reduces to the single term

$$W_{00}^{(2)} = -\frac{4\pi^2\mu^2 I}{3h^2} \tag{7 a}$$

(cf. Eq. (66), Chap. VI). Here $\mu$ and $I$ denote respectively the molecule's dipole moment and moment of inertia.

Eqs. (7), (7a) bring to light the very remarkable fact that all the contribution to the susceptibility comes from the molecules in the lowest rotational state $j = 0$.[3] This result is the very interesting quantum

---

[2] For references, see note [21] of Chap. VI.

[3] This result cannot hold when higher powers of the field strength, and the resulting saturation effects are considered, as in infinitely strong fields all molecules, regardless of $j$, aline themselves practically parallel to the field and contribute an amount $\mu$ to

analogue of the fact that with the dumb-bell model in classical theory only the molecules whose total energy is less than $\mu E$ contribute to the susceptibility. This property of the model in classical statistics was shown by Alexandrow and by Pauli.[4] In other words, classically the susceptibility arises entirely from molecules which possess so little energy that they would oscillate rather than rotate through complete circles in case their axis of rotation happened to be perpendicular to the axis of the field. Most molecules, of course, have some angular momentum about the axis of the field, so that their axes of rotation are not perpendicular to the field, and we mention the perpendicular case only because it admits a particularly simple interpretation analogous to the two types of motion for a simple pendulum. As the temperature is increased, the fraction of molecules which are located in the 'lazy' states that contribute to the susceptibility will steadily diminish, and hence we can see qualitatively why the susceptibility due to permanent dipoles decreases with increasing temperature. It must be cautioned that these theorems, both quantum and classical, that the susceptibility arises entirely from molecules of certain particularly low energies, are peculiar to the 'dumb-bell' model. In the general dynamical system to be considered in § 46, or even in the symmetrical top model, which is almost as simple as the dumb-bell, the higher rotational states will make some contribution to the susceptibility. Even then usually the bulk of the contribution comes from molecules with small rotational energies, since all rotational motions show at least a little resemblance to that of the dumb-bell, and since the susceptibility experimentally almost invariably decreases with increasing temperature. In the old quantum theory the susceptibility did not arise uniquely from the lowest rotational state even with the dumb-bell model, and this is perhaps one reason why the old theory gave such nonsensical results on dielectric constants (§ 28).

When we substitute (7) and (7 a), and utilize the familiar expression $j(j+1)h^2/8\pi^2 I$ (Eq. (57), Chap. VI) for the field-free energy of the rigid rotator, the quantitative expression (6) for the susceptibility becomes

$$\chi = \frac{8\pi^2 N\mu^2 I/3h^2}{\sum\limits_{j=0}^{\infty}(2j+1)e^{-j(j+1)h^2/8\pi^2 IkT}}. \tag{8}$$

the polarization $P$. This is also evident from the classical analogy, as when $E$ is arbitrarily large even the higher rotational states have original kinetic energies small compared to $\mu E$, and so then correspond to classical motions which contribute to the susceptibility.

[4] W. Alexandrow, *Phys. Zeits.* **22**, 258 (1921); W. Pauli, Jr., *Zeits. f. Physik*, **6**, 319 (1921).

If the temperature is sufficiently high so that most molecules have fairly large values of $j$, as is ordinarily the case, the summation in the denominator of (8) does not differ appreciably from the integral

$$\int_0^\infty 2je^{-j^2h^2/8\pi^2IkT}\,dj = \frac{8\pi^2IkT}{h^2}.$$

The formula (8) for the susceptibility, with this approximation, becomes $\chi = N\mu^2/3kT$, which is exactly the same as the part of the classical Langevin-Debye formula which arises from the permanent dipoles. Characteristic deviations from the classical theory will, however, be found at low temperatures, where the summation cannot be replaced by an integral. In classical theory it is not legitimate near $T = 0$ to neglect saturation effects and consider only the first term in the expansion of the Langevin function (4), Chap. II, as the ratio $x = \mu H/kT$ becomes very large. At $T = 0$ the classical theory will by (4), Chap. II, give the full saturation polarization $N\mu$ for infinitesimal fields, and hence an infinite susceptibility for such fields. On the other hand, the quantum theory expression (8) for the susceptibility has the finite value $8\pi^2N\mu^2I/3h^2$ at $T = 0$, as here only the state $j = 0$ gives a significant term in the denominator of (8). Thus even at the absolute zero the polarization is proportional to the field strength unless the latter is exceedingly large.

After the asymptotic derivation of the Langevin-Debye formula for the dumb-bell model, the next calculations of the susceptibility were made for the symmetrical top model (p. 153) independently by Kronig and by Manneback.[5] Here also it is found that the susceptibility has asymptotically the Langevin-Debye value at high temperatures. We shall not give the details of the calculations, as the results are all a special case of the general derivation to be given in § 46. We may, however, mention that it is unnecessary to replace the summation over the quantum number $\Lambda$ used on p. 153 by an integration, as $\Lambda$ drops out of the formulae on integrating over $j$. Hence the results apply for either use of the symmetrical top model mentioned on p. 153, viz. either to represent the rotational motion of a polyatomic molecule with two equal moments of inertia, in which $\Lambda$ is a quantum number assuming

---

[5] R. de L. Kronig, *Proc. Nat. Acad.* **12**, 608 (1926); C. Manneback, *Phys. Zeits.* **28**, 72 (1927). These writers considered the application of the model to polyatomic molecules. The application to diatomic molecules was treated by the writer, the details being unpublished except in abstract (*Nature*, **118**, 226 (1926)). Kronig and Manneback summed over $\Lambda$ so that their publications do not show explicitly that each value of $\Lambda$ contributes the same susceptibility.

a large and sensibly continuous range of values like $j$ at ordinary temperatures, or to represent the motion of a diatomic molecule not in a $\Sigma$ state, in which $\Lambda$ is regarded as a fixed electronic quantum number.

*Induced Polarization.* We have so far considered only the part of the susceptibility arising from the permanent dipoles. It is clear that the contribution of the induced polarization (p. 29) should also be considered. If we adopt the common but rather cowardly artifice of attributing the induced polarization to a set of isotropic harmonic oscillators, the calculation is, as usual, particularly simple. The wave equation for a harmonically bound particle of charge $e_i$ and mass $m_i$ subject to an impressed field $E$ along the $z$ direction is

$$\frac{\partial^2\psi}{\partial x^2}+\frac{\partial^2\psi}{\partial y^2}+\frac{\partial^2\psi}{\partial z^2}+\frac{8\pi^2h^2}{m_i}\{W-\tfrac{1}{2}a_i(x^2+y^2+z^2)+e_iEz\}\psi = 0. \qquad (9)$$

If we make the substitutions $z'=z-e_iE/a_i$, $W'=W+\tfrac{1}{2}e_i^2E^2/a_i$, this wave equation is of exactly the same form as in the absence of the field. Hence the characteristic values in the field differ from those in its absence by an amount $\tfrac{1}{2}e_i^2E/a_i$, so that[6] $W^{(1)}=0$, $W^{(2)}=-e_i^2/2a_i$, $W^{(k)}=0$, $(k=3,4,...)$. By Eq. (1) the polarization of one oscillator is $Ee_i^2/a_i$. To obtain the total polarization per unit-volume we must sum over all the oscillators in the molecule and multiply by the number of molecules per c.c. Weighting of the various states in accordance with the Boltzmann factor is unnecessary because the polarization of the oscillators has turned out not to involve the vibrational quantum numbers. If we set $\alpha = \sum_i e_i^2/a_i$, and if we assume that the induced polarization from the oscillators can be superposed additively on the polarization previously calculated for the permanent dipoles, we have the full Langevin-Debye formula

$$\chi = N\left(\frac{\mu^2}{3kT}+\alpha\right). \qquad (10)$$

## 46. General Derivation of the Langevin-Debye Formula[7]

The models used in the preceding section to obtain Eq. (10) are clearly too special, especially the ascription of the induced polarization to

---

[6] One can also verify as a nice easy example of perturbation theory that Eqs. (24) and (26), Chap. VI, when specialized to the harmonic oscillator, give these same expressions for $W^{(1)}$ or $W^{(2)}$. This is done in Condon and Morse, *Quantum Mechanics*, p. 122. These writers also give and solve the wave Eq. (9) as above. The displacement $-\tfrac{1}{2}e_i^2E^2/a_i$ in energy caused by the field $E$ is, incidently, exactly the total internal and external potential energy in the classical theory at the position $r = e_iE/a_i$ of static equilibrium between the electric field and the restoring force.

[7] This method was given by J. H. Van Vleck, *Phys. Rev.* **29,** 727 (1927).

harmonic oscillators, which involves the same kind of crude over-simplification as the first or preliminary classical treatment given in § 11. In the present section we shall therefore give a general derivation of the asymptotic validity of the Langevin-Debye formula at high temperatures, which frees us from the necessity of using special models. Thus in dealing with the polarization due to the permanent dipoles, we are no longer compelled to assume that the molecule has two equal moments of inertia, as in the symmetrical top model. Also, especially, the induced polarization can arise from real elec-tronic motions rather than from harmonic oscillators. The vibrations of the nuclei are, to be sure, very approximately simple harmonic, but have been shown in § 15 to give only a very small portion of the total induced polarization, which is mainly elec-tronic. The general derivation is really simpler than the special ones, and is illuminating in that it shows generally under what conditions departures from the Langevin-Debye formula should be expected, and hence what is the meaning of such departures when observed experimentally (cf. § 47).

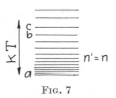

FIG. 7

The only two assumptions which it is necessary to make in the general demonstration are that the atom or molecule has a permanent moment, and that the moment matrix involves only frequencies which are 'low' or 'high' compared to $kT/h$. What is meant by the latter terminology may be explained more fully as follows. We shall classify a state as 'normal' if its Boltzmann distribution factor $e^{-W/kT}$ is appreciably different from zero, i.e. if its excess of energy over the very lowest state is either smaller than or comparable with $kT$. An 'excited' state is one which has such a small Boltzmann factor that its probability of being occupied is negligible, and whose energy thus exceeds the energies of the normal states by an amount large compared to $kT$. An energy-level diagram illustrating graphically the delineation into normal and excited states is given in Fig. 7. In order for the Langevin-Debye formula to be valid, it is vital for the electrical moment to involve no 'medium frequency' elements, which involve energy changes of the same order of magnitude as $kT$. Thus here and throughout the remainder of the volume, the equipartition allowance $kT$ of energy enters as the unit for determining whether an energy change is 'large' or 'small' for our pur-poses, or in other words, whether a frequency is 'high' or 'low'. It is essential that the spacing between consecutive normal states or energy-levels be small compared to $kT$. In Fig. 7 an interval such as $b$–$c$ must be much less than $kT$. It is not necessary to demand that the energy-difference between two widely separated normal states, such as $a$–$c$ in Fig. 7, be small compared to $kT$, as ordinarily there will be selection principles which require that the matrix elements connecting two normal states be zero, or at least very small, unless the two states are adjacent, or nearly so (cf. the familiar selection rule $\Delta j = 0, \pm 1$ for the inner quantum number, as a special example). It is clear that it is impossible to require that the energy-differences of two widely separated normal levels such as $a$–$c$ be small compared to $kT$, as the equipartition theorem demands that at high temperatures the average excess of rotational energy over the very lowest state be $kT$ itself. At very low temperatures the 'unit' $kT$ will become much smaller, and the separation between adjacent normal states will become comparable with $kT$. Special calculations, depending on the model, must then be made, which yield a more complicated variation with temperature than that given by the Langevin-Debye formula. An example of a case where such calculations are required will be encountered in § 67 in connexion with the magnetic susceptibility of NO. Dielectric constants do not appear to have been measured at low enough temperatures to make the corrections to the Langevin-Debye formula appreciable, as will be discussed more fully in § 47.

The various normal levels usually result from giving the molecules different amounts of 'temperature' rotation about their centres of gravity, different orientations relative to the external fields, or from allowing the spin axis of the electron to assume different orientations relative to the rest of the system. Hence the frequencies $\nu = (W_1 - W_2)/h$ associated with transitions between any two normal energy-levels $W_1$, $W_2$ are connected by the correspondence principle with classical frequencies of rotation or precession. Thus another way of stating the fundamental assumptions is that the molecule possesses a permanent moment which has precession and rotation frequencies all small compared to $kT/h$. It is to be understood that such terms as precession are not to be taken too literally in quantum mechanics, as the atom has no ordinary space-time geometry. It is immaterial for the proof how many frequencies are superposed, i.e. how complicated the motion.

*The low- and high-frequency elements will be found to contribute respectively the first and second terms of the Langevin-Debye formula* (10). Thus the high-frequency elements of the moment matrix are responsible for the induced polarization term, while only the low-frequency elements contribute to the permanent dipole term which is inversely proportional to temperature. The hypothesis of a permanent dipole moment means that the square of the low-frequency part of the moment matrix has the same value $\mu^2$ for all the normal states. This is not at all a drastic assumption, as it is involved in all permanent dipole theories, and without it the expression $\mu$ in (10) would have no meaning. In non-polar molecules $\mu$ may be regarded as having the special value 0, and then the moment matrix will contain exclusively elements of the high-frequency type.

Let $\mathbf{p} = \sum e_i \mathbf{r}_i$ be the vector moment matrix of the molecule. A typical element (exclusive of the exponential time factor) of its component in the direction of the applied field may be denoted by $p_E(njm; n'j'm')$. Such an element is associated with a transition from a state specified by indices $n$, $j$, $m$ to one by $n'$, $j'$, $m'$. We shall let the first of the three indices be identified with quantum numbers (e.g. 'electronic' and 'vibrational') which have an effect on the energy large compared to $kT$, so that one particular value of this index gives states of especially low energy. This value will be denoted by $n$, and yields the normal levels of the atom or molecule. The second index $j$ or $j'$ corresponds to quantum numbers (e.g. 'inner', 'rotational', 'spin') whose effect on the energy is comparable with or smaller than $kT$. We do not, however, include in the second index the 'axial' (also called 'equatorial' or 'magnetic') quantum number which specifies the spacial orientation by quantizing angular momentum about some fixed direction in space. Instead, the third index $m$ or $m'$ is to be considered as representing the axial quantum number. Thus the various component levels of the normal state correspond to fixed $n$ but different values of $j$ and $m$, whereas the excited states have an index $n'$ different from $n$. It is clearly to be understood that each index, except the third, in general symbolizes more than one quantum number. Hence we designate $n, j, m$ as 'indices' rather than quantum numbers. Our proof is thus by no means confined to systems with three quantum numbers or degrees of freedom.

If we substitute in Eq. (4) the formulae for $W^{(1)}$, $W^{(2)}$ given in Eq. (49) of Chapter VI, generalized to three rather than two indices (or what is equivalent, substitute in (1) the formula for the perturbed moment given in (50) of Chapter VI and expand as in § 44), the formula for the susceptibility becomes

$$\chi = B \sum_{j,m} \left\{ \left[ \frac{p_E^0(njm; njm)^2}{kT} - \sideset{}{'}\sum_{n',j',m'} \frac{2|p_E^0(njm; n'j'm')|^2}{h\nu(njm; n'j'm')} \right] e^{-W^0_{njm}/kT} \right\}, \quad (11)$$

with the abbreviation

$$B = \frac{N}{\sum\limits_{j,m} e^{-W^0_{njm}/kT}}. \tag{12}$$

In (11), as in § 34, the prime means that the state $n' = n$, $j' = j$, $m' = m$ is to be excluded from the inner summation.

Eq. (11) is a perfectly general expression for the susceptibility not requiring either of the two fundamental hypotheses of a permanent moment, and of the existence of solely 'low'- and 'high'-frequency elements in the moment matrix. It is perhaps well to restate these two hypotheses in equation form. The latter of them is that

$$|h\nu(njm; n'j'm')| \gg kT \qquad (n' \neq n),$$

and that $\quad p_E(njm; nj'm') = 0 \quad$ unless $\quad |h\nu(njm; nj'm')| \ll kT.$ \right\} \tag{13}

To exhibit most explicitly the significance of the other hypothesis of a permanent moment, it will be convenient to use a distinctive notation for the unperturbed matrix elements of the low-frequency part of **p**. We shall therefore use **μ** to denote the matrix formed from $\mathbf{p}^0$ by dropping the high-frequency elements $n' \neq n$ associated with transitions to excited states, so that

$$\mu_q(jm; j'm') = p_q^0(njm; nj'm') \qquad (q = x, y, z). \tag{14}$$

It is unnecessary to use an index $n$ or $n'$ in $\mu$, as it is formed from those elements of $p^0$ in which the first index has the same value $n$ in both the initial and final states. The matrix $\mu$ is thus just a small square out of the larger matrix $p^0$, and is what Born and Jordan call a 'Teilmatrix'. The assumption of a permanent moment means that the scalar magnitude of the vector matrix **μ** is constant with respect to time, and the same for the various normal states. The vector **μ** will usually not be constant in direction. Hence the individual Cartesian components $\mu_x$, $\mu_y$, $\mu_z$ will vary with time, having 'low'-frequency elements arising from the various precessions and rotations. These time variations, however, drop out of the scalar magnitude $\mu$ which is independent of $j$, $m$, and thus

$$\sum_{q=x,y,z} \sum_{j',m'} \mu_q(jm; j'm')\mu_q(j'm'; j''m'') = \delta(jm; j''m'')\mu^2, \tag{15}$$

with $\delta$ as on p. 132. In other words, $\mu^2$ is assumed to be a diagonal matrix whose elements are all equal, and in the terminology of Dirac it would be called a '$c$-number', which is the square of the moment $\mu$ entering in Eq. (10).

In terms of the distinctive notation introduced for the low-frequency elements, Eq. (11) becomes

$$\chi = \frac{B}{kT} \sum_{j,m} |\mu_E(jm;jm)|^2 e^{-W^0_{njm}/kT} -$$

$$-2B \sum_{j,m,j',m'}{}' \frac{|\mu_E(jm;j'm')|^2}{h\nu(njm;nj'm')} e^{-W^0_{njm}/kT} + \qquad (16)$$

$$+2B \sum_{j,m,n',j',m'(n'\neq n)} \frac{|p^0_E(njm;n'j'm')|^2}{h\nu(n'j'm';njm)} e^{-W^0_{njm}/kT}.$$

Here the first two and third lines represent respectively the contributions of the low- and high-frequency elements. To bring out the fact that the third line is inherently positive, we have here introduced the positive or emission frequencies $h\nu(n'j'm';njm)$ in place of the negative or absorption frequencies $h\nu(njm;n'j'm')$. In (16) we have written $|\mu_E(jm;jm)|^2$ for $[\mu_E(jm;jm)]^2$, which is legitimate since the diagonal elements of Hermitian matrices are real.

The terms in the summation in the second line of (16) may be grouped together in pairs of the form

$$P_{12} = -2B\left\{ \frac{|\mu_E(j_1m_1;j_2m_2)|^2}{h\nu(nj_1m_1;nj_2m_2)} e^{-W^0_{nj_1m_1}/kT} + \frac{|\mu_E(j_2m_2;j_1m_1)|^2}{h\nu(nj_2m_2;nj_1m_1)} e^{-W^0_{nj_2m_2}/kT} \right\}.$$
$$(17)$$

Now $\mu_E(j_2m_2;j_1m_1)$ is the conjugate of $\mu_E(j_1m_1;j_2m_2)$, and so has the same absolute magnitude. Also the denominator of the second term of (17) is the negative of that of the first term. We next make the substitution $W^0_{nj_2m_2} = W^0_{nj_1m_1} + h\nu(nj_2m_2;nj_1m_1)$ in the second exponential of (17) and develop this exponential as a power series in the ratio

$$w = \frac{h\nu(nj_1m_1;nj_2m_2)}{kT}. \qquad (18)$$

Then (17) becomes

$$P_{12} = -\frac{2B}{wkT} |\mu_E(j_1m_1;j_2m_2)|^2 e^{-W^0_{nj_1m_1}/kT}[1-1-w-\tfrac{1}{2}w^2-\tfrac{1}{6}w^3...]. \quad (19)$$

If the fundamental hypothesis (13) is valid, $w$ will be a very small quantity, and we may without serious error neglect terms of the order $w^3$ and beyond in the bracketed factor of (19). With this approximation, (19) is the same as

$$P_{12} = \frac{B}{kT}[|\mu_E(j_1m_1;j_2m_2)|^2 e^{-W^0_{nj_1m_1}/kT} + |\mu_E(j_2m_2;j_1m_1)|^2 e^{-W^0_{nj_2m_2}/kT}]. \quad (20)$$

It may be objected by some readers that by giving the molecule sufficient quanta of rotation, the ratio (18) may be made as large as we

please, as the separation of consecutive energy-levels for the simple
dumb-bell model by Eq. (57), Chap. VI, increases linearly with $j$. In
other words, the spacing of the normal levels is not uniform as in Fig. 7,
but becomes steadily greater as we go to higher normal states. Fortunately, however, this consideration gives no trouble, for the numerical
magnitude of the exponent in the Boltzmann distribution factor $e^{-W/kT}$
increases much more rapidly than $w$. (One varies approximately as the
square, the other as the first power of the rotational quantum number.)
Hence terms for which $w$ is comparable with unity will have such a
small exponential factor or probability that they can be disregarded.
As still further assurance that the higher powers of $w$ can be discarded
under the hypothesis (13), we shall give in § 47 the quantitative correction to the Langevin-Debye formula which results when the development is broken off after $w^4$ rather than $w^2$. This correction proves to
be very small if the fundamental hypothesis (13) is valid.

When we utilize (20), Eq. (16) becomes

$$\chi = \frac{B}{kT} \sum_{j,m,j',m'} |\mu_E(jm;j'm')|^2 e^{-W_{nj}^0/kT} +$$

$$+2B \sum_{j,m,n',j',m'(n' \neq n)} \frac{|p_E^0(njm;n'j'm')|^2}{h\nu(n';n)} e^{-W_{nj}^0/kT}, \qquad (21)$$

where now the first sum includes the diagonal elements $njm; njm$.
The first two lines of (16) have been melted into a single line in (21),
as the first line of (16) supplies just the diagonal elements wanting from
its second after the simplification (20).

In writing (21) we have introduced two simplifications. Firstly, in
the second line we have replaced $\nu(n'j'm';njm)$ by a number $\nu(n';n)$
independent of the indices $j$, $m$, $j'$, $m'$. This is clearly allowable as the
separations between the various normal states are by hypothesis small
compared to the interval between normal and excited states, and hence
the 'high' frequencies $\nu(n';n)$ $(n' \neq n)$ are affected but little by $j$, $m$,
$j'$, $m'$. Secondly, we have replaced $W_{njm}^0$ by an expression $W_{nj}^0$ which
is independent of $m$. This presupposes that the influence of orientation,
i.e. of the axial quantum number $m$ on the unperturbed energy $W_{njm}^0$,
is small compared to $kT$, a condition which is certainly fulfilled with
a high degree of precision in gases. In fact the ideal case ordinarily
considered is that in which the molecule is subject to no external field
except $E$, and then the unperturbed energy (i.e. the energy in the
absence of $E$) is independent of orientation, so that the index $m$ has
absolutely no effect on $W^0$. To allow for the possibility of simultaneous

electric and magnetic fields, or inter-molecular fields in liquids and solids, we admit the more general assumption that $W^0_{njm} - W^0_{nj}$ is not identically zero but small compared to $kT$. Thus our derivation of the Langevin-Debye formula is applicable to solids provided, of course, the two fundamental hypotheses given on p. 187 are fulfilled, and provided the effect of orientation is small compared to $kT$. In other words, the 'turning over' of an atom or molecule against the inter-molecular field must require the expenditure of an amount of work considerably less than $kT$. This condition is really already embodied in our second fundamental hypothesis, as the requirement $|W^0_{njm} - W^0_{njm'}| \ll kT$ is a special case of (13).

It was proved in § 35 that in virtue of the high degree of spectroscopic stability characteristic of the new quantum mechanics, an expression of the form

$$\sum_{m,m'} |A_z(njm; n'j'm')|^2$$

is invariant of the direction of the axis of quantization, and equals

$$\tfrac{1}{3}\sum_{m,m'} |A(njm; n'j'm')|^2, \text{ where } |A(njm; n'j'm')|^2 = \sum_{q=x,y,z} |A_q(njm; n'j'm')|^2.$$

This consequence of spectroscopic stability is vital, as it underlies the general occurrence of the factor $\tfrac{1}{3}$ in the temperature term of the Langevin-Debye formula. Let us suppose that the field $E$ is along the $z$ axis. Then by taking $A = \mu$ $(n = n')$ and $A = p^0$ $(n \neq n')$, one sees that (21) may be written

$$\chi = \frac{B}{3kT} \sum_{j,m,j',m'} |\mu(jm; j'm')|^2 e^{-W^0_{nj}/kT} +$$

$$+ \tfrac{2}{3}B \sum_{j,m,n',j',m'\,(n'\neq n)} \frac{|p^0(njm; n'j'm')|^2}{h\nu(n';n)} e^{-W^0_{nj}/kT}. \qquad \textbf{(22)}$$

*Simplification of Low-frequency Elements.* From the rule for matrix multiplication (Eq. (9), Chap. VI) it follows that

$$\sum_{j',m'} |\mu(jm; j'm')|^2 = (\mu_x^2 + \mu_y^2 + \mu_z^2)(j;j) = \mu^2(j;j). \qquad \textbf{(23)}$$

Here the right-hand side is a diagonal element of the matrix $\mu^2$, which is the square of the absolute magnitude of the vector matrix $\mu$ formed from the complete moment $\mathbf{p}$ by deleting the high-frequency elements. The index $m$ is not needed on the right side of (23) because the magnitude of a vector is independent of its spacial orientation.

Now if the hypothesis of a permanent moment is valid, we may apply

Eq. (15), which makes (23) independent of $j$, and the first line of (22) becomes

$$\frac{B\mu^2}{3kT} \sum_{j,m} e^{-W^0_{nj}/kT}.$$ (24)

Now we have already supposed that $W^0_{njm}$ can be replaced by $W^0_{nj}$ in the exponential factors, and so the sum in (24) is identical with the denominator of (12). Hence (24) is simply $N\mu^2/3kT$, which is the 'temperature part' of the Langevin-Debye formula (10). It is clear that if the hypothesis of a permanent moment were not valid, the first line of (22) would become instead

$$\frac{N}{3kT} \frac{\sum\limits_{j,m} \mu^2(j;j)e^{-W^0_{nj}/kT}}{\sum\limits_{j,m} e^{-W^0_{nj}/kT}} = \frac{N\overline{\overline{\mu^2}}}{3kT}.$$ (25)

Here $\overline{\overline{\mu^2}}$ denotes the statistical mean square of the moment $\mu$, i.e. the time average $\mu^2(j;j)$ of $\mu^2$ for a given state $j$, $m$, with this average in turn averaged over all the normal states weighted in accordance with the Boltzmann factor. Eq. (25) represents a sort of generalized Langevin formula, somewhat analogous to the generalized classical expression which we derived in (22), Chap. II.

*Simplification of High-frequency Elements.* The important thing about the second line of (22) is that for given $N$ it is independent of temperature and so may be denoted by a constant $N\alpha$, as in Eq. (10). The demonstration is an easy consequence of the 'sum-rules'[8] for intensities, applied to absorption rather than emission, for it is the essence of these rules that an expression of the form

$$\sum_{j',m'} |p^0(njm; n'j'm')|^2$$ (26)

is independent of the indices $j$ and $m$. The sum-rules were first established on semi-empirical grounds, but the work of Born, Heisenberg, and Jordan, and of Dirac shows that they are required by the quantum mechanics,[9] provided $j$ is associated with the one type of precession

---

[8] For references and description of the sum-rule see Pauling and Goudsmit, *The Structure of Line Spectra*, p. 137. The ordinary statement of the sum-rule for the inner quantum number is that the sum of the intensities of the multiplet components which have a common initial (or else common final) state $j$ is proportional to its *a priori* probability $g_j$. This statement, however, presupposes a summation over $m$ inasmuch as the Zeeman components are assumed unresolved. The sum-rule for the magnetic quantum number shows that all the $g_j$ components of the state $j$ contribute equally to the sum over $m$. Consequently when, as in (26), we do not sum over $m$, but only over $m'$, the factor $g_j$ cancels out.

[9] Born, Heisenberg, and Jordan, *Zeits. f. Physik*, **35**, 605 (1926). P. A. M. Dirac, *Proc. Roy. Soc.* **111**A, 281 (1926). The former deduce the formulae of Goudsmit and Kronig for the intensities of Zeeman components. Dirac proves the more difficult formu-

ordinarily identified with the inner (or rotational) quantum number. Actually we have already stated that the index $j$ may correspond to several quantum numbers, and hence represent the effect of several superposed precessions: e.g. simultaneous precessions resulting from interaction with electron spin and from molecular rotation. However, Dirac [9] notes that there is no difficulty in extending the proof of the intensity- or sum-rules to systems that are composed of any number of parts, and that so contain any number of precessions, provided the parts are coupled together by 'secular' forces which do not distort the motion but which instead give rise only to pure precession. This result is also obvious from the correspondence principle, inasmuch as the sum-rule is the quantum analogue of the fact that classically the intensity of radiation is not appreciably affected by precessions which do not sensibly alter the sizes and shapes of the orbits. This rules out centrifugal expansion and similar effects, but their effect is only subordinate, as we shall see more fully in § 47. The observed existence of a term in the dielectric constant which is independent of temperature, also especially the allied independence of the index of refraction of temperature [10], discussed in § 16, must be regarded as indirect but nevertheless very good experimental evidence for the validity of the sum-rules.

From what has been said in the preceding paragraph we may replace (26) by an expression $|p^0(n; n')|^2$ independent of $j$ and $m$, and so the second line of (22) reduces to

$$\tfrac{2}{3}B \sum_{n'(n' \neq n)} \left\{ \frac{|p^0(n; n')|^2}{h\nu(n'; n)} \sum_{j,m} e^{-W_{nj}^0/kT} \right\}. \tag{27}$$

The double sum in this equation is, as before, the same as the denominator of (12). Thus (27) becomes an expression

$$N\alpha = \tfrac{2}{3}N \sum_{n'(n' \neq n)} \frac{|p^0(n; n')|^2}{h\nu(n'; n)}, \tag{28}$$

which is independent of $T$ and which constitutes the 'constant' part of the Langevin-Debye formula. Combination of the simplifications affected in the high- and low-frequency parts of (22) yields the complete Langevin-Debye formula (10).

lae of Kronig, Russell, Sommerfeld and Hönl (note [52], Chap. VI) for intensities in multiplets. These formulae contain more information than the sum-rules, but necessarily demand the validity of the latter.

[10] The proof that refractivities in the optical region are independent of temperature is similar to that of Eq. (28). Cf. *Phys. Rev.* **30**, 41 (1927).

*Review.* Now that the proof is over, it is perhaps well to caution against the misconception prevalent among many physicists that the reapportionment of molecules among the different stationary states due to alteration of the Boltzmann factors by the applied field is responsible for the term of the Langevin-Debye formula which is inversely proportional to $T$, and that the distortion of the motion within a stationary state gives rise to the term independent of $T$. Actually the distortion usually contributes to both terms, if we use the word 'distortion' in the sense of *any* change in the motion produced by the field, such as, for instance, alteration in the end-over-end rotation. (Alteration in the internal structure of the molecule, such as stretching of the orbits, &c., as distinct from changes in the motion of the molecule as a whole, or perhaps its coupling to the spin, does, to be sure, give a term independent of $T$.) In fact, in the dumb-bell model (§ 45) it was not necessary to consider the reapportionment at all, i.e. it was adequate to take $W = W^0$ in the Boltzmann factors, as the first-order Stark effect $W^{(1)}$ vanished. (Note that in § 44 we showed that to obtain the portion of the susceptibility independent of field strength, the energy is needed to the approximation $W^{(2)}$ in connexion with the moment factors (1) involved in (3), but need be carried only to the approximation $W^{(1)}$ in the Boltzmann factors.) It may seem rather surprising that distortion without reapportionment can give rise to a term inversely proportional to $T$, but the situation is roughly the following. The 'low-frequency part' of the distortion of the moment by the applied field may be enormous because of the 'low frequencies' $\nu(njm; nj'm')$ in the denominator, but the different normal states would just compensate each other as regards this part, except for their differences in the value of the unperturbed Boltzmann factor, which after series expansion are found to have the effect of introducing $kT$ in the denominator in place of $h\nu$ (cf. Eq. (19)). Only in the special case of the magnetic susceptibilities of atoms without spin or else with very wide multiplet structures does the $1/T$ term arise entirely from $W^{(1)}$ without the aid of the low-frequency part of $W^{(2)}$ (cf. Eq. (13), Chap. IX). The popular misconception has doubtless arisen as an incorrect generalization of this special case. The high-frequency part of $W^{(2)}$, of course, gives the term independent of $T$.

*Case of a Simultaneous Magnetic Field.* The expression (28), also of course the permanent moment $\mu$, does not involve the index $m$, or the direction of the axis of quantization, and so the choice of this axis cannot influence either term of the Langevin-Debye formula. Hence, unlike the old quantum theory (§ 31), a magnetic field cannot distort the dielectric constant merely by changing the direction of the axis of quantization. Instead a magnetic field will influence the dielectric constant only through higher-order terms, which we have neglected and which are analogous to saturation effects. Because of the spectroscopic stability characteristic of the true quantum mechanics, these small terms will be proportional to $H^2$, and of the same order of magnitude as we calculated in § 31 with classical theory.

*Special Case that E is the only External Field.* In case other external fields, such as, for instance, the magnetic one just considered, are absent, the axis of quantization will coincide with the direction of $E$. The third index $m$ will then have no influence on the energy in the absence of $E$, and consequently all frequencies of the form $\nu(njm; njm')$ will vanish, as it is understood throughout that the frequencies $\nu$ appearing in the denominators are to be calculated for the unperturbed system. Nevertheless, there will be no trouble with zero denominators,[11] inasmuch as the matrices $p_E$ or $\mu_E$ will contain no elements in which $m \neq m'$, since the component of moment in the direction of $E$ clearly cannot involve the frequency of precession about the direction of $E$, which is the frequency associated with the quantum number $m$. Thus the summation over $m'$ may be replaced by the substitution $m' = m$.

## 47. Limit of Accuracy of the Langevin-Debye Formula

It is clear that if the temperature is diminished sufficiently, the separation of the normal levels cannot continue to remain small compared to $kT$. Hence at low temperatures there should be appreciable departures from the Langevin-Debye formula, which is, strictly speaking, in quantum mechanics only an asymptotic formula valid at high temperatures. This has already been emphasized in § 45 in connexion with the 'dumb-bell' model. It was shown that for this model, Eq. (8) is a rigorous expression (neglecting saturation) for the susceptibility, valid right down to $T = 0$, whereas the Langevin-Debye formula is not. One could form an idea of the range of temperatures over which the latter formula is substantially valid with this model by determining the critical temperature at which it begins to depart appreciably from Eq. (8). We shall not do this, but instead shall give an approximate correction for the departures from the Langevin-Debye formula with a more general

---

[11] Conceivably there might be degeneracies other than the spacial one, and which give rise to zero denominators. There is, however, no difficulty, as the degeneracy may be removed by applying a hypothetical infinitesmal field which removes the degeneracy, and the theorem of spectroscopic stability shows that the results are invariant of the way the degeneracy is removed.

model of a molecule, with three moments of inertia none of which are necessarily equal. This correction consists in determining the effect of the retention of terms to $w^4$ inclusive rather than to $w^2$ as previously in the series expansion made in the bracketed part of Eq. (19). A rigorous formula would involve the retention of all terms in this expansion, but such a formula would be intractable and unilluminating except for simplified models such as the dumb-bell or symmetrical top. The temperatures at which the terms in $w^3$, $w^4$ begin to appreciably modify the susceptibility are evidently the temperatures at which we may begin to expect appreciable corrections to the Langevin-Debye formula. We shall not give the details [12] of the calculation of this second approximation to the susceptibility by including the effect of $w^3$, $w^4$, but shall merely state the result, viz.

$$\chi = \frac{N\mu^2}{3kT}[1 - f(T)] + N\alpha, \tag{29}$$

where

$$f(T) = \frac{h^2}{48\pi^2\mu^2 kT}\left[\mu_{x'}^2\left(\frac{1}{B} + \frac{1}{C}\right) + \mu_{y'}^2\left(\frac{1}{C} + \frac{1}{A}\right) + \mu_{z'}^2\left(\frac{1}{A} + \frac{1}{B}\right)\right]. \tag{30}$$

Here $A$, $B$, $C$ denote the moments of inertia of the molecule about its three principal axes $x'$, $y'$, $z'$, and $\mu_{x'}$, $\mu_{y'}$, $\mu_{z'}$ are the components of the permanent moment $\mu$ along these axes. For either the 'dumb-bell' or symmetrical top models, i.e. for either diatomic or symmetrical polyatomic molecules, we may take $\mu_{z'}' = \mu$, $\mu_{x'} = \mu_{y'} = 0$, $A = B = I$, and (30) then reduces to

$$f(T) = \frac{h^2}{24\pi^2 IkT} = \frac{1\cdot32 \times 10^{-39}}{IT}. \tag{31}$$

The factor $1 - f(T)$ evidently enters in (31) as a correction to the Langevin-Debye formula. To obtain a numerical estimate of its importance let us consider the particular case of HCl. Substitution in (31) of the value $I = 2\cdot65 \times 10^{-40}$ gm. cm.$^2$ appropriate to HCl yields $f = 5\cdot0/T$, so that at room temperatures $f(T)$ is only $0\cdot016$. To make the correction as great as 5 per cent. it would be necessary to reduce the temperature to $100°$ K., or below the freezing-point of HCl, which is obviously not feasible. Gases which have low boiling-points, and which hence might be measured when the denominator of (31) is small, are invariably non-polar (e.g. $O_2$, $H_2$) or nearly so. CO and NO are two

---

[12] See J. H. Van Vleck, *Phys. Rev.* **30**, 46 (1927). The correction (31) appropriate to diatomic and symmetrical molecules has also been deduced by Kronig and by Manneback (*l.c.*[5], also ref. 21 of Chap. VI) by a different method than ours. In the case of the dumb-bell model their method consists in finding a somewhat better approximation to the denominator of (8) than merely replacing the sum by an integral as on p. 185. An analogous method is also used for the symmetrical top.

common slightly polar gases which have relatively low boiling-points, but this feature is more than offset by their moments of inertia being over five times that of HCl, so that the values of $f(T)$ obtainable experimentally for them are even smaller than for HCl.

These numerical considerations show that the correction $f(T)$ to the Langevin-Debye formula is ordinarily far too small to be of consequence, and experiments would have to be very sensitive to detect the departures from linearity which it occasions in the graph of $\chi$ against $1/T$ at constant density. The main value of the calculation of the second approximation involving $f(T)$ is hence primarily to reassure us that in the case of dielectric constants the asymptotic agreement of classical and quantum theories is nearly completed at any temperatures ordinarily obtainable (barring possible 'internal rotations' in organic molecules discussed on p. 76). (In magnetism, because of the spin multiplets,[13] we shall later see that there may be important deviations from the classical Langevin law even at room temperature.) The correction factor $1-f(T)$ does modify slightly the experimental values of the electric moment determined by the method I which was described in § 19. In this method $\mu$ is ordinarily calculated from the temperature coefficient of $\chi$ in the vicinity of a room temperature $T_0$, and hence with the correction $\mu^2$ must be increased by a factor about $1+2f(T_0)$ to give this coefficient the same value as previously. Correspondingly the effect of this correction is to increase the contribution of permanent dipoles to the susceptibility by a factor $[1+2f(T_0)][1-f(T_0)] \sim 1+f(T_0)$ and hence to diminish $N\alpha$, as determined by method I, by an amount $N\mu^2 f(T_0)/3kT_0$. In case most of the susceptibility arises from the permanent polarity, this diminution in $\alpha$ may reduce slightly the discrepancy between the values of $N\alpha$ determined by methods I and II (respectively temperature variation and extrapolation of optical data), discussed at length in §§ 14, 15, 19. In HCl, for instance, the correction raises the value of $\mu$ with Zahn's temperature data from $1\cdot034\times10^{-18}$ to $1\cdot050\times10^{-18}$, and correspondingly diminishes $4\pi N\alpha$ from $0\cdot00104$ to $0\cdot00099$, in somewhat better accord with the optical value $0\cdot000871$ furnished by method II.

---

[13] Spin multiplets comparable with $kT$ may exist in the present electrical case, but do no harm. This is primarily because the electrical moment has no matrix components between states which differ solely as regards the alinement of the spin relative to the rest of the molecule, thus avoiding the complication of 'medium frequency elements'. Although the multiplet structure thus does not influence the electric susceptibility, it does modify the Stark effect, as the latter involves the stationary states individually rather than collectively in summations.

*Correction for Centrifugal Expansion.* Because of centrifugal force the moment $\mu$ is never rigorously 'permanent', i.e. the same for all rotational states as supposed in § 46, but increases slightly with the rotational quantum number and hence with $T$. We may calculate quantitatively the correction resulting from this effect by replacing the first term of the Langevin-Debye formula by the more general expression (25), which does not assume a permanent moment. To evaluate $\overline{\overline{\mu^2}}$ let us take a diatomic molecule whose nuclear separation, moment of inertia, and electrical moment are respectively $r_0$, $I_0$, and $\mu_0$ when the molecule is at rest, completely devoid of rotation or vibration. If now the molecule rotates with an angular velocity $\omega$, the centrifugal force $Mr\omega^2$ must equal the restoring force $4\pi^2\nu^2M(r-r_0)$. Here $\nu$ is the frequency of vibration, supposed simple harmonic. A small expansion of the molecule by an amount $r-r_0$ increases the electrical moment by $e_{\text{eff}}(r-r_0)$, where $e_{\text{eff}}$ is by definition the 'effective charge' (see p. 47). Consequently we have approximately

$$\overline{\overline{\mu^2}} = \mu_0^2 + 2\mu_0 e_{\text{eff}}(\overline{\overline{r}}-r_0) = \mu_0^2 + \frac{\mu_0 e_{\text{eff}} r_0\overline{\overline{\omega^2}}}{2\pi^2\nu^2} \quad \text{or} \quad \overline{\overline{\mu^2}} = \mu_0^2 + \frac{\mu e_{\text{eff}} r_0 kT}{I\pi^2\nu^2},$$

since classically the mean of the rotational kinetic energy $\frac{1}{2}I\omega^2$ is $kT$, and quantum mechanically this value is valid at ordinary temperatures, as they are high enough to make rotational specific heats have substantially the classical equipartition magnitude. The effect of centrifugal expansion is thus only a contribution $\mu_0 e_{\text{eff}} r_0/3\pi^2I\nu^2$ to the constant $\alpha$ in Eq. (10). This contribution is, unlike the correction (31) previously considered, as important at high as at very low temperatures, but is usually quite negligible. In HCl, for instance, if we use Bourgin's value (§ 15) of the effective charge, the centrifugal expansion gives rise to only 1 per cent. of $\alpha$, and so may be neglected without appreciable error.

*Correction for Vibrational Distortion.* By supposing a permanent moment we have assumed that the electrical moment is independent of the vibrational quantum number or else that all vibrational states but the lowest have negligible Boltzmann factors. The latter assumption is sufficiently warranted in ordinary stable diatomic molecules such as HCl at ordinary temperatures, but complicated polyatomic molecules may have some of their vibrational degrees of freedom less firmly bound, and so sometimes be in higher vibrational states where the moment of inertia and hence the electrical moment is appreciably different from in the normal state. This effect has been considered in considerable detail by Zahn.[14] The correction can again be calculated approximately by replacing the first term of (10) by (25). For stable diatomic molecules such as HCl it is readily seen to be of the same order of magnitude as that for rotational distortion and likewise independent of the temperature. In complicated polyatomic molecules where the vibrations are of large amplitude and not simple harmonic, this vibrational correction may be more important and yield a complicated temperature dependence. We have already mentioned on p. 76 that in molecules possessing pliable bonds there will be departures from this formula if the radicals are only partially free to turn. This is closely akin to the effect considered by Zahn, the difference being that the non-rigidity is due to twisting rather than stretching.

*Correction for Saturation.* By neglecting terms beyond $E^2$ in Eq. (2) we have disregarded all saturation effects. The effect of including terms through $E^4$ in (2)

---

[14] C. T. Zahn, *Phys. Rev.* **35**, 1047, 1056 (1930). His Eq. (10) is essentially the same as (25). The departure from the Debye formula which he finds experimentally in acetic acid is probably due to molecular association; cf. *Phys. Rev.* **37**, 1516 (1931).

has been calculated by Niessen[15] for the general quantum dynamical system, with the two same fundamental hypotheses as in § 46. His results, especially the mode of temperature dependence have already been discussed in § 22. The numerical estimates there given show that the saturation effects are very small at the largest field strengths $E$ yet obtainable experimentally, but have nevertheless been detected by Herweg and others (§ 22). We may mention that if one considers only the permanent dipole moment, or in other words retains only the low-frequency part of the total moment $\mathbf{p}$, then Niessen has shown that it is possible to calculate asymptotically the effect of all powers of $E$ in Eq. (2). He finds that then the complete Langevin formula $NL(\mu E/kT)$ (Eq. 4, Chap. II) for the polarization is valid, but it may be cautioned that this result applies only when the correction for saturation is larger than, or at least of greater interest than, corrections such as (30) for the finite magnitude of rotational energy intervals. In other words saturation is the main correction if $\mu E \gg kT'$ and $kT' \ll kT$, where $T'$ is the molecule's 'characteristic temperature' $h^2/8\pi^2Ik$. Existing experiments on electric saturation are not made at fields so large that $\mu E \gg kT'$, although made at temperatures for which $T' \ll T$. Under these conditions one can still use Niessen's value of the correction for saturation, as the corrections for finite intervals and for saturation are approximately additive if neither of them is great.

*Comparison with Experiment.* As the quantum mechanics has restored the Langevin formula under ordinary conditions, the comparison with experiment, and deduction of numerical dipole values from the latter, proceeds as in classical theory, and so the material given in Chapter III is still applicable. The discussion of the effect of infra-red vibrations proceeds exactly as in § 15. We have seen on pp. 30 and 186 that the classical and quantum theories give exactly the same value $\sum c_i^2/a_i$ for the polarizability $\alpha$ of a system of isotropic harmonic oscillators. The identity of results is also readily established[16] in the more general case of periodic rather than static impressed fields, and of one-dimensional harmonic oscillations along the figure axis instead of isotropic ones. Spectroscopic stability shows that the factor $\frac{1}{3}$ arises from the spacial orientation, regardless of the type of spacial quantization or molecular rotation.[17] Thus (4), Chap. III, which was

---

[15] K. F. Niessen, *Phys. Rev.* **34**, 253 (1929).

[16] See *Phys. Rev.* **30**, 44 (1927).

[17] Complete similarity with classical results on harmonic oscillators is an almost invariable characteristic of the new mechanics. On the other hand, the 'anharmonic correction' which results because the restoring forces on the nuclei are not strictly linear, has a different effect on the susceptibility than in classical theory. S. Boguslawski (*Phys. Zeits.* **15**, 283, 1914) and K. Czukor (*Verh. d. Deut. Phys. Ges.* **17**, 73 (1916) showed that classically this correction modified somewhat the nature of the temperature dependence of the dielectric constant, whereas in quantum mechanics it merely alters slightly the magnitude of $\alpha$, inasmuch as (28) is a perfectly general expression for the contribution of high-frequency elements. Such a divergence from classical results is, of course, only possible because the vibrational energy intervals, as distinct from the rotational, are usually large compared to $kT$ in stable diatomic molecules. The vibrational intervals

our focal point for discussing infra-red vibrations, still retains its validity.

cease to be large compared to $kT$ when there is an appreciable vibrational specific heat. The correction which then results to the Langevin-Debye formula is, however, very slight, as the nuclear vibrations are usually very nearly simple harmonic, and solution of Eq. (9) has shown that harmonic oscillators have exactly the same polarizability in all stationary states. The form of temperature dependence is altered only by super-position of the anharmonic correction and that for the excitation of higher vibrational states than the lowest.

# THE DIELECTRIC CONSTANTS AND DIAMAGNETIC SUSCEPTIBILITIES OF ATOMS AND MONATOMIC IONS

IT may seem strange that we mix electric and diamagnetic susceptibilities in the same chapter, but in the monatomic case it is convenient to discuss them together because of parallelism in the rigorous theory for hydrogen and in the adaptation to other atoms by the method of screening constants.

## 48. The Dielectric Constant of Atomic Hydrogen and Helium

As the electrons are on the time average symmetrically located with respect to any plane containing the nucleus, atoms and monatomic ions have no permanent moments, and so have only the term $N\alpha$ of the Langevin-Debye formula which arises from 'high-frequency' matrix elements (cf. Chap. VII). It has so far been possible to determine the numerical magnitudes of $\mu$ and $\alpha$ for *molecules* only by the experimental methods of § 19, but on the other hand it is easy to calculate by pure theory the absolute value of $\alpha$ for monatomic hydrogen.

The rigorous proof that atoms have no permanent moments runs as follows.[1] In the absence of external fields, the wave equation of any atom or molecule composed of $\eta$ particles is invariant with respect to the substitution

$$x^{'} = -x_i, \qquad y_i^{'} = -y_i, \qquad z_i^{'} = -z_i \qquad (i = 1,...,\eta). \qquad \textbf{(A)}$$

Hence its solutions $\psi_n$ may always be chosen to be either even or odd as regards the substitution (A). The conjugate $\psi_n^*$ is even or odd like $\psi_n$, and $\psi_n^*\psi_n$ is then even. If we take $f = \Sigma e_i r_i$, $n' = n$ in the fundamental quadrature (14), Chap. VI, its integrand $\psi_n \psi_n^* \Sigma e_i r_i$ is odd with respect to the substitution (A) and so the integral is zero when taken over the entire coordinate space. Hence the unperturbed electric moment of any atom or molecule has no diagonal elements. To be sure, Eq. (1) of this chapter and (71) of Chap. VI display first-order Stark effects, which would seem to imply the existence of such elements, but (1) neglects the relativity and spin precessions,[2] and the 'symmetrical top' model used to obtain (71) is too simple to include 'Λ-type doubling' (see note 28 of Chap. VI and § 70). To prove that there is no permanent moment we must show that the moment matrix has no low-frequency as well as no diagonal elements. There can be no low-frequency elements if the separation of all levels, other than those differing only as regards spacial quantization or of quantization of spin relative to the rest

---

[1] E. Wigner, *Zeits. f. Physik*, **43**, 646 (1927).

[2] For calculation of the Stark effect of atomic hydrogen to a first approximation inclusive of these precessions see R. Schlapp, *Proc. Roy. Soc.* **119**A, 313 (1928); V. Rojansky, *Phys. Rev.* 33, 1 (1929). Because of a fortuitous degeneracy with respect to the azimuthal quantum number $l$, the excited states of atomic hydrogen in the new quantum mechanics retain a portion of their linear Stark effect even when the relativity and spin corrections are included. This was not true in the old quantum theory.

of the atom, are separated by intervals large compared to $kT$. In other words this condition is that there be only one 'normal electronic' level. This is ordinarily the case in atoms, as electronic absorption frequencies are certainly large compared to $kT$, but not in molecules, as there is always a sequence of closely spaced rotational levels. Although we have thus shown the desired result that ordinary atoms have no 'dipole term' proportional to $1/T$ in the Langevin-Debye formula, such a term would be found for excited hydrogen atoms. Such atoms are exceptional because of degeneracy with respect to the azimuthal quantum number $l$. The calculation of the $1/T$ term for excited hydrogen is, of course, a purely academic affair,[3] which we omit, as susceptibilities involve only normal states, and the normal state of hydrogen has only the one $l$-value 0, and hence no bothersome degeneracy and no first-order Stark effect even in Eq. (1). When there is near degeneracy, an experimentally obtainable field may greatly distort the symmetry properties of the wave function, and so the linear Stark effects predicted by (71) of Chap. VI and by (1) are a good approximation to reality in strong fields. In non-hydrogenic atoms the effect of $l$ on the energy is usually large, and there is no first-order Stark effect, except perhaps for a few excited states of very small quantum defect. The kinematical meaning of this is that non-hydrogenic atoms have fast orbital precessions owing to the departures of the field from Coulomb character, whereas hydrogen atoms have only the slow relativity precession which is easily stopped by an applied field resulting in the alinement of the semi-major axis in this field and a first-order Stark effect.[4]

To determine the moment of hydrogen in a definite stationary state one has only to calculate to terms in $E^2$ the characteristic values of its wave equation in an electric field—in other words, to compute its second-order Stark effect. This has been done by Wentzel, Waller, and Epstein[5] with neglect of relativity corrections and spin, which permits a separation of variables and which does no harm for the normal state owing to the absence of fine structure (cf. end of fine print, p. 213). They find

$$W = -\frac{chRZ^2}{n^2} + \frac{3h^2n(n_1-n_2)E}{8\pi^2meZ} -$$

$$-\frac{n^4h^6E^2}{1024\pi^6Z^4e^6m^3}[17n^2-3(n_1-n_2)^2-9n_3^2+19], \qquad (1)$$

[3] For this calculation see J. H. Van Vleck, *Proc. Nat. Acad.* **12**, 665 (1926); and especially revision in footnote 31 on p. 37 of *Phys. Rev.* **30** (1927).

[4] For amplification and references on this distinction between hydrogenic and non-hydrogenic atoms see Ruark and Urey, *Atoms, Molecules, and Quanta*, pp. 147, 343, or the writer's *Quantum Principles and Line Spectra*, pp. 62 and 131. A wealth of theoretical and experimental work on the border-line case of the Stark effect of non-hydrogenic atoms, especially neutral He, so highly excited that the field is nearly Coulomb, has been performed by J. S. Foster and by Miss Dewey, *Proc. Roy. Soc.* **117**A, 137 (1927), *Phys. Rev.* **30**, 770 (1927), and references; also Y. Fujioka, *Sc. Rep. Phys. Chem. Res. Tokyo*, **10**, 99 (1929).

[5] G. Wentzel, *Zeits. f. Physik*, **38**, 527 (1926); I. Waller, *ibid.* **38**, 635 (1926); P. S. Epstein, *Phys. Rev.* **28**, 695 (1926).

where $n_1$, $n_2$, $n_3$ are a set of parabolic quantum numbers, such that the principal quantum number $n$ is $n_1+n_2+|n_3|+1$, while $n_3$ quantizes the angular momentum about the field and so is similar to the quantum number $m_l$ of § 39.

The normal state of hydrogen has $n_1 = n_2 = n_3 = 0$, $Z = 1$, so that by (1) its moment $-\partial W/\partial E$ is $9h^6E/128\pi^6e^6m^3 = 6\cdot63\times10^{-25}E$, with the usual neglect of saturation effects resulting from higher powers of $E$ not included in (1). Its polarizability is thus $\alpha = 6\cdot63\times10^{-25}$. The corresponding numerical value of the 'molar polarizability' $4\pi L\alpha/3$ introduced on p. 53 is $\kappa = 1\cdot68$, and of the dielectric constant at $0°$, 76 cm., is $\epsilon = 1\cdot000225$. Unfortunately it has not yet been possible to make a direct experimental confirmation of these unambiguous theoretical values, as it would be necessary to have a gas composed entirely of monatomic rather than molecular hydrogen.

The dielectric constant of neutral helium has been calculated independently and simultaneously by Atanasoff[6] and by Hassé.[7] Both utilize the fact that the perturbed wave functions of the normal state are of the form $\psi = \psi^0(r_1, r_2, r_{12}) + E\{z_1 f(r_1, r_2, r_{12}) + z_2 f(r_2, r_1, r_{12})\}$ (neglecting $E^2$, $E^3$, &c.) and determine $f$ by the Ritz method, while they take $\psi^0$ from the work of Hylleraas. The dependence on the coordinates can be shown to be necessarily of this form by extension of Wigner's methods, though this is not demonstrated explicitly in either paper.[8] If one uses Birge's 'most probable values' of the atomic constants, Atanasoff's solution yields $\epsilon = 1\cdot0000653$ at $0°$ C., 76 cm., while Hassé's first calculation gives $1\cdot0000691$ in excellent accord with the experimental value $1\cdot0000693$. This gratifying agreement, however, turns out to be rather accidental, as in his second paper Hassé finds $1\cdot000079$, using a presumably more accurate unperturbed wave function $\psi_0$. Still more recently, a theoretical value $1\cdot0000715$ is reported by Slater and Kirkwood,[9] also by the Ritz method. The diversity in results seems to arise largely because the calculations are exceedingly sensitive to the choice of the unperturbed wave function.[10]

[6] J. V. Atanasoff, *Phys. Rev.* **36**, 1232 (1930).

[7] H. R. Hassé, *Proc. Camb. Phil. Soc.* **26**, 542 (1930); **27**, 66 (1931).

[8] The proof consists in showing that $\psi^{(1)}$ involves a rotational group ('Darstellung') of the type $L = 1$ since $\psi^0$ is of the type $L = 0$ and $\mathcal{H}^{(1)}$ is proportional to $\cos\theta$. Properties of the rotational groups are developed by Wigner, *Zeits. f. Physik.* **43**, 640 (1927).

[9] Slater and Kirkwood, *Phys. Rev.* **37**, 682 (1931).

[10] By a well-known theorem, the Ritz method always yields too high a value for the total energy, but one cannot tell whether it yields too high or too low a value of the coefficient of $E^2$, as the $E^2$ term is only a portion of the total energy. Hence it may yield too small or too large a dielectric constant. A small alteration in $\psi^0$ can make

## 49. The Diamagnetism of Atoms, especially Hydrogen and Helium

In considering diamagnetism, we may suppose the atoms in singlet $S$ states, as otherwise there is an overwhelming paramagnetism. In such states the paramagnetic terms in the Hamiltonian function, which were given in Eq. $\langle 97 \rangle$, Chap. VI, and which yield a perturbative potential proportional to the first power of $H$, disappear completely. This is so inasmuch as in *atoms* the squares of the orbital and spin angular momenta are respectively $L(L+1)$ and $S(S+1)$, and consequently in the $^1S$ states, which have $S = L = 0$, there cannot be even an instantaneous magnetic moment in the absence of external fields. It may be cautioned that *molecules* have such a moment even in $^1\Sigma$ states, and for them the following formula (2) must be modified, as will be done in § 69. In $^1S$ atoms, there remains only the diamagnetic term in the perturbative potential, which is proportional to $H^2$, and the magnetic moment is entirely an induced one coming from the Larmor precession. The resulting change in energy due to this term was seen in Eq. (105), Chap. VI, to be $(e^2/8mc^2) \sum \overline{(x^2+y^2)}H^2$; and furthermore, it was shown in § 35 that on averaging over the different spacial orientations one may replace $x^2+y^2$ by $\frac{2}{3}r^2$ because of spectroscopic stability. This, of course, assumes that the Boltzmann factor is sensibly the same for the different allowed spacial orientations, which it surely is in gases, and also in solids as long as the energy of orientation in the solid's intermolecular field is small compared to $kT$. If we suppose that the atoms are all in the same stationary state except for spacial orientation, as is usually the case because the first excited states involve energy increments large compared to $kT$, it is unnecessary to average over different electronic states weighted in accordance with the Boltzmann factor. The susceptibility $L\overline{(-\partial W/\partial H)}/H$ per gramme mol is then

$$\chi_{\mathrm{mol}} = -\frac{e^2 L}{6mc^2} \sum \overline{r^2} = -2\cdot 832 \times 10^{10} \sum \overline{r^2}, \tag{2}$$

where $\overline{r^2}$ is the time-average value, i.e. the diagonal matrix element for the state under consideration. Eq. (2) is exactly the same as the Pauli form of Langevin's formula in classical theory, already given in (2), Chap. IV. Thus again the new mechanics restores a classical formula.

Eq. (2) is valid regardless of whether or not the atom is hydrogenic. For hydrogen-like atoms, we may, however, proceed farther and use

a considerable error in the coefficient of $E^2$, as only the unperturbed energy is stationary with respect to the parameters varied in obtaining the unperturbed wave function.

the formula for the mean value of $r^2$ given in (107), Chap. VI, and then

$$\chi_{\text{mol}} = -2 \cdot 832 \times 10^{10} \left( \frac{h^2}{4\pi^2 Z e^2 m} \right)^2 [\tfrac{5}{2}n^4 - \tfrac{3}{2}n^2 l(l+1) + \tfrac{1}{2}n^2]$$

$$= -0 \cdot 790 \times 10^{-6} \left[ \frac{5n^4 - 3n^2 l(l+1) + n^2}{2Z^2} \right]. \tag{3}$$

The normal state of atomic hydrogen has $n = 1$, $l = 0$, $Z = 1$, and thus its molar diamagnetic susceptibility is $-2 \cdot 37 \times 10^{-6}$. This value cannot, of course, be tested directly because of the difficulty of dissociating molecular hydrogen, also because monatomic hydrogen has a $^2S$ normal state and hence would be highly paramagnetic because of the spin. Instead we have only Pascal's [11] indirect value $-2 \cdot 93 \times 10^{-6}$, obtained by applying the additivity method to diamagnetic organic compounds containing hydrogen. Exact agreement cannot be expected, as we have seen in § 21, on refractivities, that the analysis of compounds by assumed additivity rules does not necessarily furnish true atomic properties. The error, however, is probably not so great as to permit the discrepancy by a factor about $3\frac{1}{2}$ which there was between his value and that $-0 \cdot 79 \times 10^{-6}$ furnished by the old quantum theory (p. 210). Thus Pascal's result must be regarded as distinct evidence favouring the new mechanics in preference to the old.

*Direct Calculation of $\overline{r^2}$ from the Wave Functions for Helium.* Turning now to non-hydrogenic atoms, the theoretical calculation of diamagnetic susceptibilities is much easier than of the electric, as in the diamagnetic case it is only necessary to know the *unperturbed* wave function of the normal state. Once this is known, the requisite mean value needed for (2) is given by the simple quadrature

$$\int \dots \int |\psi_n|^2 \sum r^2 \, dv, \tag{4}$$

the integration of course being over the coordinate space of all the electrons. On the other hand, to make calculations of electric susceptibilities such as were quoted on p. 205 one must know the effect of the perturbing electric field on the wave function. This is because the perturbing potential was linear in the field rather than quadratic as in the magnetic case; and so to obtain the energy to the second power of the field strength, as needed for susceptibilities, it was necessary to find a second rather than a first approximation to the effect of the perturbation, which demands knowledge of the wave functions to the 1st rather than 0th approximation in $E$.

---

[11] A. Pascal, numerous references listed in *Jahrb. d. Rad. und Elektr.* **17**, 184 (1920); cf. also Weiss, *J. de Physique*, **1**, 185 (1930).

The requisite quadrature (4) has been performed for neutral helium by Slater,[12] using a wave function which he shows to be a good approximation to the three-body problem of the normal state of helium. He thus finds $\chi_{mol} = -1\cdot85 \times 10^{-6}$, in gratifying accord with Hector and Wills' experimental value $-1\cdot88 \times 10^{-6}$. The discrepancy is less than the experimental error, as well as less than the amount of uncertainty in our knowledge of the helium wave functions. The quadrature for helium has also been evaluated independently by Stoner[13] with Hartree's wave functions. He finds $\chi_{mol} = -1\cdot90 \times 10^{-6}$, likewise in exceedingly good agreement with experiment.

Direct calculations of $\sum \overline{r^2}$ from the wave functions obtained with the Hartree method of the self-consistent field[14] have been made for the alkali ions and for $Cl^-$ by Stoner.[13] His results will be given in § 52. Similar calculations are at present wanting for other heavy atoms. Because it is easy, it is tempting to try calculating the mean value of $r^2$ and hence the susceptibility for the general heavy atom by means of the Thomas-Fermi[15] charge distribution $\rho$. In the Thomas-Fermi theory the mean value of $\sum r^2$ is $e^{-1} \iiint \rho r^2 \, dxdydz$, where the integration is 3 rather than $3Z$-dimensional as in (4). One thus finds that $\chi_{mol} = -10^{-5} Z^{\frac{4}{3}}$, where $Z$ is the atomic number, and where the factor $10^{-5}$ has been estimated by a very crude numerical quadrature.[15a] This formula is not in accord with experiment, as according to Ikenmeyer (§ 52) observed susceptibilities in heavy atoms fit roughly the formula $\chi_{mol} = -0\cdot8 \times 10^{-6} Z$. The disagreement is not surprising, as the Thomas-Fermi field is primarily a good approximation to the distribution of the large number of inner electrons, rather than the few outer electrons that contribute the bulk of the susceptibility. The sensitiveness to errors in the outer distributions is illustrated by the fact that, according to Stoner, 33 per cent. of the susceptibility of $Cl^-$ comes from the 3·46 per cent. of the charge at a distance greater than 2·06 Å from the nucleus. Better results than with the Thomas-Fermi charge distribution are obtainable not only by the more refined Hartree self-consistent field, but also by the method of shielding constants to be now given.

[12] J. C. Slater, *Phys. Rev.* **32**, 349 (1928).

[13] E. C. Stoner, *Proc. Leeds Phil. Soc.* **1**, 484 (1929).

[14] D. R. Hartree, *Proc. Cambr. Phil. Soc.* **24**, 89, 111, 426 (1928).

[15] L. H. Thomas, *Proc. Cambr. Phil. Soc.* **23**, 542 (1927); E. Fermi, *Zeits. f. Physik*, **48**, 73; **49**, 550 (1928).

[15a] This proportionality to $Z^{\frac{4}{3}}$ has also been noted by T. Takeuchi, *Phys. Math. Soc. Japan* **12**, 300 (1930).

## 50. Adaptation to Other Atoms by Screening Constants

Because direct tests on monatomic hydrogen have so far been precluded by the difficulty of obtaining complete dissociation, the best existing way of testing the formulae for the susceptibilities of hydrogen atoms is to apply them to non-hydrogenic atoms by using screening constants. As a rough approximation one may assume the orbits are like those of hydrogen except that the effective nuclear charge is $Z_{eff}e$ instead of the true charge $Ze$. The simplest illustrations are the helium atom and hydrogen molecule, even though the latter is not an atom, as each contains two electrons and so may be assumed to behave like two hydrogenic atoms in the normal state $n = 1$ but with the effective charge $Z_{eff}e$. The formulae for the energy, dielectric constant, and diamagnetic susceptibilities are, then, respectively

$$W = -27 \cdot 1\, Z_{eff}^2 \text{ volts}, \quad \epsilon = 1 + 0 \cdot 000450\, Z_{eff}^{-4}, \quad \chi_{mol} = -4 \cdot 74 \times 10^{-6}\, Z_{eff}^{-2}.$$

These may now be equated to the experimental values,[16] viz.

(He) $W = -78 \cdot 8$, $\epsilon = 1 \cdot 0000693$, $\chi_{mol} = -1 \cdot 88 \times 10^{-6}$;

(H$_2$) $W = -31 \cdot 4$, $\epsilon = 1 \cdot 000273$, $\chi_{mol} = -3 \cdot 94 \times 10^{-6}$.

We then have three independent estimates of the effective charge $Z_{eff}$, as follows:[17]

*Effective Charge $Z_{eff}$*

| From: | Energy. | Dielectric Constant. | Diamagnetism. |
|---|---|---|---|
| He | 1·71 (1·71) | 1·59 (1·10) | 1·59 (0·92) |
| H$_2$ | 1·08 (1·08) | 1·14 (0·78) | 1·11 (0·63) |

[16] The value 1·0000693 for He is that obtained by Herzfeld and Wolf, *Ann. der Physik*, **76**, 71 and 567 (1925), by extrapolation of the optical refraction, and is probably more accurate than direct determinations. The value 1·000273 for H$_2$ is that obtained by Tangl; it is for 0° C. rather than 20° C., contrary to the statement in the Landolt-Bornstein tables (5th ed., p. 1041), and so is in good agreement with dispersion data. The diamagnetic values are those of Wills and Hector, *Phys. Rev.* **23**, 209 (1926); also Hector, *ibid.* **24**, 418. Their measurements are the only reliable ones at present available for He, while in the case of H$_2$ they reassuringly agree within 2 per cent. with an independent determination by Soné, *Phil. Mag.* **39**, 305 (1920). A much higher value $5 \cdot 1 \times 10^{-6}$ for H$_2$ is reported by Lehrer, *Ann. der Physik*, **81**, 229 (1926), but he himself states this may not be accurate because of uncertainties in calibration. A value even higher than Lehrer's is apparently indicated by the graphs in a preliminary paper by C. W. Hammar, *Proc. Nat. Acad.* **12**, 594 and 597 (1926), but here likewise it is not clear whether there has been an accurate calibration of absolute values.

[17] This table is taken from *Proc. Nat. Acad.* **12**, 662 (1926). The calculations of the theoretical dielectric constant 1·000225 of atomic H from the Stark effect formulae of Wentzel, Waller, and Epstein, and of its diamagnetism (3) from the quantum-mechanical mean square radius were given independently by the writer in this paper and by Pauling, *Proc. Roy. Soc.* **114**A, 181 (1927). In reproducing the table slight revisions in the numerical values have been made due to use of Birge's recent estimates of the most probable values of the atomic constants (*Phys. Rev.*, Supp. July 1929). We have not, however, made the corresponding small revisions due to these new atomic constants in quoting Pauling's numerical calculations on the following pages.

The results which would have been obtained with the old quantum theory are included in parentheses. In the new mechanics the values of $Z_{\text{eff}}$ obtained by the different methods are seen to be roughly the same, and vastly more consistent and reasonable than with the old theory. Exact agreement between the various estimates cannot be expected even in the new, since screening constants are only crude representations of the interplay between electrons. Calculations of the dielectric constant of He by the Ritz method and of the diamagnetism of He directly from the wave functions have already been mentioned in §§ 48 and 49, and, of course, represent a much higher degree of refinement. A similar improved calculation of the diamagnetism of $H_2$ by means of wave functions has been made by Wang and will be described in § 69.

To calculate the values in parentheses it has been necessary to know the old formulae analogous to (1) and (3). These can be shown to be

$$W = -\frac{chRZ^2}{n^2} + \frac{3h^2n(n_1-n_2)E}{8\pi^2meZ} - \frac{n^4h^6E^2}{1024\pi^6Z^4e^6m^3}[17n^2-3(n_1-n_2)^2-9n_3'^2], \quad (\mathbf{1}\text{a})$$

$$\chi_{\text{mol}} = -0.790\times10^{-6}\left[\frac{5n^4-3n^2l'^2}{2Z^2}\right], \tag{3a}$$

where $n = n_1+n_2+|n_3'|$ and where $n_3'$ and $l'$ are axial and azimuthal quantum numbers one unit larger in numerical magnitude than in the new mechanics. Thus the normal state of hydrogen has $|n_3'| = 1$, or $l' = 1$, and $S, P, D, F$ terms mean respectively $l' = 1, 2, 3, 4$ as compared to $l = 0, 1, 2, 3$. In (1a) and (3a) we have tacitly supposed the field strong enough for spacial quantization in the electric case, but not in the magnetic. In the old quantum theory one cannot use the Pauli formula (2) unless one assumes random orientations, as otherwise $\overline{x^2+y^2} \neq \frac{2}{3}\overline{r^2}$ and one has all the 'Glaser effect' difficulties discussed in § 29. If instead one assumed spacial quantization in the magnetic field $H$, one would have $x^2+y^2=r^2$ for the normal state, the susceptibility would be increased by a factor $\frac{3}{2}$, and the values in parentheses in the last column would become 1·13 and 0·78. This would demand a powerful field, as diamagnetic effects are quadratic in $H$. Similarly other old values for use in the second column could be obtained if we supposed the electric field too weak to effect spacial quantization, or to overpower the relativity corrections, there being thus a double degeneracy difficulty.

The divergence between (1) (3), and (1a) (3a) is, of course, most accentuated for small quantum numbers, and hence for the state $n = 1$ such as is involved in the table. For normal monatomic hydrogen (1a) and (3a) give $\epsilon-1 = 0.000050$, $\overline{r^2} = (0.528\times10^{-8})^2$ as compared to the new $\epsilon-1 = 0.000225$, $\overline{r^2} = 3(0.528\times10^{-8})^2$. In other words the quadratic Stark effect and mean square radius for the normal state of hydrogen are respectively $4\frac{1}{2}$ and 3 times as large in the new mechanics as in the old. For larger values of $n$, the discrepancies are, naturally, much less pronounced, and so we shall not bother to include a comparison with the old theory in the discussion that follows of gases heavier than He. We may mention that for the excited states of hydrogen, the new formula (1) is favoured over the old (1a) by a certain amount of direct, though difficult experimental spectroscopic evidence on the second-order Stark effect.[18]

*Application to Heavier Atoms.* The most comprehensive and searching application of Eqs. (1) and (3) to non-hydrogenic atoms by using screening constants has been made by Pauling.[19] He considers primarily inert gases and ions with 'closed' electron shells, owing to the difficulty of obtaining reliable experimental data on other monatomic media. By the Pauli exclusion principle no two electrons have all their quantum numbers the same, and as the axial spin quantum number $m_s$ can have the two values $\pm\frac{1}{2}$ (cf. § 38), there are exactly two electrons for each set of orbital quantum numbers in a given complete shell. Thus one can find the total Stark effect for such a shell by multiplying Eq. (1) by 2 and summing over all positive integral values of $n_1$, $n_2$ (including zero) and positive or negative of $n_3$ consistent with given $n = n_1 + n_2 + |n_3| + 1$. Insertion of the Boltzmann distribution factor $e^{-W/kT}$ would be extraneous, as we have here really a case of the Pauli-Fermi-Dirac statistics, although this name is rather formidable for the simple idea that orbits either occur twice or else practically not at all. On performing these summations[20] and remembering that the moment is $p_E = -\partial W/\partial E$ (Eq. (46), Chap. VI) one thus finds for the 'molar polarizability' $\kappa = 4\pi L \sum p_E/3E$ of an atom which has all shells completed up to $n = n^\dagger$ inclusive

$$\kappa = \frac{Lh^6}{64\pi^5 e^6 m^3} \sum_{n=1}^{n^\dagger} \frac{(5n^8 + 7n^6)}{(Z - \sigma_n^{(e)})^4} = 0{\cdot}281 \sum \frac{5n^8 + 7n^6}{(Z - \sigma_n^{(e)})^4}. \tag{5}$$

Similarly, on noting that for given $l$ there are $2l+1$ possible values of $m_l$ and two of $m_s$, one finds from (3) for the molar diamagnetic susceptibility

$$\chi_{\text{mol}} = -0{\cdot}790 \times 10^{-6} \sum_{n=1}^{n^\dagger} \sum_{l=0}^{l_n} \left[ \frac{n^2(2l+1)(5n^2 - 3l^2 - 3l + 1)}{(Z - \sigma_{nl}^{(m)})^2} \right]. \tag{6}$$

In these equations we have assumed that the true nuclear charge $Z$ is screened by an amount $\sigma$, which may depend on $n$ in (5) and on both

---

[18] Besides work quoted by Wentzel and Waller see also H. R. v. Traubenberg and R. Gebauer, *Zeits. f. Physik*, **54**, 307, **56**, 254, **62**, 289; *Naturwissenschaften*, **17**, 442 (1929); C. Lanczos, *ibid.* **18**, 329 (1930); M. Kiuti, *Zeits. f. Physik*, **57**, 658 (1929).

[19] L. Pauling, *Proc. Roy. Soc.* **114**A, 181 (1927).

[20] To perform this summation one notes that $n_1 - n_2$ and $n_3$ can each assume integral values ranging from $-(n-1)$ to $n-1$, and that the weight of any given value of $n_1 - n_2$ is $2(n - |n_1 - n_2|)$ and of $n_3$ is $2(n - |n_3|)$. These weights follow from counting the number of values of $n_1$, $n_2$, $n_3$ consistent with given $n$ and with given $n_1 - n_2$ or $n_3$, and then multiplying by 2 on account of the spin. The resulting sums can be evaluated by means of Eq. (17a) of Chap. IX. Passage from (5) to (7) involves multiplication by $(2l+1)/n^2$ as there are $2n^2$ electrons in a complete shell and $4l+2$ in a closed sub-shell.

$n$ and $l$ in (6). There is an important distinction between (5) and (6). Eq. (5) supposes that if a shell of principal quantum number $n$ occurs at all, it has its maximum allowance $2n^2$ of electrons. Such a shell we shall call 'completed'. On the other hand, in (6) it has been assumed that if any state of given $n$ and $l$ is present, it has its full quota $4l+2$ of electrons, but it has not been necessary to assume that all values of $l$ are represented which are possible for a given $n$. In other words, for a given $n$ in (6) we have summed over $l$ up to some value $l_n$, which is not necessarily as great as $n-1$. A full group of electrons with given $n$ and $l$ we shall call a 'closed' shell or sub-shell, as its resultant angular momentum is zero by the Pauli principle. A closed shell is with this usage not necessarily a complete shell, as it may be a subdivision of the latter. The outermost shells of inert gases beyond neon are closed rather than complete. Pauling assumes that (5) may be apportioned *pro rata* among the constituent closed shells composing a complete one, and makes use of the fact that practically all the electric polarizability comes from states with the maximum occurring value of $n$. He thus uses the formula

$$\kappa = 0 \cdot 281 \sum_{l=0}^{l_n} \frac{(5n^6 + 7n^4)(2l+1)}{(Z - \sigma_{nl}^{(e)})^4}, \tag{7}$$

where now we write simply $n$ rather than $n\dagger$ for the maximum $n$. In our opinion Eq. (7) is not rigorous, since the principle of spectroscopic stability applies only to complete shells, as elaborated below. However, the use of (7) probably does not introduce serious error, as the method of screening constants itself is but an approximation.

Eq. (1) is based on a separation of variables in parabolic coordinates peculiar to a Coulomb field, and does not apply to non-Coulomb central fields, such as Hartree[14] has shown can be so chosen as to portray fairly well non-hydrogenic atoms. Although (1) fails completely for individual states in such fields, it does nevertheless yield a first approximation when one sums over all the states in a closed shell. This can be seen as follows. Consider first the part of the perturbative potential due to an electric field which is diagonal in $n$. Its effect on the energy is yielded by solution of a secular equation of finite order, embodying all the states having a given $n$. By the 'invariance of the spur' (p. 142) the sum of its roots is invariant of the system of quantization, and so there is no trouble arising from degeneracy, at least for diagonal elements in $n$, when we sum over a complete shell, but this does not apply to incomplete though closed shells. Incidentally, this sum is readily verified to be zero in the present problem, meaning that the first-order Stark effect characteristic of a Coulomb field, also the part of the second-order effect which has $h\nu(nl;nl\pm1)$ in the denominator in a non-Coulomb central field, disappears on summing over a complete shell.

Consider now the effect of non-diagonal elements in $n$ having any given initial and final values of $n$, say $n$, $n'$. Their effect on the energy of the state $n, l, m_l$ is, by (26) of Chap. VI, given by an expression of the form

$$E^2 \sum_{l', m_l} \frac{|p_E^0(nlm_l; n'l'm_l')|^2}{h\nu(nl; n'l')}. \tag{8}$$

Now if we sum this expression over all values of $l$, $m_l$ consistent with $n$, and if we can neglect the dependence of the frequency in the denominator on $l$ (as we can approximately unless there are very great departures from Coulomb character), the sum is invariant of the system of quantization, by Eq. (42) of Chap. VI. (Here $l$, $m_l$ and $l'$, $m_l'$ correspond to $m$ and $m'$ of (42), Chap. VI.) Thus the sums could be equally well taken over a set of parabolic quantum numbers of given $n$ or $n'$ instead of over $l$, $m_l$. Here again the invariance applies only to complete shells.

It is evident that it is much less warranted to use (7) for incomplete than complete shells. Even with complete shells there is some lack of rigour as soon as one lets the screening constant $\sigma$ depend on $l$, as this implicitly assumes that (5) can be apportioned *pro rata* to different $l$'s. The resulting error is, however, probably no greater than other unavoidable errors, such as, for instance, those resulting from the assumption that the denominator of (8) does not depend on $l$.

The normal state of hydrogen, discussed in § 48, has no fine structure and so it is not even necessary to sum expressions such as (8) over $l$, $m_l$ (in distinction from $l', m_l'$) to establish invariance of the system of quantization. Thus Eq. (1) gives the Stark effect of the lowest state of hydrogen regardless of whether or not the field is able to overpower the relativity correction. This has also been verified by Epstein[21] by making the perturbation calculation for the wave equation in polar coordinates. He finds the same result $\epsilon = 1{\cdot}000225$ as ours.

Pauling calculates the screening constants $\sigma_{nl}$ in an interesting fashion by means of the old quantum theory, but with the substitution of $l(l+1)$ for $l^2$. The various groups of electrons are assumed to influence each other like surface spherical distributions of electricity. Thus he makes approximate allowance for the large 'penetration' effects, but not for the smaller polarization terms to be given in § 51. He neglects all powers above the first order in $\sigma/Z$, which seems legitimate in view of the approximate character of the calculations. The following table gives the values he thus calculates for the screening constants for the electric susceptibility of various closed configurations first reached at the listed atom or ion. The table also gives for comparison the 'experimental' values of these screening constants which are deduced from observed values of the dielectric constant or polarizability of the atom or ion in question by means of Eq. (7).[22]

[21] P. S. Epstein, *Proc. Nat. Acad.* **13**, 432 (1927).

[22] The experimental values of the refractivities for the inert gases used by Pauling are those of C. and M. Cuthbertson, *Proc. Roy. Soc.* **84**A, 13 (1911), extrapolated to infinite wave-length by Born and Heisenberg.[26] The values for Cu+, Ag+, Au+ are derived by the additivity method from Heydweiller's data on salt solutions, with details as explained by Pauling, and are, of course, somewhat less certain than the direct measurements on the inert gases.

|  | $\sigma_{nl}^{(e)}$ Calc. | $\sigma_{nl}^{(e)}$ Expt. |
|---|---|---|
| He $(n = 1; l = 0)$ | 0·391 | 0·397 |
| Ne $(n = 2; l = 0, 1)$ | 4·45,  5·64 | 4·31,   5·50 |
| Ar $(n = 3; l = 0, 1)$ | 9·70,  10·99 | 11·11,  12·40 |
| Kr $(n = 4; l = 0, 1)$ | 21·28,  22·92 | 26·69,  28·33 |
| Xe $(n = 5; l = 0, 1)$ | 34·29,  36·63 | 42·26,  44·60 |
| Cu$^+(n = 3; l = 0, 1, 2)$ | 14·4,  16·1,  19·5 | 14·9,  16·6,  20·0 |
| Ag$^+(n = 4; l = 0, 1, 2)$ | 25·7,  27·5,  31·1 | 32·2,  33·9,  37·5 |
| Au$^+(n = 5; l = 0, 1, 2)$ | 46·0,  48·1,  52·4 | 59·9,  62·0,  66·3 |

The Cu$^+$, Ag$^+$, Au$^+$ ions which are involved are, of course, in closed $^1S$ states. The values separated by commas represent the various sub-shells having the same $n$. As Eq. (7) involves a sum over $l$, the 'experimental method' is not able to isolate the individual $\sigma_{nl}$'s connected by commas, and in making the calculation from observed data for column 2, Pauling assumes that their separations are as given by his theory in column 1. Thus only a comparison of the means rather than differences of the values separated by commas serves as a real test of the theory. The agreement between the theoretical and experimental values is on the whole quite gratifying, especially for He and Ne. For He it is no greater than the experimental error. It must, however, be mentioned that a small error in $\sigma$ reflects itself in a much greater percentage error in $\kappa$, as (7) involves $Z-\sigma$ to the inverse fourth power. Thus, if one attempts to compute $\kappa$ for the rare gases from Eq. (7) with the 'calculated' values for the screening constants given above, one obtains the following results, which show a rather wide discrepancy with observed values in the case of heavy atoms.

|  | He | Ne | Ar | Kr | Xe |
|---|---|---|---|---|---|
| $\kappa$ calc. | 0·506 | 1·14 | 1·72 | 0·72 | 0·88 |
| $\kappa$ obs. | 0·513 | 0·995 | 4·132 | 6·25 | 10·16 |

Pauling also makes analogous theoretical calculations of the screening constant to be used in the formula (6) for diamagnetic susceptibilities. We shall not give his numerical results in detail, or enter upon certain rather elaborate distinctions between his procedures in the electric and diamagnetic cases. We must, however, not neglect to mention that his theory yields different screening constants for the same configuration for use in (6) than in (7), and it is to emphasize this distinction that we have used different notations $\sigma^{(m)}$ and $\sigma^{(e)}$ in these two equations. He finds smaller screening constants in the diamagnetic than in the electric case, in agreement with experiment as regards sign of the difference. Thus Pauling's calculations represent considerable refinement in certain respects, though not in others. The agreement with experiment is of about the same order as in the electric case, with greatest divergence for the heavy atoms, as shown by the following table for the inert gases: [23]

|  | He | Ne | Ar | Kr | Xe |
|---|---|---|---|---|---|
| $\chi_{mol} \times 10^6$ obs. | 1·88 | 6·7 | 18·1 | 37·0 | 59·0 |
| $\chi_{mol} \times 10^6$ calc. (Pauling) | 1·54 | 5·7 | 13·6 | 17·2 | 25·4 |
| $\chi_{mol} \times 10^6$ calc. (Slater) | 1·64 | 5·6 | 18·5 |  |  |

On the last line we add the susceptibilities obtained by using a general system of screening constants recently proposed by Slater.[24] Zener [25] calculated these screening constants by the Ritz method for the first period (He–F), while Slater extrapolated them to heavier atoms. They do not possess the refinement of being designed specifically for dia-magnetism, but probably possess a more immediate wave-mechanical basis than those of Pauling.

## 51. Polarizability of the Atom-Core from Spectroscopic Quantum Defect

Born and Heisenberg [26] first derived the following rather ingenious way of determining ionic polarizabilities spectroscopically. If one valence electron moves in a much more highly excited state than all other electrons, spectral energy-levels can be represented by the well-known Rydberg-Ritz formula

$$W = -\frac{chRZ_0^2}{(n-\Delta)^2},\tag{9}$$

where $R = -2\pi^2 me^4/ch^3$, and $Z_0 = 1$ in arc, 2 in spark, 3 in doubly enhanced spectra, &c. The quantum defect $\Delta$, which measures the amount of departure from a hydrogen-like formula, owes its origin primarily to three causes: (a) penetration of the inner regions of the atom by the excited electron, (b) the Heisenberg exchange effect, (c) polarization of the atom-core. By the atom-core is meant the ion obtained by stripping the atom of its valence electron. The effect (a) is preponderant if the perihelion distance of the excited electron is small.

[23] The experimental values quoted for He, Ne, Ar are those of Hector and Wills, while those for Kr, Xe are only indirect determinations from Koenigsberger's work on salt solutions. The theoretical values are not the same as those which Pauling gives in his table VI, as the latter are based on semi-empirical shielding constants obtained by analogy with experimental refractive ones rather than from pure theory. It may be cautioned that while Pauling neglects the contribution of all but the outermost shell in the calcula-tion of refractivities, he is obliged to include that of some of the inner shells in the calculation of the diamagnetism. He mentions, for instance, that the next to the outer-most shell of xenon contributes only 4 per cent. of the total refractivity, and hence can be approximately neglected in the optical case, whereas it contributes 20 per cent. of the diamagnetism.

[24] J. C. Slater, *Phys. Rev.* **36**, 57 (1930).

[25] C. Zener, *Phys. Rev.* **36**, 51 (1930).

[26] Born and Heisenberg, *Zeitsf. Physik*, **23**, 388 (1924); or Born, *Atommechanik*, p. 191.

If, however, its azimuthal quantum number exceeds a certain value, usually greater for heavy than light atoms, the orbit is nearly non-penetrating, and the effect (c) then may give rise to most of $\Delta$. To calculate this polarization effect (c) we proceed as follows. If the radius $r$ of the valence electron's orbit is large compared to the dimensions of the atom-core, this electron will exert a sensibly homogeneous electric field $e/r^2$ on the rest of the atom, and so induce a dipole moment $\alpha e/r^2$ in the core, where $\alpha$ is the latter's specific polarizability. This dipole will in turn react on the valence electron with an attractive force $F(r) = 2\alpha e^2/r^5$, since a dipole of strength $\mu$ gives a field $2\mu/r^3$ at points along its axis. Thus the potential energy $\int F(r)\, dr$ due to polarization of the atom-core by the valence electron is

$$V_{\text{per}} = -\frac{1}{2}\frac{\alpha e^2}{r^4}. \tag{10}$$

If we regard this as a perturbative potential superposed on the ordinary Coulomb attraction, and if we neglect squares of $\alpha$, then the change in quantized energy due to (10) is by (24), Chap. VI,

$$W^{(1)} = -\tfrac{1}{2}\alpha e^2 \frac{\overline{1}}{r^4} = -\tfrac{1}{2}\alpha e^2 Z_0^4 \left(\frac{4\pi^2 m e^2}{h^2}\right)^4 \times$$

$$\times \left[\frac{3}{2n^3(l-\frac{1}{2})l(l+\frac{1}{2})(l+1)(l+\frac{3}{2})} - \frac{1}{2n^5(l-\frac{1}{2})(l+\frac{1}{2})(l+\frac{3}{2})}\right]. \tag{11}$$

Here we have inserted the time average or diagonal element of $1/r^4$ obtained [27] by evaluating the integral (14), Chap. VI, with hydrogenic wave functions and with $f = 1/r^4$. Now the departure of (9) from the Coulomb value is approximately $-2\Delta ch R Z_0^2/n^3$, assuming that only the first term in the Taylor's development in $\Delta$ need be retained. Comparing this with (11) we see that

$$\Delta = \frac{\alpha e^2}{4ch R}\left(\frac{4\pi^2 m e^2}{h^2}\right)^4 Z_0^2 \left[\frac{3}{2(l-\frac{1}{2})l(l+\frac{1}{2})(l+1)(l+\frac{3}{2})} - \frac{1}{2n^2(l-\frac{1}{2})(l+\frac{1}{2})(l+\frac{3}{2})}\right]$$

$$= 1{\cdot}34\,\kappa Z_0^2[\ldots]. \tag{12}$$

The parts of the quantum defect which are independent of $n$ and proportional to $1/n^2$ are known as respectively the Rydberg and Ritz corrections. In the second form of (12) we have substituted numerical values of the atomic constants and introduced the 'molar polarizability' $\kappa = 4\pi L \alpha/3$.

The simplest test of (12) is furnished by the spectra of neutral helium and of ionized lithium. Here the atom-cores are respectively He$^+$ and

[27] For details of the evaluation see I. Waller, *Zeits. f. Physik*, **38**, 635 (1926).

$Li^{++}$, which are exactly like the normal hydrogen atom except that the nuclear charge is $2e$ or $3e$ instead of $e$. Hence, by the theory of the dielectric constant of hydrogen given in § 48, the values of the molar polarizability $\kappa$ should be respectively $1·68/16$ and $1·68/81$. Substitution of these $\kappa$'s in (12) then yields the following quantum defects compared to the observed [28] for the $P$, $D$, and $F$ series of He and $Li^+$.

|  | He: $P$ | He: $D$ | He: $F$ | $Li^+$: $P$ | $Li^+$: $D$ |
|---|---|---|---|---|---|
| $\Delta$ calc. | $0·056-$ | $0·0026-$ | $0·00045-$ | $0·044-$ | $0·0021-$ |
|  | $-0·04n^{-2}$ | $-0·005n^{-2}$ | $-0·002n^{-2}$ | $-0·03n^{-2}$ | $-0·004n^{-2}$ |
| $\Delta$ obs. | $0·029$ | $0·0025$ | $0·001$ | $0·020$ | $0·0022$ |

We have omitted $S$ states as too penetrating, and have taken the mean of the experimental values of $\Delta$ for par- and ortho-helium (or $Li^+$), as the par-ortho distinction is due to the Heisenberg exchange effect and taking this mean can be shown approximately equivalent to neglecting this effect. The agreement is at least qualitatively good. More painstaking computations of Sugiura [29] based on systematic perturbation theory rather than the assumed polarization effect (11) yield $\Delta = 0·022$, $0·031$, $0·020$ for the ortho-par means of He $2P$, He $3P$, and $Li^+$ $2P$ respectively.

The calculations for He and $Li^+$ given in the preceding table were made by Waller and by Wentzel (for He only) soon after the advent of the new mechanics. Analogous calculations in the old quantum theory were unsuccessful, as helium always was its stumbling-block. Born and Heisenberg [26] showed that somewhat better results attended its application to the alkalis and analogous ions. The formula for $\Delta$ in the old theory was exactly like (12) except that the bracketed factor was $(3/2l'^5)-(1/2n^2l'^3)$ (with $l'$ as on p. 210) because of a different mean value of $1/r^4$. The following table compares values of the molar polarizability $\kappa$ obtained by the old and new mechanics from the spectroscopic quantum defects for the neutral alkalis and hence singly charged atom-cores.

|  | $Li^+$ | $Na^+$ | $K^+$ | $Rb^+$ | $Cs^+$ |
|---|---|---|---|---|---|
| $\kappa$ calc. (new theory) | $0·09$ | $0·48$ | $1·97$ |  | $7·6$ ? |
| $\kappa$ calc. (old, int. $l'$) | $0·80$ | $1·03$ | $4·27$ |  | $16·5$ ? |
| $\kappa$ calc. (old, half-int. $l'$) | $0·19$ | $0·53$ | $2·21$ |  | $8·5$ ? |
|  | He | Ne | A | Kr | Xe |
| $\kappa$ obs. | $0·51$ | $0·99$ | $4·13$ | $6·25$ | $10·2$ |

[28] The experimental values for $Li^+$ are from Werner, *Nature*, **116**, 574 (1925); **118**, 154 (1926).

[29] Y. Sugiura, *Zeits. f. Physik*, **44**, 190 (1927); the direct experimental values for He $2P$, He $3P$, and $Li^+$ $2P$, ortho-para means are $0·0274$, $0·0278$, $0·0207$, whereas the table gives the experimental Rydberg correction which best approximates experiment for all values of $n$.

The question-mark indicates that the spectroscopic data for Cs are somewhat uncertain. Since the nuclear binding charge is larger, the polarizability of an alkali ion should always be lower than that of the preceding inert gas, which is directly revealed by ordinary measurements of the gas's dielectric constant. Reference to the table shows that this condition is met in the new mechanics but not in the old without the artificial introduction of half-quantum numbers—another victory for the new theory. The reason that Born and Heisenberg found half-quantum numbers worked better is now apparent, as the denominators in the bracketed part of (12) are the same as $2(l+\frac{1}{2})^5$, $2n^2(l+\frac{1}{2})^3$ if in each case we keep only the two highest powers in $l$. This is a special case of Kramers' [30] theorem that half-quantum numbers in the old quantum theory are a better approximation to the new mechanics than are whole integers. The table shows an unusually large difference between the old and new theories for Li⁺, merely because the values are here calculated from $P$, rather than from $F$ terms as for the others. The difference is naturally greater for $l = 1$ than $l = 3$.

A crucial test of (12) is found in the examination of whether the different spectroscopic values of $\Delta$ for the different non-penetrating terms of a given atom all yield the same value of $\kappa$ from (12). This test was extensively applied by Schrödinger [31] in the old theory. He found it was not well fulfilled, and this is also true of the new. Constancy of $\kappa$ is unfortunately secured over only a limited range of terms or series. The following examples of Li⁺ and Mg⁺⁺, in which we revise some of Schrödinger's calculations in accordance with the new mechanics, are typical and by no means the worst.

|  | | 2P | 3P | 4P | 5P | 3D | 4D | 5D | 6D | 4F | 5F |
|---|---|---|---|---|---|---|---|---|---|---|---|
| Li⁺ | $\kappa =$ | 0·096 | 0·094 | 0·093 | 0·094 | 0·068 | 0·076 | 0·011 | −0·04 | −0·22 | −1·3 |
| Mg⁺⁺ | $\kappa =$ | | | | | 0·398 | 0·434 | 0·447 | 0·450 | 0·194 | 0·195 |

The negative values for Li⁺ are, of course, nonsense. Eq. (12) does rather better in the dependence on $Z$ than that on $n$, $l$, as in § 52 we shall see that values of $\kappa$ deduced from (12) decrease in approximately the correct fashion as we go from left to right in an iso-electric sequence.

Comparison of the value 0·28 for Mg⁺⁺ given in the table on p. 222 with the values given above shows that Born and Heisenberg's and Schrödinger's estimates of the polarizability of the Mg⁺⁺ ion by the spectroscopic method do not agree, even when one uses only the latter's estimates from $F$ terms. This discrepancy, which is not as bad as that between them for some other ions, exemplifies the rough character of the method, and arises in part because Schrödinger calculated

[30] H. A. Kramers, *Zeits. f. Physik*, **39**, 828 (1927).
[31] E. Schrödinger, *Ann. der Physik*, **77**, 43 (1925).

the polarizability by equating (12) to the entire experimental quantum defect for individual terms while Born and Heisenberg took a representation of the experimental data by the Ritz formula $RZ_0^2/(n+a+b/n^2)^2$ and equated $a$ to the corresponding part of (12).[32] Test of the theory by examination of the values of $b$ is more difficult, as $b$ is hard to determine accurately experimentally. According to (12) the ratio $-b/a$ should be respectively 0·67, 2, 4 for $P$, $D$, $F$ terms (1·3, 3, 5·3 according to the old quantum theory). Some experimental values are: $P$ terms, Li 0·63; $D$ terms, Na 2·4, Mg+ 2·2, Al++ 2·6, Si+++ 2·4; $F$ terms, Na 3·2, Mg+ 3·6, Al++ 3·6, Si+++ 4·8.

If a frequency of motion (in the quantum sense) of the excited electron nearly coincides with an absorption frequency of the atom-core, clearly it is no longer a good approximation to regard the latter as subject to a static in distinction from periodic polarizing field. Near such coincidence we may surmise that $\Delta$ is abnormally large because of the resonance. Such resonance phenomena do not exist in alkali spectra, as ions homologous to inert gases have absorption frequencies too far in the ultra-violet, but are actually

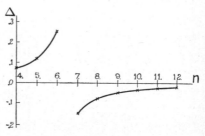

FIG. 8.

sometimes found in the spectra of atoms or ions with two valence electrons. An example is shown in Fig. 8, from Schrödinger's paper, in which the observed quantum defect is plotted against the principal quantum number $n$ for the $^3F$ terms of Al+. The similarity to anomalous dispersion curves is obvious. As the lines $3^3D-6^3F$ and $3^3D-7^3F$ of Al+ have wave numbers 43,000 and 47,700 cm.$^{-1}$ respectively, it appears that Al++ might have an absorption line near 46,000 cm.$^{-1}$, and the important line $1^2S-2^2P$ of the Al++ spectrum does indeed have a wave number 53,918. (The latter line is written $3S-3P$ if the principal quantum number is used as the ordinal number.) Exact agreement of the resonance point with an Al++ line cannot be expected, as the presence of the valence electron doubtless displaces somewhat the frequencies of the atom-core. Schrödinger shows that the observed variation of $\Delta$ can be nicely fitted by an 'undamped' dispersion curve.

$$\kappa = 7\cdot0 + 3\cdot1\nu_0^2/(\nu_0^2 - \nu^2),$$

with $\nu_0 = 46,000$ cm.$^{-1}$. The value 3·1 is about one-eighth that of the corresponding constant in the dispersion of sodium, which is very reasonable since Al++ should be harder to polarize than Na+. This

[32] Both Born and Heisenberg and Schrödinger obtain the experimental values of the quantum defect from a comprehensive paper by A. Fowler, *Proc. Roy. Soc.*, **103**A, 413 (1923).

beautiful resonance phenomenon, discovered by Schrödinger in the last days of the old quantum theory has been too much overlooked in the commotion of the new, although at the beginning of the latter it was considered quite noteworthy, though now perhaps commonplace, that the resonance frequencies in this phenomenon are those given by the Bohr frequency condition rather than the orbital frequencies of the old quantum theory. The need of more often using defects $\Delta$ with resonance points in spectroscopy has recently been emphasized by Langer.[33] We may also point out that this Schrödinger phenomenon is quite like the so-called 'perturbations' in band spectra,[34] wherein irregularities in the bands are found when rotational levels of two electronic states nearly coincide. If $H_{12}$ be the matrix element of the Hamiltonian function giving the interaction between two states otherwise of energy $W_1$, $W_2$, then the secular equation (Eq. (35), Chap. VI) has the solution $W = \frac{1}{2}(W_1 + W_2) \pm \frac{1}{2}[(W_1 - W_2)^2 + 4H_{12}^2]^{\frac{1}{2}}$. When $W_1 \neq W_2$ the effect of $H_{12}$ on $W$ is thus of the second order, but at the point $W_1 = W_2$ it becomes of the first order. There is, then, a kink in the energy-curve at this point quite similar to that of a damped dispersion curve, or to the state of affairs in Fig. 8. This figure thus shows that there are 'perturbations' even in atomic spectra. The analysis of the secular problem connected with the inter-electronic interactions is, of course, a more complete way of handling the polarization phenomena than is the description by means of Eq. (10). This is especially true near resonance, as the dispersion analogy is only a more or less qualitative one. The perturbation analysis for the $F$ terms of Al+ is to be given in detail in future papers by Langer and by Whitelaw. They show that a $3p3d\ ^3F$ term (not previously classified as a vagrant) intrudes itself among the members of the $F$ series, otherwise of the type $3snf\ ^3F$. The interaction with this intruder distorts the other members and accounts for the irregularities in $\Delta$ and especially for the anomalies in multiplet widths. (This stray term is usually mislabelled $7^3F$). Do not confuse with the $7^3F$ term of the revised notation used on p. 219.)

## 52. Ionic Refractivities and Diamagnetic Susceptibilities

The polarizabilities of ions which are iso-electronic with the inert gases may be obtained in the following four ways:

(a) Application of the additivity method to salt solutions.

(b) Application of the additivity method to salt crystals.

[33] R. Langer, *Phys. Rev.* **35**, 649 (1930).

[34] R. de L. Kronig, *Zeits. f. Physik*, **50**, 347 (1928) (theory); J. Rosenthal and F. A. Jenkins, *Proc. Nat. Acad.*, **15**, 381, 896 (1929) (experiment).

(c) Use of the theoretical Eq. (7) with screening constants.

(d) The spectroscopic method of § 51.

Method (a) has been extensively used by Heydweiller,[35] and by Fajans and Joos [36] with Heydweiller's measurements, while (b) has been used by Wasastjerna,[37] and by Born and Heisenberg [26] with Spangenberg's [38] measurements. As already intimated, (c) has been employed by Pauling,[19] and (d) by Born and Heisenberg,[26] and by Schrödinger.[31] Each method has its limitations. Those of (c) and (d) have already been described. With (a) and (b) it is always necessary to assume some one ion as having a known refractivity, so that by subtracting this from that of the salt one obtains the refractivity of the other ion. Different values will, of course, be obtained depending on what values are assumed for the known ion. In the solid state (method b) the ions may well be considerably distorted by the inter-atomic forces, while in (a) there is always a more or less uncertain correction for the effect of hydration, or, in other words, for the distortion and saturation of the surrounding water molecules of coordination. This is especially evident in the light of the work of Sack and others (§ 22) on saturation effects in ionic solutions, but these effects are not nearly as large for the optical region as for the static case considered in § 22, as the bulk of the static saturation effect is due to polarization by orientation. The polarizabilities or, what is the same thing, the 'refractivities' which we shall give in the following tables are usually for infinite wave-length, but fortunately differ but little from those in the ordinary optical region (sodium $D$ lines) as the absorption lines of inert gas configurations are well in the ultraviolet. Hence in methods (a) or (b) the refractivities should be determined in the optical region, to rule out large orientation effects on the water molecules in (a) and the effect of atomic (i.e. crystalline) vibrations in (b). An extrapolation of the ionic refractivity thus obtained to infinite wave-lengths can then be made if desired.

The approximate character of the additivity methods is shown by the fact that different refractivities for a given ion are obtained depending on the particular salt used. According to Born and Heisenberg, the values obtained for $Na^+$ from various salts are respectively 0·48 (NaF), 0·53 (NaCl), 0·51 (NaBr), 0·33 (NaI), utilizing respectively assumed values for the contributions of the $F^-$, $Cl^-$, $Br^-$, and $I^-$ ions.

---

[35] Heydweiller, *Phys. Zeits.* **26**, 526 (1925), and references to earlier work.

[36] Fajans and Joos, *Zeits. f. Physik*, **23**, 1 (1924); K. Fajans, *Zeits. f. Elektr.* **34**, 502 (1928).

[37] Wasastjerna, *Comm. Fenn.* **1**, 7 (1913); summary in *Phys. Ber.* **5**, 226 (1924).

[38] Spangenberg, *Zeits. f. Krist.* **53**, 499 (1923); **57**, 517.

In the following table we compare by way of illustration some values for the refractivities of ions iso-electronic with neon which have been obtained by the various methods.

IONIC REFRACTIVITIES

|  |  | F$^-$ | Ne | Na$^+$ | Mg$^{++}$ | Al$^{+++}$ | Si$^{++++}$ |
|---|---|---|---|---|---|---|---|
| (a) (Fajans & Joos[36]) | $\kappa =$ | 2·50 | (1·00) | 0·50 | 0·28 | 0·17 | 0·1 |
| (b) (B. & H. from Spang.[26]) |  | 2·51 | (1·00) | 0·46 |  |  |  |
| (c) (Pauling[19]) |  | 2·65 | (1·00) | 0·46 | 0·24 | 0·14 | 0·08 |
| (d) (B. & H., Spectro.[26]) |  |  | (1·00) | 0·49 | 0·28 | 0·15 | 0·10 |

The value in parentheses is C. and M. Cuthbertson's direct measurement[22] of the refractivity of gaseous neon. The decrease in the refractivity as we go from left to right in the sequence is in good accord with the variation as $(Z-\sigma)^{-4}$ predicted theoretically by (7), since (a), (b), (d) agree quite well with (c).

For the determination of ionic diamagnetic susceptibilities methods like (a), (b), (c) are available. Until recently the only calculations by the additivity method (a) were those of Joos[39] from old measurements of Koenigsberger and others. Recently, however, new determinations of the diamagnetic susceptibilities of alkali and alkaline earth halides in solution have been made by Ikenmeyer,[40] and of the halogen acids by Reicheneder.[41] The measurements with the acids have the advantage that the isolation of the individual ionic contributions by the additivity method is unique, inasmuch as the diamagnetism of H$^+$ is clearly zero. The method (b) based on measurement of solid salts has been extensively used by Pascal.[42] In the following table, which compares typical results with the various methods, we use Pauling's[19] resolution of Pascal's data into the contribution of the individual ions. This differs from that originally proposed by Pascal, as a different contribution for the Na$^+$ ion is assumed as the starting-point. Still other resolutions have been proposed by Weiss.[11] As illustrative of method (c) we include purely theoretical calculations by Stoner,[13] in which the mean value of $r^2$ needed for Eq. (2) is calculated by Hartree's method of the self-consistent field.[43]

[39] Joos, *Zeits. f. Physik*, **19**, 347 (1923); Joos and Fajans, *ibid.* **32**, 835 (1925).

[40] K. Ikenmeyer, *Ann. der Physik*, **1**, 169 (1929).

[41] Reicheneder, *Ann. der Physik*, **3**, 58 (1929).

[42] Pascal, *Comptes Rendus*, **158**, 37; **159**, 429 (1914); **173**, 144 (1921). For other measurements on solid salts see Landolt-Börnstein's tables and Pauling's comment on p. 203 of his paper.

[43] We for brevity omit from our tables the various estimates of refractivities and diamagnetic susceptibilities of doubly charged alkaline earth ions. See the original paper for these.

MOLAR DIAMAGNETIC SUSCEPTIBILITIES $\times 10^6$

|                          | Li+ | F-   | Na+  | Cl-  | K+   | Br-  | Rb+  | I-   | Cs+  |
|--------------------------|-----|------|------|------|------|------|------|------|------|
| (a) (Joos)               | 1·3 | 11·5 | 6·5  | 19·5 | 14·5 | 39·5 |      | 60·5 |      |
| (a) (Iken.)              | 4·0 | 13·9 | 10·4 | 20·4 | 16·9 | 34·8 | 31·3 | 49·3 | 45·7 |
| (a) (Reich.)             |     |      |      | 21·9 |      | 32·5 |      | 50·2 |      |
| (b) (Pascal & Pauling)   | 0·2 | 10·3 | 5·2  | 24·1 | 14·5 | 34·6 | 23·2 | 48·6 | 37·0 |
| (c) (Stoner)             |     |      | 5·5  | 40·4 |      |      | 30·1 |      |      |

The molar susceptibility for an inert gas should, of course, be intermediate between those of the corresponding halogen and alkali ions,
which should be respectively greater and smaller. In view of Hector
and Will's[16] very careful values 1·88, 6·7, and 18·1 for He, Ne, and A,
it would appear that Ikenmeyer's determinations for Li+ and Na+ are
somewhat too high. Ikenmeyer finds that for a given column of the
periodic table the molar susceptibility is almost exactly a linear function[44] $(c_1 Z + c_2) \cdot 10^{-6}$ of the atomic number, where $c_2$ is respectively
5·9, 2·4, and −3·5 for halogen, alkali, and alkaline earth ions, and $c_1$ is
0·80 for all three. In the light of Eq. (2) this means, since $c_2$ is small
compared to $c_1 Z$ except near the top of the periodic table, that the
mean square radius per electron is approximately $0·80 \times 10^{-16}/2·83$ or
$(0·53 \times 10^{-8})^2$ for all except the very lightest atoms.[45] This must mean
that the effect of increasing nuclear charge and increasing mean quan-
tum number nearly compensate as regards $\overline{\overline{r^2}}$ as we go down the periodic
table. It is to be understood that this value $\overline{\overline{r^2}}$ is the mean over all
classes of electrons. The outermost or valence electrons will have much
larger values. Joos[39] notes that if one assumes that the outermost shell
is responsible for practically all the diamagnetism, then his values of
$\chi_{mol}$ yield atomic radii 0·54, 0·71, 0·80, 0·92 × 10$^{-8}$ cm. respectively for
Na+, F−, K+, Cl−, which are in remarkably close agreement with the
ionic radii 0·63, 0·75, 0·79, 0·95 × 10$^{-8}$ respectively deduced by Fajans
and Herzfeld[46] from the grating energies of salt crystals. Only a rough
agreement could be expected, as the discrepancies in the table show
that there is considerable uncertainty in the diamagnetic measurements,
while the estimate from grating forces is a purely classical one not
utilizing the quantum 'exchange forces'.

[44] In our opinion these linear relations should not be taken too literally except perhaps
for heavy atoms. In fact his analogous relation for the alkaline earths extrapolates into
a paramagnetic susceptibility for Ba++, an absurdity. Ikenmeyer assumed the coefficient
c to be the same for all ions in order to isolate their individual contributions in the salts,
and this perhaps explains why his values for Na+ and Li+ are too high.

[45] H. Kulenkampff, Ann. der Physik, 1, 192 (1929) notes that this is exactly the radius
of a one quantum hydrogen orbit in the old quantum theory. However, any agreement
beyond that in order of magnitude is clearly fortuitous.

[46] K. Fajans and K. F. Herzfeld, Zeits. f. Physik, 2, 309 (1920).

One could go on with no end of numerical discussion on the best way of juggling the results in additivity methods, and we shall close by reproducing a semi-empirical table of ionic refractivities and diamagnetic susceptibilities given by Pauling, which is probably as reliable as any. The values of the refractivities are obtained by assuming that the direct experimental values for the inert gases can be extrapolated to other members of an iso-electronic sequence by assuming a formula like Eq. (7) except that the effective charge is taken to be

$$Z - \sigma_{nl}^{(e)} + a_{nl}^{(e)}(Z - Z_0)$$

instead of $Z - \sigma_{nl}^{(e)}$. Here $\sigma_{nl}^{(e)}$ is determined from the experimental $\kappa$ for an inert gas of atomic number $Z = Z_0$, and $a_{nl}^{(e)}$ is a small, more or less empirical correction term, which is determined so as to best fit experiment in some cases (solution values for the $Br^-$ and $I^-$ ions) and by extrapolation in others.[47] The values for the diamagnetic susceptibility are calculated from Eq. (6), but with the assumption of an effective charge $Z - \sigma_{nl}^{(m)} + a_{nl}^{(m)}(Z - Z_0)$. The values of $\sigma_{nl}^{(m)}$ and $a_{nl}^{(m)}$ are not determined from experimental diamagnetic measurements, but by alteration of his theoretical $\sigma_{nl}^{(m)}$ described on p. 213. This is accomplished by analogy [48] with the alterations in the theoretical $\sigma_{nl}^{(e)}$ necessary to secure agreement with the experimental refractivities, and by adaptation of the empirical $a_{nl}^{(e)}$. This analogy involves some rather bold extrapolations, and so the diamagnetic part of the table is probably not as dependable as the refractive part.

[47] The extrapolation is performed by assuming empirically that (in going from one row to another of the periodic table) the expression $a_{nl}^{(e)}$ is proportional to the difference between the theoretical and experimental shielding constants for the inert gases given in the table on p. 214.

[48] Pauling alters the calculated imperfection in shielding of an outer group by any given inner group by the same empirical factor as was required to give agreement with experiment on refractivities. For details see p. 201 of Pauling's paper.

## The Molar Polarizability and Diamagnetic Susceptibility of Atoms and Ions

In each cell the upper value is $\kappa$ and the lower value is $-\chi_M \cdot 10^6$.

| −4 | −3 | −2 | −1 | 0 | +1 | +2 | +3 | +4 | +5 | +6 | +7 |
|---|---|---|---|---|---|---|---|---|---|---|---|
| | | | | H<br>1·691<br>2·415 | He+<br>0·1058<br>0·604 | Li++<br>0·0209<br>0·268 | | | | | |
| | | | H⁻<br>25·65<br>8 | | | | | | | | |
| | | | | He<br>0·513<br>1·54 | Li+<br>0·074<br>0·63 | Be+2<br>0·020<br>0·34 | B+3<br>0·0076<br>0·21 | C+4<br>0·0034<br>0·15 | N+5<br>0·0018<br>0·11 | | |
| C⁻4<br>5400<br>50 | N⁻3<br>72·6<br>22 | O⁻2<br>9·88<br>12·6 | F⁻<br>2·65<br>8·1 | Ne<br>0·995<br>5·7 | Na+<br>0·457<br>4·2 | Mg+2<br>0·238<br>3·2 | Al+3<br>0·136<br>2·5 | Si+4<br>0·084<br>2·1 | P+5<br>0·054<br>1·7 | S+6<br>0·036<br>1·4 | Cl+7<br>0·025<br>1·2 |
| Si⁻4<br>950<br>110 | P⁻3<br>105<br>65 | S⁻2<br>26·0<br>40 | | Ar<br>4·13<br>21·5 | K+<br>2·12<br>16·7 | Ca+2<br>1·19<br>13·3 | Sc+3<br>0·73<br>10·9 | Ti+4<br>0·47<br>9·0 | V+5<br>0·31<br>7·7 | Cr+6<br>0·22<br>6·6 | Mn+7<br>0·16<br>5·7 |
| | | | | | Cu+<br>1·08<br>13 | Zn+2<br>0·72<br>11 | Ga+3<br>0·50<br>9·5 | Ge+4<br>0·36<br>8·5 | As+5<br>0·26<br>7·5 | Se+6<br>0·19<br>6·5 | Br+7<br>0·15<br>6·0 |
| Ge⁻4<br>276<br>140 | As⁻3<br>72·6<br>95 | Se⁻2<br>26·8<br>70 | Br⁻<br>12·14<br>54 | Kr<br>6·26<br>42 | Rb+<br>3·57<br>35 | Sr+2<br>2·18<br>28 | Y+3<br>1·41<br>24 | Zr+4<br>0·95<br>20 | Nb+5<br>0·66<br>17 | Mo+6<br>0·48<br>15 | |
| | | | | | Ag+<br>4·33<br>44 | Cd+2<br>2·74<br>37 | In+3<br>1·84<br>32 | Sn+4<br>1·26<br>28 | Sb+5<br>0·91<br>24 | Te+6<br>0·66<br>20 | I+7<br>0·49<br>17 |
| Sn⁻4<br>228<br>180 | Sb⁻3<br>80·6<br>130 | Te⁻2<br>35·6<br>105 | I⁻<br>18·07<br>80 | Xe<br>10·16<br>66 | Cs+<br>6·15<br>55 | Ba+2<br>3·94<br>46 | La+3<br>2·64<br>38 | Ce+4<br>1·86<br>33 | Bi+5<br>1·15<br>37 | | |
| | | | | | Au+<br>4·75<br>65 | Hg+2<br>3·14<br>55 | Tl+3<br>2·19<br>48 | Pb+4<br>1·56<br>42 | | | |

# THE PARAMAGNETISM OF FREE ATOMS AND RARE EARTH IONS

## 53. Adaptation of Proof of Langevin-Debye Formula given in § 46

The general proof of the Langevin-Debye formula was given in Chapter VII explicitly only for electric polarization, but can be applied to the magnetic case merely by substituting everywhere the magnetic moment vector $\mathbf{m} = -(\mathbf{L}+2\mathbf{S})he/4\pi mc$ for the electric moment vector $\mathbf{p}$ used in §§ 44 and 46. There are, however, two points which require comment.

In the first place, besides the paramagnetic part $(L_z+2S_z)Heh/4\pi mc$ (§ 42) of the Hamiltonian function, there is ever present the diamagnetic term proportional to $\sum (x^2+y^2)$ which has been discussed in §§ 43 and 49, and which has no analogue in the electric case. Therefore, to all formulae for the susceptibility calculated by the methods of Chapter VII, we must add the expression for the diamagnetic susceptibility given in Eq. (2), Chap. VIII.

The second point is the following. The magnetic moment in general consists of two parts, viz. the 'orbital' and 'spin' portions. In the different 'normal states' (cf. p. 187) these two parts may be inclined to each other at different angles. This will be the case if the normal states embrace a spin multiplet whose components are separated by intervals small compared to $kT$, as these different components correspond to different relative alinements of $L$ and $S$ ranging in atomic spectra from the 'anti-parallel' alinement $J = |L-S|$ to the parallel one $J = L+S$ (cf. § 40). Because of this flexibility in the coupling of $L$ and $S$ we cannot in general suppose that the resultant magnetic moment is 'permanent', i.e. the same for all normal states, and so we cannot always effect the simplification made in passing from Eq. (22) to (24) in Chapter VII. Instead we must use the more general expression (25), Chap. VII, for the contribution of the low-frequency elements, which does not require the hypothesis of a permanent moment.

If, then, we make only the fundamental assumption that the moment matrix involves only elements whose frequencies are either small or large compared to $kT/h$, the analysis in § 46 shows that the formula for the susceptibility is

$$\chi = \frac{N\overline{\overline{\mu^2}}}{3kT} + N\overline{\overline{\alpha}}, \tag{1}$$

where $\overline{\mu^2}$ is defined as in Eq. (25), Chap. VII, and is thus the time average of the square of the low-frequency part $\mu$ of the magnetic moment vector, this average itself being averaged over the various normal states weighted in accordance with the Boltzmann factor $e^{-W^0_{nj}/kT}$. The term $N\overline{\alpha}$ in (1) is the joint contribution of the high-frequency elements of the paramagnetic moment, and of the diamagnetic effect, similarly arranged. Consequently by (28), Chap. VII, and (2), Chap. VIII,[1]

$$N\alpha = \tfrac{2}{3}N \sum_{n' \neq n} \frac{|m^0(n;n')|^2}{h\nu(n';n)} - \frac{Ne^2}{6mc^2} \sum \overline{r^2}. \tag{2}$$

In practice the diamagnetic correction given in the second term of (2) is relatively small if the material is really paramagnetic, as usually molar paramagnetic and diamagnetic susceptibilities are respectively of the orders $10^{-4}$–$10^{-2}$ and $10^{-6}$–$10^{-5}$. Consequently we shall henceforth omit writing the diamagnetic term except when we explicitly consider diamagnetism in § 69 and § 81. Of course allowance for diamagnetism ought to be made in the most refined calculations of paramagnetic moments from observed susceptibilities. Most of the experimental measurements of the susceptibilities of paramagnetic salts which we quote in the balance of the volume, also the 'effective Bohr magneton numbers' deduced therefrom, are corrected for the diamagnetism of the anion but not that of the cation. In other words, the quoted suscepti-bilities are the measured susceptibilities of the compound augmented by the absolute magnitude of the diamagnetism of the non-paramagnetic ingredient (anion), but not that of the paramagnetic ingredient itself (cation). One reason why the correction for the diamagnetism of the cation is usually omitted in the literature is that the diamagnetism of rare earth ions is rather hard to estimate quantitatively.[2]

It is convenient to introduce as a unit of magnetic moment the Bohr magneton

$$\beta = \frac{eh}{4\pi mc} = (0{\cdot}9174 \pm 0{\cdot}0013) \times 10^{-20}\,\text{erg. gauss}^{-1}. \tag{3}$$

---

[1] We tacitly assume that the internal spin of the electron gives rise to no diamagnetic term. There is no term of this character in Dirac's 'quantum theory of the electron', and irrespective of the latter it appears quite obvious that any such term would necessarily be negligibly small since the orbital diamagnetic term is proportional to $r^2$, and since the radius of the electron is negligible compared to that of an orbit.

[2] It must be cautioned that even though the diamagnetic correction is inconsequential for the given atom or ion itself, it can well be exceedingly important in solutions, since ordinary solvents are diamagnetic, or in salts of high 'magnetic dilution', where the diamagnetic atoms or ions greatly outnumber the paramagnetic. In these cases the total diamagnetism can clearly be appreciable compared to the paramagnetism.

Then the formula for the molar susceptibility corresponding to (1) takes the numerical form

$$\chi_{\text{mol}} = L\left(\frac{\overline{\overline{\beta^2 \mu_B^2}}}{3kT} + \overline{\overline{\alpha}}\right) = 0{\cdot}1241\frac{\overline{\overline{\mu_B^2}}}{T} + 6{\cdot}064 \times 10^{23}\,\overline{\overline{\alpha}}$$

$$= 0{\cdot}00506\frac{\overline{\overline{\mu_W^2}}}{T} + 6{\cdot}064 \times 10^{23}\,\overline{\overline{\alpha}},$$

(4)

where $\mu_B$ denotes the low-frequency part of the magnetic moment measured in Bohr magnetons. If instead of the molar we used the susceptibility per unit-volume at 0° C., 76 cm. in the gaseous state, the numerical factors in the first and second forms of (4) would become respectively $5{\cdot}54 \times 10^{-6}$, $2{\cdot}705 \times 10^{19}$ and $2{\cdot}258 \times 10^{-7}$, $2{\cdot}705 \times 10^{19}$. Since the Weiss magneton is so commonly found in the literature and is in a sense also a convenient measure of moments, we have given in the second line of (4) the form which the formula takes if we measure $\mu$ in multiples of the Weiss magneton $1{\cdot}853 \times 10^{-21}$ e.m.u.[3] Historically it looked for a while[4] as if all atoms and molecules might turn out to have moments which are integral multiples of the Weiss magneton. Although many molecules are still found to have moments which are integral multiples of the Weiss magneton within the experimental error,[5] this is probably purely fortuitous, for there are many reasons for believing the Weiss magneton phenomenon to be spurious. In the first place, the Weiss magneton is 1/4·95 as large as the Bohr magneton,

[3] The Weiss magneton is often multiplied by the Avogadro number $L$ to yield what may be termed a molar Weiss magneton, of magnitude 1123·5 e.m.u. We here give the value of the Weiss magneton which Weiss proposed in 1911, as this is the Weiss unit usually utilized in the literature. Later (1924–9) he raised the estimate to 1125·6 per gramme mol. (cf. Weiss and Forrer, *Annales de Physique*, **12**, 279 (1929) ); while still more recently Cabrera suggests 1124·9±0·3 per mol. or 1·855±0·5×10⁻²¹ per atom as the most probable value (Report of the Solvay Congress, 1930). Our numerical value 0·917×10⁻²⁰ of the Bohr magneton number embodies Birge's estimate of the most probable values of the atomic constants, and yields a molar Bohr magneton number of 5564 e.m.u. In the literature the Bohr magneton seems to be very often taken as 4·97 rather than 4·95 Weiss magnetons, or as 0·921 instead of 0·917×10⁻²⁰ e.m.u., due to use of older values of $e/m$ and $h$. We employ the spectroscopic value 1·761×10⁷ of $e/m$, generally conceded more reliable than the higher value sometimes furnished by the deflexion method.

[4] P. Weiss, *J. de Physique*, **5**, 129 (1924); *Annales de Physique*, **12**, 279 (1929) and references to earlier work.

[5] In this connexion we must not fail to mention that Cabrera has collected some 160 measurements of susceptibilities, primarily in the iron group, and finds that the vast majority of them seem to yield Weiss magneton numbers which do not deviate from integers by more than ±0·1 (Report of the 1930 Solvay Congress). On the other hand, existing attempts to extract integral Weiss numbers from measurements on the rare earth group appear forced and artificial, quite irrespective of the clash of such attempts with quantum mechanics.

and so has no fundamental theoretical significance. Secondly, many of the apparent Weiss magneton numbers are fairly large (20 or so), so that the integral property is not very convincing unless the experiments are very precise. Finally, as noted by Stoner,[6] the Weiss magneton, if really fundamental, should manifest itself more clearly in gases than in solids or solutions, whereas the two common paramagnetic gases $O_2$ and NO have moments which are non-integral multiples 14·2 and 9·2 respectively of the Weiss magneton. Hence we shall not mention the Weiss magneton further. At the same time it must be cautioned that one must not expect magnetic moments to be integral multiples of the Bohr magneton either, due largely to the fact that in the new quantum mechanics, the absolute value of the angular momentum is $(J^2+J)^{\frac{1}{2}}h/2\pi$ rather than an integral multiple $J$ of $h/2\pi$.

It will be desirable to discuss separately the limiting cases that the spin multiplets are very narrow or very wide compared to $kT$. These cases are particularly illuminating, and it is only to them that Eqs. (1) or (4) are applicable. It must be cautioned that not infrequently one encounters experimentally multiplet spacings comparable to $kT$, contrary to the assumption of only low- and high-frequency elements basic to the validity of (1) or (4). Thus, as already mentioned in Chapter VII, the Langevin-Debye formula is not as universal in the magnetic as in the electric case.

## 54. Multiplet Intervals Small Compared to $kT$

We shall throughout the balance of the chapter assume that the atom has Russell-Saunders coupling (§ 40). As stated in § 40, this supposition is usually fully warranted in the normal states involved in the calculation of susceptibilities. Then the orbital and spin angular momentum vectors are constant in magnitude but not in direction, and the squares of their magnitudes have respectively the values $L(L+1)$ and $S(S+1)$ (Eq. (83), Chap. VI). We throughout measure angular momentum in multiples of $h/2\pi$, as in §§ 39–42. In the absence of external fields the resultant angular momentum $\mathbf{L}+\mathbf{S}$ will be constant both in direction and magnitude, and constitutes what Dirac calls a 'constant of the motion', whereas the vector $\mathbf{L}+2\mathbf{S}$ which is important for magnetism will not be, due to the continual precession of $\mathbf{L}$ and $\mathbf{S}$ about $\mathbf{J}$. This is illustrated in Fig. 9. In this precession the component ($b$-$c$ in Fig. 9) of $\mathbf{L}+2\mathbf{S}$, which is perpendicular to $\mathbf{J}=\mathbf{L}+\mathbf{S}$, will clearly not be constant in direction. However, the only periodic or non-diagonal elements

---

[6] E. C. Stoner, *Magnetism and Atomic Structure*, p. 159.

in the moment vector $\mathbf{m} = -\beta(\mathbf{L}+2\mathbf{S})$ are those associated with the precessions of $\mathbf{L}$ and $\mathbf{S}$ about $\mathbf{J}$. Thus $\mathbf{m}$ is diagonal in all quantum numbers other than the inner quantum number $J$ and the magnetic quantum number $M$. This, incidentally, is not true in molecules (Chap. X), and is also the underlying reason why the numerical paramagnetic susceptibilities of non-hydrogenic atoms can be calculated so much more definitely than the electric, as the electric moment vector

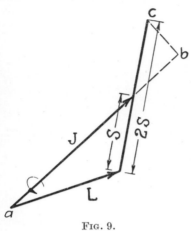

FIG. 9.

$\mathbf{p}$ involves other quantum numbers, such as, e.g., the principal quantum numbers, in a complicated way.

The preceding paragraph shows that when the multiplet intervals are small compared to $kT$ (i.e. kinematically when the precession of $\mathbf{L}$ and $\mathbf{S}$ about $\mathbf{J}$ is slow), the elements of the moment vector $\mathbf{m}$ are entirely of the low-frequency type. In other words, in the notation of Chapter VI we can dispense with the index $n$ and take $j$ to be identical with the inner quantum number $J$. Eq. (2) then

shows that the part $N\alpha$ of the susceptibility vanishes if we neglect the second or diamagnetic term. Now in the absence of high-frequency elements there is no distinction between $\mu$ and the complete moment vector $-\beta(\mathbf{L}+2\mathbf{S})$, so that

$$\overline{\mu^2} = (4\mathbf{S}^2 + \mathbf{L}^2 + 4\overline{\mathbf{L}\cdot\mathbf{S}})\beta^2. \qquad \langle 5 \rangle$$

Since the temperature factor $e^{-W^0/kT}$ for the various multiplet components may be disregarded under the supposition of intervals small compared to $kT$, the statistical average of the product $\mathbf{L}\cdot\mathbf{S}$ may be taken as zero in very strong fields, where $\mathbf{S}$ and $\mathbf{L}$ are quantized separately relative to the axis of the field (case $c$ of Fig. 6, § 40), and hence have no correlation between their directions if we average over all orientations. Furthermore, the statistical average of this product is invariant of the field strength and hence vanishes in all fields if it does in very strong ones, for use of one of the spectroscopic stability relations given in § 35 (viz. the 'invariance of the spur', p. 142) shows this average is invariant of the mode of quantization if the system is made degenerate with respect to $J$, $M$ by neglecting the energy of interaction between $\mathbf{L}$ and $\mathbf{S}$, and between $H$ and both $\mathbf{L}$ and $\mathbf{S}$. We can also verify directly that the statistical average of $\mathbf{L}.\mathbf{S}$ vanishes in weak fields, since by the 'cosine law' (Eqs. $\langle 84 \rangle$, (84a), Chap. VI) this average is proportional to the sum [7]

$$\sum_{J=|L-S|}^{L+S} (2J+1)[J(J+1)-S(S+1)-L(L+1)],$$

which is readily verified to be zero. The factor $2J+1$ appears since it is the *a priori* probability or number of $M$-components belonging to a given value of the inner quantum number $J$.

The first two right-hand members of (5) are diagonal matrices having characteristic values $4S(S+1)\beta^2$ and $L(L+1)\beta^2$ invariant of $J$, so that double bars over them are unnecessary. We have just proved the third member is zero. Hence the expression (1) for the susceptibility becomes

$$\chi = \frac{N\beta^2}{3kT}[4S(S+1)+L(L+1)]. \tag{6}$$

Eq. (6) may also be derived in the following elementary way for very strong fields adequate to produce a Paschen-Back effect. In such fields we may use the quantum numbers $M_S$, $M_L$ explained in § 40. The energy of a stationary state is then $W^{00} \mid H\beta(M_L+2M_S)+AM_L \cdot M_S$ (Eq. (103), Chap. VI), and its component of moment in the direction of the applied field is $-(M_L+2M_S)\beta$. The susceptibility is, of course, obtained by averaging over all states weighted with the Boltzmann factor (cf. Eq. (3), Chap. VII). If the multiplet widths are negligible we may neglect the term in the energy depending on $A$, and then the susceptibility is

$$\chi = -\frac{N\beta}{H} \frac{\sum\limits_{M_L=-L}^{+L} \sum\limits_{M_S=-S}^{+S} (M_L+2M_S)e^{-\beta H(M_L+2M_S)/kT}}{\sum \sum e^{-\beta H(M_L+2M_S)/kT}}$$

$$= -\frac{N\beta}{H}\left[\frac{\sum\limits_{M_L=-L}^{+L} M_L e^{-\beta H M_L/kT}}{\sum e^{-\beta H M_L/kT}} + \frac{2\sum\limits_{M_S=-S}^{+S} M_S e^{-2\beta H M_S/kT}}{\sum e^{-2\beta H M_S/kT}}\right]. \tag{7}$$

We now expand the exponents as power series in $H$, and retain as in § 44 the non-vanishing terms of lowest order in numerator and denominator. Then (7) becomes

$$\chi = \frac{N\beta^2}{kT}\left[\frac{\sum M_L^2}{2L+1} + \frac{4\sum M_S^2}{2S+1}\right]. \tag{8}$$

This agrees with (6) when we evaluate the sums by means of (68), Chap. VI.

---

[7] The sums can be evaluated by using the formulae of Eq. (17a), § 56.

The preceding elementary derivation of (6) was given only for fields adequate for a Paschen-Back effect, but the principle of spectroscopic stability, not to mention our first derivation of (6) by the methods of Chapter VII, assures us that this expression for the susceptibility is invariant of the field strength (neglecting, as everywhere, saturation), and hence the formula will hold even when the field is not able to produce a Paschen-Back effect, or only a partial one.

Since Eq. (6) is so obvious in strong fields, the writer has been frequently misquoted and misunderstood ever since he first proposed (6), even though he then explicitly said that (6) applied to all fields. Contrary to statements often made, the validity of (6) does not by any means imply $M_L$, $M_S$ quantization, and holds also with the $J$, $M$ quantization, which is a better approximation at usual field strengths. The Paschen-Back effect will usually change the formulae for individual Zeeman components (cf. Eqs. (99) and (103), Chap. VI) but will not alter the expression for the susceptibility. To dispel all doubt we shall in § 56 also prove Eq. (6) for weak fields in an elementary though tedious way that does not utilize spectroscopic stability.

## 55. Multiplet Intervals Large Compared to $kT$

When the separation of the multiplet components is large compared to $kT$, only the one component which has the lowest energy is a normal state, and the double bar is no longer needed in (1). The matrix elements of **m** now are all of the high-frequency type unless $\Delta J = 0$. Thus $J$ may be identified with the index $n$ used in Chapter VII, while the index $j$ of VII may be omitted. The low-frequency part of **m** is now only the part which is parallel to the resultant angular momentum **J** and so does not involve the now rapid precession of **L**, **S** about **J**. Hence

$$\mu^2 = \beta^2 \left[ \frac{\mathbf{L} \cdot \mathbf{J}}{|\mathbf{J}|} + 2 \frac{\mathbf{S} \cdot \mathbf{J}}{|\mathbf{J}|} \right]^2$$

$$\doteq \beta^2 \frac{[S(S+1) - L(L+1) + 3J(J+1)]^2}{4J(J+1)} = g^2 \beta^2 J(J+1),$$

where $g$ is the Landé $g$-factor

$$g = 1 + \frac{S(S+1) + J(J+1) - L(L+1)}{2J(J+1)}. \tag{9}$$

Here we have utilized, as in $\langle 84 \rangle$, $\langle 85 \rangle$ of Chapter VI, the cosine relations $2\mathbf{L} \cdot \mathbf{J} = \mathbf{L}^2 + \mathbf{J}^2 - \mathbf{S}^2$ and the fact that $\mathbf{J}^2 \doteq J(J+1)$, &c. The dot over the equality sign has the same meaning as on p. 142. Eq. (1) now becomes

$$\chi = \frac{Ng^2\beta^2 J(J+1)}{3kT} + N\alpha. \tag{10}$$

The constant $N\alpha$ no longer has the value zero, as in (6) (except for the neglected diamagnetic part), but is instead

$$N\alpha = \frac{N\beta^2}{6(2J+1)}\left[\frac{F(J+1)}{h\nu(J+1;J)} - \frac{F(J)}{h\nu(J;J-1)}\right], \tag{11}$$

with the abbreviation

$$F(J) = \frac{1}{J}[(S+L+1)^2 - J^2][J^2 - (S-L)^2]. \tag{12}$$

The existence of this $\alpha$ is a concomitant of the second-order Zeeman term in (99), Chap. VI, not to be confused with the diamagnetic second-order Zeeman term of § 43. The presence of $\alpha$, or of the second-order term in (99), is due to the component $b$-$c$ in Fig. 9, which now contributes only to the part of the susceptibility that is independent of temperature rather than as in § 54 to the ordinary Curie part proportional to $1/T$. Usually the normal state is a minimum or maximum of $J$, depending on whether the multiplet is regular or inverted (p. 166), and then the second or first term respectively of (11) vanishes, as can be verified from the formula (12) for $F$.

To prove formula (11) one might work out the expressions for $L_x+2S_x$, $L_y+2S_y$ analogous to those for $L_z+2S_z$ in (88), Chap. VI, and add their squares together in the fashion (44), Ch. VI, to get the resultant amplitudes $m^0(J;J') = \beta\sqrt{\left\{\sum_{q=x,y,z}|(L_q+2S_q)(J;J')|^2\right\}}$ needed for (2). Another way, however, which is fundamentally very little different but is easier after one has once deduced the Zeeman formula to the second order in (99), Chap. VI, is as follows. The contribution of the second-order part $H^2W^{(2)}$ of (99) to the susceptibility is $-2N\sum_{M=-J}^{+J}W^{(2)}/(2J+1)$ by (4), Chap. VII, inasmuch as under the present hypothesis of wide multiplets there is only one normal unperturbed value of $J$, and so the sum in (4), Chap. VII, reduces merely to one over $M$. The result (11) now follows on substitution of the expression for $W^{(2)}$ obtained from (99) and (88), Chap. VI, and on evaluation of the sum over $M$. The terms proportional to $M^2$ are, as usual, summed by means of (68), Chap. VI, while the other terms are very simple to sum.

Only the first term of (10) is ordinarily given in the literature. Due to the frequency factors in the denominator of (11), the second term

$N\alpha$ will ordinarily be small compared to the first if the multiplet is really wide compared to $kT$, unless perchance the normal state involves an abnormally low value of $J$, so that $a$-$b$ is small compared to $b$-$c$ in Fig. 9, p. 230. The latter case does, however, occasionally arise, as will be shown and elaborated in connexion with the susceptibilities of Eu$^{+++}$ and Sm$^{+++}$ in § 59. The first part of (10) is usually deduced in an elementary way analogous to the proof of (6) by means of (7), (8). If one uses only the first-order Zeeman formula $W_0 + Mg\beta H$ for weak fields instead of the one for strong fields and supposes that only one value of $J$ represents a normal state, then one sees that in place of (7) one has

$$\chi = -\frac{Ng\beta}{H} \frac{\sum\limits_{M=-J}^{+J} M e^{-g\beta HM/kT}}{\sum e^{-g\beta HM/kT}}. \tag{13}$$

The rest of the procedure, which converts (13) into the first part of (10), is entirely similar to that explained after Eq. (7), the only essential difference being that $g\beta$ now replaces $\beta$.

We must not forget to mention that the first part of (10) was obtained by Sommerfeld[8] and others in the old quantum theory. In that theory the Landé $g$-formula for the first-order Zeeman effect was taken as an empirical fact, and so the derivation by means of (13) could be used. There is, however, an important difference in the interpretation of (10) in the old and new mechanics. If $\theta$ denote the angle between the magnetic field $H$ and the low-frequency part $\mu$ of the magnetic moment vector, then in a weak field the first-order energy is $W_0 - |\mu| H \cos \theta$. If one uses this expression instead of the equivalent form $W_0 + Mg\beta H$ and weights the various values of $\cos \theta$ in accordance with the Boltzmann factor, then one finds after the usual series expansion of the exponentials (e.g. as in § 44 or as in passing from (7) to (8)) that, except for saturation, the susceptibility is given by the expression

$$\chi = N \frac{\overline{\mu^2 \cos^2 \theta}}{kT}. \tag{14}$$

In the old quantum theory, the value of $\mu^2$ was considered to be $g^2\beta^2 J^2$ as the magnitude of the resultant angular momentum of the atom was $Jh/2\pi$. On using this value, and equating (14) to the first part of (10), one sees that the mean value of $\cos^2\theta$ was given by

$$\text{(old)} \quad \overline{\cos^2\theta} = \frac{1}{3}\frac{J+1}{J}, \qquad \text{(new)} \quad \overline{\cos^2\theta} = \frac{1}{3}. \tag{15}$$

Here we have also included for comparison the analogous result with

[8] A Sommerfeld, *Atombau*, 4th ed., pp. 630–48 and references.

the new mechanics, which one knows must be $\frac{1}{3}$, but which one can also obtain by equating (10) and (14) with $\mu^2 = g^2\beta^2 J(J+1)$. The old value in (15) is one of the typical violations of the principle of spectroscopic stability which were so common in the old theory. This difficulty did not affect the susceptibility as long as there was spacial quantization, for then Eq. (10) was valid in the old theory, and the only difference compared to the new mechanics was that the same value of the product $\overline{\mu^2\cos^2\theta}$ was apportioned in a different way between its two factors. If, however, inter-atomic collisions were frequent, due to high temperature or density, it would not be reasonable to assume spacial orientation in the old theory. Instead one would have to assume random orientations and use the second value in (15), which, when substituted in (14) with $\mu = g\beta J$, gives $\chi = Ng^2\beta^2 J^2/3kT$ instead of (10). Thus the susceptibility might vary with density or field strength, contrary to experiment, and again the new interpretation is superior. Also in the old theory the formula (6) would be valid only in fields powerful enough for a Paschen-Back effect.

## 56. Multiplet Intervals Comparable to $kT$

Let us now turn to the general or 'intermediate' case in which the effect of the inner quantum number $J$ is comparable with $kT$. Then out of the total number of atoms a certain portion $N_J$ will have any given value $J$ of the inner quantum number. Their contribution to the susceptibility will be given by the expression (10) with $N$ replaced by $N_J$, since (10) still applies as long as all atoms under consideration have the same $J$. We must now, however, add the contributions of the atoms with various different values of $J$. The number $N_J$ is determined by the Boltzmann temperature factor, and is hence proportional to $(2J+1)e^{-W_J^0/kT}$, inasmuch as for a given $J$ there are $2J+1$ component states having different values of $M$. Thus

$$\chi = \frac{N \sum_{J=|L-S|}^{L+S} \{[g_J^2\beta^2 J(J+1)/3kT]+\alpha_J\}(2J+1)e^{-W_J^0/kT}}{\sum (2J+1)e^{-W_J^0/kT}}. \tag{16}$$

Here subscripts have been attached to $g$ and $\alpha$ to show explicitly that they are functions of $J$.

It is clear that (16) should reduce to (6) in the limiting case of very narrow multiplets. This may be verified as follows. If the dependence of $W^0$ on $J$ is negligible, it suffices to strike out entirely the exponential factors from the denominator and from the first term of the numerator, assuming for simplicity that the origin of the energy is at $J = 0$. With the second term the procedure is not so simple, as by (11) the $\alpha$'s approach infinity when the multiplets become very narrow. One can, however, evaluate the second sum in the numerator in the limit $(W_{J+1}-W_J)/kT = 0$ by using exactly the same type of expansion as in passing from (17) to (20) in Chapter VII. One thus finds that in this limit, (16) is the same as

$$\chi = \frac{N}{3kT} \frac{\sum [g_J^2\beta^2 J(J+1)(2J+1)+\tfrac{1}{2}F(J)]}{\sum (2J+1)}. \tag{17}$$

This expression can be verified with a bit of labour to be identically equal to (6) if one introduces the explicit expressions (9), (12) for $g$ and $F$ and uses the following formulae for the sums of series:

$$\sum_{x=1}^{n} x = \frac{(n+1)n}{2}, \qquad \sum x^2 = \frac{n(n+1)(2n+1)}{6},$$

$$\sum x^3 = \frac{n^2(n+1)^2}{4}, \qquad \sum \frac{1}{x(x+1)} = \frac{n}{n+1} \tag{17a}$$

in which $x$ assumes consecutive integral values from 1 to $n$. These formulae are readily proved inductively in the same fashion as explained for (68), Chap. VI, which is essentially the second of these relations.

Laporte and Sommerfeld[9] use for narrow multiplets the expression obtained by omitting the $F$ terms in (17). Their expression differs but little from the more rigorous and also more simple formula (6), the reason being that $b$-$c$ is usually small compared to $a$-$b$ in Fig. 9. For instance, Laporte and Sommerfeld calculate effective Bohr magneton numbers 2·92, 4·35, 4·97, 5·23, and 5·92 respectively for narrow $^2D$, $^3F$, $^4F$, $^5D$, $^6S$ multiplets, which are of asymptotic interest in the iron group, whereas (6) gives 3·0, 4·47, 5·20, 5·48, 5·92. In quoting their results for narrow multiplets in the iron group in § 72 we shall throughout give values modified in accordance with (6).

Before we can use formula (16) it is necessary to know quantitatively the multiplet intervals in order to evaluate the denominators in (11). These intervals should, of course, be taken if possible from direct spectroscopic data on the multiplets in question, but unfortunately such data are often not available for the type of ions encountered in paramagnetic solutions (§§ 58, 59). It is then necessary to resort to a theoretical expression for these intervals, and one uses the 'cosine law' (Eq. (84a), Chap. VI)

$$W_J = \tfrac{1}{2}AJ(J+1)+\text{constant}, \tag{18}$$

together with the proper value of $A$. All the paramagnetic ions yet encountered seem to owe their magnetic moments to an incomplete

[9] O. Laporte and Sommerfeld, *Zeits. f. Physik*, **40**, 333 (1926); O. Laporte, *ibid.* **47**, 761 (1928).

shell of 'equivalent electrons', i.e. electrons with similar $n$, $l$. Further-more, when all electrons not in closed groups are equivalent, the Hund theory of spectral terms[10] tells us that the normal or 'lowest lying' electronic state has the maximum multiplicity allowed these electrons by the Pauli exclusion principle, and also the maximum $L$ consistent with this multiplicity. (Specific examples will be cited in § 58.) With this specialization it will be shown in the next paragraph that an immediate application of Goudsmit's theory[11] for calculating $A$ yields

$$A = \pm \frac{a_{11}}{2S}, \tag{19}$$

where $a_{11}$ is the $A$-factor which would result were only one electron of the group present. The plus or minus sign is to be used according as the group is less than or more than half completed.[12] As the number of electrons in a completed sub-shell is $4l+2$, the value of $A$ is, in other words, positive if $\eta < 2l+1$, and negative if $\eta > 2l+1$, where $\eta$ is the number of electrons present of the type under consideration. The theory thus predicts that the multiplets of the normal state be respectively regular and 'inverted' for the first and second halves of the sequence formed by addition of consecutive electrons of the group. This rule is in good accord with experiment wherever spectroscopic measurements are available on multiple normal states. An abundance of such measure-ments is available for the iron group, though usually for no tas high a degree of ionization as directly involved in the study of paramagnet-ism. The value of $a_{11}$ for a hydrogenic atom is

$$a_{11} = \frac{16\pi^4 m Z^4 e^8}{c^2 h^4 n^3 l(l+1)(2l+1)}. \tag{20}$$

This is equivalent to the well-known 'relativity' or 'spin' doublet formula, and follows from Eq. (80), Chap. VI, after the mean value of $1/r^3$ involved therein is evaluated with hydrogenic wave functions.[13] It is assumed that a non-hydrogenic atom can be approximately repre-sented by introducing a screening constant $\sigma$ into the hydrogen formulae. Instead of giving directly the value of $A$, it is often convenient to use the 'over-all' multiplet width $h\Delta\nu_{\text{total}} = W_{J\text{max}} - W_{J\text{min}}$, which by (18) is $\frac{1}{2}A[(L+S)(L+S+1) - |L-S|(|L-S|+1)]$. The multiplets involved in the normal states which we need to deal with all have $S \leqslant L$. Hence

[10] F. Hund, *Linienspektren*, Chap. V.

[11] S. Goudsmit, *Phys. Rev.* **31**, 946 (1928). Eq. (19) is also derived by O. Laporte in *Handbuch der Astrophysik*, iii, p. 643.

[12] At the point $\eta = 2l+1$ at which the group is half complete, there is no trouble from ambiguity in sign, as here the 'lowest lying' state is an $S$ one without multiplet structure.

[13] See Heisenberg and Jordan, *Zeits. f. Physik*, **37**, 263 (1926).

by (19), (20) the expression for the 'over-all' width when expressed in wave numbers rather than ergs is

$$\frac{1}{c}\Delta\nu_{\text{total}} = \frac{S(2L+1)}{hc}\frac{(\pm a_{11})}{2S} = \pm\frac{5\cdot 82(2L+1)}{n^3 l(l+1)(2l+1)}(Z-\sigma)^4\,\text{cm}^{-1}. \quad (21)$$

The factor $5\cdot 82$ follows from substituting explicit numerical values for the constants $e$, $h$, $m$, $c$. It is perhaps well to reiterate the distinction between $l$ and $L$. The former is an azimuthal quantum number measuring the angular momentum of a single electron, while $L$ measures that of the whole incomplete group.

*Derivation of Eq.* (19). By application of the principle of permanence of $\Gamma$-sums (§ 42) or invariance of the spur (§ 35) to the passage from $J$, $M$ to $M_S$, $M_L$ quantization (case (b) to (c) in Fig. 6, § 40) one has, in virtue of Eqs. (84a), (103), Chap. VI, the relation

$$\sum_a \tfrac{1}{2}A[J(J+1)-L(L+1)-S(S+1)] = \sum_a AM_L M_S$$

where $\sum_a$ means a summation over all the states consistent with given $S$, $L$, $M$. By a similar application to the passage from $M_L$, $M_S$ to $m_l$, $m_s$ quantization (case (c) to (a), Fig. 6), one has $\sum_b AM_L M_S = \sum_i \sum_b a_{11}m_{l_i}m_{s_i}$, where $\sum_b$ means a summation over all the states consistent with given $M_L$, $M_S$, $n$, $l$, even though involving different $L$ or $S$, and where $\sum_i$ means a summation over all the individual equivalent electrons, which we suppose $\eta$ in number. In the first application the summation sign $\sum_a$ can be omitted when $M = J = L+S$, as there is then just one term, and the relation becomes merely $ALS = AM_L M_S$. Similarly, in the second application, the summation $\sum_b$ can be omitted when $M_L = L$, $M_S = S$, $S = \tfrac{1}{2}\eta$, and when $L$ has the maximum value $L_{\text{max}}$ which according to the exclusion principle is consistent with this $S$. This is true because there is never more than one multiplet of the type $S = \tfrac{1}{2}\eta$, $L = L_{\text{max}}$. One then has $AM_L M_S = \tfrac{1}{2}a_{11}M_L$, as each $m_{s_i}$ is necessarily $\tfrac{1}{2}$ when $M_S = \tfrac{1}{2}\eta$. Thus combining the special cases of the two applications one has $ALS = \tfrac{1}{2}a_{11}L$ or $A = a_{11}/2S$. This is the desired result for the first half of the sequence. In the second half the exclusion principle demands $S < \tfrac{1}{2}\eta$ so that the preceding method cannot be used. Instead, the value $A = -a_{11}/2S$ follows as a special case of Goudsmit's general result that $A$ values are reversed in sign in passing from the first to second half of the sequence. It is to be cautioned that we give in (19) only the formula for the lowest-lying multiplets rather than Goudsmit's necessarily more complicated relations and derivation for the general multiplet.

## 57. Susceptibilities of Alkali Vapours.

Unfortunately none of the preceding theory can easily be tested directly upon gases, as the only monatomic gases are the inert ones, which are diamagnetic. There are, to be sure, many materials whose vapours should be paramagnetic. However, the susceptibilities of vapours are very hard to measure, because of the difficulty of obtaining a sufficiently high, as well as accurately known, vapour-pressure. As far as the author is aware, the only quantitative determination of the susceptibility of a monatomic paramagnetic vapour is Gerlach's measurement[14] on potassium vapour. He finds that for temperatures between 600° and 800° C. corresponding to vapour-pressures of from 0·5 to 30 mm., the molar susceptibility of potassium vapour obeys Curie's law and is $0·38/T$. The normal states of alkali atoms are $^2S$ ones, and so by Eq. (6) the theoretical molar susceptibility is $L\beta^2/kT = 0·372/T$. It is, of course, here not necessary to worry about the width of the multiplet, as a multiplet structure is wanting in $S$ states. The agreement between the observed and theoretical Curie constants is extremely gratifying, as Gerlach's experiment is extremely difficult and he does not claim an accuracy of more than 10 per cent. Incidentally, this good agreement is a nice confirmation of the correctness of the assumed vapour-pressure curve, and shows that potassium vapour must be primarily monatomic at the temperatures employed. If diatomic, the vapour would be diamagnetic, as the normal state of the $K_2$ molecule is of the type $^1\Sigma$. Dissociation theory indicates that the fractional number of atoms associated into molecules at the temperatures employed by Gerlach should be[15] of the order $10^{-2}$, and so the neglect of molecular association is not a dominant experimental error. Incidentally, magnetic measurements should be a sensitive means of determining the degree of molecular association when appreciable. Hence it would be of interest if Gerlach's experiments could be extended to conditions where there is more molecular association, viz. to still higher vapour-pressures (which means higher temperatures) in potassium, or to sodium or lithium. Compared to potassium, molecular association at a given $p, T$ is favoured in Li and Na by their molecules having higher heats of dissociation (about 1·2 and 0·8 volt respectively) than that of K (about 0·6 volt).[16]

## 58. Susceptibilities of the Rare Earths

Because of the difficulty of obtaining paramagnetic materials in the vapour state, the best that can usually be done is to study the suscepti-

[14] W. Gerlach, *Atti del Congresso Internazionale dei Fisici*, **1**, 119 (1927).

[15] Cf. R. W. Ditchburn, *Proc. Roy. Soc.* **117A**, 486 (1928), or Gibson and Heitler's formula given on p. 175 of Ladenburg and Thiele, *Zeits. f. Phys. Chem.* **7**, 161 (1930).

[16] Loomis and Nusbaum, *Phys. Rev.* **37**, 1712 (1931); ($Li_2$): Loomis, *Ibid.* **31**, 323 (1928); Kinsey, *Proc. Nat. Acad.* **15**, 37 (1929); Polanyi, Schay, and Ootuka, *Zeits. f. Phys. Chem.* **1B**, 30 (1929), **7B**, 407 (1930); Ladenburg and Thiele, *l.c.*, all $Na_2$. H. Ootuka, *Zeits. f. Phys. Chem.* **7B**, 422 (1930); Ditchburn, *l.c.*[15]; A. Carrelli and P. Pringsheim, *Zeits. f. Physik*, **44**, 643 (1927); W. O. Crane and A. Christy, *Phys. Rev.* **36**, 421 (1930), all $K_2$.

bilities of solutions containing paramagnetic salts, or of these salts in the solid state, preferably hydrated. One *hopes* that in some of these cases the ions responsible for the paramagnetism may be so nearly free as far as orientation is concerned that the calculations for the gaseous phase may be utilized. We shall later see that disturbances from other atoms prevent realization of this hope in most instances. In the first place the number of paramagnetic ions is rather limited. In most atoms the only incomplete shells with an outstanding magnetic moment are those belonging to the valence electron, and in solution or in salts the atom is stripped of these valence electrons, leaving only ions with closed shells. For instance, Na or Cl atoms each contain an odd number of electrons, and are thus paramagnetic, but in NaCl or in solutions containing NaCl, the sodium and chlorine atoms respectively lose and capture one electron, yielding only closed configurations. The reason that solid pure alkali metals are not appreciably paramagnetic is rather complicated and will be considered in § 80.

There are, however, certain well-known places in the periodic table in which inner as well as outer groups of electrons are in process of formation. These cases are found in the iron, palladium, rare earth, and platinum groups, where respectively sub-shells of ten $3d$, ten $4d$, fourteen $4f$, and ten $5d$ electrons have not been completely filled.[17] Generally speaking, atoms in these groups lose all the valence electrons of their outer incomplete shells when in solution or in salt compounds, but not necessarily the electrons of the inner incomplete shells, so that paramagnetism may result. For instance, the Sm atom contains five $4f$, two $5d$, and one $6s$ electrons, besides other electrons not in closed shells. This atom usually reacts trivalently, so that in, e.g., $Sm_2(SO_4)_3$, solid or dissolved, it loses the $5d$ and $6s$ electrons, but keeps the five $4f$ ones. To quote Bohr,[17] 'On the whole a consideration of the magnetic properties of the elements within the long periods gives us a vivid impression of how a wound in the otherwise symmetrical inner structure is first developed and then healed as we pass from one element to another.'

The one case where one might expect the gaseous theory to apply better than usual is to salts or solutions containing the rare earths. The rare earths as a rule exhibit a trivalent behaviour, losing their two

---

[17] We assume the reader has at least a little familiarity with Bohr's well-known theory of the perodic table. See, for instance, N. Bohr, *The Theory of Spectra and Atomic Constitution*, Essay 3. The relation of magnetic properties to the structure of the periodic table has also been extensively discussed by Ladenburg, *Zeits. f. Electrochem.* **26**, 263 (1920); *Zeits. f. Phys. Chem.* **126**, 133 (1927).

$5d$ and one $6s$ electrons as in the typical example of Sm cited above. Thus the paramagnetism of rare earth ions arises from the $4f$ electrons, and such electrons are well in the interior of the atom, far more so than, e.g. the $3d$ electrons in the iron group, as the $4f$ electrons are surrounded by eight electrons (viz. two $5s$ and six $5p$) of higher principal quantum number, whereas the ions of the iron group of the type involved in paramagnetism have no electrons of principal quantum number greater than 3. Thus we must not become too surprised in § 72 at the complete failure of the ordinary gaseous theory in the iron group. The nearly identical chemical properties of the different rare earths, despite the fact that they have different numbers of $4f$ electrons ranging from 0 to 14, is direct evidence that these electrons are but little affected by the fields from other atoms, and hence by their neighbours in solutions or solid compounds.

Before one can calculate the susceptibilities of rare earth ions it is necessary to know the values of the quantum numbers $L$, $S$, $J$ to be used in the equations of §§ 54–6. This information as to the 'lowest lying' spectral term is supplied by a theory of Hund.[10] When there are a number of equivalent electrons, the possible spectral terms are rather severely limited in number by the Pauli exclusion principle, and Hund supposes that out of the possible terms that of highest multiplicity has the lowest energy. In case several values of $L$ are possible when the multiplicity $2S+1$ has its maximum value, then the greatest $L$ consistent with this $S$ is assumed to give the least energy. All other states are assumed to have so much greater energy that they are not normal ones. For example, with two equivalent $f$ electrons, the Pauli exclusion principle can be shown to admit the $^1S$, $^3P$, $^1D$, $^3F$, $^1G$, $^3H$, $^1I$ and to rule out the $^3S$, $^1P$, $^3D$, $^1F$, $^3G$, $^1H$, $^3I$ states. Out of the former, the $^3H$ term alone is a normal state under Hund's assumptions. The normal states which he obtains with various numbers of equivalent $f$ electrons are shown in the table in the next paragraph. Generally speaking, Hund's assumptions are well confirmed spectroscopically, though in the particular case of the rare earths direct spectroscopic evidence is as yet wanting, so that here the only experimental confirmation is by means of the magnetic theory itself. A first-order perturbation calculation by Slater[18] has confirmed theoretically Hund's assumptions in the case of the iron group, and similar confirming calculations could doubtless be made for the rare earths.

It is, of course, necessary to know something about the effect of $J$ as

[18] J. C. Slater, *Phys. Rev.* **34**, 1293 (1929).

well as of $L$, $S$ as above, on the energy, so as to determine whether to use the theory of § 54, 55, or 56. Hund[19] himself first calculated the susceptibilities under the assumption that the multiplets are very wide compared to $kT$. As discussed in § 56 (Eqs. (18), (19), &c.), the component with minimum or maximum $J$ is alone supposed to be a normal state depending on whether the multiplet is respectively 'regular' or inverted, i.e. whether in the rare earth ions the number of $4f$ electrons is less or greater than 7. The results of Hund's calculations made by formula (10) without the term $N\alpha$ are shown under the column headed 'Hund' in the following table and in Fig. 10. Various experimental values are shown for comparison. The entries throughout are what we shall call the 'effective Bohr magneton number', defined by the equation

$$\mu_{\text{eff}} = \sqrt{\frac{3\chi kT}{N\beta^2}}. \tag{22}$$

It is to be clearly understood that the $\mu_{\text{eff}}$ thus defined is a function of temperature if Curie's law $\chi = \text{const.}/T$ is not obeyed. Thus under Hund's assumptions $\mu_{\text{eff}}$ should be independent of $T$, but not if instead the term $N\alpha$ of (10) is important, or if it is necessary to use the 'intermediate formula' (16). The experimental values given in the table, also the theoretical values of Van Vleck and Frank (*V. V. & F.*), where different from Hund's, relate to room temperatures. The juxtaposition of theoretical and experimental values of $\mu_{\text{eff}}$ is merely one way of comparing the calculated and observed absolute susceptibilities, as $\mu_{\text{eff}}$ is proportional to $\chi^{\frac{1}{2}}$. A 'theoretical' or 'experimental' $\mu_{\text{eff}}$ is obtained according to the kind of value of $\chi$ which is used. Only when Curie's law is obeyed, is either the theoretical or experimental $\mu_{\text{eff}}$ defined by (22) to be identified with the permanent moment $\mu$ of the atom.

Cassiopeium (Cp), of course, has a complete shell and so has no paramagnetism. Stefan Meyer's value 2·77 is for Pr++++ rather than Ce+++, and its moderately good agreement with the values for Ce+++ by other observers is in fair accord with the Sommerfeld-Kossel rule that ions with equal number of electrons often have very similar properties.[20] The smaller and larger values for Sm and Eu in the column *V. V. & F.* correspond respectively to use of values 33 and 34 for the screening number $\sigma$ in (21), as will be elaborated in §§ 59, 60. For the

[19] F. Hund, *Zeits. f. Physik*, **33**, 855 (1925).

[20] Cabrera and Duperier[28] find a susceptibility for PrO$_2$ which gives an effective Bohr magneton number 2·24 for Pr++++, or 2·74 if the Weiss modification of (22) is used, in which $T$ is replaced by $T+\Delta$.

other ions it makes no appreciable difference which of these values is used.

| | THEORETICAL $\mu_{eff}$ | | | EXPERIMENTAL EFF. BOHR MAGNETON NUMBER $\mu_{eff}$[27] | | | | |
|---|---|---|---|---|---|---|---|---|
| $+++Ion$[21] | Term | Hund | $V. V.$ & $F.$ | Cabrera[22] Sulph. | Meyer[23] Sulph. | Z. & J.[24] Sulph. | Decker[25] Sol. | Williams[26] Oxide |
| La | $^1S$ | 0·00 | 0·00 | | | | | diam. |
| Ce | $4f\ ^2F_{5/2}$ | 2·54 | 2·56 | 2·39 | 2·77 | 2·37 | 2·10 | 0·23 ? |
| Pr | $4f^2\ ^3H_4$ | 3·58 | 3·62 | 3·60 | 3·47 | 3·47 | 3·41 | 2·29 ? |
| Nd | $4f^3\ ^4I_{9/2}$ | 3·62 | 3·68 | 3·62 | 3·51 | 3·52 | 3·45 | 3·43 |
| Ill | $4f^4\ ^5I_{4..}$ | 2·68 | 2·83 | .. | .. | .. | .. | .. |
| Sm | $4f^5\ ^6H_{5/2..}$ | 0·84 | $\begin{Bmatrix}1·55\\1·65\end{Bmatrix}$ | 1·54 | 1·32 | 1·53 | 1·63 | 1·57 |
| Eu | $4f^6\ ^7F_{0..}$ | 0·00 | $\begin{Bmatrix}3·40\\3·51\end{Bmatrix}$ | 3·61 | 3·12 | .. | .. | .. |
| Gd | $4f^7\ ^8S$ | 7·94 | 7·94 | 8·2 | 8·1 | 7·81 | 7·86 | 7·46 |
| Tb | $4f^8\ ^7F_6$ | 9·7 | 9·7 | 9·6 | 9·0 | 9·4 | 9·8 | .. |
| Ds | $4f^9\ ^6H_{15/2}$ | 10·6 | 10·6 | 10·5 | 10·6 | .. | 10·9 | 10·0 |
| Ho | $4f^{10}\ ^5I_8$ | 10·6 | 10·6 | 10·5 | 10·4 | 10·3 | 10·4 | 10·1 |
| Er | $4f^{11}\ ^4I_{15/2}$ | 9·6 | 9·6 | 9·5 | 9·4 | 9·6 | 9·5 | 9·2 |
| Tu | $4f^{12}\ ^3H_6$ | 7·6 | 7·6 | 7·2 | 7·5 | .. | .. | .. |
| Yb | $4f^{13}\ ^2F_{7/2}$ | 4·5 | 4·5 | 4·4 | 4·6 | 4·4 | 4·5 | .. |
| Cp | $4f^{14}\ ^1S$ | 0·00 | 0·00 | | diam. | diam. | 1·2 ? | 0·49 ? |

The experimental results call for some comment, especially in view of the different materials used. Cabrera, St. Meyer, and Zernicke all made their measurements primarily[28] on solid hydrated sulphates of the form $M_2(SO_4)_3 . 8H_2O$. Decker used solutions in which sulphates were dissolved, except that nitrates instead were dissolved for La, Ce,

[21] Throughout the balance of the chapter we omit attaching three plus signs to the abbreviations for the chemical elements, and it is to be uniformly understood that we are concerned with trivalent ions unless otherwise stated.

[22] B. Cabrera, *Comptes Rendus*, **180**, 668 (1925).

[23] St. Meyer, *Phys. Zeits.* **26**, 51, 478 (1925).

[24] Zernicke and James, *J. Amer. Chem. Soc.* **48**, 2827 (1926).

[25] H. Decker, *Ann. der Physik*, **79**, 324 (1926).

[26] E. H. Williams, *Phys. Rev.* **12**, 158 (1918); **14**, 348 (1919); **27**, 484 (1926).

[27] In the calculation of the effective Bohr magneton number from experimental data there may be slight differences in the method of computation because different writers use different values of the atomic constants in (22), and especially different estimates of the diamagnetic corrections. We have not attempted to iron out these small inconsistencies, as we give in the table the effective magneton numbers quoted by Hund from Meyer's and Cabrera's older data, and by Decker from his own work, while the calculation is our own for the other data, including that given on p. 245. Zernicke and James make the claim that the proper diamagnetic correction raises Meyer's value for the molar susceptibility of Sm to $960 \times 10^{-6}$, which gives a magneton number 1·51 in improved agreement with other observations.

[28] Cabrera, however, used a penta- rather than octohydrate for Ce. Meyer used oxides rather than sulphates for Tb and Tu.

and Pr. The good agreement of the values for solid sulphates with those for solutions and with the theoretical values for gases must mean that even in solids the ions are virtually free as far as the $4f$ electrons are concerned. The similarity of the results with oxides, which have been measured not only by Williams but also by Cabrera and Duperier,[29] to those for sulphates, is especially remarkable, as oxides are firmer chemical compounds than sulphates, and lack the 'magnetic dilution' of hydrated sulphates. The strikingly low value which Williams finds for Ce presumably means that he had largely [30] $CeO_2$ rather than $Ce_2O_3$, as $Ce^{++++}$ should be diamagnetic like $La^{+++}$, or else possibly that by

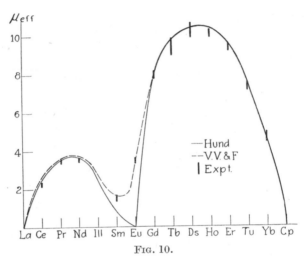

FIG. 10.

exception the inter-atomic forces on the $4f$ electron are here so large that the gaseous theory no longer holds. The rather wide discrepancies between some of the experimental values on the sulphates themselves are probably due to use of different samples or preparations of the rare earth salts, since the experimental error is due far more to difficulties of chemical purification than of magnetic technique. Zernicke and James[24] suggest that close agreement between two different observers does not necessarily imply that more weight should be attached to their results, but may simply arise because they used salts from the same original source of preparation. Cabrera and Duperier,[29] on the other hand, find remarkably consistent and reassuring values even with salts of different

---

[29] Cabrera and Duperier, *Comptes Rendus*, **188**, 1640 (1929).

[30] Although trivalent valencies are the rule for the rare earths, there are exceptions near the beginning of the sequence, and the oxides $CeO_2$, $Ce_2O_3$, $Ce_4O_7$ are all known to exist. See Hevesy, *Die seltenen Erden vom Standpunkte des Atombaues*, pp. 52, 74.

preparation, which are given in detail below. Impurities doubtless explain the paramagnetic moments sometimes reported for Cp, also the abnormally low value found by Williams for $Pr_2O_3$, but not confirmed by Cabrera and Duperier.[29]

*Additional Experimental Values.* Unfortunately space compels us to omit in the table the older measurements by Du Bois, Urbain, and Wedekind. For a good summary of this older work, and references, see Zernicke and James, *l.c.*[24] Roughly speaking, the older determinations agree fairly well with the newer work, but differ erratically in a few instances. Measurements in the Leiden laboratory on Gd, Er, Ds, Ce will be cited on p. 254. The data of Freed[31] yield $\mu_{\text{eff}} = 1\cdot57$ for Sm at room temperatures. Zernicke and James measured anhydrous as well as hydrated $Gd_2(SO_4)_3$, finding the same effective magneton number $7\cdot8$ in both cases.

It is particularly interesting and noteworthy that in addition to Cabrera's earlier work[22] on hydrated sulphates given in the table, Cabrera and Duperier[29] have recently also measured the anhydrous sulphates and oxides, often from different sources of preparation. Their results for anhydrous sulphates and oxides yield in (22) the following effective Bohr magneton numbers: Pr, $3\cdot47$†, $3\cdot32$*; Nd, $3\cdot52$†, $3\cdot40$*; Sm, $1\cdot58$†, $1\cdot50$*; Eu, $3\cdot54$†, $3\cdot32$‖; Gd, $7\cdot9$†, $7\cdot7$‖; Tb, $9\cdot6$†,—; Ds, $10\cdot3$†, $10\cdot2$‖; Ho, $10\cdot4$†, $10\cdot2$†; Er, $9\cdot4$†, $9\cdot3$†; Tu, $7\cdot0$†, $6\cdot8$†; Yb, $4\cdot3$†, $3\cdot9$†. The first and second values are respectively for anhydrous sulphates and oxides, and the † * ‖ denote preparations obtained respectively from Auer v. Welsbach, Prandtl, and Urbain. Zernicke and James, and Williams used salts prepared respectively in the New Hampshire and Illinois laboratories, while Cabrera's, Meyer's, and Decker's measurements reported in the table are with salts prepared by Auer v. Welsbach (except that Decker's, Co, Pr, Nd were by Prandtl).

In case the temperature variation is in accord with the Weiss generalization $\chi = C/(T+\Delta)$ of the Curie law, it is probably preferable to deduce the effective Bohr magneton number from experiment by using a modified form of (22) in which $T$ is replaced by $T+\Delta$, provided $\Delta$ is really due to inter-atomic forces rather than primarily (as in Sm, Eu) to natural multiplet structures. If we apply this modification to Cabrera's measurements on the anhydrous sulphates and oxides, the only data refined enough to permit use of this modification, one obtains the following effective Bohr magneton numbers instead of those given in the preceding paragraph: Pr, $3\cdot76$, $3\cdot71$; Nd, $3\cdot79$, $3\cdot71$; Gd, $7\cdot9$, $7\cdot9$; Tb, $9\cdot7$, —; Ds, $10\cdot5$, $10\cdot5$; Ho, $10\cdot6$, $10\cdot5$; Er, $9\cdot6$, $9\cdot5$; Tu, $7\cdot5$, $7\cdot2$; Yb, $4\cdot8$, $4\cdot5$. (In the cases of Pr, Nd, Tu, Yb, Cabrera and Duperier find that $1/\chi$ is not really a linear function of $T$ as implied by the Weiss formula, but as a rough approximation we take $\Delta$ equal to the value of $-(d\log\chi/dT)^{-1}-T$ at room temperature.)

## 59. The Special Cases of Europeum and Samarium

(The trivalent ions are to be understood throughout. Cf. note 21.)
It is seen that Hund's calculations agree with experiment, within the discrepancies of the latter among themselves, except for Sm and Eu, where his theoretical values are much too low. Hund[19] himself, and also Laporte,[32] have suspected that this is perhaps because the multiplet

---

[31] S. Freed, *J. Amer. Chem. Soc.* **52**, 2702 (1930).

[32] O. Laporte, *Zeits. f. Physik*, **47**, 761 (1928).

intervals in Sm and Eu are not really infinitely large compared to $kT$. This requires us to make a more careful examination of multiplet structures by means of (18). This formula shows that the various components are not evenly spaced, and instead crowd together for small values of $J$, as by (18) the interval between two consecutive components $J, J+1$ equals $A(J+1)$. Now if the multiplicity $2S+1$ is fairly large,

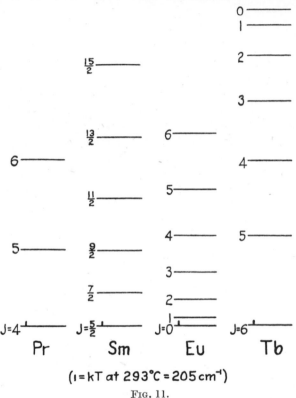

$$(\mathtt{i} = kT \text{ at } 293°C = 205\,cm^{-1})$$

Fig. 11.

and if $L$ and $S$ are nearly equal, so that $J_{\min} = |L-S|$ is small, the separation between the components with the two lowest values of $J$ may well be small compared to $kT$, even though the 'over-all' multiplet width is considerably greater than $kT$. This is just the situation which arises *par excellence* in Eu, and to a lesser degree in Sm. In Eu the interval between the lowest multiplet components is only $1/21$ of the over-all width, as for a $^7F$ term

$$\tfrac{1}{2}[J_{\max}(J_{\max}+1)-J_{\min}(J_{\min}+1)] = \tfrac{1}{2}6\times7-0 = 21, \qquad J_{\min}+1 = 1.$$

The corresponding value for Sm is $7/55$. The multiplets for Eu and Sm are illustrated in Fig. 11 (Grotrian diagrams). The cases of Pr and Tb are also shown for comparison as illustrative of ions in which the lowest interval is an appreciable fraction (5/11 in Pr, 6/21 in Tb) of the total width and in which Hund's calculations are confirmed experimentally.

To proceed further it is now necessary to evaluate quantitatively the multiplet intervals by determining the screening constant $\sigma$ in (21) from X-ray data. This data must be taken from atoms heavier than the rare earths, as X-ray emission lines terminating in the $4f$ level are observed only after the $4f$ group is complete, so that there is an initial concentration of electrons in higher levels.[33] Such a method is, of course, rather indirect, but a check on its accuracy is furnished by comparison with the iron group. In the latter, optical data are available on screening constants for incomplete shells as well as X-ray data for complete ones, and it is found that the screening constants for triply charged ions of the former never differ by more than one or two units from the standard values of the latter. This is naturally in a sense a special case of the well-known Bowen-Millikan result on the similarity of X-ray and optical multiplets. The uncertainty in the X-ray determinations of $\sigma$ is, however, somewhat larger in the rare earth ($4f$) than in the iron ($3d$) group. Wentzel gives $34 \pm 4$ as the value yielded by these determinations in the case of the $4f$ shell,[34] while Coster[35] gives 33. In the table and elsewhere we have generally given the effective magneton numbers obtained both by taking $\sigma = 34$ and $\sigma = 33$. The screening number, as a matter of fact, is more accurately determined by the magnetic measurements themselves than by the X-ray data. This will be shown particularly clearly when we study the temperature variation in Sm (§ 60). Screening numbers in the ranges 30–32 and 35–38 definitely will not fit the experimental magnetic measurements on Sm, even though within Wentzel's estimate of the X-ray precision. Substitution of the value $\sigma = 34$ in (21) makes the over-all multiplet width 5,360 cm.$^{-1}$ for Eu and 7,320 cm.$^{-1}$ for Sm. The corresponding values of the intervals between the two lowest components are $5,360/21 = 255$ cm.$^{-1}$ and $7,320(7/55) = 932$ cm.$^{-1}$, while somewhat higher values are obtained if we use $\sigma = 33$. In either case these intervals are not very great com-

---

[33] Considerable work is in progress on the spectra of rare earth salts, whose analysis may ultimately yield the desired multiplet structures directly. See S. Freed and F. H. Spedding, *Nature*, **123**, 525 (1929); *Phys. Rev.* **34**, 945 (1929). A certain amount of X-ray data is available for some rare earths themselves, but this is for the neutral atom rather than trivalent ion and also the multiplet structures have not been adequately resolved and analysed; see E. Lindberg, *Zeits. f. Physik*, **50**, 82; **56**, 402 (1928–9).

[34] G. Wentzel, *Zeits. f. Physik*, **33**, 849 (1925).

[35] D. Coster, in Müller-Poulliets' *Handbuch der Physik*, ii. 2057.

pared to $kT$, inasmuch as $kT$ is $0\cdot698T$ cm.$^{-1}$ when expressed in wave numbers, and is thus about 200 cm.$^{-1}$ at room temperatures. It is therefore necessary to use the accurate 'intermediate' formula (16) instead of the asymptotic one (10). The explicit forms which (16) takes for Eu and Sm are respectively

(Eu) $\chi_{\text{mol}}$

$$= \frac{0\cdot1241}{xT} \frac{24+(13\cdot5x-1\cdot5)e^{-x}+(67\cdot5x-2\cdot5)e^{-3x}+(189x-3\cdot5)e^{-6x}+\ldots}{1+3e^{-x}+5e^{-3x}+7e^{-6x}+\ldots},$$

(Sm) $\chi_{\text{mol}}$ \hfill (23)

$$= \frac{0\cdot1241}{yT} \frac{2\cdot14y+3\cdot67+(42\cdot9y+0\cdot82)e^{-7y}+(142y-0\cdot33)e^{-16y}+\ldots}{3+4e^{-7y}+5e^{-16y}+\ldots}$$

where $x$ and $y$ are respectively 1/21 and 1/55 of the ratio of the over-all multiplet width (in ergs) to $kT$. If $\sigma = 34$, then $x = 365/T$, $y = 191/T$, while with $\sigma = 33$ the values are $x = 418/T$, $y = 220/T$. We give the formulae in a form not requiring these specialized values of $x$ and $y$ to allow for the fact that in the future the multiplet widths will doubtless be known more accurately.

When formula (23) is used, effective Bohr magneton numbers of $3\cdot51$ and $1\cdot65$ respectively are obtained for Eu and Sm if $\sigma = 34$, while $3\cdot40$ and $1\cdot55$ result if $\sigma = 33$. Either of these values is in as good agreement with experiment as for the other members of the rare-earth series,[36] so that the agreement is now quite satisfactory for the entire series. Reference to the table in § 58 shows that the confirmation in Eu and Sm is particularly close if one accepts the other experimental values in preference to St. Meyer's. It is altogether probable that his values for Sm and Eu are too low,[37] especially in view of the very careful recent work of Cabrera and Duperier.

Calculations for the other rare earths can also be made by means of

---

[36] These theoretical values were given by Miss Frank and the writer, *Phys. Rev.* **34**, 1494, 1625 (1929), and clearly show that explanation of the susceptibilities of Eu and Sm does not require modification of the Bohr-Hund configurations for these ions. Such modifications, whereby the numbers of $4f$ electrons in Sm$^{+++}$ and Eu$^{+++}$ were taken to be different from 5 and 6 respectively, were formerly debated because Hund's original calculations did not agree with experiment; cf. Hevesy, *Die seltenen Erden*, p. 44 and references.

[37] Cf. especially Cabrera and Duperier's additional recent measurements given on p. 245, also Zernicke and James' contention given at the end of note [27]. Their value for Sm should presumably be quite accurate, as they used the same preparation of Sm as employed for an atomic weight determination (Stewart and James, *J. Amer. Chem. Soc.* **39**, 2605, 1917). Meyer[23] intimates that the usual values for Eu may be high on account of contamination by Gd, but this is disputed by Cabrera,[29] who states that in his own work the impurity is Sm, which would lower rather than raise the susceptibility.

the accurate formula (16) instead of the asymptotic one (10), and the resulting values are given in the column of the table marked $V. V. \& F.$ The corrections other than those for Sm and Eu already studied are important only in the rare and magnetically unmeasured element Ill. The absence of any revision in the bottom half of the table is because here the multiplets are inverted, so that the relatively narrow intervals separate only components which are excited rather than normal states. The diagram for Tb, for instance, is similar to that for Eu turned upside down (cf. Fig. 11).

It is to be emphasized that in Eu and Sm it is very essential that one does not omit the commonly forgotten term $\alpha_J$ in (16). Laporte [32] showed that without this term the effective Bohr magneton number for Eu is only 1·7 instead of 3·51. As the susceptibility varies as the square of this number, the second-order Zeeman effect hence contributes about 3/4 of the susceptibility of Eu. The kinematical origin of such an abnormal situation can readily be comprehended from Fig. 9, p. 230, for if $J$ is very small compared to $S$ and $L$, as in Eu, then $\sin(J, S)$ is substantially unity, and the component $b$-$c$ in Fig. 9 is much larger than the ordinary component $a$-$b$.

## 60. Temperature Variation in the Rare Earths—The Gyromagnetic Ratio

The dependence on temperature for Sm and Eu is quite different from that given by Curie's law, as it is necessary to use the 'intermediate' formula (16) instead of (10). The variation with temperature of the effective Bohr magneton number for Sm computed by Miss Frank [38] from (23) and (22) is exhibited in the table on p. 250.

The experimental values of various observers are included for comparison. The agreement with experiment is gratifying when it is remembered that the observations are made on solids rather than the theoretical ideal gas state. In particular, the ions in the oxides are doubtless far from free. The deviations from theory at low temperatures revealed by Freed's measurements need not cause concern, as they are to be attributed to 'cryomagnetic anomalies', i.e. distortion by interatomic forces in the solid. We shall elaborate in Chapter XI the idea that the values for free ions should apply only as long as the work required to 'turn over' an ion against the inter-atomic forces is assumed

---

[38] A. Frank, *Phys. Rev.*, in press. In *Proc. Lon. Phys. Soc.* **42**, 388 (1930), W. Sucksmith also has noticed that the anomalies in the temperature variation in Sm and Eu are to be attributed to Van Vleck and Frank's second-order Zeeman correction.

small compared to $kT$, a supposition clearly not warranted if the temperature is too low.

EFFECTIVE BOHR MAGNETON NUMBERS FOR $Sm^{+++}$

| | $\mu_{\text{eff}}$ Theory | | $\mu_{\text{eff}}$ Experiment | | | |
| | | | Williams[26] | Freed[31] | Cabrera & Dup.[39] | |
| $T$ | $\sigma = 33$ | $\sigma = 34$ | (oxide) | (hyd. sul.) | (oxide) | (anh. s.) |
|---|---|---|---|---|---|---|
| 0° K | 0·84 | 0·84 | .. | .. | .. | .. |
| 20 | 0·91 | 0·92 | .. | .. | .. | .. |
| 74 | 1·07 | 1·09 | .. | 0·91 | .. | .. |
| 85 | 1·09 | 1·12 | .. | 0·96 | .. | .. |
| 112 | 1·16 | 1·20 | .. | 1·08 | .. | .. |
| 123 | 1·18 | 1·23 | 1·08 | .. | .. | .. |
| 170 | 1·29 | 1·35 | .. | 1·26 | .. | .. |
| 205 | 1·37 | 1·43 | .. | 1·35 | .. | .. |
| 240 | 1·44 | 1·52 | .. | 1·44 | .. | .. |
| 293 | 1·55 | 1·65 | 1·58 | 1·57 | 1·50 | 1·58 |
| 375 | 1·73 | 1·85 | 1·77 | .. | 1·69 | .. |
| 400 | 1·78 | 1·91 | .. | .. | 1·75 | .. |
| 500 | 2·00 | 2·15 | .. | .. | 1·97 | .. |
| 543 | 2·09 | 2·25 | 2·14 | .. | 2·06 | .. |
| 600 | 2·20 | 2·38 | .. | .. | 2·17 | .. |
| 800 | 2·58 | 2·78 | .. | .. | .. | .. |
| 1000 | 2·91 | 3·14 | .. | .. | .. | .. |

A particularly interesting feature in Sm is that somewhat above room temperatures the susceptibility should reach a minimum and then increase slowly as the temperature is raised still further, in marked contrast to the usual Curie decrease with increasing temperature. This is shown in Fig. 12.

From (23) Miss Frank finds that the temperature at which this minimum is located is approximately $T_{\text{min}} = 0\cdot0628(Z-\sigma)^4$, e.g. 386° K. with $\sigma = 34$ or 444° with $\sigma = 33$. Precise experimental observation of this temperature would thus determine the screening constant $\sigma$ accurately, but such precision would be difficult as the curve is so flat near the minimum. The measurements of Cabrera and Duperier [40] do, however, definitely show that there is experimentally a minimum somewhere between 350° and 425° K., perhaps at 400°. Furthermore, Williams finds a lower susceptibility at 375° than at either 293° or 543°. This is a striking confirmation of an unusual feature of the theory.

[39] The experimental values by Cabrera and Duperier given in the tables for Sm and Eu at various temperatures are obtained from a personal letter from Professor Cabrera giving more detail than ref. [29].

[40] The writer is indebted to Professor Cabrera for personal communication of this fact, not stated in the paper of Cabrera and Duperier.

The theoretical effective Bohr magneton numbers for Eu at various temperatures are shown in the following table, along with the data of Cabrera and Duperier.

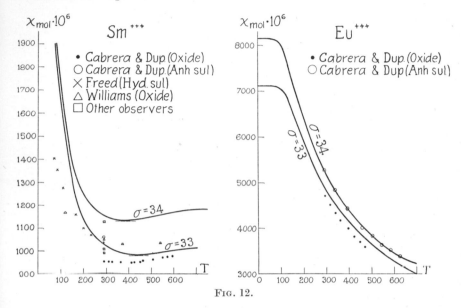

FIG. 12.

EFFECTIVE BOHR MAGNETON NUMBERS FOR Eu[+++]

| | $\mu_{\text{eff}}$ Theory | | $\mu_{\text{eff}}$ Experiment (Cabrera & Dup.)[39] | |
|---|---|---|---|---|
| $T$ | $\sigma = 33$ | $\sigma = 34$ | oxide | anh. s. |
| 0° K | 0·0 | 0·0 | .. | .. |
| 20 | 1·07 | 1·15 | .. | .. |
| 70 | 2·01 | 2·14 | .. | .. |
| 100 | 2·38 | 2·53 | .. | .. |
| 200 | 3·09 | 3·20 | .. | .. |
| 293 | 3·40 | 3·51 | 3·34 | 3·53 |
| 400 | 3·65 | 3·75 | 3·57 | 3·75 |
| 470 | 3·77 | 3·89 | 3·69 | 3·89 |
| 625 | 4·02 | 4·14 | .. | 4·11 |

The corresponding curves of susceptibility against temperature are shown in Fig. 12. Unfortunately no experimental data are available for Eu at low temperatures, which would be particularly interesting, as the effective Bohr magneton number should approach zero at $T = 0$. This, however, does not mean that the paramagnetic susceptibility of Eu vanishes at the absolute zero. When the inner quantum number $J$ vanishes, as in the lowest multiplet component of Eu, the first term of

(10) disappears, to be sure, but the second term $N\alpha$ is abnormally large. Thus in the vicinity of $T = 0$ Eu should have a molar susceptibility about $7\cdot1\times10^{-3}$ ($\sigma = 33$) or $8\cdot1\times10^{-3}$ ($\sigma = 34$) independent of temperature.

Reference to Fig. 12 shows that use of a screening number 34 probably gives results in better accord with experiment than does 33 as regards the temperature at which the minimum is located in Sm, although the precise location of the experimental minimum is rather uncertain. Certainly $\sigma = 34$ fits the absolute values of the experimental susceptibility for Eu better than $\sigma = 33$, if the anhydrous sulphate is considered a closer approach to gaseous behaviour than the oxide. In Sm the absolute values, in distinction from location of minimum, are perhaps in better accord with $\sigma = 33$ than with $\sigma = 34$. This need not be considered a contradiction, as any departures from gaseous behaviour tend to lower the susceptibility, and hence make the apparent $\sigma$ less than the true $\sigma$. The screening constant $\sigma$ should be somewhat greater (perhaps $0\cdot3$ more) for Eu than for Sm, due to shielding by the additional $4f$ electron. As Sm has a lower paramagnetic susceptibility than the other rare earths, the omitted correction for the diamagnetism of the cation is more important than usual here, though still small.

This correction would raise the experimental points in Fig. 12, but cannot be estimated precisely. It is perhaps about $30\times10^{-6}$ per mol. This corresponds approximately to Pauling's estimate $-38\times10^{-6}$ of the diamagnetism of $La^{+++}$, which resembles $Sm^{+++}$ except for the absence of the five $4f$ electrons and a corresponding diminution of $Z$ by five units. The $4f$ electrons contribute less to the diamagnetism than the surrounding $5s$, $5p$, shells. The diamagnetic effect of the $4f$ group is perhaps roughly counterbalanced by the fact that it screens the outer shells only imperfectly, thus contracting the 5 quantum orbits. If this is true, the diamagnetism of La and Sm is of the same order. The estimate $-28\times10^{-6}$ furnished for $Sm^{+++}$ by Slater's screening constants (§ 50) is also in accord. The low magnitude $-20\times10^{-6}$ found experimentally by Meyer for the susceptibility of $HfO_2$ suggests that even the estimate $-30\times10^{-6}$ is excessive for Sm. ($Hf^{4+}$ resembles $La^{3+}$ except for addition of the complete shell of 14 $4f$ electrons.) As the molar susceptibility of $O^{--}$ is $-13\times10^{-6}$, his determination would demand that $Hf^{4+}$ be without appreciable magnetism, but possibly his low value is due to counterbalancing of the true diamagnetism by paramagnetic impurities.

It is interesting to contrast the temperature coefficients $-\chi^{-1}d\chi/dT$ of the susceptibilities of Sm and Eu at room temperatures with the value 1/293 predicted by Curie's law. The theoretical value for Sm is 1/1517 ($\sigma = 33$) or 1/2525 ($\sigma = 34$), while the experimental determinations are 1/1600 (Williams[26]), 1/1700 (Zernicke and James[24]), 1600 (Freed[31]). For Eu the corresponding theoretical values are 1/542 ($\sigma = 33$) and 1/525 ($\sigma = 34$), while Cabrera and Duperier find 1/522 and

1/500 for the oxide and anhydrous sulphate respectively. The agreement is as good as can be expected. The abnormally small value for Sm is because increasing temperature increases the concentration of ions in the states with larger values of the inner quantum number $J$ and hence larger magnetic moments. This effect tends to offset the decrease with increasing temperature due to the factor $T$ in the usual Curie denominator. In Eu the lowest state $J = 0$ has an abnormally large second-order term $N\alpha$, so that promotion to higher values of $J$ does not increase the susceptibility as much as in Sm. This is reflected in the temperature coefficient being nearer the ordinary Curie value in Eu than in Sm.

The rare earths other than Eu, Sm, and Ill should conform very approximately to Curie's law and have a temperature coefficient about 1/293 at room temperatures, as for these other ions the difference between the columns headed *Hund* and *V. V. & F.* in the table of § 58 is negligible. In Nd, for instance, Miss Frank's calculations show that the correction for the effect of the multiplet structure only changes this coefficient from 1/293 to 1/303, while for the remaining ions Hund's calculations apply still more accurately and the changes are smaller still. Some experimental results on the reciprocal of the temperature coefficient in the vicinity of 293° K. for ions in various salts are given in the following table.

| $-\chi/(d\chi/dT)$ | Ce | Pr | Nd | Gd | Tb | Ds | Ho | Er | Tu | Yb |
|---|---|---|---|---|---|---|---|---|---|---|
| Anh. Sulph. Cabrera[41] | .. | 344 | 341 | 292 | 296 | 304 | 301 | 304 | 322 | 369 |
| Hyd. Sulph. Z. & J.[24] | 290 | 358 | 348 | 305 | 327 | .. | 320 | 252 | .. | 292 |
| Oxide { Cabrera[41] | (438) | 366 | 344 | 306 | 316 | 312 | 307 | 308 | 330 | 390 |
| Oxide { Williams[26] | .. | .. | 337 | 305 | .. | 308 | .. | 306 | .. | .. |

The discrepancy between different observations on the same salt shows that the experimental error is considerable. The deviations from 293 are, in most cases, relatively small, and, when real, are doubtless caused primarily by inter-atomic forces in the solid, and so shed no particular light on the ideal gas theory, but do reveal how much the orientations of the ions are constrained by inter-atomic forces. It is usually found that the temperature variation of the susceptibility can be fairly well represented at least over a range of a few hundred degrees and barring possible anomalies at very low temperatures by the Weiss generalization $\chi = C/(T+\Delta)$ of the Curie formula. The value of $\Delta$ is approxi-

[41] Computed from Cabrera and Duperier's empirical formulae $\chi = -k+C/(T+\Delta)$ given in ref. [29]. An earlier paper (*J. de Physique*, **6**, 252, 1925) gives other temperature coefficients differing by 5 per cent. or so in some cases. Zernicke and James report a value 283 for anhydrous $Gd_2(SO_4)_3$.

mately $-\chi(d\chi/dT)^{-1}-T$, and is thus about 50 for, e.g. Nd. If the inter-atomic forces are adequate to produce this large $\Delta$ in Nd, they should produce deviations between theory and experiment in Sm at low temperatures, of about the order of magnitude found experimentally (p. 250).

Because $T$ occurs in the denominator, measurements at very low temperatures are particularly desirable. At Leiden $Ds_2O_3$,[42] $CeF_3$,[43] and $Er_2(SO_4)_3 8H_2O$ [44] have been measured down to the temperature of liquid hydrogen ($c.$ 14° K.) and $Gd_2(SO_4)_3 8H_2O$ [45] down to that of liquid helium (1·3° K.). Usually the law $\chi = C/(T+\Delta)$ is found to hold remarkably well down to the lowest temperature studied, with the following values of $\Delta$: $Ds_2O_3$, 16; $CeF_3$, 62; $Er_2(SO_4)_3 8H_2O$, 1·9; $Gd_2(SO_4)_3 8H_2O$, 0·0 (or possibly 0·26). In $CeF_3$, however, pronounced deviations appear below 65° K. The corresponding experimental values of the effective Bohr magneton number $\mu_{eff}$ are 10·6, 2·51, 9·0, 7·8, in quite satisfactory agreement with the theoretical values 10·6, 2·54, 9·6, and 7·9 respectively. These results yield temperature coefficients 1/309, 1/355, 1/295, 1/293 respectively for $Ds_2O_3$, $CeF_3$, $Er_2(SO_4)_3 8H_2O$, $(Gd_2)_3(SO_4)_2 8H_2O$ at room temperatures. The agreement with Zernicke and James's value 1/252 for $Er_2(SO_4)_3 8H_2O$ (see table) is poor, but the latter observers do not claim a high degree of precision, so that 1/295 is doubtless very close to the true value. The measurements at low temperatures are particularly interesting because they reveal the order of magnitude of the inter-atomic forces tending to orient the $4f$ orbits in the rare earths, which turn out to be surprisingly small. When the multiplet structure is so wide that the Langevin formula should hold for the ideal gas state, as is the case in the rare earths except for Ill, Sm, Eu, the theoretical considerations of Chapter VII show that departures from the Langevin or Curie law should first be expected in a solid when the temperature becomes so low that the energy required to 'turn over' an atom against the inter-atomic field becomes comparable with $kT$. Thus $k\Delta$ is a

[42] Onnes and Oosterhuis, *Leiden Communications*, 129 b, 132 e.

[43] W. J. de Haas and C. J. Gorter, *Leiden Communications*, 210 c, or *Proc. Amsterdam Acad.* 33, 949 (1930).

[44] W. J. de Haas, E. C. Wiersma, and W. H. Capel, *Leiden Communications*, 201 b or *Proc. Amsterdam Acad.* 32, 739 (1929).

[45] H. R. Woltjer, *Leiden Communications*, 167 b; H. R. Woltjer and H. Kamerlingh Onnes, *ibid.* 167 c; earlier work, mostly at higher temperatures, by Onnes and Perrier and by Onnes and Oosterhuis, *Leiden Communications*, 122 a, 129 b, 140 d. Jackson and Onnes find that gadolinium ethyl sulphate obeys Curie's law $\chi = C/T$ down to $T = 14°$ K., the lowest temperature they employed for this material (*Leiden Communications*, 168 a or *Comptes Rendus*, 177, 154, 1923); the value of $C$ yields an effective magneton number 7·5, nearly the same as for the hydrated sulphate.

measure of the orientation energy in the crystal. In the case of Nd ions, for instance, this energy is of the order 30 cm.$^{-1}$, as here $\Delta = 50$, while $kT/hc = 0.7T$ cm.$^{-1}$. The fact that the unmodified Langevin formula holds so beautifully for hydrated gadolinium sulphate right down to the temperature of liquid helium is a consequence of the fact that the Gd ion is in a $^8S$ state and has a paramagnetic moment only in virtue of the spin, so that questions of orbital dissymmetry do not arise. This point will be elaborated in §§ 73–74. That $Ds_2O_3$ and $CeF_3$ have a larger $\Delta$ than $Er_2(SO_4)_3 8H_2O$ is probably because hydration causes 'magnetic dilution', and also because oxides and fluorides are firmer compounds than sulphates.

*The Gyromagnetic Effect.* Besides the ordinary measurements on susceptibilities, the theory for the rare earths is confirmed by evidence of another sort, viz. the limited amount of data available on the gyromagnetic effect [46] for these materials. To magnetize a body to the extent demanded by our formulae, it is necessary to supply the atoms with angular momentum. The atoms can secure this angular momentum only by stealing it from the body as a whole. Such a theft demands that the body acquire a mass rotation if it is at rest before the field is applied. (The angular momentum supplied by the field can be shown very generally to be only of the order of magnitude corresponding to the Larmor precession,[47] regardless of whether his theorem is applicable. Hence the field only supplies a small fraction $k$ of the necessary angular momentum, where $k$ is of the order of the ratio of diamagnetic to paramagnetic susceptibility.) A free atom's angular momentum in the direction of the field is $Mh/2\pi$, if measured now in ordinary rather than quantum units. The total angular momentum demanded per c.c. by the atoms is thus $N \sum\limits_{J,M} \dfrac{Mh}{2\pi} e^{-W/kT} \Big/ \sum e^{-W/kT}$. As $W = W_J^0 + Mg_J\beta H$, this expression may be simplified as in passing from (13) to (10). The complication of a term analogous to $N\alpha$ in the susceptibility formulae does not enter in dealing with angular momentum, as the angular momentum is a constant of the motion not perturbed by the field except for a small,

---

[46] For an account of the ordinary gyromagnetic experiments and references, see Stoner, *Magnetism and Atomic Structure*, Chap. VIII. This, however, is not recent enough to include Sucksmith's experiments on paramagnetic materials. Another summary, by Weiss, is given in the report of the 1930 Solvay Congress.

[47] This point has caused considerable uncertainty in the literature, as it has sometimes been incorrectly conjectured that the field might supply an appreciable fraction of the angular momentum, thus invalidating the gyromagnetic experiments. The writer hopes to discuss this subject more fully in a future paper.

essentially diamagnetic correction which we have neglected (viz. the difference between $p_{\gamma_1}$ and $\sum m_i \rho_i^2 \phi_i$ in an analysis such as that in § 8). The ratio $\theta$ of the angular momentum to the magnetic moment $\chi H$ is thus found to be

$$\theta = \frac{2mc \sum_J g_J J(J+1)(2J+1)e^{-W_J^0/kT}}{e \sum [g_J^2 J(J+1)+3kT\alpha_J \beta^{-2}](2J+1)e^{-W_J^0/kT}} \tag{24}$$

after use of the formula (16) for $\chi$. It can be shown that the expression given by (24) is also the same as the ratio $H/\Omega$ in the converse (Barnett) experiment on magnetization by rotation, where $H$ is the magnetic field which would produce the same magnetization as rotation of the solid with an angular velocity $\Omega$.

If the multiplet is small compared to $kT$, (24) reduces to

$$\theta = \frac{2mc}{e} \frac{[2S(S+1)+L(L+1)]}{[4S(S+1)+L(L+1)]}$$

(cf. Eq. (6)). If it is large compared to $kT$, and if the terms proportional to $\alpha_J$ may be neglected, then $\theta = 2mc/g_J e$, where $g_J$ is the ordinary Landé $g$-factor. In dysprosium the theoretical value of $g_J$ is 1·33. Sucksmith's determination[48] of the gyromagnetic ratio $\theta$ for $Ds_2O_3$ yields $g = 1·28 \pm 0·07$. The agreement is especially gratifying when it is remembered that gyromagnetic experiments are vastly more difficult in paramagnetic than in the ferromagnetic bodies usually measured.

In Sm and Eu it is, of course, necessary to use the 'intermediate' formula (24) without simplification, and the gyromagnetic ratio should vary with temperature. The numerical magnitudes of the values of (24) appropriate to various temperatures will be found in Miss Frank's paper.[38] At $T = 0$ the ratio vanishes for Eu, while at room temperatures $\theta = 0·270\ mc/e$ if $\sigma = 33$ or $0·306\ mc/e$ if $\sigma = 34$. Measurements bravely undertaken by Sucksmith[49] on Eu at $T = 293$ have not yet achieved quantitative accuracy but definitely favour in a qualitative way these values as opposed to the higher value 1·33 $mc/e$ which would be obtained if one forgot the terms proportional to $\alpha_J$ in (24) contributed by the second-order Zeeman effect.

Gyromagnetic measurements are at present wanting on rare earths other than Ds and Eu.

[48] W. Sucksmith, *Proc. Roy. Soc.* **128**A, 276 (1930).
[49] W. Sucksmith, paper presented at 1930 meeting of British Association.

## 61. Saturation Effects

Hitherto we have supposed the field strength sufficiently small so that only the portion of the moment per c.c. which is linear in the field $H$ need be retained. However, in the limiting cases of multiplets which are exceedingly narrow or wide compared to $kT$ there is no difficulty in obtaining closed expressions for $\chi$ even when the latter cannot be treated as independent of $H$. Namely, the right-hand sides of (7) and (13) can be summed without the necessity of expanding the exponents in series as previously. The denominator of (13) is summed by making the substitution $x = e^{+g\beta H/kT}$ and using the elementary formula $x^{-J}(1+x+x^2+...+x^{2J}) = (x^{-J}-x^{J+1})/(1-x)$ for the sum of a geometric progression. Differentiation of this formula with respect to $x$ yields a relation which sums the numerator of (13). One thus finds that (13) becomes

$$M_H = NJg\beta B_J\left(\frac{Jg\beta H}{kT}\right),\qquad(25)$$

with the abbreviation

$$B_J(y) = \frac{2J+1}{2J}\coth\left(\frac{2Jy+y}{2J}\right) - \frac{1}{2J}\coth\frac{y}{2J}.\qquad(26)$$

In Eq. (25) we have given the formula for the magnetic moment $M_H$ per unit-volume instead of the susceptibility. This difference is trivial, as $M_H = H\chi$. It is convenient to have a name for the function (26), and so we shall call it a Brillouin function, as it was employed in the new quantum mechanics by Brillouin,[50] although also previously used in the old theories by Debye[51] and others. One can also similarly evaluate Eq. (7) for narrow multiplets accurately, which becomes $M_H = 2NS\beta B_S(2S\beta H/kT) + NL\beta B_L(L\beta H/kT)$. This formula, however, is not especially useful, as temperatures low enough to permit experimental production of appreciable saturation effects do not warrant the assumption of multiplet intervals small compared to $kT$.

When $J$ becomes very great and $\beta$ is imagined to become small to keep $\beta J$ finite, the Brillouin function passes over asymptotically into the classical Langevin function $L(x) = \coth x - (1/x)$ in the following way, $\lim_{J=\infty} B_J(y) = L(y)$. The saturation moment predicted by (25) and (26) is $NJg\beta$, or $N(J/J+1)^{\frac{1}{2}}\mu_{\text{eff}}\beta$, where $\mu_{\text{eff}}$ is the effective Bohr magneton number for weak fields, defined in the fashion (22) applied to (10).

[50] L. Brillouin, *J. de Physique*, **8**, 74 (1927).
[51] P. Debye in Marx, *Handbuch der Radiologie*, vi. 713; also Stoner, *Magnetism and Atomic Structure*, p. 116. Introduction of the term 'Debye function' might lead to confusion with his specific heat function.

The Langevin expression $M_H = N\mu L(\mu H/kT)$ gives a saturation moment $N\mu_{\text{eff}}$, which is $(J+1/J)^{\frac{1}{2}}$ times greater than that given by the Brillouin for the same value of $\mu_{\text{eff}}$, i.e. for the same initial slope of the magnetization curve. This difference is readily understandable, as the maximum (i.e. saturation value of the) $z$ component of angular momentum is $P_z = Jh/2\pi$, so that even here $P_x^2$, $P_y^2$ never vanish, inasmuch as $P_x^2 + P_y^2 + P_z^2 \doteq J(J+1)h^2/4\pi^2$. Thus even the 'most parallel' alinement of magnetic moment is in a certain sense necessarily incomplete in quantum mechanics. On the other hand, in the electric case complete

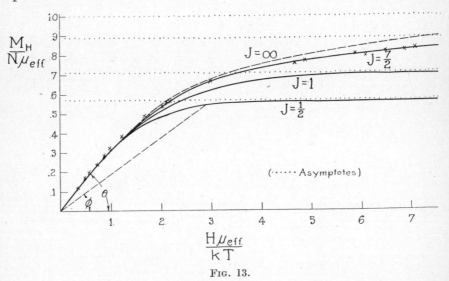

Fig. 13.

alinement of the permanent electric moment vector of the molecule is possible, as in § 47 we mentioned that the complete Langevin formula for electric polarization is obtained when saturation effects are considered (assuming the rotational fine structure to be narrow compared to $kT$). The difference between the magnetic and electric cases may seem strange, but Niessen [52] shows that it is due fundamentally to the fact that the various Cartesian components of angular momentum do not commute with each other in matrix multiplication, whereas the components $\sum e_i x_i$, $\sum e_i y_i$, $\sum e_i z_i$ of electric moment do. Various typical Brillouin curves are contrasted with the Langevin one in Fig. 13. The ordinates and abscissae are taken as $M_H/N\mu_{\text{eff}}$, $H\mu_{\text{eff}}/kT$ rather than $M_H$, $H$, in order to make all curves have the same initial slope 1/3. The dotted line is drawn for later use and explanation in § 77.

[52] K. F. Niessen, *Phys. Rev.* **34**, 253 (1929).

To test Eq. (25) one has the celebrated Leiden measurements[45] on hydrated gadolinium sulphate. As far as the writer is aware, these are the only observations on true 'gaseous' saturation produced directly by the applied magnetic field, rather than through the agency of the molecular field as in ferromagnetic solids. The saturation is made appreciable by the use of a material with a comparatively large $\mu_{\text{eff}}$ (7·9), and also primarily by the use of exceedingly low temperatures (down to 1·3° K.). At room temperatures the deviations due to saturation are too small to be detectable even with Kapitza's machinery (300,000 gauss)! Distortions from the theoretical gaseous behaviour are minimized by using a material whose paramagnetic ion is in an $S$ state and which has a high 'magnetic dilution' in virtue of the eight water-molecules of hydration. The experimental results have usually been interpreted in terms of the classical Langevin function, but the Brillouin one $B_{7/2}(7\beta H/kT)$ should, of course, be used instead. The value 7/2 of $J$ in Gd is sufficiently large that the difference between these two functions is not great. With the latter the saturation moment is $0·88\,N\mu_{\text{eff}}$ instead of $N\mu_{\text{eff}}\,(= 7·94N\beta)$. The experimental points are indicated by crosses in Fig. 13. At the highest field strength and lowest temperature used by Woltjer and Onnes the magnetization reached $0·84N\mu_{\text{eff}}$, or about 95 per cent. of the full saturation allowance, $0·88N\mu_{\text{eff}}$. The theoretical value at this $H$ and $T$ is $0·831N\mu_{\text{eff}}$, whereas the Langevin value is $0·859N\mu_{\text{eff}}$. Reference to the figure shows that the agreement of experiment with the theoretical curve is very gratifying. As remarked by Giauque,[53] it is even better than with the classical Langevin formula. In fact, Woltjer and Onnes were puzzled with the perceptible, though small, deviations from the latter.

## 62. Lack of Influence of Nuclear Spin

The 'hyperfine' structure of series spectra makes it certain that nuclei possess internal spins, having an angular momentum of the same order of magnitude as that of electrons.[54] However, the narrowness of the hyperfine structure shows that the attendant magnetic moment is only of the order $10^{-3}\beta$, where $\beta$ is the Bohr magneton[55] $he/4\pi mc$. The direct

---

[53] W. F. Giauque, *J. Amer. Chem. Soc.* **49**, 1870 (1927). See this paper for numerical calculation of the Brillouin function for Gd at various field strengths.

[54] For a good discussion of the hyperfine structure and attendant evidence on the magnitude of nuclear spin and magnetic moment see Pauling and Goudsmit, *The Structure of Line Spectra*, Chap. XI.

[55] This small value for the magnetic moment of the nucleus is in part understandable because the ratio of charge to mass of a nucleus is of the order $10^{-3}$ times the corresponding ratio for an electron. There is, however, the difficulty emphasized by Kronig

effect of the nuclear spin on the susceptibility is clearly negligible, as it should be of the order $10^{-6}N\beta^2/kT$ or $10^{-9}$ e.m.u. per gramme mol. at ordinary temperatures, whereas even diamagnetic susceptibilities are of the order $10^{-6}$ or greater.

One might inquire whether the nuclear spin could indirectly modify the susceptibility by causing the ordinary extra-nuclear (i.e. orbital + spin) angular momentum to be quantized in space in a different way. If $I$ be the quantum number measuring the nuclear spin angular momentum, then in the absence of external fields the resultant of $\mathbf{I}$ and $\mathbf{J}$ has a quantized value $F$, just as $\mathbf{L}$ and $\mathbf{S}$ form a quantized resultant $\mathbf{J}$ in case (b) of Fig. 6, § 40. Here $J$ and $F$ measure the total angular momentum of the atom respectively exclusive and inclusive of nuclear spin. Because the interaction of $\mathbf{I}$ and $\mathbf{J}$, which yields the hyperfine structure, is small, an external field of ordinary magnitude could easily produce a Paschen-Back effect, so that $\mathbf{I}$ and $\mathbf{J}$ would have separate spacial quantization, analogous to case (c) for $\mathbf{L}$, $\mathbf{S}$ in Fig. 6. If one did not have spectroscopic stability, as, for instance, in the old quantum theory, this would be an excellent opportunity to detect experimentally a dependence of susceptibility on field strength in virtue of the change in quantization. However, the analysis in Chapter VII and especially in § 54 of the present chapter has made it sufficiently apparent that such an effect will not exist as long as the 'hyper-multiplet' width is small compared to $kT$. This condition is always met in practice (except possibly at the temperature of liquid helium) as the hyperfine structure $\Delta\nu_{\mathrm{hyp}}$ is of the order 1 cm.$^{-1}$ or less. Just as we showed that Eq. (6) applied in either weak or strong fields, one can prove that when the nuclear spin is considered the susceptibility is

$$\chi = \frac{N\beta^2}{3kT}[g^2J(J+1)+g_{\mathrm{nuc}}^2 I(I+1)] \tag{27}$$

regardless of whether the field distorts the hyperfine structure, provided only that one supposes that $h\Delta\nu_{\mathrm{hyp}}/kT$ is small. As the nuclear $g$-factor

(*Naturwissenschaften*, **16**, 335, 1928) that nuclei known from atomic weights to contain an odd number of electrons possess only this small magnetic moment. In ordinary (i.e. extra-nuclear) atomic dynamics there is always an odd multiplicity and hence a non-vanishing spin magnetic moment of the order of magnitude of a Bohr magneton $\beta$, whenever there is an odd number of electrons. Consequently the mechanics within the nucleus must be still more complicated than the ordinary quantum dynamics, presumably in virtue of the close packing and very high velocities. If the spin magnetic moments of electrons within the nuclei did not very nearly compensate each other, our whole theory of susceptibilities would be upset, as it would be forced to involve nuclear properties (isotope effects, &c.) rather than just the configurations of the extra-nuclear electrons.

$g_{\mathrm{nuc}}$ is of the order $10^{-3}$, the additive term in (27) due to nuclear spin is negligible, and so the susceptibility can be calculated with disregard of the nuclear spin. In (27) we have supposed for concreteness that the ordinary (not hyper) multiplet is wide compared to $kT$, and that saturation effects do not need to be considered, but the extension to other cases occasions no difficulty.

# THE PARA- AND DIAMAGNETISM OF FREE MOLECULES

## 63. Spectral Notation and Quantization in Diatomic Molecules

Except in §§ 68–70, we shall consider exclusively diatomic molecules in the present chapter. Probably the most important distinction between quantization in atoms and in diatomic molecules is that in the latter the *resultant* orbital electronic angular momentum is no longer constant in time and is thus incapable of quantization. Instead the combined field due to the two nuclear attracting centres has axial rather than central symmetry, and so only the *parallel component* of this angular momentum is conserved. This component can, however, be given a quantized value $\Lambda$. When we use the terms 'parallel' or 'perpendicular' in the present chapter we always mean relative to the axis of figure of the molecule, and we always measure angular momentum in multiples of the quantum unit $h/2\pi$. A term is called of the $\Sigma$, $\Pi$, $\Delta$, $\Phi$ type according as $|\Lambda| = 0$, 1, 2, 3, &c. As in § 40, small letters are used if it is desired to isolate the quantum numbers of individual electrons. Thus a notation[1] such as

$$1s\sigma^2\, 2p\pi\, 5f\delta\; {}^3\Phi_4,\tag{1}$$

which is the molecular analogue of (86), Chap. VI, means that there are two electrons having $n = 1$, $l = \lambda = 0$, one having $n = 2$, $l = |\lambda| = 1$, and one having $n = 5$, $l = 3$, $|\lambda| = 2$; furthermore, especially that the total orbital angular momentum $\Lambda = \sum \lambda$ about the axis of figure is 3 and that the multiplicity $2S+1$ is 3. Here $S$ is the resultant spin, $n$ is the usual principal quantum number, and $l$ measures approximately an electron's total angular momentum, while $\lambda$ does the parallel component thereof. This significance of the quantum numbers $l$, $\lambda$ is only an asymptotic one appropriate to small departures from central character, as the inter-electronic interactions destroy the constancy of an individual electron's angular momentum even to the parallel component. Besides the quantum numbers revealed by (1) there is the nuclear vibrational quantum number $v$, and the rotational quantum number $J$ which orders the band structure and which determines the complete molecular angular momentum due jointly to nuclear and electronic orbits and to electron spin.

---

[1] For a fuller account of approved notation in molecular spectra see R. S. Mulliken, *Phys. Rev.* **36**, 611 (1930). The paper in which the writer first gave most of the theory in the present chapter (*Phys. Rev.* **31**, 587 (1928)) used an earlier notation in which Greek letters were less in vogue than now.

The matrix elements of the perpendicular components of orbital electronic angular momentum can readily be shown [2] to be exclusively of the type $\Delta\Lambda = \pm 1$. Essentially this point was already proved for a very special case in (75), Chap. VI, when allowances are made for differences in notation.[2] As molecular fields are far from central, the effect of the quantum number $\Lambda$ on the energy is usually very large compared to $kT$; or, interpreted kinematically, the electronic orbital angular momentum vector precesses very rapidly about the axis of figure. This means that these perpendicular components contain exclusively high-frequency matrix elements, and so by the theory of Chapter VII contribute to the susceptibility only a small additive term which is independent of temperature, and which we shall usually neglect except in § 69. Hence the square of the low-frequency part of the orbital moment is proportional to $\Lambda^2$ instead of $L(L+1)$ as in the atomic case when the multiplets are narrow.[3]

We must now consider the spin. Hund [4] has emphasized that we must distinguish between two kinds of coupling of the spin axis relative to the rest of the molecule, which he designates as types (a) and (b). In (a) the energy of interaction between the spin and orbital angular

---

[2] The $z$ axis in (75), Chap. VI, corresponds to the axis of symmetry and so $m_l$ to $\Lambda$ (or better still to $\lambda$). Eq. (75) was very special in that it assumed only one electron and central rather than merely axial symmetry. The substitution of axial for central symmetry does not affect the factor involving $\phi$ in (74), Chap. VI, although it in general makes the factor involving $\theta$ different. This change will alter the explicit form of the elements $\Delta m_l = \pm 1$ but does not modify the vanishing of other elements, our present concern. The generalization to more than one electron is accomplished by noting that in the coordinate system used in (52), (53), Chap. I, the wave function involves $\gamma_1$ only through an exponential factor; cf., for instance, Kronig, *Band Spectra and Molecular Structure*, p. 20.

[3] At first thought it may appear as though $\Lambda(\Lambda+1)$ should appear in place of $\Lambda^2$, as a similar combination appears so often in quantum mechanics. However, the square under consideration is one of a constant component rather than of the entire magnitude of a vector, and so proves to have the same value $\Lambda^2$ as in the old quantum theory. (In the hydrogen atom, for example, the square of the $z$ component of orbital angular momentum is $m_l^2$ not $m_l(m_l+1)$, if for simplicity we assume no coupling with the spin.) Similarly, the square of the parallel spin component is $\Sigma^2$ not $\Sigma(\Sigma+1)$. On the other hand, the squares of the angular momenta associated with the quantum numbers $J$, $K$, $S$ are $J(J+1)$, &c., as these numbers measure resultants, rather than components.

[4] F. Hund, *Zeits. f. Physik*, **36**, 657 (1926); **42**, 93 (1927). We omit many other types of coupling which as a rule occur in excited rather than normal states. For these see Hund, *l.c.*, also Mulliken, *Rev. Mod. Phys.* **2**, 60 (1930). For instance, the magnetic interaction between spin and orbit destroys the rigorous constancy of the parallel components of spin and orbital angular momenta even for a stationary molecule, although not affecting that of the sum measured by $\Omega$. For this reason, the quantum numbers $\Lambda$, $\Sigma$ sometimes cannot be used, but we assume that the distortion through this cause is negligible. This is warranted for the molecular states with which we shall be concerned.

momenta is large compared to that between the spin and the angular momentum due to rotation of the molecule as a whole, and consequently the spin axis is firmly quantized relative to the molecular axis. The parallel component of spin angular momentum can then be assigned a quantized value $\Sigma$. The various values $\Sigma = -S, ..., +S$ yield the different components of a multiplet.[5] The notation $\Omega$ is employed for the sum $\Lambda + \Sigma$. Thus $\Omega$ gives the parallel component of spin and orbital angular momentum combined, and can be used in place of $\Sigma$ to specify the multiplet component. In notation such as (1) the value of $\Omega$ is indicated by a subscript after the final Greek capital, but this subscript has a direct meaning only in case $(a)$. In (1), for instance, $\Omega = 4$, and

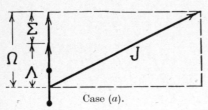
Case $(a)$.

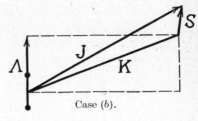
Case $(b)$.

Fig. 14.

so $\Sigma = \Omega - \Lambda = 1$. In $(b)$ the magnetic coupling between spin and orbit is overpowered by the centrifugal forces caused by the molecular rotation. The spin axis then no longer makes a fixed angle with the axis of figure. Instead the angular momentum of the molecule exclusive of spin is first quantized to a resultant $\mathbf{K}$, and then $\mathbf{K}$ and $\mathbf{S}$ are compounded vectorially to give the total angular momentum determined by $\mathbf{J}$. This is shown in $(b)$, Fig. 14. Large rotational quantum numbers favour case $(b)$, especially in light atoms where the multiplets are narrow and the magnetic coupling is easily broken down.

As in Chapter IX, it is convenient to consider the limiting cases of multiplets which are very small or very large compared to $kT$.

### 64. Multiplet Intervals Small Compared to $kT$

In this case the matrix elements of the spin will be entirely of the low-frequency type, for the only motion of the spin vector relative to the rest of the molecule is a precession about the axis of figure, whose frequency is correlated with the multiplet intervals. The square of the low-frequency part of the moment is therefore identical with the square of $(2\mathbf{S} + \mathbf{L}_{par})\beta$. Furthermore, the statistical average of the product

---

[5] Do not confuse the quantum number $\Sigma$ and $\Sigma$ states. This double burden of the letter $\Sigma$ is approved usage.

$S \cdot L_{par}$ is zero, for with narrow multiplets we may neglect the Boltzmann temperature factor, so that the components in which the sign [6]
of $\Sigma$ is the same as or opposite to that of $\Lambda$ have the same weight.
Furthermore, we have $S^2 \doteq S(S+1)$ and $L_{par}^2 \doteq \Lambda^2$. Thus the expression given for the susceptibility in (1), Chap. IX, becomes, with neglect
of the small term $N\alpha$,

$$\chi = \frac{N\beta^2}{3kT}[4S(S+1)+\Lambda^2]. \tag{2}$$

Formula (2) will apply regardless of whether the coupling is of type (*a*),
type (*b*), or intermediate, provided only that the multiplets are small
compared to $kT$. This is just another example of the 'spectroscopic
stability' or invariance of the susceptibility of the mode of quantization
so long as the magnitudes of frequencies relative to $kT/h$ are unaltered.

## 65. Multiplet Intervals Large Compared to $kT$

Here the coupling will in general be of type (*a*), whereas in § 64 it could
be of either type. This is true because cases (*a*) and (*b*) arise when the
multiplets are respectively very large and small compared to the spacing
between the different rotational energy-levels, and because, further, this
spacing is usually small [7] compared to $kT$.

In the present case of wide multiplets the quantum number $\Sigma$
assumes in the normal state only the one value which gives the lowest
energy. The matrix elements representing the perpendicular component
of spin belong exclusively to the neglected 'high-frequency' category,
for they represent transitions [8] $\Delta\Sigma = \pm 1$ to other multiplet components
which must now be classed as excited states. The square of the low-
frequency part of the moment is thus identical with the square of the
parallel component of orbital and spin moment combined, and is thus
$(\Lambda+2\Sigma)^2\beta^2$. By (1), Chap. IX, the susceptibility is hence

$$\chi = \frac{N\beta^2}{3kT}(\Lambda+2\Sigma)^2. \tag{3}$$

---

[6] The introduction of the quantum number $\Sigma$ presupposes coupling of type (*a*) and
so ostensibly restricts our proof to this case. However, the principle of spectroscopic
stability or invariance of the spur assures us that the statistical average of the product
$S \cdot L_{par}$ will be invariant and hence zero with other types of coupling. For type (*b*) this
can also be verified explicitly by averaging the diagonal matrix elements for this product
in (*b*) given by Hill and Van Vleck, *Phys. Rev.* **32**, 250 (1928); especially their Eq. (17).

[7] Cf. the observation on p. 192 that $w$ is usually small compared to $W/kT$.

[8] The quantum number $\Sigma$ plays the same role for spin as $\Lambda$ for orbit. Analogy to the
orbital case studied in note 2 thus shows that the perpendicular spin elements will be
exclusively of the form $\Delta\Sigma = \pm 1$.

## 66. The Oxygen Molecule

The only two common paramagnetic gases are $O_2$ and NO. Other important diatomic molecules have $^1\Sigma$ normal states and are diamagnetic. The case of the oxygen molecule is interesting because it is paramagnetic, despite containing an even number of electrons.[9] Its normal state is of the type $^3\Sigma$, constituting something of an exception to the Heitler-London valence rule that saturated valences yield singlet configurations. The $^3\Sigma$ character of the normal state was first known from its magnetic behaviour (Eq. (4) below) but has subsequently been confirmed spectroscopically in a careful analysis of oxygen bands by Mulliken.[10]

Molecular $\Sigma$ states are practically devoid of multiplet structures, although experimentally [10] and theoretically [11] they do have a small fine structure, of the order 1 cm.$^{-1}$ or less, if there is an outstanding spin, as in oxygen. Hence the susceptibility can certainly be calculated under the assumption that the multiplet structures are small compared to $kT$. With $S = 1$, $\Lambda = 0$ Eq. (2) yields a value

$$\chi_{mol} = \frac{8L\beta^2}{3kT} = \frac{0{\cdot}993}{T} \tag{4}$$

for the molar susceptibility, corresponding to an effective Bohr magneton number $8^{\frac{1}{2}} = 2{\cdot}83$. As usual, $L$ denotes the Avogadro number. At $20°$ C., Eq. (4) gives a molar susceptibility $3{\cdot}39 \times 10^{-3}$. The value observed by Bauer and Piccard,[12] which seems to be usually accepted as the most accurate, is $3{\cdot}45 \times 10^{-3}$. The early determinations of Curie [13] yield $3{\cdot}35 \times 10^{-3}$ when recalibrated [14] on the basis of $0{\cdot}72 \times 10^{-6}$ rather than $0{\cdot}79 \times 10^{-6}$ as the mass susceptibility of water. Still other observations are: $3{\cdot}31 \times 10^{-3}$ by Onnes and Oosterhuis,[15] $3{\cdot}33 \times 10^{-3}$ by Soné,[16] $3{\cdot}48 \times 10^{-3}$ by Wills and Hector,[17] and more recently $3{\cdot}34 \times 10^{-3}$ by

---

[9] All odd molecules are necessarily paramagnetic. Paramagnetic even ones are very rare except in the monatomic case of incomplete inner shells (cf. § 58). By analogy with $O_2$, one would expect $S_2$ to have a $^3\Sigma$ ground state and be paramagnetic. This is confirmed spectroscopically by Naudé and Christy, *Phys. Rev.* **37**, 490 (1931).

[10] R. S. Mulliken, *Phys. Rev.* **32**, 880 (1928).

[11] H. A. Kramers, *Zeits. f. Physik*, **53**, 422, 429. The fine structure in $\Sigma$ states is somewhat greater for $S > \frac{1}{2}$ than for $S = \frac{1}{2}$. In the latter case there is only the very minute 'rho-type doubling', of the order $0{\cdot}01J$ cm$^{-1}$, due to rotational distortion; cf. J. H. Van Vleck, *Phys. Rev.* **33**, 497 (1929).

[12] Bauer and Piccard, *J. de Physique*, **1**, 97 (1920).

[13] P. Curie, *Ann. Chim. Phys.* **5**, 289 (1895); Œuvres, p. 232.

[14] Cf. Stoner, *Magnetism and Atomic Structure*, p. 126.

[15] H. Kamerlingh Onnes and E. Oosterhuis, *Leiden Communications* 134 d.

[16] T. Soné, *Phil. Mag.* **39**, 305 (1920).

[17] Wills and Hector, *Phys. Rev.* **23**, 209 (1924).

Lehrer,[18] also $3 \cdot 42 \times 10^{-3}$ by Woltjer, Coppoolse, and Wiersma.[19, 20] It is thus not improbable that Bauer and Piccard's value is slightly too high.

Before the writer's theory with the new quantum mechanics, it was observed by Sommerfeld,[21] Stoner[22], and others that the susceptibility of the oxygen molecule is the same as that of an atom in a $^3S$ state. Such an atom likewise gives formula (4), since the atomic and molecular formulae (6), Chap. IX and (2), X, respectively are the same for $S$ and $\Sigma$ states, and these only. This can be seen by comparing (2) with (6), Chap. IX. The atomic formula for $S$ states is usually derived in an elementary way (cf. Eq. (7), Chap. IX) under the assumption that the spin is quantized relative to the applied field. Hence in the old quantum theory it was obvious that (4) would apply to an oxygen molecule only in the event that the applied field is able to break down the coupling of the spin relative to the rest of the molecule. (This coupling is of the type (b), Fig. 14, as the oxygen multiplet structure is very narrow.) In other words, the field must be adequate for a Paschen-Back effect. The triplet width for the normal oxygen molecule is about $1 \cdot 4$ cm$^{-1}$, whereas the normal Zeeman displacement is $4 \cdot 67 \times 10^{-5}H$ cm$^{-1}$, and so the magnetic field would have to be of about the order of $10^5$ gauss to produce a complete Paschen-Back effect. Ordinary experimental fields thus become of just the transition range in which the susceptibility would presumably change with field strength in the old quantum theory because of the change in quantization. The principle of spectroscopic stability or our derivation of (4) by the general theory of Chapter VII shows that the susceptibility will, however, be invariant in the new mechanics. Derivations of (4) by the elementary method (7), Chapter IX, without appealing to this principle are obviously inadequate.

Particularly significant is the mode of temperature variation. As the multiplet structure is almost negligible in width, Curie's law should be obeyed with considerable accuracy. This was first verified by Curie[13] himself over the range $290°$–$720°$ K. At lower temperatures the validity of this law was confirmed approximately for oxygen over the interval $143°$–$290°$ K. by Onnes and Oosterhuis.[15] Recently more refined experiments have been made by Woltjer, Coppoolse, and Wiersma[19] down to $157°$ K. and by Stössel[23] down to $136 \cdot 5°$ K. Both sets of observations agree in showing that Curie's law is at least very nearly valid. Stössel finds no perceptible departure from this law even at $136 \cdot 5°$ K. Woltjer, Coppoolse, and Wiersma, on the other hand, contend that even after

[18] E. Lehrer, Ann. der Physik, **81**, 229 (1926).

[19] H. R. Woltjer, C. W. Coppoolse and E. C. Wiersma, Leiden Comm. 201 or Proc. Amsterdam Acad. **32**, 1329 (1929).

[20] They do not give explicitly their absolute determination of the susceptibility, but this may be obtained by calibrating all their observations by means of their '1st series', instead of by comparison with Bauer and Piccard, and then extrapolating to zero pressure.

[21] A. Sommerfeld, Atombau, 4th ed., pp. 630 ff.

[22] E. C. Stoner, Phil. Mag. **3**, 336 (1927).

[23] R. Stössel, Ann. der Physik, **10**, pp. 393–436 (1931). The writer is indebted to Dr. Stössel for communication of his results in advance of publication.

their data are extrapolated to zero density to avoid interference effects between molecules, there is below 175° K. a small deviation of 2 per cent. which is beyond the experimental error. This is not alarming. In the first place the experiment is a difficult one and no deviation is found by Stössel. Secondly, the theory has involved three distinct approximations: (1) disregard of the additive term $N\alpha$ due to high-frequency elements and to diamagnetism (cf. Eq. (2), Chap. IX); (2) assumption that the spacing of rotational states is small compared to $kT$, or, in other words, that the 'characteristic temperature' $h^2/8\pi^2 Ik$ of the molecule is negligible compared to $T$; and (3) assumption that the multiplet structure is likewise of negligible width.

Of these (1) probably is to be most seriously considered, as the other corrections appear exceedingly small. If one assumes that $N\alpha/\chi_{291}$ is about 0·04, then $\chi_{291}/\chi - T/291$ increases from 0 at $T = 291°$ K. to about 0·01 at $T = 150°$ K., in accordance with the Leiden observations.[19] This makes the graph of this difference against $T$ concave downwards, whereas experimentally it seems to be upwards, but the curvature is a second-order effect which is very hard to measure. Such a value of $N\alpha$ appears rather large, some 200 times larger than we shall calculate in § 69 for the effect of the high-frequency elements in $H_2$. However, as the normal state of the O atom is of the type $^3P$, the oxygen molecule is composed of $^3P$ atoms rather than $^1S$ like $H_2$, and so the perpendicular orbital component responsible for these elements might conceivably be considerably greater than in $H_2$. The agreement on absolute values is made somewhat worse by assuming this $N\alpha$ as the calculated susceptibility at room temperature becomes about 2·2 per cent. greater than Bauer and Piccard's value, instead of 1·8 per cent. lower, and deviates still more from the lower values found by most other observers.

A wealth of Leiden data[24] exists on the susceptibility of liquid and solid oxygen, both pure and diluted in different amounts of $N_2$. Great variations with density and abrupt discontinuities at certain critical temperatures are reported. Between these critical points a law of the Weiss form $\chi = C/(T+\Delta)$ is usually obeyed, where $\Delta$ increases rapidly with the concentration in numerical magnitude. (This Weiss generalization of Curie's law must also be used even for the gaseous state when at very high pressures.) Only the extrapolation to zero density, obtained by dissolving the oxygen in successively greater amounts of nitrogen, is of interest for the present theory, where forces between the molecules are disregarded. It is gratifying that within the rather large experimental error the extrapolations to zero density for the liquid conform to a Curie formula with the same constant $C$ as for oxygen gas. We may note parenthetically that the existence of a $\Delta$ term in the Curie denominator which increases in magnitude with density is in at least

[24] A. Perrier and H. Kamerlingh Onnes, Leiden Comm. 139. Good summary on pp. 141–4 of Stoner's *Magnetism and Atomic Structure*.

qualitative accord with Heisenberg's theory of ferromagnetism to be developed in Chapter XII (cf. Eq. (39) of XII).

## 67. The Nitric Oxide Molecule

Nitric oxide gas furnishes the most striking confirmation of our entire theory, both because the NO band-spectrum furnishes unambiguous term-assignments and because the doublet width is comparable with $kT$ and so furnishes a test for the finer points of the theory. The normal state of the NO molecule is known spectroscopically [25] to be a regular $^2\Pi$ doublet of width $h\Delta\nu$ approximately [26] $120 \cdot 9$ cm$^{-1}$. The effective magneton number for very high temperatures is 2, as seen by taking $S = \frac{1}{2}$, $\Lambda = 1$ in Eq. (2). Eq. (3) shows that at very low temperatures the effective magneton number is zero, for the lower doublet component has $\Sigma = -\frac{1}{2}$, $\Lambda = 1$. The susceptibility observed by Bauer and Piccard [12] and by Soné [27] at $20°$ C. is $1 \cdot 46 \times 10^{-3}$ per gramme mol. These measurements yield an effective Bohr magneton number $1 \cdot 86$ intermediate between the two asymptotic values just calculated. This is not surprising, for $kT$ is about 200 cm.$^{-1}$ at room temperature, making $h\Delta\nu/kT$ about $0 \cdot 6$. Thus ordinary temperatures fall in the critical region in which the doublet width $h\Delta\nu$ is comparable with $kT$, and in which deviations from Curie's law should hence be expected. To verify the theory quantitatively, it is necessary to make calculations for the more complicated intermediate case, rather than the asymptotic ones previously considered. Such calculations will be made on pp. 271–2. It will there be shown that the effective Bohr magneton number (defined by Eq. (22), Chap. IX) is the following function of temperature:

$$\mu_{\text{eff}} = 2\sqrt{\left/\left(\frac{1-e^{-x}+xe^{-x}}{x+xe^{-x}}\right)\right.} \quad \text{with} \quad x = \frac{h\Delta\nu}{kT} = \frac{173}{T}. \tag{5}$$

At $20°$ C. this yields $1 \cdot 836$. The discrepancy of about 1 per cent. with the experimental value $1 \cdot 86$ of Bauer and Piccard and of Soné is not excessive in view of experimental difficulties in absolute determinations, and of the fact that the theory itself involves certain small approxima-

---

[25] Cf., for instance, R. T. Birge, *Nature*, Feb. 27 (1926); Jenkins, Barton, and Mulliken, *Phys. Rev.* **30**, 150 (1927).

[26] We take the doublet interval as $120 \cdot 9$ cm$^{-1}$, rather than the value $124 \cdot 4$ quoted by Jenkins, Barton, and Mulliken, as for our purposes it is better to use energy differences which are inclusive rather than exclusive of the term $-h^2\Omega^2/8\pi^2 I$ in the rotational energy. (This term has been encountered in Eq. (70), Chap. VI, but we there neglected spin, so that $\Lambda$ appeared rather than $\Omega$.) It makes little difference which value is used, as (5) shows that the corresponding change in the effective number of Bohr magnetons is only $\frac{1}{2}$ per cent.

[27] T. Soné, *Tohoku Univ. Sci. Reports*, **11**, (3), 139 (1922).

tions (viz. items (1) and (2), p. 268; also other approximations mentioned in notes 4 and 30).

When the theoretical formula (5) was first developed by the writer,

CALCULATED AND OBSERVED MAGNETON NUMBERS FOR NO AS A
FUNCTION OF TEMPERATURE.

| Temp. | $\mu_{\text{eff}}$ Calc. | $\mu_{\text{eff}}$ Obs. | Temp. | $\mu_{\text{eff}}$ Calc. | $\mu_{\text{eff}}$ Obs. |
|---|---|---|---|---|---|
| 0·0° K. | 0·0 | .. | 238·4° K. | 1·794 | (1·794)(W.,deH.,& C.) |
| 50·0 | 1·098 | .. | 250·6 | 1·807 | (1·807) (St.) |
| 100·0 | 1·489 | .. | 289·2 | 1·833 | 1·841 (St.) |
| 112·8 | 1·546 | 1·535(W.,deH.,& C.[29a]) | 290·2 | 1·834 | (1·834) (Ah. & S.) |
| 135·5 | 1·624 | 1·627 (St.[23]) | 292·1 | 1·836 | 1·852 (W., deH., & C.) |
| 157·2 | 1·678 | 1·679 (St.) | 296·0 | 1·837 | (1·837) (Bit.) |
| 165·4 | 1·695 | 1·691 (W., deH., & C.) | 350·0 | 1·864 | .. |
| 178·0 | 1·718 | 1·713 (St.) | 500·0 | 1·908 | .. |
| 194·7 | 1·744 | 1·732 (Ah. & S.[29]) | 1000·0 | 1·955 | .. |
| 216·0 | 1·771 | 1·768 (Bit.[28]) | ∞ | 2·000 | .. |

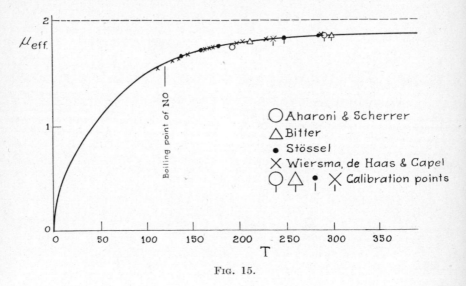

FIG. 15.

there existed only the experimental data at room temperatures, so that it was then impossible to test the predicted dependence of magneton number on temperature or, in other words, the deviation from Curie's law. Subsequently this has been tested by Bitter,[28] by Aharoni and Scherrer,[29] by Stössel,[23] and by Wiersma, de Haas, and Capel,[29a] each

[28] F. Bitter, *Proc. Nat. Acad.* **15**, 632 (1929).
[29] Aharoni and Scherrer, *Zeits. f. Physik*, **58**, 749 (1929).
[29a] Wiersma, de Haas, and Capel, *Leiden Communications* 212 b.

to a lower temperature than the preceding. As the boiling-point of NO is $142°$ K., it would be very difficult to go much below the lowest temperature $112·8$ employed by Wiersma, de Haas, and Capel. The effective magneton numbers yielded by (5) for various temperatures, together with the experimental values reported by these different observers, are shown in the table opposite, and in Fig. 15. We, for brevity, include only two of Wiersma, de Haas, and Capel's measurements at ten temperatures intermediate between $112·8°$ and $292·1°$.

The experimental measurements are all relative ones made on the ratios of the susceptibilities at different temperatures rather than on absolute magnitudes. In the table and figure, the data of Bitter, Aharoni and Scherrer, Stössel, and Wiersma, de Haas, and Capel have been calibrated so as to make them fit exactly the theoretical values at $296°$, $290·2°$, $250·6°$, and $238·4°$ K. respectively.

This quantitative verification of the deviations from Curie's law in NO must be regarded as a convincing proof of the correctness of the quantum theory of magnetic susceptibilities in gases. These deviations form a marked contrast to the validity of this law in $O_2$. They are rather more striking than indicated in the figure, as the Curie constant varies as the square of the effective magneton number. It may be mentioned that although the effective magneton number vanishes at $T = 0$, the product $\mu_{\mathrm{eff}}^2/T$ remains finite there, and in consequence the theoretical molar susceptibility approaches the finite limit

$$4L\beta^2/3h\Delta\nu = 2·87 \times 10^{-3} \text{ at } T = 0.$$

*Proof of Eq.* (5). As explained in § 63 we may neglect the perpendicular component of orbital magnetic moment because changes in the electronic quantum number $\Lambda$ give rise only to very high frequencies. On the other hand, we must not forget the perpendicular component of spin moment, because the effect on the energy of the spin quantum number $\Sigma$ is comparable with $kT$ (cf. p. 269). The same is also true of $\Omega$, since $\Omega = \Sigma + \Lambda$ differs from $\Sigma$ only by an additive constant $+1$ in a $\Pi$ state. As we have discarded transitions to excited orbital states, all elements diagonal in $\Omega$ will be of the low-frequency type, as they involve at most only changes in the molecular rotation $j$. Elements involving transitions in $\Omega$ connect the various spin components (here only two in number), and so are of the 'medium frequency type'. We must now adapt the work of Chapter VII to admit a 'medium frequency' quantum number $\Omega$ in place of the high-frequency one $n$. With this modification the expression in magnetic notation corresponding to (22), Chap. VII, retains its validity if one adds a summation over the quantum number $\Omega$ inasmuch as there is an appreciable Boltzmann factor for all values of $\Omega$. Also the low-frequency moment will now involve $\Omega$ as a parameter, so that the notation $m^0(\Omega jm; \Omega j'm')$ is better than $\mu(jm; j'm')$. By (22), Chapter VII, the susceptibility is thus[30]

$$\chi = \frac{B}{3kT} \sum_{\Omega j m j' m'} \left| m^0(\Omega jm; \Omega j'm') \right|^2 e^{-W^0(\Omega j)/kT} +$$

$$+ \frac{2B}{3} \sum_{\Omega j m \Omega' j' m' (\Omega' \neq \Omega)} \frac{|m^0(\Omega jm; \Omega'j'm')|^2}{h\nu(\Omega'; \Omega)} e^{-W^0(\Omega j)/kT},$$

(6)

with the abbreviation (cf. Eq. (12), Chap. VII).

$$B = \frac{N}{\sum_{\Omega j m} e^{-W^0(\Omega j)/kT}}.$$

(7)

The summations over $\Omega$ and $\Omega'$ each embrace only the two values $\frac{1}{2}$, which give the two doublet components of the $^2\Pi$ state. The index $j$ may be identified with the molecular rotational quantum number $J$, while $m$ is the component of $J$ along the field.

The first and second lines of (6) arise respectively from the parallel and perpendicular components of moment. This follows from the fact that changes in $\Omega$ are identified kinematically with precessions about the axis of figure and so appear only in the perpendicular component. Hence we have

$$\sum_{j'm'} |m^0(\Omega jm; \Omega j'm')|^2 = m^2_{\text{par}}(\Omega; \Omega) = (\Lambda + 2\Sigma)^2\beta^2 = (1\pm1)^2\beta^2,$$

(8)

since by the foregoing and the rules for matrix multiplication the sum in (8) is the square of the parallel component of combined spin and orbital moment. Similarly

$$\sum_{\Omega'j'm'(\Omega' \neq \Omega)} |m^0(\Omega jm; \Omega'j'm')|^2 = m^2_{\text{perp}}(\Omega; \Omega) = 4(S^2+S-\Sigma^2) = 2\beta^2,$$

(9)

where $m_{\text{perp}}$ is the perpendicular component of purely spin moment. The value of $m^2_{\text{perp}}$ is that given in (9) since the square of the total spin magnetic moment is the sum of the squares of the perpendicular and parallel components, and since the square of the parallel spin component is $4\Sigma^2\beta^2 = \beta^2$ (as $\Sigma = \pm\frac{1}{2}$). These results would not be true if any part of the spin were of the discarded high-frequency type such as all the perpendicular orbital component, but actually the motion of the spin axis is very closely that of a regular precession about the axis of figure without appreciable nutations. Now $\nu(\frac{3}{2}; \frac{1}{2}) = -\nu(\frac{1}{2}; \frac{3}{2}) = \Delta\nu$, and also we may set $W(\frac{3}{2}, j) = W(\frac{1}{2}, j) + h\Delta\nu$ as $\nu(\frac{3}{2}jm; \frac{1}{2}jm)$ is approximately the doublet width $\Delta\nu$. Since furthermore, the expressions (8) and (9) have values independent of $j$, $m$, the sum over $j$, $m$ is by (7) a common factor which can be cancelled from numerator and denominator of (6). With these observations substitution of (7)–(9) in (6) yields (5). (The effective magneton number involved in (5) is of course defined as in (22), Chapter IX.)

## 68. Polyatomic Molecules

We saw that in diatomic molecules the perpendicular component of orbital moment was of the high-frequency type. When the molecule

---

[30] Eq. (6) assumes that to a sufficient approximation $\nu(\Omega'j'm'; \Omega jm)$ can be replaced by $\nu(\Omega'; \Omega)$, as an equivalent assumption was made in (22), Chap. VII. As $\Omega$ has less effect on the energy than an electronic quantum number $n$, the resulting error is somewhat larger than in the case of electronic frequencies. The ensuing error in the suceptibility is hard to estimate with precision, but is perhaps 1 per cent.; see *Phys. Rev.* **31**, footnote, p. 611 (1928) for details.

is polyatomic, i.e. contains more than two atoms, the entire orbital moment will be of this type unless the molecule has unusual symmetry. The first step in demonstrating this is to prove the following theorem:

*The existence of a mean magnetic moment for an atom or molecule in the absence of external fields implies the existence of at least a twofold degeneracy, i.e. at least two states of identical energy.* The proof is as follows. If the degeneracy is completely removed, the wave functions are necessarily real in the absence of external magnetic fields. For when one supposes all the electrons are subject to only electrical forces (which can be external as well as internal to the atom), the wave equation does not involve $i = \sqrt{-1}$, as the potential energy is a real function, while the kinetic energy involves the imaginary momentum operators only in squares. It can also be shown that $i$ occurs only in squares even when the magnetic coupling between spin and orbit is included. Hence, if it is possible to utilize what we shall call 'complex' wave functions of the form $P(x_1, x_2,...) + iQ(x_1, x_2,...)$, where $P$ and $Q$ are *different* (i.e. linearly independent) real functions of the coordinates, then the real and imaginary parts must separately be solutions of the wave equation belonging to the same energy. The existence of two such linearly independent solutions would, of course, require at least a twofold degeneracy. Furthermore, whenever the wave functions are real, the average or diagonal part of the orbital angular momentum is zero, for if we take $n' = n$ and take $f$ to be the operator corresponding to any component of magnetic moment, say $L_z = i^{-1}\left(x\dfrac{\partial}{\partial y} - y\dfrac{\partial}{\partial x}\right)$, the fundamental quadrature (14) of Chapter VI vanishes, as it contains then as one factor either the expression $\displaystyle\int_{-\infty}^{+\infty} \psi_n^* \dfrac{\partial \psi_n}{\partial y}\, dy$ or $\displaystyle\int \psi_n^* \dfrac{\partial \psi_n}{\partial x}\, dx$, which is clearly zero when $\psi_n^* = \psi_n$ if $\psi_n$ vanishes at infinity in the fashion proper to the characteristic functions for bound electrons. This argument no longer applies if $\psi_n$ is complex, as then $\psi_n^* \neq \psi_n$. Hence the existence of some degeneracy is a necessary, though not a sufficient, condition for the existence of an average unperturbed magnetic moment.

In diatomic molecules there is the twofold degeneracy associated with the fact that the sense of rotation about the axis of figure is immaterial, or, in other words, that the states $+\Omega$ and $-\Omega$ give the same energy (neglecting a small rotational distortion effect to be mentioned in § 70). This is why diatomic molecules could have (barring this distortion) a constant orbital magnetic moment parallel to the axis of figure. In polyatomic molecules, however, there is no axis of symmetry about which the angular momentum is conserved, and this type of degeneracy is no longer encountered. In some cases the nuclei may be arranged with such a high degree of symmetry that some other degeneracy appears in its stead. The symmetry conditions necessary for this have been studied in detail by Bethe,[31] and his work will be further discussed in § 73. He studied ostensibly the effect of different symmetries in external fields, but his arguments are so general that they relate equally well to the fields arising from nuclei in polyatomic molecules. He shows that even if the fields are highly symmetrical, usually the states of lowest quantum number still do not admit complex wave functions. Hence we may assume that ordinarily in the normal states of polyatomic molecules the diagonal elements of the orbital magnetic moment are zero. (This is true even when the moment is referred to axes fixed in the molecule so that the frequencies of molecular rotation are avoided.) As all electronic quantum numbers in molecules usually have an effect on the energy which is large compared to $kT$, the non-diagonal elements of the orbital moment will be entirely of the high-frequency type. As there are no diagonal elements, this completes the proof that only such a type occurs.

*Molecules with a Resultant Spin.* If the molecule has a spin quantum number $S$ different from zero, virtually all the paramagnetism will result from the spin, as we have seen that all the orbital moment is of the ineffective, high-frequency type. The multiplet structure which couples the spin relative to the rest of the molecule will usually be small compared to $kT$, for it becomes an effect of the second order, as in the $\Sigma$ states of diatomic molecules, rather than of the first order, as in the ordinary case of atoms and diatomic molecules not in $\Sigma$ states. This small size of the multiplet structure is a consequence of the fact that the average orbital moment vanishes. This will be shown in the analysis in § 73.[32] The spin is thus composed entirely of low-frequency elements, and is entirely free as far as the susceptibility is concerned. The latter is hence

$$\chi = \frac{4N\beta^2 S(S+1)}{3kT} + N\alpha, \qquad (10)$$

where $N\alpha$ is the small residual effect of the high-frequency orbital

[31] H. Bethe, *Ann. der Physik*, **3**, 133 (1929); *Zeits. f. Physik*, **60**, 218 (1929).

[32] In adapting this analysis to the present context, the 'spacial separation' (§ 73) is to be considered due to the dissymmetry in the field from the molecule's own nuclei rather than to an external field. It is thus probably greater than for the external case considered explicitly in Chap. XI, so that the inequality (4) of XI is more apt to be satisfied.

elements (Eq. (2), Chap. IX). All odd polyatomic molecules should presumably conform to this formula (unless some unusual case should arise where the orbit is less completely quenched, or else the spin is more firmly bound than we have anticipated). Experimental data for odd molecules are apparently available only for $ClO_2$ and $NO_2$.

The molar susceptibility observed by Taylor[33] for $ClO_2$ in solution at $20°$ C. is $1.34 \times 10^{-4}$, while (10) gives $1.27 \times 10^{-4}$ if we take $S = \frac{1}{2}$, $\alpha = 0$. The discrepancy is scarcely greater than Taylor's estimate of the experimental error as 5 per cent. Furthermore, part of the difference might be due to the effect $N\alpha$ of the high-frequency elements, which could conceivably be larger than in diatomic molecules. The appropriate value of $S$ cannot yet be deduced spectroscopically for polyatomic molecules, but we can note that our assignment $S = \frac{1}{2}$ is consistent with the fact that $ClO_2$ has an odd number of electrons. Very likely due to ionization or polymerization, the $ClO_2$ molecule loses its identity in solution, but the theoretical result $1.27 \times 10^{-4}$ is still applicable if one ionic unit of spin quantum number $\frac{1}{2}$ is formed for each molecule of $ClO_2$ which is dissolved.

On the other hand, Soné[27] finds that at $20°$ C. the $NO_2$ molecule has a molar susceptibility $+2.1 \times 10^{-4}$, a value less than one-fifth that given by (10) with $S = \frac{1}{2}$. Perhaps this low value is to be attributed to polymerization or some other spurious cause, for new measurements on $NO_2$ have just been completed by G. Havens, at the University of Wisconsin, and he finds a susceptibility which agrees with (10) (taking $S = \frac{1}{2}$) within 5 per cent., which is less than the experimental error.

*Molecules without a Resultant Spin.* When a polyatomic molecule has a spin quantum number zero, the commonest value for even molecules, there remains only the contribution of the orbital moment's high-frequency elements, represented by $m^0(n; n')$ $(n' \neq n)$ in the notation of Chapter IX. The susceptibility is thus given by the expression (2), Chap. IX, viz.:

$$\chi_{\text{mol}} = -\frac{Le^2}{6mc^2} \sum \overline{r^2} + \tfrac{2}{3} L \sum_{n' \neq n} \frac{|m^0(n'; n)|^2}{h\nu(n'; n)} \tag{11}$$

per gramme mol., and so should be very small and independent of temperature. The material is diamagnetic or paramagnetic depending on whether the first or second term of (11) is the greater. Nitrous oxide $(N_2O)$, for instance, is found to be diamagnetic, showing that here the first term has the greater magnitude. A more interesting and less

[33] N. W. Taylor, *J. Amer. Chem. Soc.* **48**, 854 (1926).

common situation arises when the second term of (11) predominates. The substance should then have a feeble paramagnetism independent of temperature. Examples of materials containing complex ions which exhibit this behaviour will be cited on p. 302. These ions, of course, occur in solution or in solid salts, rather than as a gas, but they seem to have a distinct and fairly stable existence, so that they may be classed with gaseous polyatomic molecules for our purposes.

*Invariance of* (11) *of Origin.* The reader has possibly wondered what point should be used as the origin for computing $r$, $m$ in equations such as (11). This choice is immaterial, as (11) is invariant of the origin. To see this, let us change the origin of $x$, for instance, by an amount $\delta x$. The resulting change in the right side of (11) is

$$-\frac{Le^2}{6mc^2}[2\delta x\, x^0(n;n)+(\delta x)^2]+$$

$$+\frac{Le^2\delta x}{6m^2c^2}\sum_{q=y,z}\sum_{n''}\sum_{n'\neq n}\left\{\frac{p_q^0(n;n')[p_q^0(n';n'')x^0(n'';n)-p_x^0(n';n'')q^0(n'';n)]}{h\nu(n';n)}+\right.$$

$$\left.+\frac{[p_q^0(n;n'')x^0(n'';n')-p_x^0(n;n'')q^0(n'';n')]p_q^0(n';n)+\delta x p_q^0(n;n')p_q^0(n';n)}{h\nu(n';n)}\right\}$$

$$\tag{12}$$

inasmuch as (letting $q$ denote $y$ or $z$) $\delta x(n;n)=\delta x$, $\delta x(n;n')=0$ $(n'\neq n)$, $\delta p_q=0$, $m_q=\pm(e/2mc)(p_q x-p_x q)$, &c., where $p_x$, $p_y$, $p_z$ are the components of linear momentum. To simplify printing we have supposed that there is only one electron and have neglected the part of $m_q$ due to spin; but removal of these restrictions occasions no difficulty. (As the radius of the electron is negligible, one can take $\delta\mathbf{s}=0$ in the spin terms.) The frequency factors may be removed from the denominator by utilizing the relations

$$p_y(n;n')=-p_y(n';n)=2\pi imv(n;n')y(n;n'),\ \&\mathrm{c}.$$

The expression (12) can be shown to vanish identically if we simplify the products by using repeatedly the quantum conditions and commutation rules given in ⟨12⟩, ⟨13⟩ of Chap. VI, applied to Cartesian coordinates. (See e.g. Eq. (4), Chap. XIII, for the explicit form of the first relation of ⟨12⟩, Chap. VI, in Cartesian coordinates.)

## 69. The Diamagnetism of Molecules

The fact that most gases are diamagnetic shows that ordinarily the first term of (11) is the greater in magnitude. It is therefore now convenient to turn to consideration of the diamagnetism of molecules. Our discussion will include both diatomic and polyatomic molecules, for both are governed by formula (11). The only difference is that in the former the high-frequency matrix elements $m^0(n; n')$ $(n' \neq n)$ arise only from the perpendicular component of orbital moment, while in the latter the components along all three of the principal axes of the molecule will contribute such elements. If a diatomic molecule is diamagnetic, it is in a $^1\Sigma$ state, and the parallel component vanishes. Previously we neglected the feeble paramagnetic contribution of the perpendicular component, given by the second term of (11), but in dealing with small susceptibilities such as diamagnetic ones,[34] its inclusion is necessary.

Without the second term, Eq. (11) would be the ordinary Langevin formula for the diamagnetism of atoms in the form given by Pauli (cf. Eq. (2), Chap. IV). Because of this term, however, *Pauli's formula does not apply to non-monatomic molecules.*[35] This is closely connected with the fact that the validity of Larmor's theorem is confined to atoms (§ 8). Because the additional term is inherently positive, Pauli's formula will always be an upper limit to the diamagnetism, and estimates of the mean square orbital radii deduced from observed susceptibilities by means of this formula will tend to be somewhat too large except in atoms.

One may inquire whether the second term of (11) can ever vanish, but this is possible only in atoms. The disappearance of this term would require that all the matrix elements $P(n; n')$ of the orbital angular momentum originating in the normal state $n$ equal zero. As

$$P^2(n; n) = \sum_{n'} P(n; n')P(n'; n) = \sum_{n'} |P(n; n')|^2, \tag{13}$$

this in turn demands that the mean square angular momentum $P^2(n; n)$ vanish for the normal state. The mean angular momentum $P(n; n)$ can, to be sure, vanish for diatomic molecules, but the mean square $P^2(n; n)$ cannot. By taking in (14), Chap. VI, $f$ to be the operator corresponding to the square of the orbital angular momentum, it is not hard to show [36] that $P^2(n; n)$ can vanish only if the wave function be invariant under a rotation of the coordinate system for the electrons without a corresponding rotation of the coordinate system for the nuclei. In case there

---

[34] We nevertheless neglect the paramagnetic term contributed by the molecular rotation, as we throughout disregard the contribution of the nuclei to the susceptibility. Due to their large masses this term is in itself small compared even to (11); see F. Bitter, *Phys. Zeits.* **30**, 497 (1929) for estimate. Furthermore, it is largely compensated by the diamagnetic contribution of the nuclei. This is true because the rotational quantum numbers are so large that we can almost use the classical theorem (§ 24) on the cancelling of dia- and paramagnetism, as far as the nuclei are concerned.

[35] Contrary to an incorrect statement once made by the writer, *Proc. Nat. Acad.* **12**, 662 (1926).          [36] For details see J. H. Van Vleck, *Phys. Rev.* **31**, 600 (1928).

is only one electron, this requirement may be more simply stated by saying that $\psi$ must be a function of $r$ alone. In any case, this demand can be satisfied only if the nuclear field is centro-symmetric. The latter, however, implies that there is only one attracting centre, i.e. an atom. In diatomic molecules, the physical interpretation of this non-disappearance of $P^2(n;n)$ is that the two nuclei together exert a torque which causes fluctuations in the perpendicular component of orbital electronic angular momentum. The combined electronic and nuclear angular momentum is necessarily constant, but there are continual transfers back and forth between electrons and nuclei.

As to the relative magnitude of the second term of (11), the fact that reasonable estimates of orbital radii can be obtained even in molecules by means of Pauli's formula shows that often this term must be fairly small compared to the first. Also Pascal's discovery [37] that the additivity method can be used to represent the diamagnetic suscepti-bilities of many organic compounds can only mean that atomic orbits are but little distorted by these molecular bonds, and that here the influence of the second part of (11), which is an interference effect between atoms, is subordinate.[38]

Quantitative calculation of the two parts of (11) has been attempted only for the hydrogen molecule. Even here, direct evaluation of the sum over the excited states $n'$ would be excessively difficult, and it is necessary to adopt the artifice of replacing the variable denominator $\nu(n';n)$ by a constant $\nu_1$. Then $\nu_1$ is a sort of mean absorption frequency which refractive data [39] lead one to take as $1 \cdot 23R$, where $R$ is the Rydberg constant. The elements of orbital magnetic moment differ from those of the angular momentum measured in multiples of $h/2\pi$, only by a constant factor $\beta$. With the aid of the multiplication rule (13) the second term of (11) now becomes

$$\frac{Le^2}{6m^2c^2h\nu_1} P^2(n;n) \left(\frac{h^2}{4\pi^2}\right) = 0\cdot271 \frac{Le^2}{mc^2} \left(\frac{h^2}{4\pi^2e^2m}\right)^2 P^2(n;n). \tag{14}$$

Miss Frank and the writer [40] showed that with Wang's [41] wave func-

[37] Pascal, various papers in *Ann. Chim. Phys.* 1908–13.

[38] In this connexion we may cite particularly a paper by F. W. Gray and J. Farquharson, who examine critically the departures from additivity observed for various compounds, *Phil. Mag.* **10**, 191 (1930). Cf. also Gray and Dakers, *ibid.* **11**, 81, 297 (1931).

[39] If, following Unsöld (*Ann. der Physik*, **82**, 380 (1927)), we replace $1/\nu(n';n)$ by $\nu(n';n)/\nu_1^2$; in Eq. (28), Chap. VII, the summation in the latter equation is readily per-formed in virtue of the quantum conditions. See Eq. (4), Chap. XIII. The evaluation of $\nu_1$ is then achieved by equating (28) to the observed electric susceptibility of $H_2$.

[40] J. H. Van Vleck and A. Frank, *Proc. Nat. Acad.* **15**, 539 (1929).

[41] S. C. Wang, *Phys. Rev.* **31**, 579 (1928).

tions for the normal state of the hydrogen molecule, its mean square angular momentum $P^2(n;n)$, which can be evaluated by the usual quadrature (14) of Chapter VI, is 0·394. This makes the expression (14) $0·51 \times 10^{-6}$ per mol. Wang [42] calculated the first term of (11) to be $-4·71 \times 10^{-6}$. The computed molar susceptibility of $H_2$ is hence $-4·20 \times 10^{-6}$. The experimental values [43] are $-3·94 \times 10^{-6}$ (Wills and Hector) and $-3·99 \times 10^{-6}$ (Soné). The agreement with these is quite satisfactory since the wave functions are not accurately known.

Although the second term of (11) is only a little over 10 per cent. of the first in $H_2$, it is quite probable that it is a somewhat larger fraction in other molecules where the nuclear field is less nearly centro-symmetric. That $H_2$ departs less from atomic symmetry than most molecules seems to be evidenced by the fact that it alone among molecules has a normal Verdet constant in the Faraday effect (§ 84). It is to be emphasized that there is no sharp dividing-line between diamagnetic molecules and feebly paramagnetic ones, mentioned in § 68, where the second term of (11) predominates. One would expect this term to be particularly large for molecules formed out of atoms not of the $^1S$ type, and also molecules for which Mulliken's united atom, formed by collapsing the nuclei together, is not of the type $^1S$, for in these cases there is an overwhelming paramagnetism at large and small internuclear distances respectively.

## 70. Absence of Magneto-Electric Directive Effects

It has often been conjectured [44] that especially in diatomic molecules with both electric and magnetic moments parallel to the molecular axis of figure, application of a magnetic field would produce electric as well as magnetic polarization, and that vice versa an electric field would magnetize the body. There would then be what may be termed a magneto-electric directive effect. The ground for this belief is the idea that when the molecules are oriented by an applied field of either nature, the electric and magnetic dipole axes would be alined together.

Actually, experiments endeavouring to detect this effect have always yielded null results, even in liquids and solids.[45, 46] The only important diatomic gas for which such an effect might be expected is NO, for

[42] S. C. Wang, *Proc. Nat. Acad.* **13**, 798 (1927).

[43] Wills and Hector, *Phys. Rev.* **23**, 209 (1924); Hector, *ibid.* **24**, 418 (1924); T. Soné, *Phil. Mag.* **39**, 305 (1920).

[44] Debye and Huber, *Physica*, **5**, 377 (1925); Debye, *Zeits. f. Physik*, **36**, 300 (1926).

[45] Perrier and Borel, *Archives des Sciences*, **7**, 289 and 375 (1925); Szivessy, *Zeits. f. Physik*, **34**, 474 (1925); A. Perrier, *Physica*, **5**, 380 (1925).

[46] A. Huber, *Phys. Zeits.* **27**, 619 (1926).

nitric oxide is the only common polar paramagnetic gas. The electric moment of the NO molecule is, to be sure, so small that it has not yet been measured quantitatively, but is undoubtedly different from zero, as the N and O atoms are not identical. The very sensitive experiments of Huber[46] show that even when extremely intense magnetization is produced by applying a magnetic field to liquid NO, there is no observable electric polarization.

Despite the considerations advanced in the first paragraph, there is no difficulty in explaining theoretically why experiments invariably reveal no directive effect. The standard explanation is one first proposed specifically for NO by de Haas,[47] though previously suggested by Piccard[48] in connexion with experiments on certain solids. De Haas suggests that there are two kinds of NO molecules, in which the electrons circulate respectively clockwise and counter-clockwise about the axis of electric polarity. These left- and right-handed molecules would presumably be present in equal amounts. There is then on the average no correlation between the directions of electric and magnetic moments, and hence no magneto-electric directive effect.

Recent developments in the theory of band spectra, too complicated for us to give in much detail, show that this explanation by Piccard and de Haas is not quite correct. There are indeed two kinds of NO molecules, corresponding to the two components of what spectroscopists call a $\Lambda$-type doublet,[49] but each kind is in itself both left- and right-handed at once. There would thus be no directive effect even if we could isolate one of the kinds. The existence of such 'ambidextrous' molecules is a characteristic quantum effect which cannot very well be explained in terms of ordinary geometrical pictures. It arises because the molecular rotation removes the degeneracy associated with the identity of energies for the states $\Omega$, $-\Omega$ in a stationary molecule. The correct wave function proves to be a linear combination of those corresponding to the states $\Omega$ and $-\Omega$. The parallel component of electronic angular momentum is thus of indeterminate sign, though of definite numerical magnitude $|\Omega|$, when referred to an axis having invariably

---

[47] W. J. de Haas, *Kon. Akad. Wet. Amsterdam,* **35,** 221.

[48] A. Piccard, *Archives des Sciences,* **6,** 404 (1924).

[49] This was formerly called a $\sigma$-type doublet. The term $\Omega$-type doubling would be the most expressive, as with spin the signs of $\Lambda$ and $\Sigma$ must be reversed together to give the degeneracy in a stationary molecule. For theory of this doubling see R. de L. Kronig, *Zeits. f. Physik,* **46,** 814; **50,** 347 (1928–9), *Band Spectra and Molecular Structure,* Chap. II; J. H. Van Vleck, *Phys. Rev.* **33,** 467 (1929); R. S. Mulliken, *ibid.* **33,** 507 (1929). The $\Lambda$-doubling is superposed on the much coarser true multiplet structure, such as e.g. the spin doublet in NO, and should not be confused with the latter.

the N atom on one given end and the O atom on the other. We talked in §§ 63–7 as if this component were constant in both magnitude and sign, which we now see it is not, but this inaccuracy is admissible on two grounds. First, the frequency of oscillation in sign is measured by the width of a 'Λ-type doublet', and is hence very small compared to $kT$, so that this component always remains of the very low-frequency category and hence as good as constant as far as the magnetic suscepti-bility is concerned. Secondly, it would be equally logical to say that the electric moment of the molecule fluctuates in sign relative to the magnetic axis of the molecule, as the choice of axis is somewhat arbitrary. If one uses axes fixed in space the fluctuations in sign prove to be in the electric rather than magnetic moment.[50] This is because the two Λ-doublet components are respectively even and odd with respect to the transformation (A), p. 203, and so have no first-order Stark effect, as there explained, although there is a first-order Zeeman one. A very powerful electric field, however, produces a Paschen-Back transformation on the doublet and gives a first-order Stark effect.[51] The hypothesis of Piccard and de Haas is then correct. In any field strength there is on the average no correlation between the electric and magnetic axes, and hence no directive effect.

[50] As the rotational frequencies enter in the direction cosines connecting a coordinate system fixed in space with one fixed in the molecule, expressions which average to zero in one system do not necessarily in the other. Note that the mean angular momentum relative to axes fixed in the molecule definitely vanishes in a diatomic molecule only in virtue of removal of the degeneracy by the molecular rotation; in a stationary one it is really ambiguous because any linear combination of the wave functions for the states $\Omega$, $-\Omega$ could be used. On the other hand, in a polyatomic molecule, the disappearance (§ 68) is due to dissymmetry in the nuclear field, and so found even in stationary molecules.

[51] Cf. Penney, *Phil. Mag.* **11**, 602 (1931).

# THE PARAMAGNETISM OF SOLIDS, ESPECIALLY SALTS OF THE IRON GROUP

## 71. Delineation of Various Cases

We shall stress primarily only the new quantum developments rather than the innumerable classical theories of magnetization in solids. As the present and following chapters are a digression from our intent to study only rarefied media, and as the quantum theory of magnetism of solids has so far achieved success more in the bold qualitative outlines of the phenomena rather than quantitative detail, we shall not document the experimental measurements quite as completely as in the two preceding chapters. A whole volume would be required to digest the copious experimental work on the iron family alone.

Different solids can exhibit susceptibilities of entirely different natures, and it may be well to outline in advance the various cases which can occur and in what materials they are commonly found.

(a) Instances where the inter-atomic forces are so small that the magnetism can be calculated by treating the atoms of the solid to be as free as in an ideal gas. The criterion for this is that the work required to orient an atom against the inter-atomic forces be small compared to $kT$. This case is exemplified remarkably well by rare earth salts, which have consequently been discussed at length in Chapter IX on free atoms and ions. As noted to the writer by Professor Bohr, the extraordinary freeness of the $4f$ orbits is revealed not only by the magnetism but also by the sharpness of the spectral lines from rare earth salts. This can only mean that the $4f$ wave functions of the various rare earth atoms project out very little from the interiors of their respective atoms and so 'overlap' other atoms only very slightly even in the solid state.

(b) Solids or solutions in which inter-atomic forces quench the orbital angular momentum but leave the spin free. This is what probably occurs in most salts of the iron group, as we shall see in § 72.

(c) Solids in which there is such strong internal magnetic coupling, i.e. such wide multiplets, that irrespective of the Heisenberg exchange effect the inter-atomic forces of necessity quench the spin angular momentum when they do the orbital. It is hard to distinguish experimentally between this case (c) and (e), (f) below, but case (c) is possibly sometimes realized in some salts of the platinum and palladium groups (§ 75).

(d) Solids in which the Heisenberg exchange forces tend to aline the spins parallel and so create ferromagnetism. This is, of course, the case of iron, nickel, cobalt, also a few alloys which are ferromagnetic.

(e) Solids in which these forces have the opposite sign from that in (d) and so tend to aline the spins antiparallel and destroy magnetism.

(f) Materials in which the spin angular momenta compensate each other because of the restrictions imposed by the Pauli exclusion principle rather than because of the exchange effect.

In cases (e) and (f) any orbital angular momentum is ordinarily quenched as in (b). Hence in (c), (e), and (f) the orbital and spin magnetic effects are both largely destroyed, so that these cases all give feeble paramagnetism, or even diamagnetism. One of these cases must be the commonest of all, as most elements (distinct as from salts) exhibit only a feeble paramagnetism, if any, in the solid state. Cases (e) and (f), which will be discussed in § 80, are more probable than (c).

We throughout use the term 'quenched' when the constancy of angular momentum is so completely destroyed by inter-atomic forces as to blot out most of the paramagnetism which would be found in the ideal gas state. The distinction between the various cases is, of course, usually not a hard and fast one. Besides (a)–(f) there is also the trivial case of solids composed exclusively of atoms which are in $^1S$ states when free and which are hence without appreciable magnetism.

The Heisenberg 'exchange' or *Austausch* forces[1] play a very important role in the magnetism of solids, especially in ferromagnetism. As far as the present chapter is concerned, it will be sufficient to say that the exchange forces have the effect of introducing a very strong coupling between the spins of paramagnetic atoms or ions. Diamagnetic atoms or ions have no resultant spin and so do not give rise to any exchange forces tending to orient the spins of other atoms. The mathematical basis for these statements will be given in Chapter XII. The important thing for present purposes is that the exchange forces become of subordinate importance in media of considerable 'magnetic dilution', i.e. media in which the density of paramagnetic atoms or ions is low because the great majority of the atoms are diamagnetic. Such media are the primary concern of the present chapter, and so it seems best to defer until Chapter XII the detailed description of the nature and workings of the Heisenberg exchange effect.

---

[1] W. Heisenberg, *Zeits. f. Physik*, **38**, 411 (1926); **49**, 619 (1928).

## 72. Salts and Solutions Involving the Iron Group

Pure solid elements of the iron group have high magnetic concentrations and large exchange effects, leading to the ferromagnetic phenomena to be discussed in the next chapter. On the other hand, most salts involving ions of the iron group are only paramagnetic, except possibly at extremely low temperatures. In these salts the magnetic dilution is usually sufficient to warrant neglect of the exchange forces. This is perhaps obvious only if the salt is in solution, or is highly hydrated in the solid state. However, it is found that in true salts (not oxides) the susceptibility is usually affected comparatively little (not over 10 per cent. in many cases) by whether or not water molecules are present to increase the magnetic dilution.

One is first tempted to try calculating the susceptibilities of salts of the iron group in the same fashion as for the rare earths, viz. under the assumption that the paramagnetic ions are perfectly free. The general nature of the procedure with the aid of the Hund spectroscopic theory has been fully explained in connexion with §§ 58 and 59 on the rare earths, and so need not be repeated. The difference is that the incomplete inner group is now one of $3d$ rather than $4f$ electrons.[2] The comparison of theory with experiment is given in the table on p. 285, which corresponds to that in § 58 for the rare earths.

The values in the columns headed $\Delta \nu = 0$ and $\Delta \nu = \infty$ are those obtained from the asymptotic formulae (6) and (10) of Chapter IX applicable respectively to multiplets which are very narrow and very wide compared to $kT$. These limiting cases were first studied by Laporte and Sommerfeld.[3] The column 'actual $\Delta \nu$' gives the values obtained at 293° K. by means of the accurate formula (16), Chap. IX, which must be used when the multiplet widths are comparable to $kT$. Such calculations were first made by Laporte,[4] and the reader is referred to his important paper for the details of the estimates of the screening constants $\sigma$ used to determine the multiplet width by means of Eq. (21), Chap. IX. As a rule the values of $\sigma$ represent only a slight extrapolation from optical or X-ray data on other atoms and ions. The calculations in the column

---

[2] For details of the spectroscopic theory of the iron group see Hund, *Linienspektren*, § 33. Besides the $3d$ electrons and the closed groups already completed at argon, the neutral atoms of the iron group contain from one to two $4s$ electrons, but these $4s$ electrons are presumably the first to be lost when there is any ionization, so that all the ions involved in the table have only argon-like shells plus the $3d$ electrons.

[3] O. Laporte and A. Sommerfeld, *Zeits. f. Physik*, **40**, 333 (1926). Somewhat similar calculations have also been made independently by Fowler, and the results briefly given in his *Statistical Mechanics*, p. 303.

[4] O. Laporte, *Zeits. f. Physik*, **47**, 761 (1928).

## EFFECTIVE BOHR MAGNETON NUMBERS FOR IONS OF THE IRON GROUP[5]

| Term | Ion | Theoretical $\mu_{\text{eff}}$ | | | | Experimental $\mu_{\text{eff}}$ | |
|---|---|---|---|---|---|---|---|
| | | $\Delta\nu = 0$ | $\Delta\nu = \infty$ | Actual $\Delta\nu$ | Spin only | Solutions | Salts |
| $3d^0\ {}^1S$ | $K^+ ... V^{5+}$ | 0·0 | 0·0 | 0·0 | 0·0 | 0·0 | 0·0 |
| $3d^1\ {}^2D_{3/2,\,5/2}$ | $Sc^{++}$ | 3·0 | 1·55 | 2·57 | 1·73 | .. | .. |
| | $Ti^{+++}$ | 3·0 | 1·55 | 2·18 | 1·73 | .. | .. |
| | $V^{++++}$ | 3·0 | 1·55 | 1·78 | 1·73 | 1·75 | 1·79 |
| $3d^2\ {}^3F_{2,..}$ | $Ti^{++}$ | 4·47 | 1·63 | 3·36 | 2·83 | | .. |
| | $V^{+++}$ | 4·47 | 1·63 | 2·73 | 2·83 | 2·76–2·85 | .. |
| $3d^3\ {}^4F_{3/2,.}$ | $V^{++}$ | 5·20 | 0·77 | 3·60 | 3·87 | 3·81–3·86 | .. |
| | $Cr^{+++}$ | 5·20 | 0·77 | 2·97 | 3·87 | 3·68–3·86 | 3·82 |
| | $Mn^{++++}$ | 5·20 | 0·77 | 2·47 | 3·87 | 4·00 | .. |
| $3d^4\ {}^5D_{0,.}$ | $Cr^{++}$ | 5·48 | 0·0 | 4·25 | 4·90 | 4·80 | .. |
| | $Mn^{+++}$ | 5·48 | 0·0 | 3·80 | 4·90 | .. | 5·05 |
| $3d^5\ {}^6S$ | $Mn^{++}$ | 5·92 | 5·92 | 5·92 | 5·92 | 5·2–5·96 | 5·85 |
| | $Fe^{+++}$ | 5·92 | 5·92 | 5·92 | 5·92 | 5·94 | 5·4–6·0 |
| $3d^6\ {}^5D_4$ | $Fe^{++}$ | 5·48 | 6·70 | 6·54 | 4·90 | 5·33 | 5·0–5·5 |
| $3d^7\ {}^4F_{9/2}$ | $Co^{++}$ | 5·20 | 6·64 | 6·56 | 3·87 | 4·6–5·0 | 4·4–5·2 |
| $3d^8\ {}^3F_4$ | $Ni^{++}$ | 4·47 | 5·59 | 5·56 | 2·83 | 3·23 | 2·9–3·4 |
| $3d^9\ {}^2D_{5/2}$ | $Cu^{++}$ | 3·0 | 3·55 | 3·53 | 1·73 | 1·8–2·0 | 1·8–2·2 |

'actual $\Delta\nu$' are inclusive of the term $\alpha_J$ in (16), Chap. IX, which Laporte neglected. This term is much less important in the iron group than in the rare earths $Sm^{+++}$ and $Eu^{+++}$ (§ 59), and has an appreciable influence only in $V^{++}$, $Cr^{+++}$, $Mn^{++++}$, $Cr^{++}$, $Mn^{+++}$, where Laporte's original values were 3·23, 2·61, 2·01, 3·74, 3·16 instead of 3·60, 2·97, 2·47, 4·25, 3·80. The values given in the table for $Sc^{++}$–$V^{+++}$ inclusive are only slightly higher (about 5 per cent.) than Laporte's, while those in the bottom half are identical with his, as here the inversion of the multiplets makes the effect of $\alpha$ negligible. The rare earths other than Sm and Eu had such wide multiplet widths that the magneton number could be calculated without appreciable error under the supposition of multiplet widths extremely great compared to $kT$, but comparison of the columns '$\Delta\nu = \infty$' and 'actual $\Delta\nu$' shows that this is very often not the case in the iron group. This is, of course, because here the atoms are lighter than in the rare earths, and the multiplets thus narrower.

Because the multiplet widths are more precisely known, the present theoretical calculations for free ions of the iron group should be more accurate than for the rare earths, but comparison of the columns 'actual $\Delta\nu$' and 'experiment' shows that the agreement with observations on

[5] The experimental magneton numbers quoted in the table are the same as those given by Stoner in a survey in *Phil. Mag.* **8**, 250 (1929), except that we have added Freed's measurements on the vanadium ion to be cited in § 74. A very complete documentation of experimental data is given by Cabrera in the report of the 1930 Solvay Congress.

salts and solutions is miserable, in marked contrast to the situation in the rare earths. One must therefore grope for some other explanation of the measured susceptibilities. As noted by Sommerfeld,[6] Bose,[7] and Stoner,[8] the latter are represented quite well if we use the formula

$$\chi = \frac{N\beta^2}{3kT}[4S(S+1)] \tag{1}$$

instead of the theoretical expressions based on the ordinary spectroscopic theory for free ions. Here $S$ is the spin quantum number for the appropriate spectral term listed in the table. For instance, $S$ is 3/2 for $Cr^{+++}$, as the multiplicity $2S+1$ of a $^4F$ term is 4. The magneton numbers calculated from (1) are given in the column marked 'spin only' and are seen to be in fairly good agreement with experiment.

*Mechanism for Leaving Only Spin Free.* Our problem is now to obtain a theoretical justification for Eq. (1), which gives the same susceptibility as though we substituted $S$ for $D$ and $F$ terms throughout the first column of the table, with the multiplicity unaltered. Two possibilities immediately suggest themselves. One is that the Hund theory of the assignment of spectral terms is in error, and that the ions in question are normally all in $S$ states even when free. This proposal appears to have actually once been made by Sommerfeld, but is now abandoned by him. In our opinion it must be quite definitely rejected, as there is an abundance of experimental spectroscopic evidence for the correctness of the Hund theory in the iron group, not to mention Slater's perturbation calculation [9] which confirms the Hund predictions on the lowest-lying terms. In fact, $S$ terms of the necessary multiplicity are not allowed by the Pauli exclusion principle, unless one supposes that there is some other incomplete group besides that of the equivalent $d$ electrons.

Another possibility, and one which we advocate, is that the assignment of spectral terms is correct, and that the theoretical calculations in the column 'actual $\Delta\nu$' would be confirmed by experiment if measurements could be made on atoms or ions which are really free. The absence of such a confirmation is to be attributed to the fact that the existing observations are not on vapours or gases, but instead on solutions or salts, where there are inevitably large inter-atomic forces. If, then, these inter-atomic forces quench the magnetic effect of the orbital

[6] A. Sommerfeld, *Atombau*, 4th ed., p. 639, or *Phys. Zeits.* **24**, 360 (1923); *Zeits. f. Physik*, **19**, 221 (1923).        [7] D. M. Bose, *Zeits. f. Physik*, **43**, 864 (1927).

[8] E. C. Stoner, *Phil Mag.* **8**, 250 (1929).

[9] J .C. Slater, *Phys. Rev.* **34**, 1293 (1929).

angular momentum but leave the spin free, one will have precisely the expression (1) for the susceptibility. This point has been particularly emphasized by Stoner. The whole problem thus resolves itself into showing that from a theoretical standpoint it is reasonable to expect that the inter-atomic forces have a quenching effect of this type which blots out the orbital magnetic moment but not the spin. Stoner [8] showed that the necessary quenching could be obtained if one assumes that the inter-atomic forces are equivalent to extremely large random magnetic fields which are rather mysteriously supposed to act on only the orbital angular momentum. A somewhat similar assumption of random magnetic fields was successfully used in Kapitza's theory [10] of the influence of magnetic fields on electrical conduction, although the true explanation of Kapitza's experiments is much more complicated. Stoner did not propose his calculation by means of random magnetic fields except in a preliminary, suggestive way. It should not be taken literally, as inter-atomic forces are, of course, primarily electrostatic rather than magnetic in nature, and the magnetic portion would be much too weak to do the requisite quenching. In the following section, however, we shall show that precisely the type of quenching that leads to Eq. (1) ensues if each atom or ion is subjected to sufficiently asymmetrical electrical forces.[10a] In our opinion such asymmetrical electrostatic fields are probable, and are the real explanation of the quenching phenomena first proposed and roughly described by Stoner. The reason why, on the other hand, the ordinary theory for free ions is applicable to the susceptibilities of rare earth salts is doubtless, as already stated, that their 4f electrons are sequestered in the interior of the atom and so are not influenced nearly as much by neighbouring atoms as the 3d electrons involved in the iron group.

## 73. Quenching of Orbital Magnetic Moment by Asymmetrical External Fields

In a solid or liquid, the electrons of a given atom may to a first approximation be regarded as in an inhomogeneous external electric field which represents to this approximation the effect of other atoms on a given atom. This method has been extensively used by Bethe [11] and by Kramers,[12] and is admissible inasmuch as the other atoms are

---

[10] P. Kapitza, *Proc. Roy. Soc.* **123A**, 342 (1929).

[10a] During the printing of the present volume this point has also been emphasized in a paper by Pauling, *J. Amer. Chem. Soc.*, **53**, 1367 (1931).

[11] H. Bethe, *Ann. der Physik*, **3**, 133 (1929); *Zeits. f. Physik*, **60**, 218 (1930).

[12] H. A. Kramers, *Proc. Amsterdam Acad.* **32**, 1176 (1929).

approximately in the same configuration as in the absence of the given atom. Let us expand the potential energy of any electron of the given atom in this external field as a Taylor's series about the centre (nucleus) of the atom. The terms of successive order in the expansion usually involve the inter-atomic separation ('grating spacing') to successive negative powers so that the series converges rapidly. If there are similar equidistant atoms on either side of the given atom the linear terms disappear from the expansion, and the 'cross' products in the quadratic terms can, of course, be made to vanish by a proper rotation of axes. The terms of lowest non-vanishing order in the expansion of the external potential energy are then

$$A \sum x_i^2 + B \sum y_i^2 + C \sum z_i^2, \tag{2}$$

where the summation extends over all the electrons of the given atom. We do not necessarily claim that a simple quadratic form like $\langle 2 \rangle$ is a good quantitative representation of the interactions between atoms. However, only a rough qualitative portrayal, which is conveniently accomplished by means of $\langle 2 \rangle$, is needed to show that sufficient dissymmetry will quench out the magnetic effect of the orbital angular momentum.

Until further notice we shall neglect the spin and also any dissymmetries occasioned solely by higher-order terms in the Taylor's expansion than $\langle 2 \rangle$. We assume throughout that the external fields are never strong enough to destroy appreciably the Russell-Saunders quantization of the atom. In other words, electrostatic forces within the atom are supposed greater than forces from without the atom, so that the squares of the orbital and spin angular momentum are approximately $L(L+1)$ and $S(S+1)$, even though we shall see that the spacial quantization is greatly disturbed by the external fields.

*Case $A = B = C$.* If all three coefficients in $\langle 2 \rangle$ are equal, then the atom is as freely oriented in a solid as in a gas. The ideal magnetic theory for free atoms or ions should then apply.

*Case $A = B$, $B \neq C$.* In case two of the three coefficients are equal, say $A$ and $B$, the component of orbital angular momentum which is parallel to the $z$ axis is conserved, and can be assumed to have a quantized value $M_L$ (in multiples of $h/2\pi$) as the $z$ axis now becomes one of symmetry. On the other hand, the matrix elements of the $x$ and $y$ components of angular momentum will be exclusively of the form $\Delta M_L = \pm 1$ (cf. Eq. (89), Chap. VI). In other words, $L_z$ is a diagonal matrix, while $L_x$, $L_y$ contain no diagonal elements. If the effect of $M_L$

on the energy is large compared to $kT$, which means that

$$|A-C| \sum \overline{x_i^2} \gg kT,$$

then the contributions of $L_x$, $L_y$ to the susceptibility when calculated by the methods of Chapter VII will be entirely of the high-frequency type, and hence will be relatively ineffective, as they then give terms having the high frequencies instead of $kT$ in the denominator (cf. Eq. (28), Chap. VII). Thus only the contribution of the $z$ component $L_z = M_L$ remains. If one assumes that the axes of symmetry of the micro-crystals can have a random spacial distribution, as in, e.g. a crystal powder, then on neglecting high-frequency elements one easily finds that $\chi = N\overline{\overline{M_L^2}}/3kT$. Hence, supposing $|A-C|x^2 \gg kT$, one has $\chi = 0$ or $\chi = NL^2/3kT$ according as the minimum in energy corresponds to a minimum or maximum in $|M_L|$. In the former case the normal state has $M_L = 0$; in the latter, $M_L = \pm L$. The present situation is similar to that in the well-known Lenz-Ehrenfest [13] classical theory of magnetism, which was developed under the assumption that the atom has two positions of equal potential energy in a crystal, corresponding to the fact that in the present case $A = B$ this energy is independent of the sign of $M_L$. If one included higher-order 'saturation' terms in the field strength one would obtain the so-called Ehrenfest function as an expression for the paramagnetism.[14] Under the present supposition $A = B$, only two of the three components of orbital angular momentum are necessarily quenched. The third or $z$ component is also quenched if one assumes that the level $M_L = 0$ is alone a normal state, but it is doubtful whether this could be the case universally enough to explain the widespread applicability of (1). In the following paragraphs, however, we shall show that all three components are indeed quenched if instead we assume that all three coefficients $A$, $B$, $C$ are unequal, so that there is complete dissymmetry.

*Case A, B, C All Unequal.* Here the important fact is that the spacial degeneracy is completely removed. This is true inasmuch as ⟨2⟩ leads to the same secular problem as that of the asymmetrical top, which is non-degenerate unless two or more of the coefficients in the quadratic form are equal. For this observation the writer is indebted to Professor Kramers.[15] Quite irrespective of the formal mathematical analogy to

---

[13] W. Lenz, *Phys. Zeits.* **21**, 613 (1920); P. Ehrenfest, *Proc. Amsterdam Acad.* Dec. 18, 1920, or *Leiden Communications*, Suppl. 44 b.

[14] For elaboration on the Ehrenfest function see p. 712 of Debye's article in vol. vi of the *Handbuch der Radiologie*.

[15] The Hamiltonian function involved in the problem of the asymmetrical top is the quadratic form $aP_{x'}^2 + bP_{y'}^2 + cP_{z'}^2$, where $P_{x'}$, $P_{y'}$, $P_{z'}$, are the components of angular

the asymmetrical top it seems quite obvious that there is no remaining degeneracy when all three coefficients become unequal, as there was only the twofold degeneracy $M_L = \pm |M_L|$ even when two coefficients were equal. In the present case there is no axis of symmetry about which the angular momentum is conserved, so that there is no longer this degeneracy associated with the equivalence of left- and right-handed rotations about such an axis.

Now in § 68 we showed that when the degeneracy is completely removed it becomes necessary to use real wave functions, and that hence the average magnetic moment is zero. Thus when the coefficients in ⟨2⟩ are all unequal, the orbital magnetic moment matrix contains no diagonal elements. If the separation of energy-levels occasioned by removal of the degeneracy is large compared to $kT$, the contribution of the orbital angular momentum to the susceptibility will be entirely of the high-frequency type (Eq. (2), Chap. IX) and hence relatively small. Hence, if the coefficients $A$, $B$, $C$ in ⟨2⟩ are sufficiently large and unequal, the magnetic effect of the orbital angular momentum becomes practically entirely quenched. The residual effect of the high-frequency elements never disappears entirely but becomes negligible if the spacial separation is of the order $10^3$ to $10^4$ cm.$^{-1}$ or greater. Here and elsewhere we use the term 'spacial separation' for the difference in energy between the various non-degenerate states into which the energy-levels are separated by ⟨2⟩ or by an asymmetric inter-atomic field in general. If, on the other hand, the spacial separation is small compared to $kT$, the general theorem of Chapter VII shows that the orbital angular momentum will make its full contribution to the susceptibility.

Even though the potential ⟨2⟩ is probably not a close quantitative

momentum referred to the principal axes, and where $a$, $b$, $c$, are half the reciprocals of the principal moments of inertia. A general theorem of group theory shows that the resulting secular problem is similar to that of ⟨2⟩ inasmuch as $x$, $y$, $z$ and $P_{x'}$, $P_{y'}$, $P_{z'}$, transform similarly under a rotation of axes. The term 'secular' is here to be construed as meaning that we retain only the portion of ⟨2⟩ which is diagonal in $L$; otherwise the dynamical problem arising from ⟨2⟩ is more complicated than that of the asymmetrical top. The retention of only the diagonal elements is equivalent to our assumption that ⟨2⟩ does not destroy the Russell-Saunders coupling. The quantum numbers $J$, $\Lambda$ in the asymmetrical top correspond to $L$, $M_L$ in ⟨2⟩; this is a formal mathematical rather than physical correspondence; the asymmetrical top involves as a third quantum number a spacial quantum number physically somewhat similar to $M_L$, but this does not enter in its secular problem. That the asymmetry removes the degeneracy as regards the sign of $\Lambda$ has been shown independently by Kramers and Ittmann, *Zeits. f. Physik*, **53**, 553; **58**, 217; **60**, 663 (1929–30), and rather more explicitly by Wang, *Phys. Rev.* **34**, 243 (1929); cf. especially his Eq. (12). The formal correspondence of the quantum numbers $J$, $\Lambda$ and $L$, $M_L$ appears particularly clearly in the work of Klein, *Zeits. f. Physik*, **58**, 730 (1930).

approximation to the perturbing effect of other atoms, the preceding considerations nevertheless make it evident that sufficiently large and unsymmetrical external fields will quench the contribution of the orbital angular momentum to the susceptibility. In regular crystals it is usually necessary to retain higher-order terms than the second in the Taylor's expansion in order to reveal the exact degree of symmetry. An elaborate investigation of the effect of external fields of various types of crystalline symmetry has been made by Bethe, and readers interested in details are referred to his papers.[11] He finds that there can be at most only a rhomboidal symmetry if the spacial degeneracy is completely removed. Ordinary tetragonal, cubic, or hexagonal symmetries will not remove all the degeneracy. With these types of symmetries at least two of the coefficients in ⟨2⟩ are equal, but when higher-order terms in the Taylor's development are included (e.g. the fourth-order terms $D \sum (x_i^4 + y_i^4 + z_i^4)$ if there is cubic symmetry) then there is no longer an axis of symmetry about which angular momentum is conserved, and no component of the latter is what Dirac terms a 'constant of the motion'. Bethe shows[16] that nevertheless there is still a partial degeneracy, so that it is possible to use complex solutions and obtain an average magnetic moment, leading to an expression for the susceptibility of the form $NC/3kT$, where in general $0 < C < L(L+1)\beta^2$, so that there is only a partial quenching. For instance, he finds that an $F$ term is split by an external field with cubic symmetry into two triply degenerate states and one single or non-degenerate state. The orbital magnetic moment can be completely quenched only if the single or non-degenerate state has so much less energy than the multiple ones that it alone is a normal state.[17] The situation is thus somewhat analogous to that when $A = B$, $B \neq C$ in ⟨2⟩, as there we found the quenching was complete only if the state $M_L = 0$ had much less energy than the pairs of states corresponding to each $|M_L| > 0$. Thus sufficiently large external fields of rhomboidal or lower symmetry always

---

[16] H. Bethe, *Zeits. f. Physik*, **60**, 218 (1930).

[17] Even if the degeneracy is not completely removed, so that two or more wave functions, say $P$, $Q$, represent states of identical energy, it can sometimes happen that there is no magnetic moment, as the most general linear combination of $P$, $Q$ may still yield a non-magnetic state. In other words the ability to use complex wave functions is a necessary but not sufficient condition for the existence of magnetic moments. For instance, Bethe shows that a $D$ term splits in a field with cubic symmetry into one triply and one doubly degenerate state, but the doubly degenerate state is non-magnetic so that the orbital magnetic moment is quenched if the doubly degenerate state has the lower energy. With tetragonal instead of cubic symmetry, however, the multiple levels are necessarily magnetic, according to Bethe's analysis.

quench completely, while with more symmetry the quenching is complete only if certain states are the lowest lying.

Bethe shows that when an average magnetic moment persists despite the absence of an axis of symmetry (i.e. when there is more than rhomboidal but less than axial symmetry) that there can be a first-order Zeeman effect but that the selection rules are no longer the usual ones, and unusually large changes are permitted in the spacial quantum number, which no longer has the usual kinematical significance as proportional to a component of angular momentum. Bethe's theory finds a direct confirmation in Becquerel's observation of abnormally large Zeeman effects in certain crystals containing rare earths. The external fields which Bethe utilizes to explain Becquerel's [18] observations do not necessarily contradict the calculation in Chapter IX of the susceptibilities of rare earth ions on the assumption that the latter are free, as these fields might produce a spacial separation small compared to $kT$, and hence not quench the orbital angular momentum as far as susceptibilities are concerned. Bethe shows that the appearance of the anomalous Zeeman lines is not contingent on the absolute value of the spacial separation, but only on the ratio of the fourth- to second-degree terms in the Taylor's expansion of the potential. This ratio must not be too small compared to unity. We have repeatedly emphasized that susceptibilities depend on second- as well as first-order Zeeman terms, and so are not necessarily altered when the usual spectroscopic Zeeman patterns are changed. A more serious difficulty is that Bethe needs fields with more than rhomboidal symmetry to explain Becquerel's results. If one assumes that crystals involving iron ions have fields of the same symmetry but of much greater magnitude than Becquerel's rare earth compounds so that the separation of non-coinciding levels becomes greater rather than smaller than $kT$, the quenching of orbital angular momentum would not in general be as complete as needed for the validity of Eq. (1). Independently of Becquerel's work, Eq. (1) is found to be valid in crystals of the iron group in which it is known that there is more than rhomboidal symmetry. An example is NiO, which conforms roughly to (1), at least at room temperature, but which has cubic symmetry like NaCl. Unfortunately X-ray analyses of crystal structure seem to be wanting for the sulphates of the iron group, for which the magnetic data are the most complete. When (1) is found to apply despite more than rhomboidal symmetry, the simplest [17] explanation is that for some reason a 'single' level lies below the multiple ones, a pos-

[18] J. Becquerel, *Zeits. f. Physik*, **58**, 205 (1929).

sibility discussed at the end of the preceding paragraph. (Do not confuse this use of the terms 'single' and 'multiple' as regards the splitting due to inter-atomic fields with the 'singlets' and 'multiplets' introduced in connexion with spin fine structure.) The fact that most molecules are diamagnetic indeed seems to indicate that in complexes the non-magnetic states usually have the least energy.

In solutions there is surely no difficulty in believing that the fields have the degree of dissymmetry required to quench the angular momentum, for in liquids the atoms are doubtless rather irregularly spaced. The coefficients $A$, $B$, $C$ in $\langle 2 \rangle$ might even be regarded as functions of the time which vary with the approach and recession of atoms from each other. Also linear as well as quadratic terms in $x_i$, $y_i$, $z_i$ may be required. However, it is quite possible that in solutions the ions are not free, but attach themselves to water molecules, their so-called water molecules of coordination. In fact many chemists believe that an ion has the same definite number of water molecules attached to it in solutions as in the hydrated solid salt. A divalent ion containing iron, for example, would then really be of the form $Fe^{++} . nH_2O$ rather than $Fe^{++}$. The theory of polyatomic molecules ought, then, really to be invoked. This point has been particularly emphasized by Freed.[19] The magnetic theory for molecules has been discussed in Chapter X and shows a certain amount of resemblance to the various cases just presented. For instance, a diatomic molecule is somewhat similar to the case $A = B$, $B \neq C$, as there is an axis of symmetry and the orbital magnetic moment perpendicular to this axis is blotted out, while the parallel component is quenched only if one particular state (viz. the $\Sigma$ state $\Lambda = 0$) falls below the others in energy. A molecule with more than two atoms is similar to the case in which $A$, $B$, $C$ are all unequal, since we showed in § 68 that in general the orbital magnetic moment is largely quenched in unsymmetrical polyatomic molecules. This, we now see, is because all symmetry in the fields is lost in complicated molecules. Of course, the electrons in a molecule circulate freely from one atom to another, so that the representation of inter-atomic forces within the molecule as equivalent to a constant external field on each atom is but a poor quantitative approximation, but this does not affect the symmetry considerations. Furthermore, the individual atomic configurations probably preserve their identities rather more in complexes such as $Fe^{++} . nH_2O$ than in true molecules, as these complexes are doubtless held together by weak polarization forces rather than true valence

[19] S. Freed, *J. Amer. Chem. Soc.* **49**, 2456 (1927).

forces. One might wonder whether it would not be possible to find a solvent in which the dissolved ions did not form such complexes, as then the ions would be less disturbed and it might be possible to test experimentally the theory for free ions. Unfortunately, however, the ability to attach molecules of coordination is probably the criterion for solubility, as well as for the dissociation of the dissolved salt into ions.

It is conceivable that in certain solids the unit of crystalline structure is the molecule rather than the atom, in which case the considerations of the preceding paragraph or of Chapter X can be used. It is, of course, impossible to delineate sharply the point at which molecules or clusters begin to be formed in solids or liquids, and the representations by external fields and by isolated molecular entities are only asymptotic ones, but it seems quite safe to interpolate to intermediate or transition cases the result that sufficient dissymmetry quenches the orbital magnetic moment.

We have ostensibly assumed throughout that the atom of the iron group loses all of its $s$ electrons and exists in a definite ionic form. However, the quenching considerations based on symmetry clearly apply equally well in the event of non-polar or 'coordination' bonds in which these electrons are merely shared or even traded, provided only that they are so grouped as to have zero resultant spin, thus leaving only the $d$ electrons not in closed configurations.

We have gone to considerable length to show that inter-atomic forces can quench out the magnetic effect of the orbital angular momentum. The question now arises as to why the spin is free and unquenched. There is no difficulty in understanding that forces from other atoms do not perturb the spin. The only inter-atomic forces which can have an appreciable orienting influence on the spin are the exchange forces between paramagnetic atoms or ions, cited on p. 283. It was there explained that the media studied in the present chapter are of sufficient 'magnetic dilution' to make this influence unimportant. We must, however, show that the spin is free as regards the magnetic forces which arise from within the atom and which are responsible for spin multiplets. (Magnetic forces between different atoms are, of course, negligible.) These internal magnetic forces will not quench the spin magnetic moment if the spin multiplet width in the ideal gas state is small compared to the spacial separation defined on p. 290. To show this let us take as an unperturbed system the atom without spin in a powerful external asymmetrical electronic field such as is embodied in $\langle 2 \rangle$. Introduce as a perturbing potential the magnetic coupling

$$A'\mathbf{L} \cdot \mathbf{S} \qquad \langle 3 \rangle$$

between spin and orbit (cf. Eq. $\langle 84 \rangle$, Chap. VI. To avoid confusion with coefficients in $\langle 2 \rangle$ a prime is attached to $A$ in $\langle 3 \rangle$). This case is, of course, unlike the ordinary ideal gas one, as the orbital magnetic moment has been already greatly distorted by the external potential $\langle 2 \rangle$ and no longer has matrix elements of the form (88) or (89), Chap. VI. In fact the quenching effect considered above has robbed $L$ of all diagonal matrix elements. By (24), Chap. VI, this means that to a first approximation in $A'$, the perturbing potential $\langle 3 \rangle$ has no effect on the energy. When the second approximation (26), Chap. VI, is considered, however, $\langle 3 \rangle$ causes energy displacements of the order of magnitude $A'^2/h\nu_{\text{sep}}$, as $L$, $S$ are of the order unity. Here $h\nu_{\text{sep}}$ is an expression of the order of magnitude of the 'spacial separation', or of $|A-B| \sum \overline{x_i^2}$, assuming $|A-B| \leqslant |A-C| \leqslant |B-C|$. Thus the effect of the internal magnetic coupling is of the order $A'^2/h\nu_{\text{sep}}$, to be contrasted with the order $A'$ for free ions. The theory of Chapter VII, especially the remarks on p. 193, show that the spin will make its full contribution (1) to the susceptibility, provided that the work required to 'turn over' the spin is small compared to $kT$. The only force interfering with the freedom of orientation of the spin is the coupling arising from $\langle 3 \rangle$. Thus the requirement is that [20]

$$A'^2 \ll kT \cdot h\nu_{\text{sep}}. \qquad (4)$$

In the ions of the iron group with which we are concerned, the over-all multiplet width ranges from about $4 \times 10^2$ ($Ti^{+++}$) to $2 \times 10^3$ cm.$^{-1}$ ($Cu^{++}$). The corresponding values of $A'$ are roughly $1 \cdot 6 \times 10^2$ to $0 \cdot 8 \times 10^3$ cm.$^{-1}$. Large departures from (1) (or more precisely from the Weiss formula (6)) seem first to appear when $T$ is reduced below about $70° K$. (see p. 304), or in terms of wave numbers when $kT$ is less than $50$ cm.$^{-1}$. Hence, for (4) to be satisfied down to this temperature, the spacial separation must be of the order $10^3$ to $10^4$ cm.$^{-1}$, or $0 \cdot 1$ to $1$ volt. This requires fields of the order $10^7$ to $10^8$ volts/cm., as $x$, $y$, $z$ are of the order $10^{-8}$. Fields of this magnitude are perhaps not unreasonable, although they seem a bit high. In particular the higher estimate of 1 volt is plausible only if the ions are intimately attached in complexes,

---

[20] The inequality (4) must be satisfied in order for the spin to be free even if the quenching of the orbital angular momentum ensues not because of complete dissymmetry, but because a non-magnetic component might have the least energy when there is more than rhomboidal symmetry. The inequality (4) is still needed, as the non-diagonal matrix elements of $\mathbf{L}$, such as are involved in the second approximation to the effect of $\langle 3 \rangle$, never vanish regardless of the amount of symmetry or of quenching.

so that the inter-atomic forces are large. It is perhaps well to compare (4) with the requirement that the spacial separation be large enough to quench the orbital angular momentum, which is

$$h\nu_{\text{sep}} \gg kT. \tag{5}$$

At room temperatures in the first half of the iron period the multiplets are of the same order of magnitude as $kT$, so that fulfilment of (5) ensures that of (4). At lower temperatures and in the second half where multiplets are wider, (5) is a less severe condition than (4), as it only demands spacial separations of the order $10^3$ cm.$^{-1}$.

It is to be emphasized that our estimate by means of (4) and (5) of the magnitude of the spacial separation required to quench the orbital momentum and still leave the spin free is only a very crude one, and may well be in error by a factor, say 10 to $10^2$. If, for instance, one used in the left side of (4) the 'over-all multiplet width' produced by $\langle 3 \rangle$ in free ions, rather than the proportionality factor $A'$, one would find the spacial separation would have to be 1 to 10 volts, which seems rather too high. However, we believe the estimate by using $A'$ comes closer to the truth, as what counts is the differences rather than absolute values of the energies of the various spacial spin quantizations produced by $\langle 3 \rangle$. The differences may well be considerably smaller than the absolute values. We must further caution that (4) and (5) cease to be good approximations when the multiplet structure for free ions is not small compared to $\langle 2 \rangle$, as then it is not allowable to treat $\langle 3 \rangle$ as a small perturbation superposed on $\langle 2 \rangle$. Hence we must not rely too exactly on (4) and (5) near the end of the group ($Ni^{++}$, $Cu^{++}$) where the multiplets are wider.

We must mention that even if the inequality (4) is not satisfied, the spin can sometimes be at least in part free, as some degeneracy may exist even in the secular problem connected with the superposition of $\langle 3 \rangle$ on $\langle 2 \rangle$. Kramers [21] shows that all states remain doubly degenerate when there is an odd number of electrons. This is because the inner quantum numbers for free ions are then half-integral, so that there is a 'Zweideutigkeit' in the representation of rotational transformations by group theory.[22] Even the persistence of this double degeneracy will leave the spin only partly free, except in doublet spectra, where it is very much freer than usual. Partial freedom of the spin when (4) is not satisfied would not explain an accurate validity of (1), but might mean that the departures from (1) are not very great even if the left side of

[21] H. A. Kramers, *Proc. Amsterdam Acad.* **33**, 959 (1930), especially § 2.
[22] Cf. pp. 153ff. of Bethe's first paper.

(4) is somewhat greater than the right. The table on p. 304 shows that $CuSO_4.5H_2O$ (an odd ion, $^2D$ type) obeys Curie's law closer than $NiSO_4.7H_2O$ (even, $^3F$). This is a beautiful manifestation of Kramers' degeneracy effect.

Bethe estimates that the spacial separation in crystals is of the order 250 cm.$^{-1}$ if caused by fourth-order terms in the Taylor's expansion. He informs the writer that this estimate should be increased by a factor about 10 if the dissymmetries already appear in the second-order terms such as $\langle 2 \rangle$. There is also a further increase by a factor $Z^2$ in the second-order terms if the ions have a $Z$-fold rather than single ionization. The size of the second-order terms then agrees well with our estimate from (4), but Bethe supposes ionic crystals, and so for our purposes his estimates ought to be lowered if the units in solvents and hydrated salts are primarily neutral rather than ionic. One would conjecture that the dipole-fields from water molecules might be responsible for part of the quenching in solutions. On the other hand, Bethe does not consider clusters, which would raise the estimates. An obvious difficulty occurs should Eq. (1) be found valid in crystals of sufficient symmetry (e.g. cubic) so that the dissymmetry is occasioned only by the fourth-order terms, as then one has only a spacial separation of the order $250Z^2$ cm.$^{-1}$.

Joos [23] has particularly emphasized in connexion with the problem of magnetism that the colours of solutions containing ions of the iron group must be associated with transitions between different energy-levels of complexes, as these ions when free have no normal absorption lines softer than 1300 Å. If the characteristic colours are due to transitions between different levels which we have ascribed to spacial separation, the latter must be about 2 or 3 volts, in good agreement with our upper estimate from (4). There is sometimes good evidence that similar associations are formed both in crystals and in solution, and this perhaps explains why the susceptibilities also are often so similar. The absorption spectra of cobalt compounds, for example, leads to the conclusion that both in solids and solutions the cobalt ion is associated with four groups in the blue compounds and with six in the red.[24]

## 74. Further Discussion of Salts of the Iron Group

In the present section we shall cite a number of experimental facts (a)–(h) which can for the most part be nicely correlated in a qualitative

---

[23] G. Joos, *Ann. der Physik*, **81**, 1076 (1926); **85**, 641 (1928).
[24] Quoted by Stoner from R. Hill and O. R. Howell, *Phil. Mag.* **48**, 833 (1924).

way with the theory just developed in § 73, and which seem to preclude any other explanation of the susceptibilities of the iron salts. Probably the only alternative that warrants any consideration is that the orbital angular momentum is not fully quenched, but that the multiplet intervals are greatly distorted in solution or solids, and the susceptibility thus altered. However, a very serious objection to this alternative is that some experimental susceptibilities fall outside the limits for infinitely narrow or wide multiplets in the latter half of the iron group (see table, § 72). The only escape would be the highly improbable supposition that in the solid or liquid state the multiplets become turned 'upside down' as compared to the gaseous state, and thus become regular rather than inverted in the last half of the period. (To illustrate, the limiting magneton number for $Cu^{++}$ for $\Delta\nu = \infty$ would then become 1·55, the value for an infinitely wide regular $^2D$ multiplet; cf. $Sc^{++}$ in table.)

Many of the points which we now give as favourable to Eq. (1) have already been mentioned by Stoner,[8] though not with exactly our quenching mechanism, and we have found the discussion in his paper very helpful in writing the present section.

(a) *Near Constancy of the Magneton Number in an Iso-electronic Sequence.* Reference to the table in § 72 shows that as we pass down the sequence $V^{++}$, $Cr^{+++}$, $Mn^{++++}$ the magneton number should decrease in the ideal gas state (cf. column 'actual $\Delta\nu$'). This is because the multiplet width is increasing. On the other hand, the experimental susceptibility for $Mn^{4+}$ is apparently higher than for $Cr^{+++}$. Hence all traces of the natural multiplet structure must be pretty well quenched.

(b) *Small Variations with Concentration.* If the anomalies in susceptibility were due to a fortuitous alteration (as distinct from quenching) of the multiplet structure by inter-atomic forces, there should presumably be tremendous variations with the precise character of the inter-atomic fields, and hence with the concentration, nature of solvent, or nature of salt in solid compounds. There are some variations, but they are usually comparatively small, at least relative to the discrepancy between experiment and theory ('actual $\Delta\nu$', p. 285) for free ions, as reference to the upper and lower limits to the experimental values given in the table of § 72 will show. Even the same salt may behave differently according to its thermal treatment. The extensive investigations of Chatillon[25] yield magneton numbers for the cobaltous ion ranging from

[25] A. Chatillon, *Annales de Physique*, **9**, 187 (1928).

4·4 to 5·2. Birch [26] has measured the magnetic moment of the cupric ion under no less than twenty different conditions (different solvents, concentrations, solid compounds, and temperature intervals) and finds the magneton number ranges from 1·8 to 2·0, so that the total variation is 10 per cent.[27] On the other hand, de Haas and Gorter [27a] have recently found that solid $CuSO_4 . 5H_2O$ follows the Weiss-Curie law (Eq. (6), p. 303) almost perfectly even down to 14° K., with $\mu_{eff} = 1·92$ and with $\Delta$ only 0·70.

Variations of the order of magnitude of those mentioned in the preceding paragraph are understandable on the ground that the external fields such as ⟨2⟩ may not be adequate to quench the orbital angular momentum completely. Even if the inequality (5) is fulfilled, there is always some residual effect of the high-frequency elements which may vary from one material to another. Also it is quite likely that the left side of (4) is not entirely negligible compared to the right side, so that the spin is not completely free. In some cases Eq. (1) is a remarkably good quantitative approximation. For $V^{++++}$, $V^{+++}$, $V^{++}$ in solution Freed [19] finds 1·745, 2·760, and 3·805–3·855, respectively for the effective Bohr magneton numbers, whereas the theoretical values predicted by (1) are 1·732, 2·828, and 3·873. Freed even endeavours to distinguish between vanadium ions which have attached an oxygen atom to them and those which have not. Freed thinks his value given above for $V^{++++}$ is probably really for $VO^{++}$ rather than free $V^{++++}$, but that the other values are for free ions, except for water molecules of coordination. The value quoted for $V^{+++}$ was for the green variety. Freed suggests that the brown variety involves really $VO^+$ instead of $V^{+++}$, but the magneton number which he finds for it is 2·813–2·848, and thus in even closer accord with (1) than for the green variety. If the $V^{+++}$ ion really attaches itself to an O atom to form a diatomic ion, the latter must be in a $^3\Sigma$ state to explain the validity of (1). Perhaps the unusually good agreement for the vanadium ions is because (4) is better fulfilled in the first than second half of the iron period, as the multiplets are narrower. Also reference to the table shows that the discrepancy between (1) and the values 'actual $\Delta\nu$' is, rather fortuitously, unusually small for the V ions, so that the susceptibility would be only slightly altered even if the quenching is only partial, provided, however, the ions are monatomic rather than diatomic. For this reason Freed's data on vanadium

[26] Birch, *J. de Physique*, **9**, 137 (1928).

[27] For further comparisons of the magneton numbers for the same ion in different salts see the table to be given in item (*h*).

[27a] W. J. de Haas and C. J. Gorter, *Leiden Communications* 210d.

perhaps do not furnish quite as crucial a test of (1) as would equally careful measurements on other ions.

(c) *Experimental Values often Intermediate between* (1) *and Those for Free Ions*. This should, of course, be the case if the quenching is only partial. Reference to the columns 'spin free', 'actual $\Delta\nu$', and 'experiment' in the table of § 72 shows that this is indeed usually the case, especially in the last half of the period, where the divergence between the values 'spin free' and 'actual $\Delta\nu$' is greatest. Occasionally some of the experimental values lie outside these limits, but not very far. As the quenching condition (5) is better fulfilled at low temperatures, one might expect the beginning of a transition from (1) to the values for free ions to manifest itself as the temperature is raised. Stoner notes that a limited amount of experimental data seems to reveal just this situation. Theodorides[28] finds a magneton number 3·2 for $Ni^{++}$ in the temperature interval 15–125° C., and 3·4 for 150–500°C., to be compared with the values 2·83 and 5·56 given respectively by (1) and Laporte's theory for free ions.

(d) *Experiments on the Gyromagnetic Effect*. This is one of the most satisfying arguments. Such experiments on rotation by magnetization, or the converse, yield a $g$-factor approximately[29] 2 when made as usual on Fe, Ni, Co, or alloys thereof. Now 2 is just the $g$-factor characteristic of the spin alone, and so is indicative that the orbital magnetic moment is completely quenched. The usual experiments are, to be sure, made on the ferromagnetic pure metals and alloys rather than the paramagnetic salts now being studied, but since ferromagnetism is a spin phenomenon (§ 77) there can be but little doubt but that the quenching

---

[28] Theodorides, Dissertation, Zurich, 1921; *Comptes Rendus*, **171**, 948 (1920); *J. de Physique*, **3**, 1 (1922). Honda and Ishiwara find that the graph of $1/\chi$ against $T$ for $CuCl_2$ is non-linear with the concave side of the curvature towards the $T$ axis (*Sci. Rep. Tohoku Univ.*, vols. 3–4) and Birch finds a similar curvature for $CuSO_4$ between 10 and 537° C. This is the type of curvature to be expected if the magneton number is beginning to change from the 'spin only' value 1·73 to that 3·53 appropriate to free ions. Birch gives a magneton number 1·82 for $CuCl_2$ in solution from 0–40° and 2·0 from 40–85° C. This difference gives, however, a rather exaggerated impression of the amount of curvature, as the magneton number is taken by Birch to be proportional to $[\chi.(T+\Delta)]^{\frac{1}{2}}$ and there are nearly compensating changes in $\Delta$, which he gives as respectively $-10$ and $+65$ in the two intervals. If the magneton number is taken proportional to $(\chi T)^{\frac{1}{2}}$ i.e., without the Weiss modification in the Curie formula, it has nearly identical values, viz. 1·85 and 1·86 in these two intervals.

[29] It is usually stated that gyromagnetic experiments yield a $g$-factor which is 2 within the experimental error. However, the very careful recent work of S. J. Barnett and L. J. H. Barnett (*J. Amer. Acad.* **60**, 127 (1925); *Phys. Rev.* **31**, 1116 (1928) ) yields a $g$-factor 1·87 for pure iron, quite definitely less than 2. This is doubtless because the orbital magnetic moment is not completely quenched. The $g$-factor for a free $Fe^{+++}$ ion is 2, but that for $Fe^{++}$ is 3/2, and both types of ions are perhaps present.

on the orbital part is similar in both cases.  Also particularly pleasing is the fact that gyromagnetic experiments made instead very recently by Sucksmith[30] on a paramagnetic salt containing $Cr^{+++}$ still reveal a $g$-factor 2, in marked contrast to the agreement of his gyromagnetic experiments on the rare earths with the theory for free ions (cf. § 60).

(e) *Confirmation in* $Fe^{+++}$ *and* $Mn^{++}$.  These ions are in $S$ states, so that there are no questions of multiplet structure, and Eq. (1) gives the same result as the theory for free ions.  Hence the calculations should hold more closely than usual.  Now it is noteworthy that $Mn^{++}$ does indeed have a remarkably constant magneton number.  In a careful study of solutions of the chloride, sulphate, and nitrate, Cabrera[31] and his collaborators have found in each case a number close to 5·92 independent of the concentration.  On the other hand, a variation of nearly 10 per cent. in the magneton number of the $Fe^{+++}$ ion is observed when solutions of different concentrations or acid content are prepared. Perhaps this variation is due to chemical effects, such as the attaching of water molecules of coordination, or possibly, a suggestion made by Stoner, a partial formation of diamagnetic complex ions.

(f) *Complex Salts*.  There are many so-called complex salts in which the ion of the iron group is known to be present only as one of the constituents of a complicated radical.[32]  Very often such salts have susceptibilities which can be approximately represented by (1) if $S$ is given the proper value.  For instance, $[Cu(NH_3)_4(NO_2)_2]$ and also other similar complex cupric salts usually have magneton numbers somewhere between 1·8 and 2·0; $Cr(NH_3)_6I_3$ and other chromic salts numbers from 3·4 to 3·8; and $Ni(NH_3)_6Br_2$, &c., numbers ranging from 2·6 to 3·2.  These values are nearly the same, though usually somewhat higher than those 1·73, 3·87, and 2·83 given by (1) with $S$ respectively 1/2, 3/2 and 1. These are just the values of $S$ for isolated $Cu^{++}$, $Cr^{+++}$, and $Ni^{++}$ ions, and this suggests that the iron group ions often have a fairly independent existence even in the complex salts.  Hence in (h) we shall draw freely on the temperature data for complex salts.  In any case the obvious interpretation is that the complex radical has a nearly free resultant spin, and that any excess over (1) is due to an only partial quenching of the orbital angular momentum.

There are, however, many complex salts, e.g. $KMnO_4$, $K_2Cr_2O_7$, many

[30] W. Sucksmith, paper communicated to the British Association, 1930.

[31] B. Cabrera and A. Duperier, *J. de Physique*, **6**, 121 (1925).

[32] For further discussion of complex salts see Stoner, *Magnetism and Atomic Structure*, pp. 325 ff.; Welo and Baudisch, *Nature*, **116**, 359, 606 (1925); S. Shaffer and N. W. Taylor, *J. Amer. Chem. Soc.* **48**, 843 (1926); Rosenbohm.[33]

ferrous complex salts, and some sixty cobaltamines measured by Rosenbohm, which are either diamagnetic or only feebly paramagnetic. The
obvious explanation is that here the resultant spin of the complex ion
is zero. This is allowable, as in each case the latter contains an even
number of electrons. The spins of the individual constituent atom-ions,
in so far as they have an isolated existence, need not be zero, but only
the vector sum over the entire radical.

(g) *Feeble Paramagnetism of Certain Salts.* Some of the complex salts
cited in the preceding paragraph are feebly paramagnetic instead of
diamagnetic. For instance, after allowing for the residual diamagnetic
effects, Rosenbohm[33] finds that the molar susceptibility of the hexa-
mines, pentamines, tetramines, and triamines of cobalt are respectively
approximately $55 \times 10^{-6}$, $60 \times 10^{-6}$, $73 \times 10^{-6}$, $97 \times 10^{-6}$. The ordinary
paramagnetic susceptibilities which we have previously been treating
are of the order $10^{-3}$ or greater. It seems reasonable to attribute this
feeble paramagnetism to the residual effect of the high-frequency matrix
elements, or, in other words, to the fact that the quenching of the
orbital angular momentum is necessarily imperfect. This idea finds a
beautiful confirmation in the fact that such feeble paramagnetism is
usually found experimentally to be independent of the temperature,[34]
or nearly so, in accord with the general theorem of Chapter VII that
high-frequency matrix elements give a contribution to the susceptibility
which is independent of temperature. In this connexion the second
term of Eq. (11), Chap. X, and remarks relating thereto should be
consulted, as it was there found that the feeble paramagnetic term is
unavoidable when the molecule or ion contains more than one atom.

Ladenburg[35] has emphasized that certain ions which are in $^1S$ states
when free sometimes seem to exhibit a small paramagnetism when in
compounds which is usually independent of temperature. For instance,
$Sc_2O_3$, $TiO_2$, $V_2O_5$, $CeO_2$ all seem to exhibit paramagnetic susceptibilities
(after allowance for diamagnetism) of the order $10^{-5}$ to $10^{-4}$ per gramme
mol. independent of temperature, despite the fact that $Sc^{3+}$, $Ti^{4+}$, $V^{5+}$,
and $Ce^{4+}$ ions all have $^1S$ configurations. Such measurements are necessarily unprecise and difficult because of the smallness of the effect and
uncertain estimate of the diamagnetism, but seem quite definite for

[33] Rosenbohm, *Zeits. f. Phys. Chem.* **93,** 693 (1919).
[34] See T. Ishiwara, *Sci. Rep. Tohoku Univ.* **3,** 303 (1914); P. Weiss and Mlle P. Collet,
*Comptes Rendus,* **178,** 2147 (1924); **181,** 1051 (1925); **182,** 105 (1926); Freed and Kasper,
*J. Amer. Chem. Soc.,* **52,** 4671 (1930). Freed explicitly mentions the agreement of his
observations on temperature variation with Eq. (11), Chap. X, or its equivalent.
[35] R. Ladenburg, *Zeits. f. Phys. Chem.* **126,** 133 (1927).

$V^{5+}$ in view of the careful work of Weiss and Mlle Collet.[34] Other convincing data have recently been given by Freed.[34] Such small residual paramagnetism finds its explanation along the lines of the preceding paragraph. Here the important thing to note is that in complicated molecules the inter-atomic forces not merely quench most of the orbital paramagnetism if the constituent atom-ions are not in $^1S$ states when free, but can actually create a small paramagnetism if they are all in $^1S$ states and hence diamagnetic when isolated from each other. This is because the square of the orbital angular momentum never vanishes (and hence cannot be $S(S+1)$ with $S=0$) when there is more than one nuclear centre, as explained in § 69.

(h) *Approximate Conformance of Temperature Variation to the Weiss Law.* It is a remarkable and illuminating fact that the temperature variations of the susceptibilities of most salts involving the iron group are represented rather well down to a certain critical temperature by the so-called Weiss formula,

$$\chi = \frac{C}{T+\Delta}, \tag{6}$$

in which Curie's law is generalized by addition of the constant $\Delta$ to the denominator. In view of (1) the approximate value of the constant $C$ is usually $4N\beta^2 S(S+1)/3k$. Whole pages could be devoted to recording the values of $C$ and $\Delta$ reported by different investigators, not always in overly good accord with each other.[36] We shall content ourselves by giving in the following table some of the measurements made by Jackson and others at Leiden,[37] as the Leiden data usually extend to lower temperatures than elsewhere, and so furnish a more crucial test of (6), usually revealing the temperature below which (6) fails.[38] Instead of

---

[36] For an excellent survey of the different experimental determinations and references, see Stoner, *Magnetism and Atomic Structure*, pp. 127, 132–7, 144–9, or Cabrera, *l.c.*[5]

[37] The measurements for the nickel and cobalt salts (except chlorides) given in the table are by Jackson, *Leiden Communications* 163, or *Phil. Trans. Roy. Soc.* **224**, 1 (1923). The values for the ferrous salts are as quoted and calculated by Jackson from earlier Leiden work. The papers on the chlorides are cited in notes 42 and 44 below. The results on the ferric and manganous salts are taken from a variety of the Leiden papers (*Communications* 129 b, 132 e, 139 e, 168 b) mostly by Onnes and Oosterhuis. For $Cu^{++}$ see ref. 27 a. The determination for $Cr_2(SO_4)_3K_2SO_4 . 24H_2O$ is by de Haas and Gorter, *Leiden Communications* 208 c.

[38] In the early days of the old quantum theory several attempts were made to explain the deviations from Curie's law at low temperatures as found at Leiden, by quantizing the rotation of a free diatomic molecule. See, for instance, F. Reiche, *Ann. der Physik*, **54**, 401 (1917); S. Rotszajn, *ibid.* **57**, 81 (1918). These attempts do not seem to have any physical significance, as an ionic crystal surely does not consist of such freely rotating molecules.

giving the Curie constant $C$, we give in each case the effective Bohr magneton number defined by $\mu_{\text{eff}} = (3kC/N\beta^2)^{\frac{1}{2}}$.

| | $\Delta$ | $\mu_{\text{eff}}$ | | $\Delta$ | $\mu_{\text{eff}}$ |
|---|---|---|---|---|---|
| $MnSO_4$ . . . . | 24 | 5·83 | $MnSO_4 \cdot 4H_2O$ . . | 0 | 5·87 |
| $Fe_2(SO_4)_3$ . . . | 31 | .. | .. | | .. |
| $FeSO_4$ . . . . | 31 | 5·16 | $FeSO_4 \cdot 7H_2O$ . . | 1 | 5·22 |
| $CoSO_4$ . . . . | 45 | 5·09 | $CoSO_4 \cdot 7H_2O$ . . | 14 | 5·05 |
| $NiSO_4$ . . . . | 79 | 3·21 | $NiSO_4 \cdot 7H_2O$ . . | −59 | 2·95 |
| | | | $CuSO_4 \cdot 5H_2O$ . . | 0·7* | 1·91 |
| | | | | | |
| $Cr_2(SO_4)K_2SO_4 \cdot 24H_2O$ . | −0·2* | 3·83 | $CrCl_3$ . . . | −32·5 | 3·61 |
| $MnSO_4(NH_4)_2SO_4 \cdot 6H_2O$. | 0* | 5·89 | $MnCl_2$ . . . | 0 | 5·61 |
| $Fe_2(SO_4)_3(NH_4)_2SO_4 \cdot 24H_2O$ | 0* | 5·84 | .. | | .. |
| $FeSO_4(NH_4)_2SO_4 \cdot 6H_2O$ | 3* | 5·55 | $FeCl_2$ . . . | −20 | |
| $CoSO_4(NH_4)_2SO_4 \cdot 6H_2O$ . | 22 | 5·00 | $CoCl_2$ . . . | −33 | 5·03 |
| $NiSO_4(NH_4)_2SO_4 \cdot 6H_2O$ . | 4 | 3·21 | $NiCl_2$ . . . | −67 | 3·17 |

As a rule the values of $\Delta$ given in the table are found when substituted in (6) to yield a formula which represents the experimental data fairly well down to about 65–135° K. Below this critical region of temperatures Eq. (6) usually ceases to be valid, and the cryomagnetic anomalies discussed below begin to set in. In a few cases, however, Eq. (6) with the constants as given in the table is found to hold quite well down to the lowest temperature investigated (usually about 14° K.). These cases are indicated by asterisks in the table.[39]

As regards the theoretical interpretation of $\Delta$, it is quite clear that it is not usually an atomic property, but is due primarily to distortions by inter-atomic forces. This is shown, for one thing, by the fact that $\Delta$ varies so much with the compound in which a paramagnetic ion of given valence occurs, in marked contrast to the comparative constancy of the magneton number $\mu_{\text{eff}}$. Chlorides, for instance, usually yield a negative $\Delta$, and sulphates a positive one. As a rule the values of $\Delta$ are lower in compounds of high 'magnetic dilution', such as the hydrated sulphates and amono-sulphates in the table. Heisenberg's theory, which we shall discuss in Chapter XII, shows that the exchange forces between paramagnetic atoms or ions have the effect of adding a constant $\Delta$ to the denominator of the usual Curie formulae, thus yielding an expression of the desired form (6). We have, however, already mentioned that the exchange forces probably play only a subordinate effect in the ordinary salts, and if all of $\Delta$ is due to the exchange effect, then $\Delta$ should vanish when the magnetic dilution is high. Reference to the table, on the other hand, shows that $\Delta$ is still appreciably different

[39] In the cases of $MnSO_4$, $MnSO_4 \cdot 4H_2O$, $FeSO_4 \cdot 7H_2O$, and $NiSO_4(NH_4)_2SO_4 \cdot 6H_2O$, the deviations from (6) at low temperatures are, however, considerably less pronounced than for the other salts not designated by asterisks in the table.

from zero even for some of the highly hydrated salts. One therefore is probably safe in attributing only a part of $\Delta$ to the exchange effect, and the balance to distortion effects involving the orbital angular momentum, probably because the inequalities (4) and (5) are not fulfilled with any great precision, although the requisite mathematical theory has not yet been developed to show that the temperature dependence is of the form (6).[40]

This view that $\Delta$ is often due mainly to the influence of orbital angular momentum finds support in the fact that $\Delta$ is usually smaller in the manganous and ferric than in most other salts. The $Mn^{++}$ and $Fe^{+++}$ ions are in $S$ states and hence devoid of orbital angular momentum. Hence, only the part of $\Delta$ arising from the exchange effect should still remain, and this disappears at infinite magnetic dilution. This is in beautiful accord with the fact that $\Delta$ is zero for $MnSO_4(NH_4)_2SO_4 . 6H_2O$ and $Fe_2(SO_4)_3(NH_4)_2SO_4 . 24H_2O$ within the experimental error. The latter of these (alum), with its 24 water molecules, of course represents an unusually high degree of magnetic dilution. Furthermore, for these two salts Curie's law holds right down to the temperature of liquid hydrogen, without the usual irregularities setting in at about $70° K$. We can, so to speak, say that in the salts of the iron group the orbital magnetic moment and all traces of gaseous multiplet structure are pretty well exterminated, manifesting themselves only indirectly in $\Delta$ and in irregularities only at very low temperatures. In $Mn^{++}$ and $Fe^{+++}$ there are no multiplets to exterminate, and this is reflected in the closer applicability of Curie's law than for other ions, except possibly $Cu^{++}$.

The data on $\Delta$ which we have previously quoted have been for solids.

---

[40] Without a detailed calculation it can be predicted that the theoretical expression for the susceptibility can be developed in a series of the form $\chi = \dfrac{C}{T} + \dfrac{a_2}{T^2} + \dfrac{a_3}{T^3} + \ldots$ when we consider corrections to (1) resulting from the fact that the left side of (4) is not negligible compared to the right side, but at the same time neglect any error resulting from the fact that the condition (5) may not be well fulfilled. This development is the same as (6) to terms of the order $T^{-2}$ if we take $\Delta = -a_2/C$. It is not clear without lengthy computations of $a_2$, $a_3$ whether or not this development and that obtained by expansion of (6) differ appreciably in the terms of order $T^{-3}$, $T^{-4}$, &c., also how much the development is spoiled because (5) is never ideally fulfilled.

In this connexion we may mention that a development of the susceptibility in descending powers of $T$ is likewise obtained in the theory of Cabrera and Palacios, *An. Soc. esp. Fis. Quim.* **24**, 297 (1926). They also have the idea that part of the susceptibility of the free ion is suppressed by inter-atomic forces, but in our opinion the numerical values of the coefficients in their series development are in error because they overlook the fact that the second- as well as first-order Zeeman terms contribute to the Curie term of the susceptibility when the frequencies in the perturbation denominators are small compared to $kT/h$.

The experimental data on $\Delta$ in solutions are rather hard to analyse, as there are complicated variations of $\Delta$ with acid content, with the temperature interval (indicating that here (6) is really not a good formula), &c. Generally speaking, $\Delta$ changes but slowly with concentration, and does not vanish at infinite dilution. This is theoretically comprehensible if there are certain clusters or complexes which maintain their existence at any dilution. The fact that the value of $\Delta$ depends somewhat on the nature of the negative radical of the dissolved salt indicates that the cluster apparently sometimes has a more complicated structure than $Fe^{++} \cdot nH_2O$, &c. Cabrera and Duperier [41] find that $\Delta$ is about $-23$ to $-28$ for aqueous solutions of manganous salts. This is rather puzzling, as the $Mn^{++}$ ion is in a $^6S$ state when free, and hence should presumably be affected but little by the surrounding molecules of hydration. In our opinion the data on hydrated solid salts furnish a more reliable and more easily analysed test of the theory than do the measurements on solutions. In particular, the determinations of $\Delta$ in solutions are often based on such restricted temperature intervals that they lack much significance (cf. end of note 28).

It is to be understood that (6) is not claimed to be an entirely accurate representation of the temperature variation even at room temperatures and higher. Instead $\Delta$ must itself be regarded as a slowly varying function of the temperature, in line with the transition effects mentioned at the end of item $(c)$. One fact, however, stands out sharply, namely, that the large departures from Curie's law do not appear experimentally in the first half of the iron group which should appear theoretically in the ideal free or gaseous state because the multiplets are comparable to $kT$. Reference to the table on p. 285 shows that in the upper half of this table the effective magneton numbers for the free state calculated for '$\Delta\nu = \infty$' or $T = 0$ are quite different from those calculated for 'actual $\Delta\nu$' or ordinary temperatures. One can, for instance, calculate the following effective magneton numbers for free $Cr^{+++}$ and $Cr^{++}$ at various temperatures.

| $T =$ | 0 | 20 | 50 | 80 | 150 | 293 | 400° K. |
|---|---|---|---|---|---|---|---|
| $Cr^{+++}$ $\mu_{eff} =$ | 0·78 | 0·95 | 1·18 | 1·44 | 2·04 | 2·97 | 3·37 |
| $Cr^{++}$ $\mu_{eff} =$ | 0 | 1·74 | 2·52 | 2·90 | 3·51 | 4·25 | 4·55 |

Analogous departures from Curie's law in the free state do not come in question in the second half of the iron period, as here the inversion of the multiplets makes the intervals between the lowest components

[41] B. Cabrera and A. Duperier, *J. de Physique* **6**, 121 (1925). For further information on the values of $\Delta$ for solutions see Cabrera's article in the report of the 1930 Solvay Congress, also Stoner, *Magnetism and Atomic Structure*, p. 127.

large compared to $kT$. Unfortunately there is a dearth of data, especially at low temperatures, on the temperature behaviour of the moments of the ions in the first half. In particular, no adequate temperature data are available for $Cr^{++}$ and $Mn^{+++}$, which resemble $Eu^{+++}$ inasmuch as the free magneton number drops to zero at $T = 0$. However, Woltjer [42] finds that $CrCl_3$ obeys the formula $\chi = N\beta^2(3\cdot61)^2/3k(T-32\cdot5)$ down to about $136°\,K$. The susceptibility thus increases more rapidly with decreasing temperature than according to Curie's law, whereas we have seen above that the effective magneton number of the free $Cr^{+++}$ ion instead diminishes with decreasing temperature, giving a departure from Curie's law in the opposite direction. This difference shows vividly how 'un-gas-like' are conditions in salts of the iron group, in marked contrast to the rare earths. De Haas and Gorter find $Cr_2(SO_4)_3K_2SO_4.24H_2O$ follows Curie's law almost perfectly down even to $14°\,K$. Turning to measurements at somewhat higher temperatures, Honda and Ishiwara [43] find that $CrCl_3$, $Cr_2(SO_4)_3$, and $Cr_2O_3.7H_2O$ all approximately obey Curie's law throughout the entire temperature range about $100$–$800°\,K$ they studied, barring oxidation effects at high temperatures and Weiss $\Delta$-corrections important only at low temperatures. This is in accord with the theory of § 73, whereby the quenching effect effaces the multiplet structure, and yields Eq. (1), thus restoring Curie's law.

*Cryomagnetic Anomalies.* We have already mentioned that (6) fails below a certain critical temperature, usually about $70°\,K$. This is at least in part understandable on the ground that the inequality (4) is less apt to be fulfilled at low temperatures, so that the coupling between spin and orbit becomes more important. Usually below the critical temperature the susceptibility increases less rapidly with decreasing temperature than predicted by (6), which is just what we should expect if the spin ceases to be free.

At very low temperatures more anomalies than merely departure from the simple temperature variation (6) sometimes manifest themselves. It is found that at the temperatures of liquid hydrogen the susceptibilities of $CoCl_2$, $CrCl_3$, $FeCl_2$, and $NiCl_2$, also $Fe_2(SO_4)_3$, are all

[42] H. R. Woltjer, *Leiden Communications* 173 b.

[43] T. Ishiwara, *Sci. Rep. Tohoku Univ.* **3**, 303 (1914); Honda and Ishiwara, *ibid.* **4**, 215 (1915). They find that the susceptibility of $Cr_2O_3$ decreases only very slowly as the temperature is raised, in marked contrast to $CrCl_3$ or $Cr_2O_3.7H_2O$. The meaning of this is not clear. The departure from Curie's law for $Cr_2O_3$ are, to be sure, in the same direction as for the free $Cr^{+++}$ ion, but it is hard to believe that in the oxide the $Cr^{+++}$ ion is more free than elsewhere, although it is conceivable that there is different crystalline symmetry in the other salts. In general, the behaviour in the vicinity of $1000°\,K.$ is very irregular for the different chromic salts presumably because of chemical effects.

dependent on the field strength $H$, in some cases increasing ($NiCl_2$, $CoCl_2$), in others decreasing ($CrCl_3$) or even increasing and then decreasing ($FeCl_2$) as the field strength is increased.[44] One has here a sort of incipient ferromagnetism, but not true ferromagnetism, in that there is no saturation or enormously high susceptibility. The explanation is probably that the exchange forces between magnetic ions, which Heisenberg shows can create ferromagnetism, may be vital at very low temperatures even though not at higher ones, as the importance of interaction energies is always gauged by comparing them with $kT$. This seems plausible since the chlorides have less magnetic dilution than many salts, so that exchange forces may be relatively more important than in the others.

We must not give the impression that all compounds of atoms of the iron group with atoms not belonging to this group are not ferromagnetic except possibly at very low temperatures. Ishiwara,[45] for instance, finds that certain nitrides of Mn are ferromagnetic above room temperatures. The forces tending to create ferromagnetism are thus here stronger than in the chlorides; possibly this has something to do with the fact that the normal state of the N atom is a quartet state. Pyrrhotite (approximately $Fe_7S_8$), magnetite ($Fe_3O_4$), haematite ($Fe_2O_3$), and the Heusler alloys are well-known examples of ferromagnetic compounds consisting only in part of atoms of the iron group. Generally speaking, the sulphides and oxides of this group, even when merely para- rather than ferromagnetic, often do not conform at all to Eq. (1) (cf. note 43). This is in marked contrast to the rare earths, where the oxides behave nearly as regularly as hydrated sulphates (§ 58). Oxides have less magnetic dilution and more symmetric and simple crystal structures than salts composed of a variety of atoms, so that we need not be surprised that they often do not obey Eq. (1).

It may be noted that Williams[46] finds that at room temperatures the pure rare earth metals, in distinction to the salts thereof, exhibit susceptibilities dependent on field strength. This is probably the same sort of phenomenon as that of the chlorides of the iron group at low temperatures, as a true state of intense ferromagnetism has not been reached but yet $\chi$ depends on $H$. That pure rare earths are thus less ferromagnetic than pure iron is doubtless because the deep sequestering

[44] Woltjer and Onnes, *Leiden Communications* 173; Woltjer and Wiersma, *ibid.* 201 a. The dependence on field strength at low temperatures was first observed in ferric sulphate by Onnes and Oosterhuis, *ibid.* 129 b.

[45] T. Ishiwara, *Sci. Rep. Tohoku Univ.* 5, 53 (1916).

[46] E. H. Williams, *Phys. Rev.* 29, 218 (1927).

of the $4f$ orbits makes the inter-atomic exchange forces smaller than in the iron group.

*Crystalline Dissymmetries.* The data which we have previously quoted have been for powders or other preparations in which the various crystalline axes cannot be isolated. In a few cases it has been found possible to use single crystals and so measure susceptibilities along the different crystal axes. Different salts behave quite differently. (We, of course, discuss primarily only paramagnetic crystals; ferromagnetic are much more complicated.) Three distinct cases which arise are:

(I) Magnetically isotropic crystals. As an example, gadolinium ethyl sulphate [47] is found to obey Curie's law with the same constant for all three axes to within one part in a thousand.

(II) Crystals in which the constant $C$ in (6) is the same for the different axes, but the constant $\Delta$ is different. As an example, Jackson [48] finds that $CoSO_4(NH_4)_2SO_4 . 6H_2O$ has $\Delta = 9 \cdot 8$, 52, 15 respectively for various axes. Usually, though not invariably, the magnitude of $\Delta$ is least along the axes along which the atoms are spaced most sparsely, in accord with the general proposition enunciated by Onnes and Oosterhuis that $\Delta$ decreases when the 'magnetic dilution' becomes greater. This is in qualitative agreement with our interpretation of $\Delta$ as due to inter-atomic forces, although a quantitative theory for crystals is wanting.

(III ?) Crystals in which the Curie constant $C$ has different values for the principal axes. Jackson and de Haas [49] report that in $MnSO_4(NH_4)_2SO_4 . 6H_2O$ the effective Bohr magneton numbers are $6 \cdot 9$, $5 \cdot 9$, and $4 \cdot 6$ for the three principal axes. As regards theory, the analysis of Chapter VII will yield Curie's law with different constants for the different axes if one abandons the isotropy relations given on p. 193, Chapter VII, and instead makes the supposition that the effect of the quantum number $m$ on the energy is large compared to $kT$. Then only the diagonal elements of the moment matrix contribute appreciably to the susceptibility. This, however, would involve quenching most of the susceptibility of the free ion, and seems irreconcilible with the fact that Jackson and Onnes find that the mean susceptibility for all three axes has the same value as for the free ion. An even greater difficulty is that it is hard to imagine appreciable forces causing magnetic dissymmetry when the ions are in $S$ states, as are those of $Mn^{++}$, Furthermore, according to the measurements of Rabi, [49a] the magnetic anisotropy of $MnSO_4(NH_4)_2SO_4 . 6H_2O$ at room temperature does not exceed one per cent., which is convincing evidence that the constant $C$ does not really depend much on the axis. It is therefore noteworthy that very recently K. S. Krishnan [49b]

[47] Jackson and Onnes, *Leiden Communications* 168 a (1923).

[48] L. C. Jackson, *Leiden Communications* 163; *Phil. Trans. Roy. Soc.* **224**, 1 (1923); **226**, 107 (1926).          [49] Jackson and de Haas, *Leiden Communications* 187.

[49a] I. I. Rabi, *Phys. Rev.* **29**, 174 (1927).

[49b] K. S. Krishnan, *Zeits. f. Physik,* **71**, 137 (1931).

claims to have found a computational error in the paper of Jackson and de Haas, and states that when proper corrections are made the dissymmetry proves to be of the usual type II.[50]

One would expect the magnetic dissymmetries in crystals to be due primarily to distortion effects involving the orbital angular momentum at least indirectly. The magnetic moment may well arise almost entirely from the spin magnetic moment and the anisotropy be in conjunction with the coupling of orbital and spin magnetic moment within a given atom. This coupling may have some disturbing effect because the left side of (4) is not negligible compared to the right, and need not be isotropic when the orbital angular momentum is exposed to an external field. The anisotropy of the crystal then makes itself felt directly on the orbital angular momentum, and hence indirectly on the spin. The beginnings of a theory based on this idea may be detected in interesting recent work by Powell,[51] though primarily in connexion with ferro- rather than paramagnetism. He subjects the spin to a Weiss molecular field having the same symmetry as the crystal. This may be regarded as a crude portrayal of the fact that the coupling $\langle 3 \rangle$ of spin and orbit will indirectly subject the spin to forces having the same type of symmetry as the crystal if the orbit is itself first quenched by the crystalline fields associated with $\langle 2 \rangle$. Powell's model is, of course, merely a substitute for the real dynamics connected with $\langle 2 \rangle$ and $\langle 3 \rangle$, but he shows that it can account quite nicely for certain crystalline dissymmetries in the magnetization curves of iron and nickel.

It should be particularly noted that the exchange forces between atoms, which create effectively a coupling between spins, do not create any magnetic anisotropy in the crystal. This is one of the consequences of Heisenberg's theory of ferromagnetism (§ 77) and is one of our main reasons for attributing the anisotropies to effects involving the orbital angular momentum.

This idea that orbital distortions cause most of the magnetic aniso- tropy seems to be nicely confirmed by the almost perfect magnetic isotropy of crystals of gadolinium ethyl sulphate. The $Gd^{+++}$ ion is in a $^8S$ state and so has none of the complications coming from orbital angular momentum. Also, Rabi[49a] finds manganous salts much more

---

[50] Besides the measurements on cobalt ammonium sulphate quoted above, Jackson measured the three principal susceptibilities of $NiSO_4 . 7H_2O$, while Foex had previously measured those of siderose. (*Annales de Physique*, **16**, 174 (1921). In each case the dis- symmetry was found to be of the type II rather than III.

[51] F. C. Powell, *Proc. Roy. Soc.* **130A**, 167 (1930). Fowler and Powell, *Proc. Camb. Phil. Soc.* **27**, 280 (1931).

isotropic magnetically than nickel, cobalt, or ferrous ones. This is what one would expect since the $Mn^{++}$ ion is in a $^6S$ state.

Even without coupling to the orbits, there can be some slight anisotropy in the part of the susceptibility coming from the spin because of the purely magnetic forces between the spins of different atoms. By a classical calculation, whose results no doubt hold in quantum mechanics, Becker[52] has shown that no anisotropy arises from this cause as long as the crystal is cubic. Also, Kramers[53] has shown that even in an $S$ state a fine multiplet structure, interfering somewhat with the freedom of the spin, comes into existence as soon as the atom is subject to a non-central field. Both these potential causes of magnetic anisotropy are second-order effects, as magnetic forces between different atoms are small, and as the Kramers fine structure effect is very narrow. However, there are reasons for believing that crystalline dissymmetries in magnetization are themselves a secondary thing in origin.

## 75. The Palladium, Platinum, and Uranium Groups

Here respectively $4d$, $5d$, and $6d$ inner shells are in process of development. The structural situation is thus like that in the iron group in that the incomplete shell is one of $d$ electrons, with a capacity of ten. The table on p. 312 sets forth the available experimental data, in comparison with the theory for free ions, and with the assumption that the spin only is effective, which was found so fruitful in the iron group. We include as ions illustrative of the various configurations only the smattering assortment with various valencies, for which experimental data are available. The salts employed by Cabrera,[54] by Bose,[55] and by Guthrie and Bourland[56] are the ordinary anhydrous chlorides, except that the values in parentheses are for oxides, and except for the values by Bose to which asterisks are attached. The latter are respectively for $KTaF_6$, $Th(CO_3)_2$, $K_2W(OH)Cl_5$, $U(C_2O_4)_2$, $K_3MoCl_6 . 12H_2O$, $K_3W_2Cl_9$, $2IrCl_3 . 3H_2O$. Thus the values designated by asterisks usually represent measurements on more complex salts of more magnetic dilution than the other data. The value for $Mo^{4+}$ ($MoO_2$) is by Berkman and Zoeller[57]

---

[52] R. Becker, *Zeits. f. Physik*, **62**, 253 (1930); related other work by G. S. Mahajani, *Phil. Trans. Roy. Soc.* **228**, 63 (1929); N. S. Akulov, *Zeits. f. Physik*, **52**, 389; **54**, 582; **57**, 249; **59**, 254; **64**, 559, 817 (1930); L. W. McKeehan, *Rev. Mod. Phys.* **2**, 477 (1930); *Nature*, **126**, 952 (1930).    [53] H. A. Kramers, *Zeits. f. Physik*, **53**, 422 (1929).

[54] B. Cabrera, *Atti del Congresso (Como) Internazionale dei Fisici*, i. 95 (1927).

[55] D. M. Bose, *ibid.* p. 119, or *Zeits. f. Physik*, **48**, 716 (1928). Besides the data given in the table, he finds a magneton number of 3·71 for $Mo^{+++}$ in $Mo(SCN)_6(NH_3)_4 . 4H_2O$.

[56] A. N. Guthrie and L. T. Bourland, *Phys. Rev.* **37**, 303 (1931)

[57] S. Berkman and H. Zoeller, *Zeits. f. Phys. Chem.* **124**, 318 (1927).

| Term. | Ion | | | Theoretical $\mu_{\text{eff}}$ | | Experimental $\mu_{\text{eff}}$ | | |
|---|---|---|---|---|---|---|---|---|
| | Pd. Gr. | Pt. Gr. | Ur. Gr. | Free Ion | Spin only | Cabrera[54] | Bose[55] | Guthrie & Bourl.[56] |
| $^1S$ | .. | Ta$^{5+}$ | Th$^{4+}$ | 0·0 | 0·0 | .. | diam.* | .. |
| $d\ ^2D_{3/2}$ | .. | .. | .. | 1·55 | 1·73 | .. | .. | .. |
| | Mo$^{4+}$ | .. | .. | 1·63 | 2·83 | (0·2) | .. | .. |
| $d^2\ ^3F_2$ | .. | W$^{4+}$ | .. | 1·63 | 2·83 | .. | 1·8* | .. |
| | .. | .. | U$^{4+}$ | 1·63 | 2·83 | .. | 2·4* | .. |
| $d^3\ ^4F_{3/2}$ | Mo$^{+++}$ | .. | .. | 0·77 | 3·87 | .. | 3·6* | .. |
| | .. | W$^{+++}$ | .. | 0·77 | 3·87 | .. | 0·4* | .. |
| $d^4\ ^5D_0$ | Ru$^{++++}$ | .. | .. | 0·0 | 4·90 | .. | .. | (0·6) |
| | Ru$^{+++}$ | .. | .. | 5·92 | 5·92 | 2·1 | 0·3 | 1·8 |
| $d^5\ ^6S$ | .. | Os$^{+++}$ | .. | 5·92 | 5·92 | .. | diam. | .. |
| | .. | Ir$^{4+}$ | .. | 5·92 | 5·92 | .. | 1·9 | (0·7) |
| | Rh$^{+++}$ | .. | .. | 6·70 | 4·90 | 0·3 | 0·4 | (0·4) |
| $d^6\ ^5D_4$ | .. | Os$^{++}$ | .. | 6·70 | 4·90 | 0·4 | .. | .. |
| | .. | Ir$^{+++}$ | .. | 6·70 | 4·90 | 0·3 | 0·5* | diam. |
| | .. | Pt$^{4+}$ | .. | .. | .. | .. | diam. | diam. |
| $d^7\ ^4F_{9/2}$ | .. | .. | .. | 6·64 | 3·87 | .. | .. | .. |
| $d^8\ ^3F_4$ | Pd$^{++}$ | .. | .. | 5·59 | 2·83 | 0·1 | diam. | .. |
| | .. | Pt$^{++}$ | .. | 5·59 | 2·83 | diam. | diam. | .. |
| $d^9\ ^2D_{5/2}$ | .. | .. | .. | 3·55 | 1·73 | .. | .. | .. |

rather than Cabrera. In connexion with the measurements on oxides, we must remember that even in the iron group the oxides often had a different and more complicated behaviour than the ordinary salts. Consequently data on oxides can scarcely furnish a crucial test of the theory.

The column headed 'spin only' gives the magneton numbers yielded by Eq. (1), while the theoretical values for free ions have been calculated under the assumption that the multiplets are infinitely wide compared to $kT$, permitting the use of Eq. (10), Chap. IX, with $\alpha = 0$. This is legitimate since in the Pd, Pt, and U groups the multiplets are much wider than in the iron group.[58]

The agreement between the measurements of Cabrera and Bose is

[58] X-ray data show that the screening constant for the multiplets involved in the Pd group is about 24. This shows that the multiplets are here roughly about 6 times as wide as in the iron group, so that Mo$^{+++}$ and Ru$^{++++}$ should have about the same magneton numbers at room temperatures as Cr$^{+++}$ and Cr$^{++}$ respectively at 50° K. Reference to the table on p. 306 shows that the theoretical values for Mo$^{+++}$ and Ru$^{4+}$ thus become approximately 1·2 and 2·5 when the corrections for finite multiplet width are considered. This value for Mo$^{+++}$ is not enough greater than that for $\Delta\nu = \infty$ to shed much light on the glaring general discrepancy between theory and experiment, while in the case of Ru$^{++++}$ experimental data are available only for the oxide. The corresponding change in the Pt and U groups is even less important, as the multiplets are still greater. The correction for finite multiplet width would be significant if adequate measurements were available for the $d^4$ configuration, which is much the most sensitive to this correction. In configurations other than $d^3$ and $d^4$ this correction becomes of subordinate importance.

none too good,[59] but the data are adequate to show that the magnetic behaviour of the Pd, Pt, and U groups is exceedingly complicated, and that here the susceptibilities do not conform except in isolated instances either to the theory for free ions so successful in the rare earths, or to the 'spin only' theory characteristic of the iron group. This is the exact opposite of the frequent conjectures made before the recent experiments that the heavier atoms with incomplete $3d$ configurations would be more amenable to theory than the iron group because the multiplet structures are wider and hence less easily distorted.

An outstanding characteristic revealed by the table is the very low experimental susceptibilities, especially in the second half of the period. One naturally seeks to explain this on the ground that the 'internal magnetic' coupling $\langle 3 \rangle$ is stronger than the inter-atomic forces responsible for the spacial separation, so that an inner quantum number $J$ can still be employed even in the presence of $\langle 2 \rangle$. One can then show that the spacial separation will tend to quench the total angular momentum rather than just the orbital part, for it is now necessary to treat the perturbations in the order $\langle 3 \rangle$ followed by $\langle 2 \rangle$ rather than $\langle 2 \rangle$ by $\langle 3 \rangle$, and so the argument used in § 73 to demonstrate quenching of orbital angular momentum now demonstrates quenching of the total angular momentum. Even should $\langle 3 \rangle$ not be larger than $\langle 2 \rangle$, it is quite possible that the inequality (4) is not satisfied, so that the spin is not free and the susceptibility is hence low. On this view that the spacial separation should leave the multiplet structure intact in heavier atoms one would expect the theory for free ions to be more nearly applicable than the assumption that the spin only is free. This is supported by the fact that the susceptibilities of $Ru^{4+}$, $W^{+++}$, and $W^{4+}$ conform much more closely to the values calculated for 'free ions' than for 'spin only', but the latter assumption seems to succeed better in $Mo^{+++}$ and $U^{4+}$.

A probably insuperable objection to the explanation attempted in the preceding paragraph is that abnormally low susceptibilities are observed for $Ru^{+++}$, $Os^{+++}$, and $Ir^{4+}$, despite the fact that these ions are in $^6S$ states. This is in marked contrast to the close conformity to theory of the analogous $Fe^{+++}$, $Mn^{++}$ ions in the middle of the iron group. In $S$ states it is, of course, no longer possible to impute the quenching of magnetic moment to ordinary (i.e. non-exchange) inter-atomic forces

---

[59] Perhaps a little of the discrepancy is due to different assumptions concerning the corrections for diamagnetism which are omitted in some cases. The latter become of course, relatively more important when the effective magneton numbers are as small as they are for many of the salts in the table. However, the diamagnetic corrections are inadequate to shed any light on the discrepancies between theory and experiment.

which act upon the orbital angular momentum and hence indirectly on the spin if the multiplets are wide. Three possibilities seem to present themselves: (a) that the Hund theory of spectral terms is inapplicable and that the lowest-lying term for $d^5$ is here not an $S$ one; (b) that the exchange forces between paramagnetic atoms are sufficiently large to quench the spin after the fashion to be explained in § 80; (c) that the ions do not exist in monatomic form, but instead form complexes or molecule-ions of zero resultant spin, possibly through electron-sharing, or something of the kind, so that one might have, e.g. $W_2$ instead of W ions. Alternative (a) does not seem likely, although some slight anomalies in the position of spectral terms have been found in the Pd and Pt groups.[60] Cases (b) and (c) resemble each other in that both suppose that the exchange forces tend to create units of zero resultant spin, in one case micro-crystalline, the other molecular. If (b) is correct the anomalies should disappear if the 'magnetic dilution' is increased by adding more water molecules of hydration, or otherwise, while in (c) the anomalies should still persist when this is done, as the molecular units still remain. (This difference is really the definition of the distinction between (b) and (c).) Measurements for $Ru^{+++}$, $Os^{+++}$, $Ir^{4+}$ in salts of different degrees of magnetic dilution would thus be of considerable interest, as in the anhydrous chlorides so far employed the density of paramagnetic atoms is probably sufficiently high so as not to preclude the explanation (b). However, (c) seems more probable, as the possibility of molecular units is cited by both Cabrera and Bose. Cabrera[54] notes that Werner and Pfeiffer have remarked that there is considerable physical-chemical evidence that the halides of Fe, Co, Ni are true salts that can be dissociated electrolytically, but that in those of Ru, Rh, Pd and of Os, Ir, Pt the atomic clustering effects seem to be predominant, and it is questionable whether their halides are truly saline in nature.

It will be noted that in the iron group as well as in the groups now under consideration the ideal theory for free ions seems to apply somewhat better in the first than in the second half of the period. This seems reasonable, as the inter-atomic perturbing forces may well increase with the number of electrons in the incomplete group.

One point at least stands out clearly. When none of the simple formulae are obeyed, Curie's law should not be followed, and Cabrera does indeed find complicated temperature variations for the salts of the

---

[60] Cf. Hund, *Linienspektren*, diagram p. 166. The peculiarities are found in the arc spectra, and are presumably much less likely to occur in the doubly and triply enhanced spectra.

Pd and Pt groups which he has studied. In general, the graph of $1/\chi$ against $T$ is curved rather than linear as given by (1) or (6). Usually the susceptibility decreases somewhat as the temperature is increased, but in one case ($PdCl_2$) it actually increases. The susceptibilities of $RhCl_3$, $IrCl_3$, $OsCl_2$ are nearly independent of temperature, suggesting immediately the predominance of 'high-frequency elements'. On the other hand, Guthrie and Bourland find that $RuCl_3$ follows Curie's law with $\Delta = 37$.

Further experimental data on the different salts of the Pd and Pt groups are greatly to be desired. Without them further discussion would be too speculative.

# HEISENBERG'S THEORY OF FERROMAGNETISM. FURTHER TOPICS IN SOLIDS

## 76. The Heisenberg Exchange Effect

An outstanding characteristic feature of the new quantum mechanics is the so-called 'Austausch' or exchange effect, first discovered by Heisenberg.[1] It is concerned with the degeneracy associated with the possibility of two electrons trading places, and is best explained by considering first a system with only two electrons and with neglect of spin. First suppose that the electrons do not influence each other and that they are subject to fields derived from similar potential functions, so that the Schrödinger wave equation is

$$\nabla_1^2 \Psi + \nabla_2^2 \Psi + \frac{8\pi^2 m}{h^2}[W - V(x_1, y_1, z_1) - V(x_2, y_2, z_2)]\Psi = 0. \qquad (1)$$

A solution of this equation is

$$\Psi_{\mathrm{I}} = \Psi_k(x_1, y_1, z_1)\Psi_m(x_2, y_2, z_2), \qquad W = W_k + W_m, \qquad (2)$$

where $\Psi_k$, $\Psi_m$ are solutions of the Schrödinger equation for a single electron subject to a potential $V$, as in the absence of interaction it is, of course, possible to consider each electron separately rather than together as in (1). We shall suppose the wave functions $\Psi_k$, $\Psi_m$ are real, orthogonal, and normalized to unity.[2] The physical interpretation of solution (2) is that electron 1 is in the state $k$ and electron 2 in the state $m$ (not necessarily states belonging to the same atom). This solution is, however, not the only one belonging to the energy $W_k + W_m$. An alternative solution is clearly

$$\Psi_{\mathrm{II}} = \Psi_k(x_2, y_2, z_2)\Psi_m(x_1, y_1, z_1), \qquad W = W_k + W_m, \qquad (3)$$

in which the electrons have traded places as compared to (2). More generally, any linear combination of (2) and (3) is a solution. The question now arises as to what is the proper combination to use when the degeneracy of interchange is removed by adding to the potential energy in (1) a potential energy $V_{12}$ of interaction between the two

---

[1] W. Heisenberg, *Zeits. f. Physik*, **38**, 411 (1926). The same effect was also discovered almost simultaneously by Dirac, *Proc. Roy. Soc.* **112**A, 661 (1926).

[2] The restriction to real solutions involves no essential loss of generality for our purposes, and avoids the necessity of introducing complex coefficients in equations such as (4) or for distinguishing between $J_{12}$ and $J_{21}$. The requirement of orthogonality is usually not met in the important case that $k$, $m$ relate to different atoms, but the resulting error is not great if the wave functions of the different atoms do not overlap too much (cf. Heitler and London, *Zeits. f. Physik*, **44**, 455 (1927)).

electrons, which we may suppose symmetrical in the coordinates $x_1$, $y_1$, $z_1$ and $x_2$, $y_2$, $z_2$. Most readers doubtless already know that the answer is the 'symmetric' and 'antisymmetric' combinations

$$\Psi_{\text{sym}} = \frac{1}{2^{\frac{1}{2}}}(\Psi_{\text{I}} + \Psi_{\text{II}}), \qquad \Psi_{\text{ant}} = \frac{1}{2^{\frac{1}{2}}}(\Psi_{\text{I}} - \Psi_{\text{II}}). \tag{4}$$

One way of proving (4) is to note that (4) diagonalizes the energy as far as the exchange degeneracy is concerned, since one can easily show that the fundamental quadrature (14), Chap. VI, vanishes if $\psi_{n'}$, $\psi_n$ are respectively symmetrical and antisymmetrical or vice versa, and if $f$ is a symmetrical function, such as $V_{12}$. Or one can set up the secular equation corresponding to the pair of wave functions (2) and (3). This is

$$\begin{vmatrix} W_0 + K_{12} - W & J_{12} \\ J_{12} & W_0 + K_{12} - W \end{vmatrix} = 0 \tag{5}$$

where $W_0$ is the energy in the absence of the interaction term $V_{12}$, and where

$$K_{12} = \int \cdots \int \Psi_{\text{I}}^* V_{12}\, \Psi_{\text{I}}\, dv_1 dv_2 = \int \cdots \int \Psi_{\text{II}}^* V_{12}\, \Psi_{\text{II}}\, dv_1 dv_2, \tag{6}$$

$$J_{12} = \int \cdots \int \Psi_{\text{I}}^* V_{12}\, \Psi_{\text{II}}\, dv_1 dv_2. \tag{7}$$

The solutions of (5) are

$$W = W_0 + K_{12} + J_{12}, \qquad W = W_0 + K_{12} - J_{12}, \tag{8}$$

and correspond respectively to the solutions $S(\text{I};1) = S(\text{II};1)$ and $S(\text{I};2) = -S(\text{II};2)$ for the simultaneous linear equations of type (33), Chap. VI, associated with the determinant (5). This agrees with (4). If we grant (4) instead of using perturbation theory the result (8), of course, follows directly from the fundamental quadrature (14) of Chapter VI on taking $n' = n$, $f = V_{12}$ and using one of the wave functions (4).

The Pauli exclusion principle demands that one use only antisymmetric wave functions.[3] The symmetry properties, however, are profoundly modified by inclusion of the spin. If we neglect the 'magnetic' coupling between the spin and orbital angular momenta, the wave functions are the product of the orbital and spin ones. Therefore, when the orbital wave function is symmetrical, the spin one must be antisymmetrical and vice versa. Now it can be shown that in a two-electron problem the spin wave function is symmetrical when the spin quantum number $S$ is 1 and is antisymmetrical when it is 0.[4] In other words, the

[3] The interpretation of the exclusion principle in terms of the symmetry of the wave functions appears to have first been given by Heisenberg and by Dirac, $l.c.$[1]

[4] Cf, for instance, Dirac, *The Principles of Quantum Mechanics*, p. 214, or Sommerfeld, *Wellenmechanischer Ergänzungsband*, p. 274.

triplet and singlet spectra (e.g. ortho- and parhelium) are respectively antisymmetrical and symmetrical in the orbital part of the wave function. Let $\mathbf{s}_1$ and $\mathbf{s}_2$ be the spin angular momentum vectors of the two electrons, measured in multiples of the quantum unit $h/2\pi$ as in previous chapters. The characteristic values of the matrix $(\mathbf{s}_1+\mathbf{s}_2)^2$, the square of the magnitude of their resultant, are $S(S+1)$, with $S$ equal to 0 or 1. (By the characteristic values of a matrix are meant its diagonal elements after it is converted into a diagonal matrix by a proper canonical transformation. Cf. § 35.) Now $\mathbf{s}_1^2$ and $\mathbf{s}_2^2$ are invariably diagonal matrices whose diagonal elements are all $\frac{1}{2}(\frac{1}{2}+1)=\frac{3}{4}$, as the spin quantum number for one electron is invariably $\frac{1}{2}$; in other words, $\mathbf{s}_1^2$ and $\mathbf{s}_2^2$ are '$c$-numbers' in Dirac's terminology. As $(\mathbf{s}_1+\mathbf{s}_2)^2 = \mathbf{s}_1^2+\mathbf{s}_2^2+2\mathbf{s}_1\cdot\mathbf{s}_2$ it now follows that the characteristic values of the scalar product $\mathbf{s}_1\cdot\mathbf{s}_2$ are $\frac{1}{2}(0-2\cdot\frac{3}{4})=-\frac{3}{4}$ and $\frac{1}{2}(2-2\cdot\frac{3}{4})=\frac{1}{4}$ corresponding respectively to $S=0$ and $S=1$, or to the symmetric and antisymmetric orbital solutions. The characteristic values of the potential energy $V_{12}$ of interaction between the electrons are seen from (8) to be $K_{12}+J_{12}$ and $K_{12}-J_{12}$ respectively for the symmetrical and antisymmetrical orbital solutions, as the remaining terms in the Hamiltonian function have the characteristic value $W_0$ independent of the symmetry. Thus the matrix $V_{12}$ has the characteristic value $K_{12}+J_{12}$ when $\mathbf{s}_1\cdot\mathbf{s}_2$ has the characteristic value $-\frac{3}{4}$, and $K_{12}-J_{12}$ when the latter has $+\frac{1}{4}$. In other words, $V_{12}-K_{12}+\frac{1}{2}J_{12}+2J_{12}\mathbf{s}_1\cdot\mathbf{s}_2$ has the characteristic values zero. Now a matrix whose characteristic values are all zero is identically zero regardless of the system of representation, as any canonical transformation applied to a null matrix clearly still gives only a null matrix. Consequently we have the matrix equality

$$V_{12} = K_{12}-\tfrac{1}{2}J_{12}-2J_{12}\,\mathbf{s}_1\cdot\mathbf{s}_2, \qquad\qquad \langle 9\rangle$$

which applies regardless of whether the matrices in question have been transformed to diagonal form.

Eq. $\langle 9\rangle$ shows that the two electrons behave as though there were a strong coupling between their two spins which apart from an additive constant is proportional to the scalar product of these spin angular momenta, or to the cosine of the angle between the two spin vectors. The latter is precisely the dependence of angle found in one term[5] of the mutual potential energy of two dipoles, so that the exchange effect has a partial semblance to a very powerful magnetic coupling between the spins. This is not at all the same as saying that actually there is

---

[5] The mutual potential energy of two dipoles is $\mu_1\cdot\mu_2/r^3-3(\mu_1\cdot\mathbf{r})(\mu_2\cdot\mathbf{r})/r^5$. Thus only the first term is of the type form $\langle 10\rangle$.

a real magnetic coupling of such magnitude, as the actual magnetic forces are so very weak that we have neglected them entirely in the present connexion. The semblance of large direct coupling between the spins is only because the exclusion principle requires one type of orbital solution when the spins are parallel and another when they are anti-parallel. Nevertheless, the interpretation ⟨9⟩, due to Dirac, of the exchange effect as formally equivalent to coupling between spins is exceedingly useful, as it enables us to picture and also to follow quantitatively the workings of the exchange effect by means of the vector model. The large par-ortho energy separations were shrouded in mystery before the new mechanics, as they require the constant of proportionality $J_{12}$ in the coupling ⟨9⟩ to be fairly large. This trouble now disappears, as $J_{12}$ is an exchange integral rather than a small magnetic factor.

Let us now pass to systems with more than two electrons, say a crystal composed of $N$ atoms each having $Z$ electrons. The exchange degeneracy now becomes exceedingly complicated. It is, in fact, $(NZ)!$-fold rather than twofold as above, since in order to treat the inter-atomic forces such as interest us for magnetism in solids it is necessary to consider the permutations of electrons not necessarily in the same atom of the crystal. Even the problem of the $Z!$-fold exchange degeneracy for a single atom is complicated. Regardless of the number of electrons, the Pauli exclusion principle requires that the wave functions still be antisymmetric in any two electrons if both the spin and orbital co-ordinates be interchanged, but they will no longer in general be symmetrical or antisymmetrical in the orbital and spin parts considered separately. (The latter characteristic is peculiar to systems with only two electrons.) Eq. ⟨9⟩ shows that this is equivalent to saying that the spins of two electrons taken at random in the crystal (or even in the same atom) will not in general be parallel or anti-parallel, a result which seems quite obvious. The proper linear combinations of the $(NZ)!$ original wave functions are usually deduced by rather involved group theory. We owe to Dirac [6] and Slater [7] the elucidation that this is not

[6] P. A. M. Dirac, *Proc. Roy. Soc.* **123A**, 714 (1929), or *The Principles of Quantum Mechanics*, Chap. XI.

[7] Another method of avoiding group theory has been given by Slater, *Phys. Rev.* **35**, 509 (1930). Slater's method could doubtless be used to obtain the mean values (22–3) which we calculate in § 78. In fact it is used by Bloch (*Zeits. f. Physik*, **57**, 545, 1930) and Pauli (Report of the 1930 Solvay Congress) to obtain the mean energy (22), or its equivalent, but they do not give the more difficult computation of the mean square energy (23). Dirac's and Slater's procedures resemble each other in that their strength arises from recognizing at the outset that the exclusion principle severely restricts the

really necessary because the exclusion principle limits so severely the allowable 'characters' in the group theory. Dirac points out that the important results can instead all be obtained in an elementary way from the fact that Eq. $\langle 9 \rangle$ shows that any two electrons $k$, $l$ in the crystal can be considered as having their spins coupled together by a potential of the form

$$-2 J_{kl} \mathbf{s}_k \cdot \mathbf{s}_l, \qquad\qquad \langle 10 \rangle$$

where the coupling constant or exchange integral $J_{kl}$ will depend on the states assumed to be occupied by these two electrons, $k$ and $l$, before allowing for the permutations. We here drop the first two right-hand terms of $\langle 9 \rangle$ as they do not depend on the orientations of the spin, and are of no interest for our problems in magnetism. These terms should, of course, be added when one requires absolute, as distinct from relative, energies. When there are more than two electrons, solution of the exchange degeneracy does not transform the matrix $\langle 10 \rangle$ into diagonal form, but only the expression

$$-2 \sum J_{kl} \mathbf{s}_k \cdot \mathbf{s}_l, \qquad\qquad \langle 11 \rangle$$

which is the total exchange energy of the crystal except for the additive term $-\frac{1}{2} \sum J_{kl}$ which we have dropped. The summation is over all the $\frac{1}{2} N Z(N Z-1)$ pairs of electrons in the crystal. The fact that individual terms in the sum $\langle 11 \rangle$ are not diagonalized does not impair the kinematical representation $\langle 10 \rangle$ of the exchange effect, as we have already mentioned that the validity of $\langle 9 \rangle$, which is basic to $\langle 10 \rangle$, $\langle 11 \rangle$, is invariant of the system of representation. We shall, for instance, show that use of $\langle 11 \rangle$ yields the mean values employed by Heisenberg in his theory of magnetism.

It is clearly to be understood that $\langle 11 \rangle$ is only an approximation, in that it embodies only the 'exchange' secular problem connected with the interaction between the various members of a family of $(N Z)!$ states having the same original energy, and neglects the interaction with the infinity of states with other unperturbed energies. An analogous approximation in the two-electron problem was made in (4)–$\langle 9 \rangle$. In other words, we use (32) rather than (15) of Chapter VI, i.e. we seek to express the perturbed wave function as a linear combination of a finite number of unperturbed wave functions, whereas an infinity is required for a complete development. This means that by solving the secular problem connected with $\langle 11 \rangle$ the energy is obtained only to a first approximation in a parameter $\lambda$ proportional to the coupling forces between electrons.

symmetry character. Slater's method is very powerful for computing purposes when spacial degeneracy in the orbital motion must be considered, but does not give quite as much kinematical insight as Dirac's.

This not only suffices to give all the essential qualitative features of the exchange effect, but is often a fair quantitative approximation in the case of inter-atomic forces, our primary interest. In the latter case the related integrals such as (6) and (7) are usually small since the wave functions of different atoms overlap but little. The most important thing for magnetism, however, is merely the fact that *the exchange effect, though entirely orbital in nature, is, because of the exclusion principle, very sensitive to the way the spin is alined, and is formally equivalent to 'cosine coupling' between the spin magnets of the various atoms.*

A very vital point is that the alinement of the spin of a given atom having a non-vanishing spin is not influenced by the interaction with atoms which have closed shells of electrons and are thus in $^1S$ states. It is not correct to say that the exchange effects disappear entirely between a pair of atoms if at least one of them is in a $^1S$ state, as there is in any case the additive exchange term $-\frac{1}{2}J_{12}$ which we have dropped in going from $\langle 9 \rangle$ to $\langle 10 \rangle$. This term, however, does not involve the spin and so is not of significance for our magnetic work. The significant part of the exchange energy for us does, however, vanish if one of the atoms is in an $S$ state. To prove this[8] consider the interaction of a given electron $k$ of one atom with a closed shell of $r$ similar electrons $(l = 1, ..., r)$ in another atom. According to $\langle 10 \rangle$ the part of the exchange energy depending on alinement of the spin is $-2J_{kl}\mathbf{s}_k \cdot \sum_l \mathbf{s}_l$. This vanishes, as $\sum \mathbf{s}_l$ is zero for a closed shell. In other words, for our purposes (viz. neglecting terms which have no alining effect on the spin), the exchange forces can be considered as existing only between the paramagnetic atoms or ions of a solid. These forces will thus be subordinate if the material has a high 'magnetic dilution', i.e. consists primarily of diamagnetic rather than paramagnetic atoms. Hence, exchange effects have played only a subordinate role in the preceding chapter.

[8] The proof here given that the expression $\langle 10 \rangle$ vanishes on being summed over a closed shell is a bit incomplete in that it takes no cognizance of the fact that in actual atoms the orbital spacial degeneracy is superposed on the exchange degeneracy. The extension of Dirac's procedure to include the former degeneracy will be given in a future paper by the writer, where Dirac's and Slater's methods will be compared in detail. It will there be shown that full generality can be achieved by allowing the coefficients $J_{12}$ to be matrix functions of the orbital angular momentum vectors. A wave function for a closed shell can be constructed by superposition and linear combination of wave functions based on $m_s, m_l$ quantization (case $(a)$, fig. 6, § 40), and the vital point is that $\sum \mathbf{s}_k \cdot \mathbf{s}_l = 0$ on summing over the two values $m_s = \pm\frac{1}{2}$ of $m_s$ possible for given $m_l$. Another proof that closed shells do not influence spins of other electrons has been given by Slater,[7] using considerations closely related to these.

## 77. Heisenberg's Theory of Ferromagnetism[9]

The explanation of ferromagnetism has long been a conundrum. The early work of Ewing, subsequently amplified by Honda and others,[10] showed that many of the phenomena of hysteresis and of magnetization in crystals could be described by assuming a large potential energy between adjacent molecular magnets. Also Weiss, in his well-known theory,[11] showed that many properties of ferromagnetic media, especially the thermal ones, could be imputed to a local field of the form $H+qM$. The portion $qM$ proportional to the intensity of magnetization $M$ is called the 'molecular field'. The great difficulty, however, has been that tremendously large values must be assumed for the constant $q$, of the order $10^4$, quite different from the value $4\pi/3$ calculated under ordinary electromagnetic assumptions (§ 5). The magnetic forces between molecules are clearly too feeble to account for such enormous values of $q$, or for the large amount of interaction between molecular magnets in the Ewing theory. Classical electrostatic forces lead to interactions of the right order of magnitude, but do not give the desired linearity of the Weiss molecular field in $M$ or, what is more or less equivalent, the right dependence of the Ewing interaction energy on the angle between the elementary magnets.[12]

This dilemma has been beautifully solved by the quantum-mechanical exchange forces described in § 76. These forces are electrostatic, but because of the constraints imposed by the Pauli exclusion principle are formally equivalent to a tremendously large coupling between spins. In fact, reference to Eq. ⟨10⟩ or ⟨11⟩ shows that this coupling is proportional to the cosine of the angle between two spins, just as in the classical theories of Weiss and Ewing. Even without the following further analysis the empirical successes of these theories are thus already qualitatively understandable.

A crystal is nothing but a large molecule. Hence, if we neglect the usually subordinate, purely magnetic coupling between spin and orbital angular momenta, the total spin of the entire crystal is conserved, like

[9] W. Heisenberg, *Zeits. f. Physik*, **49**, 619 (1928).

[10] J. A. Ewing, *Proc. Roy. Soc.* **48**, 342 (1890); *Proc. Roy. Soc. Edinb.* **47**, 141 (1927); K. Honda and J. Okubo, *Sci. Rep. Tohoku Univ.* **5**, 153; **6**, 183; **13**, 6 (1919). Summaries by Terry in *Theories of Magnetism* (Bull. Nat. Research Coun. No. 18), p. 144 or by McKeehan, *Rev. Mod. Phys.* **2**, 477 (1930).

[11] P. Weiss, *J. de Physique*, **6**, 667 (1907); **1**, 166 (1930). A good survey of the Weiss theory is given in *Theories of Magnetism*, p. 114, or Stoner's *Magnetism and Atomic Structure*, p. 75.

[12] For further discussion of this and related points and of the magnitude required for $q$ see p. 703 of Debye's article in *Handbuch der Radiologie*, vol. vi.

that of an ordinary free molecule, and its square has the characteristic values $S'(S'+1)$, where $S'$ is a whole or half-integer according as the number of electrons in the entire crystal is even or odd. Also, if we continue to neglect the magnetic forces in comparison with the larger electrostatic ones, the energy of the crystal will not depend on the orientation (as distinct from the absolute value of) its resultant spin. The truth of these propositions can be seen by invoking the formal similarity of a crystal to the arbitrary polyatomic molecule. Or they can be established more fundamentally by proving that the square $\mathbf{S}'^2 = (\sum \mathbf{s}_i)^2$ of the total spin of all the electrons of the crystal, also any Cartesian component thereof, say $S'_z$, commute in matrix multiplication with the part $\langle 11 \rangle$ of the energy which involves the spin. This can be seen from the commutation rules given in note 41 of Chapter VI. Since $\mathbf{S}'^2$, $S'_z$ commute with $\langle 11 \rangle$ and with each other, it follows that $\mathbf{S}'^2$, $S'_z$ can be assigned their characteristic values $S'(S'+1)$ and $M'_S$ in a stationary state. Instead of $S'_z$ we could equally well choose $S'_x$ or $S'_y$ for this spacial quantization, and this implies that the energy is independent of the orientation of $S'$ relative to the crystal, a result already quoted in § 74.

At this point it is perhaps well to say a word on notation. We employ primes, as in $S'$, $M'_S$, &c., to distinguish 'crystalline quantum numbers' and other expressions which relate to the entire crystal, regarded as one big molecule. Quantum numbers written in capital letters without primes, such as $S$, $M_S$, refer to a complete single atom, while those written in small letters, such as $s$, $m_s$, are, as usual, for a single electron within the atom.

If a magnetic field is applied along the $z$ direction, the $z$ component of the crystal's spin assumes a quantized value $M'_S$. Let us suppose that the crystal is composed of $n$ identical atoms each having a given spin $S$. The maximum value of $S'$ is then $nS$. The number of states $\Omega(M'_S)$ of the crystal having a given $M'_S$ is best obtained by imagining a field so strong as to break down inter-atomic coupling and give each atom individual spacial quantization of spin and orbit. That ordinary laboratory fields are not adequate to do this is immaterial since we are merely counting the number of terms. Each atom, then, has a spacial spin quantum number $M_S$, and $\Omega$ is clearly the number of different combinations of the $M_S$ consistent with the condition $M'_S = \sum M_S$. In case $S = \frac{1}{2}$, the expression for $\Omega$ takes the simple form

$$\Omega(M'_S) = \frac{n!}{(\frac{1}{2}n + M'_S)!(\frac{1}{2}n - M'_S)!}, \tag{12}$$

as here $\frac{1}{2}n+M'_S$ atoms must have $M_S=+\frac{1}{2}$, and $\frac{1}{2}n-M'_S$ must have $M_S=-\frac{1}{2}$; hence $\Omega$ is merely the number of permutations of $n$ things between two classes. For arbitrary $S$ it is readily found that

$$\Omega(M'_S) = \text{coefficient of } x^{M'_S} \text{ in } (x^S+x^{S-1}+...+x^{-S})^n. \qquad (13)$$

The number of states $\omega$ of the crystal having a given resultant spin $S'$ is[13]

$$\omega(S') = \Omega(S')-\Omega(S'+1), \qquad (14)$$

since $M'_S=-S',...,+S'$, so that $\Omega(M'_L)$ contains all states having $S' \geqslant |M'_S|$. In ferromagnetism we are interested in quite large values of $S'$. In this region $\Omega(S')\gg\Omega(S'+1)$, so that approximately

$$\omega(S') = \Omega(S'). \qquad (15)$$

The physical significance of (15) is that the great bulk of the states of a given $M'_S$ have $S' = |M'_S|$, provided $|M'_S|$ is fairly large.

Heisenberg's calculations appear to assume that the atoms are in $S$ states, but this is not really the case, as it is only necessary to suppose that the orbital angular momentum is quenched after the fashion explained in § 73. He also assumes that a given atom has an appreciable exchange coupling only with adjacent atoms, and possesses $z$ such neighbours equidistant from it. Thus $z=2$ for a linear chain, 4 for a quadratic surface grating, 6 for a simple cubic grating, 8 for body-centred cubic, and 12 for face-centred cubic. Let us further suppose that the valence electrons, or electrons not in closed shells, are in similar states. The part of the Hamiltonian function which involves inter-atomic spin coupling, and which we shall denote by $\mathcal{H}'$, is then

$$\mathcal{H}' = -2J \sum_{\text{neighbours}} \mathbf{S}_i \cdot \mathbf{S}_j. \qquad \langle 16 \rangle$$

Here $J$ is the exchange integral (7) between two valence electrons of adjacent atoms, and the summation extends over all neighbouring pairs of atoms. The result $\langle 16 \rangle$ can be seen from $\langle 9 \rangle$ or $\langle 11 \rangle$, since $\sum \mathbf{s}_k \cdot \mathbf{s}_l = \sum \mathbf{s}_k \cdot \sum \mathbf{s}_l = \mathbf{S}_i \cdot \mathbf{S}_j$ if $k$ and $l$ refer to different atoms $i$ and $j$ and if we sum over the valence electrons of both atoms. Closed shells contribute nothing to $\langle 11 \rangle$ or $\langle 16 \rangle$, as explained at the end of § 76, while exchange effects between electrons of the same atom merely give an additive constant to the energy as far as we are concerned, since we may suppose the inter-atomic forces not large enough to destroy the quantization $S$ of the spin of each individual atom.

The fundamental problem of Heisenberg's theory of ferromagnetism

---

[13] The number $\omega$ here given does not include the spacial degeneracy factor $2S'+1$ which results because different orientations yield identical energies in the absence of external fields.

is to calculate the characteristic values of $\langle 16 \rangle$ and hence the energy states belonging to various resultant spins of the crystal. Before explaining the mathematical details of how this is done, or rather circumvented, it will perhaps be illuminating to consider qualitatively three limiting cases.

1. $J/kT \gg 1$. Here the exchange coupling is so exceedingly great that the state $S' = nS$ of maximum crystalline spin has much less energy than all other states of less $S'$ and hence is the only normal state. By regarding the whole crystal as a single molecule of spin $nS$, its susceptibility is seen to be $(2nS\beta/H)B_{nS}(2nS\beta H/kT)$, where $B_{nS}$ is the Brillouin function defined in § 61. As the number $n$ of atoms is very great, virtually any field is sufficient to make $n\beta H/kT \gg 1$, and so $B_{nS} = 1$, thus giving the full saturation magnetization $2nS\beta$. The crystal is then, so to speak, infinitely ferromagnetic. In fact it would possess a magnetic moment even without an external field. This difficulty is, of course, avoided by supposing that our crystal is really a micro-crystal and that the macro-crystal is composed of a large number of micro-crystals, whose spins have random orientations and hence compensate each other without an external alining field.

2. $|J/kT| \ll 1$. Here the inter-atomic exchange coupling is negligible, and the susceptibility will be $\chi = 4NS(S+1)\beta^2/3kT$, disregarding the here negligible saturation effects. This is the case which arises in paramagnetic iron salts (Chap. XI). We may here remark that the derivation of the Langevin-Debye formula given in Chapter VII can still be applied if the unit of structure is the (micro-) crystal instead of individual atom. We showed in Eq. (6), § 54, that the orbit and spin made the same contribution to the susceptibility as though both were entirely free, provided only their interaction energy is small compared to $kT$. Similarly, one can show that the susceptibility is the same as that coming from the individual atomic spins, considered separately, provided only the inter-atomic exchange couplings are small compared to $kT$.

3. $J/kT \ll -1$. Here $J$ is negative and the energy will be lowest when as many spins as possible are anti-parallel, and the normal states are those of least $S'$. The inter-atomic coupling thus here erases practically all the paramagnetism, as will be discussed more fully in § 80.

Even ferromagnetic bodies conform to case 1 only asymptotically at $T = 0$. In such bodies the state $S' = nS$ of maximum spin for the crystal does, to be sure, represent the least energy,[14] as when the spins

---

[14] Another proof that the state of maximum spin is an extremum in energy has been given by Teller, *Zeits. f. Physik*, **62**, 102 (1930).

are all parallel, each term in the summation $\langle 11 \rangle$ has its minimum characteristic value (assuming $J > 0$). However, whereas there is only one state with the maximum spin $nS$, there are by (13)–(15) $n-1$ states of spin $S' = nS-1$, approximately $n^2/2$ states of spin $nS-2$, &c. This increasing number of states as $S'$ is diminished from its maximum is important for two reasons. First of all, strength of numbers will partially offset the smaller Boltzmann factors for spins less than the maximum. In other words, the probability of the crystal being in *some* state having a given $S' < nS$ may be appreciable even though the probability of its being in one particular designated state of this $S'$ may be negligible. Secondly, all the states with a given $S' < nS$ do not have the same energy, and a few favoured ones may have quite low energies, even though they can never lie as deep as the state $S' = nS$. Whereas the infinitely ferromagnetic case 1 is thus too much of an idealization, it may nevertheless well be that most of the crystals have very large resultant spins. This seems to be the characteristic of ferromagnetic materials. A field of ordinary magnitude is then not able to produce the true saturation magnetization $2nS\beta$, as this would require that the field be able to convert the crystal into the state $S' = nS$, and only enormous fields can have an appreciable effect on the distribution of $S'$ as distinct from $M'_S$. However, it is possible at the same time to have $HS'\beta/kT \gg 1$, though $S' < nS$, $H\beta/kT \ll 1$, so that the field is able to aline the spin of the crystal in its direction. There is then what we may term a state of pseudo-saturation, which is the saturation observed in the laboratory and which will be discussed more quantitatively on pp. 334–6. This pseudo-saturation, of course, approaches asymptotically the true saturation at $T = 0$. On the other hand, if the temperature is raised sufficiently, case 2 above will become a better approximation than case 1, in agreement with the well-known experimental fact that ferromagnetism is obliterated if the temperature is raised above a certain critical point, called the Curie point.

We must now seek to make these ideas more quantitative. If $Z$ be the partition function

$$Z = \sum e^{-W/kT} = \sum e^{-(W' + 2M'_S \beta H)/kT}, \tag{17}$$

then the magnetic moment per unit-volume in the direction of the field $H$ is

$$M = \frac{N}{n} kT \frac{\partial \log Z}{\partial H}. \tag{18}$$

These relations are readily seen to be the equivalent of (3), Chap. VII, or the quantum analogue of (59), Chap. I, applied to the magnetic rather than electric moment. In the second form of (17) we have utilized the fact that the magnetic moment is assumed to come entirely from the spin, so that the crystal, regarded as one big molecule, possesses a Zeeman term $2M'_S\beta H$ (cf. Eq. (103), Chap. VI). As usual $N$ denotes the number of atoms per c.c., so that $N/n$ is the 'density of micro-crystals'; Eq. (18) involves $N/n$ rather than $N$ as in previous chapters since our unit of structure is now the (micro-) crystal rather than the atom.

The precise determination of the unperturbed energy-levels $W'$ belonging to a given value of the spin $S'$, i.e. the determination of the characteristic values of $\langle 16 \rangle$, is virtually impossible, as it involves solution of a secular problem of degree $\omega$ (cf. Eq. (14)). Heisenberg therefore makes the approximation that the discrete succession of $\omega$ energy-levels belonging to a given $S'$ can be replaced by a continuum. He further supposes that this continuum is distributed according to the Gaussian error law about the average energy for the spin $S'$, which we shall denote by $W_{S'}$. Thus he takes the number of states of the crystal of given spin which have energies between $W_{S'}+x$ and $W_{S'}+x+dx$ in the absence of the field $H$ to be

$$\frac{\omega(S')}{(2\pi)^{\frac{1}{2}}\Delta_{S'}} e^{-x^2/2\Delta_{S'}}\, dx. \tag{19}$$

The mean energy $W_{S'}$ and the constant $\Delta_{S'}$ which determines the Gaussian 'spread' will be calculated later as functions of $S'$. The partition function (17) now becomes

$$Z = \frac{1}{(2\pi)^{\frac{1}{2}}} \sum_{S'} \left[ \frac{\omega(S')}{\Delta_{S'}} e^{-W_{S'}/kT} \int_{-\infty}^{+\infty} e^{-(x/kT)-x^2/2\Delta_{S'}^2}\, dx \sum_{M'_S=-S'}^{+S'} e^{-2M'_S\beta H/kT} \right]. \tag{20}$$

As $M'_S$, $S'$ are large numbers, the summations over $M'_S$, $S'$ may be replaced by integrations. The integration over $M'_S$ is immediate, and here to a sufficient approximation we may take

$$e^{-2M'_S\beta H/kT}\big|_{-S'}^{+S'} = -e^{2S'\beta H/kT}.$$

If we perform also the integration over $x$, Eq. (20) is transformed into

$$Z = \frac{kT}{2\beta H} \int \omega(S') e^{(2S'\beta H - W_{S'})/kT} e^{\Delta_{S'}^2/2k^2T^2}\, dS'. \tag{21}$$

*The Special Case $S = \frac{1}{2}$.* Following Heisenberg, it is best to consider first the case $S = \frac{1}{2}$ of atoms with only one electron each not in a closed shell. We shall show in § 78 that here [15]

$$W_{S'} = -\frac{zJ}{n} S'^2,$$ (22)

$$\Delta_{S'}^2 = J^2 z \frac{(n^2 - 4S'^2)(3n^2 - 4S'^2)}{8n^3}.$$ (23)

The prevalent states have sufficiently large values of $\frac{1}{2}n \pm S'$, so that the Stirling approximation $x! \sim x^x$ can be used for the factorials in (12), and (15) can be employed instead of the exact formula (14). By (22), (23), and (12), Eq. (21) now reduces to

$$Z = \frac{kT}{2\beta H} \int e^{f(S')} dS',$$ (24)

where

$$f(S') = \frac{2H\beta S'}{kT} + \frac{zJS'^2}{nkT} + \frac{J^2 z(n^2 - 4S'^2)(3n^2 - 4S'^2)}{16n^3 k^2 T^2} +$$

$$+ n \log n - (\tfrac{1}{2}n + S')\log(\tfrac{1}{2}n + S') - (\tfrac{1}{2}n - S')\log(\tfrac{1}{2}n - S').$$ (25)

As the integral (24) cannot be evaluated in closed form, it is necessary to have recourse to the method of steepest descents. This method hinges on the fact that the integrand of (24) has a sharp maximum at the value of $S'$ which maximizes $f(S')$ and which we shall denote by $S^\dagger$. It can be shown that the equation

$$\frac{df}{dS'} = 0$$ (26)

for determining $S^\dagger$ has either (a) one real root, a maximum of $f(S')$, or (b) three real roots which give respectively a maximum, a minimum, and a subordinate maximum. The correct root to use then is, of course, the dominant maximum. If we stop with quadratic terms in the Taylor's expansion of $f$ about $S' = S^\dagger$, Eq. (24) becomes

$$Z = \frac{kT}{2\beta H} e^{f(S^\dagger)} \int_{-\infty}^{+\infty} e^{-ay^2} dy = \frac{kT}{2\beta H} \sqrt{\frac{\pi}{a}} e^{f(S^\dagger)},$$ (27)

where $y = S' - S^\dagger$, $-2a = d^2f/dy^2|_{y=0}$. The limits for $y$ are not really $\pm\infty$, but this is immaterial owing to the sharp peak of the integrand at $y = 0$. The expression (18) for the magnetic moment is now, by (25) and (27),

$$M = 2S^\dagger\beta\frac{N}{n},$$ (28)

---

[15] In comparing results such as (22), (23) with Heisenberg's paper, it should be noticed that our $n$ is the same as $2n$ in his notation, and that he retains the additive term in the exchange energy which is independent of spin and which we dropped in passing from $\langle 9 \rangle$ to $\langle 10 \rangle$.

since in performing the differentiation involved in (17) the implicit dependence of $f(S^\dagger)$ on $H$ through $S^\dagger$ (which is a function of $H$) may be disregarded in virtue of (26), so that $df/dH = 2\beta S^\dagger/kT$. Also the dependence of the factor $1/Ha^{\frac{1}{2}}$ in (27) on $H$ can be considered negligible compared to that of $e^f$, as $f \gg 1$. With these observations Eq. (28) is obtained immediately. The physical significance of (28) is that $S^\dagger$ is so great that the spin $S' \sim S^\dagger$ alines itself parallel to the field.

It is convenient to use dimensionless measures of the moment, and also of the importance of the exchange integral $J$, by introducing special notations $\zeta$, $\gamma$ respectively for the ratio of the moment to its true saturation value at $T = 0$, and for the ratio of $zJ$ to $kT$. Thus

$$\zeta = \frac{M}{2N\beta S} = \frac{S^\dagger}{nS}, \qquad \gamma = \frac{zJ}{kT}. \tag{29}$$

In the present case $S = \frac{1}{2}$, but we shall later use (29) also in the general case of any $S$.

On working out the explicit form of (26) by means of (25) and using the new notation (29) it is found that

$$\zeta = \tanh y, \quad \text{with } y = \frac{\beta H}{kT} + \tfrac{1}{2}\zeta\left(\gamma - \frac{\gamma^2}{z}\right) + \frac{\gamma^2}{4z}\zeta^3 \sim aH + b\zeta + c\zeta^3. \tag{30}$$

This is Heisenberg's final result, which will be discussed after the next paragraph.

*The General Case of Arbitrary S.* Unfortunately it has not yet been possible [16] to calculate the mean square deviation $\Delta_{S'}$ of the energy for given $S'$ from its mean value $W_{S'}$ except for the special case $S = \frac{1}{2}$ of only one valence electron per atom. For $S > \frac{1}{2}$, one can therefore not yet calculate the susceptibility even under the assumption of the Gaussian distribution of characteristic values. Instead one must make the

---

[16] An attempt to extend the calculation of $\Delta_{S'}$ to the case of atoms with arbitrary $S$ has been made by Heisenberg in his article in *Probleme der modernen Physik*, p. 114 (Sommerfeld Festschrift, edited by Debye). Unfortunately, this article is marred by an error, and when appropriate corrections are made, the group theory method there used fails to give a result on $\Delta_{S'}$ except for $S = \frac{1}{2}$. The calculation of $W_{S'}$, on the other hand, is entirely correct. (Details of the error are as follows. It consists in overlooking the fact that in the case (2) considered by Heisenberg at the top of p. 119 his expression $b_{ii}{}^T {}^{T'}$ will have different values when $T$, $T'$ define transpositions from the common element to elements located in a common second atom or to elements in entirely different atoms. This is allied to the fact that even when $j$, $l$ are in different atoms from $i$, the mean value of $(s_i \cdot s_j)(s_i \cdot s_l)$ is different when $j$, $l$ are in the same atom or in different ones, as a constraint is imposed by the resultant of the spins for a single atom being $S$. Analogous difficulties are encountered in case 3. The number of different kinds of $b$'s is thus greater than Heisenberg recognized, and this complication makes them incapable of calculation in the manner sought.)

still cruder supposition that all crystalline states of the same spin have the same energy $W_{S'}$. Then $W_{S'}$ is the mean energy appropriate to the spin $S'$, which can be calculated by very elementary means for any $S$. This mean will be so shown in § 78 to have very approximately the value given in Eq. (22), regardless of the magnitude of $S$. As the preceding detailed analysis for the case $S = \frac{1}{2}$ has made it clear that the prevalent states aline themselves parallel to the field, it will not be necessary to carry through the niceties of the method of steepest descents, and we can take the partition function to be

$$Z = \sum_{S'} \omega(S')e^{\frac{2S'\beta H}{kT}+\frac{\gamma S'^2}{n}}.\tag{31}$$

Because of the sharp maximum of the summand at some particular $S'$, denoted as before by $S^\dagger$, it will suffice to retain only terms through the first order in the Taylor's expansion about $S^\dagger$, so that (31) becomes

$$Z = e^{-\frac{\gamma S^{\dagger 2}}{n}} \sum \omega(S')e^{2\gamma SS'\zeta+\frac{2S'\beta H}{kT}}.\tag{32}$$

As we may use the approximation (15), the expression (32) is, in virtue of (13), merely

$$Z = e^{-\frac{\gamma S^{\dagger 2}}{n}} (e^y+e^{-\frac{(S-1)}{S}y}+...+e^{-\frac{(S-1)}{S}y}+e^{-y})^n, \text{ with } y = \frac{2\beta SH}{kT}+2\gamma S^2\zeta.\tag{33}$$

This rather elegant observation is due to Heisenberg.[17]  In the present method we assume *ad hoc* that there is an overwhelming probability that the crystal be in the state $|M'_S| = S' = S^\dagger$. Hence the moment given by (18) must be the same as $2\beta S^\dagger(N/n)$ or $2\beta SN\zeta$ (cf. Eq. (29)). In view of (33) this means that

$$\zeta = B_S(y), \quad \text{with } y = \frac{2\beta SH}{kT}+2\gamma S^2\zeta \sim aH+b\zeta,\tag{34}$$

where

$$B_S(y) = \frac{Se^y+(S-1)e^{(S-1)y/S}+...+(-S+1)e^{(-S+1)y/S}+(-S)e^{-y}}{S(e^y+e^{(S-1)y/S}+...+e^{(-S+1)y/S}+e^{-y})}$$

$$= \frac{2S+1}{2S}\coth\left(\frac{2Sy+y}{2S}\right)-\frac{1}{2S}\coth\frac{y}{2S}.$$

[17] W. Heisenberg, *l.c.*[9], also especially Sommerfeld Festschrift, p. 122. It will be noted that quite apart from the neglect of $\Delta_{S'}$ we have used a different method of calculation for the case of arbitrary $S$ than for the case $S = \frac{1}{2}$. Our procedure for $S = \frac{1}{2}$, based on steepest descents, is taken largely from Fowler and Kapitza, *Proc. Roy. Soc.* **124**A, 1 (1929) while that for any $S$ follows more nearly the original papers of Heisenberg. The latter method avoids the necessity of using Stirling's theorem, but does not give such a good justification for the assumption of a sharp maximum without some further study, such as was given in Heisenberg's original paper.[9] We purposely use for variety one method in one case and one in the other.

The expression $B_S(y)$ is what we called the Brillouin function in § 61. When $S = \frac{1}{2}$, Eq. (34), of course, reduces to (30), provided we neglect the part of $y$ in (30) which is quadratic in $\gamma$. This part resulted from the Gaussian spread of energy-levels, now omitted.

*Discussion of Eqs.* (30) *and* (34). Either of the pairs of simultaneous equations (30) or (34) bears an obvious relation to the classical Weiss ones

$$\zeta = L(y), \quad \text{with } y = \frac{\mu(H+qM)}{kT} \sim aH + b\zeta \qquad (35)$$

obtained by taking the argument of the Langevin function

$$L(y) = \coth y - 1/y$$

to be proportional to the applied plus molecular field $H+qM$. In fact, (34) is identical in form with the Weiss expression, except for the difference, characteristic of quantum theory, that the Brillouin function occurs in place of the Langevin one.[18] We explained in § 61 how the Brillouin function merged asymptotically for very large quantum numbers (or fictitiously small $h$) into the Langevin. A classical analysis starting with $\langle 16 \rangle$ would thus yield the Weiss result [19] (35), provided one overlooks the distribution of energies for crystalline states of identical angular momentum. The major role of quantum mechanics is thus to provide a real mechanism, viz. the exchange effect, for $\langle 16 \rangle$. The term in (30) which is cubic in $\zeta$ or $M$ is a refinement resulting from the Gaussian spread, and finds no analogue in the Weiss theory, but is unimportant, at least from a qualitative standpoint. Like other writers, we henceforth for simplicity omit this term in discussing the workings of Eqs. (30) or (34).

The exposition of how Eqs. (30) or (34) yield the ferromagnetic phenomena of the Curie point proceeds largely as for the Weiss expression (35), and so need be given only briefly here.[20]

The simultaneous equations (30) or (34) will have a real positive solution for $\zeta$ even if the applied field $H$ is zero, provided the proportionality constant $b$, which measures the effect of the apparent molecular

---

[18] Even before the advent of the new quantum mechanics the substitution of the Brillouin for the Langevin function in the Weiss theory was proposed and studied by Debye, in *Handbuch der Radiologie*, vi. 718. The justification of Eqs. of the form (34) by means of the exchange mechanism was first given by Heisenberg in the Sommerfeld Festschrift, p. 122.

[19] In seeming contradiction, Ising found that classically there was no ferromagnetism regardless of the crystalline arrangement (*Zeits. f. Physik*, **31**, 253 (1925)). This, however, was because Ising arbitrarily took the coupling between elementary magnets to be proportional to $\mu_{z_1}\mu_{z_2}$ rather than to the complete scalar product $\mu_1 \cdot \mu_2$.

[20] For elaboration of the details of the Weiss theory see the references cited in note 11.

field, is sufficiently large. This is most easily seen graphically, as the solutions of (34) for $H = 0$ are the intersection of $\xi = B_S(y)$ with a straight line $\zeta = y/b$ passing through the origin in a $\zeta$-$y$ diagram. There will be a real positive solution provided the slope $\tan \phi = 1/b$ of this line is positive, but less than the initial slope $\tan \theta = (dB_S/dy)_0$ of the Brillouin curve. This is illustrated in Fig. 13, p. 258, for the case $S = \frac{1}{2}$. The critical temperature at which $\theta = \phi$ is the Curie point. Below this temperature, $\phi$ is less than $\theta$, and there is a solution of the type $\zeta > 0$ when $H = 0$, so that spontaneous magnetization is possible. Above this, $\phi$ exceeds $\theta$, and the only real, non-negative solution is the non-magnetic one $\zeta = 0$, showing that here the strength of numbers of the crystalline states with $S' \sim 0$ more than offsets the fact that some of the states with larger spins have lower energies. In other words, the prevalent states have large spins below and small spins above the Curie point, and correspondingly there is ferromagnetism below and only para-magnetism above.

To derive a quantitative expression for the Curie point, and for the paramagnetism at high temperatures, we expand the Brillouin function as a power series in $y$. Eqs. (34) then become

$$\zeta = \frac{1}{3}\frac{(S+1)}{S} y - \frac{1}{720 S^4}[(2S+1)^4 - 1]y^3, \quad \text{with } y = \frac{2\beta SH}{kT} + \frac{2JzS^2\zeta}{kT}. \tag{36}$$

The cubic term could be omitted for present purposes, but is retained for later use in § 79. As explained above, the first-degree portions of the two equations of (36) must become identical for $H = 0$ at the Curie point $T_C$. Hence

$$T_C = \frac{2Jz}{3k} S(S+1). \tag{37}$$

If instead we used (30), we would similarly find

$$T_C = \frac{2J}{k\left(1 - \sqrt{1 - \dfrac{8}{z}}\right)}. \tag{38}$$

The observed Curie temperatures are roughly of the order $10^{3}°$ K., and in view of (37) or (38) this means that the atoms in ferromagnetic bodies must be close enough together so that the exchange integral $J$ is of the order $10^3 k$ or about 0·1 volt, which does not seem unreasonable.

*Behaviour above Curie Point.* Above the Curie point it is adequate to retain only the linear portion of (36). The elimination of $y$ between the two parts of (36) can then immediately be performed, and it is thus found on using (37) that the expression for the susceptibility

$\chi = 2N\beta S\zeta/H$ may be written

$$\chi = \frac{4N\beta^2 S(S+1)}{3k(T-T_C)}. \tag{39}$$

If instead one uses the Gaussian refinement (30), the corresponding formula proves to be the same as (39), specialized to $S = \frac{1}{2}$, only if $z$ is large and if in addition the temperature is high.

Eq. (39) is in good agreement with experiment, inasmuch as the susceptibilities of ferromagnetic bodies are usually found to exhibit a temperature dependence of the form $\chi = C/(T+\Delta)$ above the Curie point. Also the constant $\Delta$ is often found to be roughly equal to the negative of the Curie temperature $T_C$, but there is sometimes the complication, not envisaged by (39), that $\Delta$ changes at the various polymorphic transitions. For instance, in iron, one of the worst offenders, $C$ has respectively the values 2·21, 1·53, 4·03, and 0·25 (per gramme mol.), and $-\Delta$ the values 1047°, 1063°, 1340°, and 1543° K. in the intervals 1047–1101°, 1101–1193°, 1193–1668°, above 1668° K. (Fe $\beta_1$, $\beta_2, \gamma, \delta$). Nickel behaves much better, as it conforms quite accurately to a formula with $C = 0\cdot325$, $\Delta = -645$ from 689–1173° K.; above 1173°, however, departures seem to set in.[21] Typical experimental values of $T_C$ for Fe and Ni are respectively 1042° K. (Terry) and 637° K. (quoted by Weiss). Different determinations vary by as much as 20°, and Weiss states that on the whole $T_C'$ seems to be about 20° less than $-\Delta$ in Ni.

We have seen in § 74 that a formula of the form $\chi = C/(T+\Delta)$ often represents quite well the temperature behaviour of purely paramagnetic bodies, such as iron salts, over considerable temperature ranges. When $\Delta$ is negative this implies, according to (39), that the paramagnetic body is really a ferromagnetic one, but with so low a Curie point that the ferromagnetic properties are not exhibited at ordinary temperatures. Some of the cryomagnetic anomalies cited on p. 307 lend some support to this view, but on the whole not as many traces of ferromagnetism are actually found at low temperatures as one would then expect. More often $\Delta$ is positive, and on Heisenberg's theory this simply means that the Curie temperature is negative. According to (34), (37) this will be the case if the molecular field (i.e. the part of $y$ proportional to $\zeta$) is negative. The question of the sign of this temperature will be discussed on p. 336, and we shall there see that one would expect negative tem-

---

[21] The experimental data above the Curie point are discussed by Stoner in *Magnetism and Atomic Structure*, p. 149 and ref. 23; also in the reports of Weiss and Cabrera for the 1930 Solvay Congress.

peratures to be the more common. However, these considerations on paramagnetic atoms may be a bit irrelevant when the atoms are not in $S$ states, as we have seen in § 74 on salts of the iron group that the primary cause of $\Delta$ is probably here not the exchange effect but the incomplete quenching of the orbital angular momentum. On the other hand, the rough equality of $-\Delta$ and $T_C$ in real ferromagnetic media

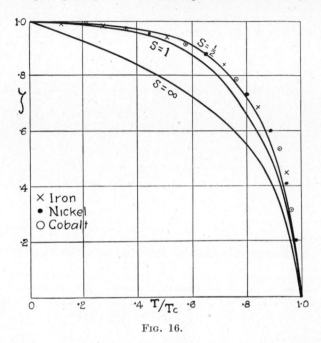

Fig. 16.

above the Curie point must mean that in the latter, $\Delta$ is really due to the Heisenberg exchange effect.

*Behaviour below Curie Point.* In this region $\zeta$ can be determined as a function of the 'reduced temperature' $T/T_C$ by numerical solution of (34). The resulting curves for various values of $S$ are shown in Fig. 16. Owing to the use of $\zeta$, $T/T_C$ instead of $M$, $T$ as variables, the curves are uniquely determined, and do not involve $J$ and $N$ as parameters. This absence of parameters constitutes the so-called 'law of corresponding states', a famous result of the Weiss theory (which behaves like $S = \infty$), and is seen to hold in quantum mechanics only for materials with the same atomic spins, as the curves do depend on $S$. As explained on p. 326, the spontaneous magnetization represented as a function of temperature in Fig. 16, is not the experimental residual magnetization in the absence of any applied field, but rather the experi-

mental saturation value, which we dubbed the pseudo-saturation
magnetization. No adequate theory has yet been developed for the
magnetization curves in weak fields or, in other words, for the transition from the compensation of the micro-crystals at $H = 0$ to the state
of pseudo-saturation.[22] According to the preceding theory this transition should take place with infinite rapidity, and there should be no
hysteresis; this defect perhaps arises because the magnetic forces between particles have been neglected in comparison with the exchange
ones. The former forces are, to be sure, usually subordinate, but might
be important during unstable equilibria involved in sensitive readjustment processes such as are involved in the study of hysteresis and
retentivity.

*Magneton Numbers.* The experimental saturation values for nickel
and iron are represented respectively by dots and crosses in Fig. 16.
The experimental points for nickel are seen to fit the quantum curve
for $S = \frac{1}{2}$ better than the original Weiss curve.[23] Also, the Curie
constant for nickel above the Curie point agrees approximately with
that obtained by taking $S = \frac{1}{2}$ in (39), as the experimental magneton
number is 1·62 from 689–1173° K., and 1·91 above 1173° K., while
$\sqrt{(4 \cdot \frac{1}{2} \cdot \frac{3}{2})} = 1 \cdot 73$. For cobalt, $\mu_{\text{eff}} = 3 \cdot 21$, $-\Delta = 1404°$ from 1443–
1514° K., and $\mu_{\text{off}} = 2 \cdot 93$, $-\Delta = 1422°$ from 1514–1576° K., while the
theoretical $\mu_{\text{eff}}$ is 2·83 for $S = 1$. The existence of an apparent spin
quantum number $\frac{1}{2}$ for Ni, and possibly 1 for Co, is a bit hard to
understand theoretically, as neutral nickel and cobalt atoms contain
respectively even and odd numbers of electrons, and so should have
respectively integral and half-integral $S$. Perhaps the explanation of
this dilemma lies in the fact that metals are composed of ions and con-

---

[22] The greatest progress along this line appears to have been made in the classical
theories of G. S. Mahajani, *Phil. Trans.* **228**, 63 (1929); N. S. Akulov, *Zeits. f. Physik*,
**54**, 582; **57**, 249, 254; **64**, 559, 817; **67**, 794; **69**, 78, 822; and R. Becker, *ibid.* **62**, 253
(1930). Discussion of these papers is beyond the scope of our chapter, primarily on
quantum developments. We may, however, mention that the question as to whether
a demagnetized crystal really consists of spontaneously magnetized micro-crystals has
been the subject of considerable controversy. Besides the papers of Akulov on this
subject see also interesting articles by Frenkel and Dorfmann, *Nature*, **126**, 274 (1930);
McKeehan, *ibid.* **126**, 952 (1930). A very interesting study of single crystals has
recently been given by Webster, *Proc. Lon. Phys. Soc.*, **42**, 431 (1930). He deduces
convincing evidence that the micro-crystals are really spontaneously magnetized. The
magnetization curves for single crystals are much more amenable to theory than those
for other ferromagnetic bodies.

[23] A particularly careful comparison of theory and experiment for nickel has been
given by F. Tyler, *Phil. Mag.* **9**, 1026 (1930). An excellent résumé of the status of the
theory of ferromagnetism in comparison with experiment is given by Stoner in *Phil. Mag.*
**10**, 27 (1930).

duction electrons rather than of ordinary neutral atoms.[24] If the conduction electrons are sufficiently free, the magnetic effect of their spins virtually disappears because of the Fermi-Dirac interference effects to be considered in § 80. If, then, an odd number (most likely one) of electrons are detached from each neutral atom of Ni or Co to become conduction electrons, the residual ions might have the desired values of $S$. A further difficulty is that the saturation moment of Ni at $T = 0$ is found[25] to be about 40 per cent. lower than the value $N\beta$ which would be expected on the basis of $S = \frac{1}{2}$. The value for Co is probably about 10 or 20 per cent. lower than that $2N\beta$ corresponding to $S = 1$. Possibly these irregularities are because interaction with the conduction electrons hinders complete alinement of the spins of the ions.

The variations in the Curie constant of iron at the polymorphic transition points are clearly too complicated to explain by any simple theory. There is thus, all told, no adequate existing theory of the numerical magneton values in ferromagnetic media, although the values of Ni and Co are, as we have seen, not entirely unreasonable.

*Question of Sign of $T_C$.* To permit a ferromagnetic solution of Eqs. (30) or (34) it is essential that the Curie temperature $T_C$ be positive.[26] Otherwise the condition $0 < \phi < \theta$ is incapable of realization, as negative or imaginary temperatures have, of course, no physical meaning. The absence of a positive $T_C$ means either that the molecular field is negative, and so opposes ferromagnetism, or else is positive but too small to have an appreciable effect. Eq. (37) shows, if one makes the crude assumption of identical energies for all crystalline states of identical spin, that the necessary and sufficient condition for ferromagnetism is that the exchange integral $J$ be positive. Heisenberg estimates that $J$ can be positive only if the principal quantum number

[24] The need of considering ionic magnetic units even in metals has been emphasized by Stoner, *Proc. Leeds Phil. Soc.* **1**, 55 (1926). Stoner is able to account more or less quantitatively for the various moments of nickel above the Curie point on the assumption that Ni, Ni$^+$ and Ni$^{++}$ atoms are present in the ratio 3: 1: 1, but this supposition seems rather arbitrary. Another interpretation of the magneton numbers in nickel has very recently been given by A. Wolf, *Zeits. f. Physik*, **70**, 519 (1931). He suggests that two states of the neutral nickel atom alternate in the crystal structure.

[25] The experimental saturation magnetization for Ni extrapolated to $T = 0$ yields a moment almost exactly 3 Weiss magnetons per atom, whereas the theoretical value for $S = \frac{1}{2}$ is 1 Bohr magneton or 4·95 Weiss magnetons.

[26] Ferromagnetism clearly cannot exist without a critical Curie temperature at which it disappears (though not necessarily discontinuously). For at very high temperatures the inter-atomic interactions become of negligible consequence and the ordinary formulae for paramagnetism in gases become applicable. Hence by raising $T$ sufficiently, one can always reach a point at which the ferromagnetism is effaced from a body.

$n$ is 3 or greater, in agreement with the fact that ferromagnetism is not found in the first two Mendeleef periods, but the fact that the normal state of $O_2$ has a spin quantum number 1 rather than 0 seems to require that $J$ can sometimes exceed zero even when $n = 2$. This exception is not surprising as Heisenberg's estimates of the sign of the exchange integrals are only very crude ones. The whole Heitler-London theory of valence [27] is based to a large extent on the idea that stable chemical compounds as a rule (barring, e.g. $O_2$) have as small spins as possible, implying that commonly $J < 0$.

Even when $J > 0$, there may still fail to be a real Curie temperature if one assumes a Gaussian distribution of energy-levels. Reference to (38) shows that with the latter distribution a real $T_C$ is achieved only if $z \geqslant 8$. Ferromagnetism should then exist only if each atom has at least eight neighbours. Heisenberg cites in nice confirmation of this theory that the common ferromagnetic crystals Fe, Ni, Co are either body-centred cubic ($z = 8$) or face-centred ($z = 12$). However, as mentioned to the writer by Dr. Wiersma, there are known ferromagnetic alloys and compounds in which the atoms of the iron group which are responsible for the ferromagnetism have themselves the simple cubic arrangement, and so have $z = 6$ if we consider only neighbours with outstanding spins. Such exceptions are not discomforting, as they can conceivably be explained on three different grounds: (a) the Gaussian distribution may be but a poor approximation to the actual distribution of energy values; (b) ferromagnetism may be due to free rather than bound electrons; (c) the behaviour may be substantially modified by the presence of an orbital magnetic moment.

Alternative (a) seems the most likely. The accuracy of the Gaussian hypothesis can be tested by calculating $\overline{(W-W_{S'})^3}$ or $\overline{(W-W_{S'})^4}$ with the methods of § 78 (or their group-theory equivalent) and examining whether these fluctuations agree with those obtained with the Gaussian distribution after the constant determining the spread has been obtained from $\overline{(W-W_{S'})^2}$. This has been done in unpublished work of Peierls, by the group method. His calculation shows that actually the Gaussian assumption is a poor approximation, but does not give enough further information to permit any real improvement in the theory. The only service of the calculation with the Gaussian distribution is to show qualitatively that there are other criteria for ferromagnetism besides a positive exchange integral.

[27] W. Heitler and F. London, *Zeits. f. Physik*, **44**, 455 (1927); Heitler, *ibid.* **46**, 47; **47**, 835; London, *ibid.* **46**, 455 (1928).

*Improved Method of Calculation near* $T = 0$. Although a rigorous solution of the $\omega(S')$-dimensional secular problem connected with $\langle 16 \rangle$ is impossibly difficult, a very ingenious approximate method of solution has been developed by Slater.[28] Unfortunately, space will not permit us to give details. The essence of the method is that by throwing away relatively few of the elements in the secular equation it can be thrown into a form which can be solved rigorously. In this way closed expressions for the different energy values belonging to a given $S'$ can be obtained. It is, of course, far preferable thus to obtain the individual energy-levels than a rough distribution curve for all the levels regarded as a continuum. Unfortunately, Slater's solution is only a good approximation when $S'$ is nearly equal to its maximum value $nS$. Hence it is useful for ferromagnetism primarily at very low temperatures, where the pseudo-saturation is nearly the true saturation, or the prevalent spins nearly the maximum spins. It does not thus aid in studying the phenomena of the Curie point. Slater did not consider his solution of the secular equation in connexion with the problem of ferromagnetism, and the application to the latter has been made in an important paper by Bloch.[29] The results, which relate entirely to atoms having $S = \frac{1}{2}$, are as follows. A linear chain, the quadratic surface grating, and hexagonal surface grating, should all not exhibit ferromagnetism. These results are the same as with Heisenberg's Gaussian calculation, as the number of neighbours is less than eight. For simple cubic and body-centred cubic crystals, Bloch finds that there can be ferromagnetism. This is an advance over the Gaussian method, as we saw that the latter did not allow ferromagnetic simple cubic crystals. The refinement of the method is evidenced by the fact that it predicts ferromagnetism for simple cubic but not for hexagonal surface gratings, despite the fact that there is the same number, six, of neighbours in each; thus the arrangement as well as number of neighbours is important. Bloch calculates that in a simple cubic crystal the moment $\zeta$ should approach its saturation value 1 in the following fashion:

$$\zeta = 1 - a \left( \frac{T}{\theta_C} \right)^{3/2}, \quad \text{where } a = \sum_{n=1}^{\infty} \frac{1}{(4\pi n)^{3/2}} = 0 \cdot 0587, \quad \theta_C = \frac{J}{k}. \quad (40)$$

For the body-centred cubic he finds the same form of temperature dependence but a different value of the coefficient $a$. Eqs. (34), on the other hand, give an asymptotic solution of the form $\zeta = 1 - S^{-1} e^{-3T_0/(S+1)T}$

[28] J. C. Slater, *Phys. Rev.* **35**, 509 (1930).

[29] F. Bloch, *Zeits. f. Physik*, **61**, 206 (1930). Summary by Pauli in Report of the 1930 Solvay Congress.

in the vicinity of $T = 0$, regardless of the form of crystalline arrangement, provided only a positive molecular field is granted. As (40) is surely more accurate than (34) near $T = 0$, the true theoretical curves should be drawn somewhat differently than in Fig. 16 in the immediate vicinity of $T/T_C = 0$. They should still remain horizontal at $T = 0$, but exhibit a more pronounced downward curvature at this point. There are not adequate data available at extremely low temperatures to test experimentally this modification. (Data [30] at ordinary low temperatures favour an empirical formula of the form $\zeta = 1 - \alpha_1 T^2 - \alpha_2 T^4 - \ldots$, but conceivably higher-order terms in $T/T_C$, neglected in obtaining (40), might make the theoretical formula sufficiently resemble the empirical one over a limited temperature range somewhat higher than covered by Eq. (40).)

*Possibility of Ferromagnetism from Free Electrons.* A variant of Heisenberg's theory has been given in another paper by Bloch.[31] Here he assumed that the electrons whose exchange effects give the ferromagnetism are the free rather than bound electrons. This corresponds to using the wave functions characteristic of the Sommerfeld [32] theory of conduction instead of the Heitler-London theory of valence. The type of crystal structure, of course, then does not enter. Instead Bloch shows that free electrons will give ferromagnetism if, and only if, the tendency towards ferromagnetism is able to conquer the tendency of the Fermi statistics or the Pauli exclusion principle to suppress the spin paramagnetism of free electrons, an effect to be discussed in § 80. Assuming that there is one free valence electron per atom, and that the temperature is below the critical degeneracy temperature of the Sommerfeld theory, Bloch shows that this requires that the inter-atomic distance be not less than $0 \cdot 22 h^2/me^2 = 0 \cdot 5. \ 10^{-7}$ cm. This is only a rough approximation, but it is noteworthy that the actual inter-atomic distances are considerably less than this critical value in the alkalis, thus giving insight into why the latter are only feebly paramagnetic. Stoner [33] further points out that if ferromagnetism were due to free electrons, the Curie point would have to be higher than the critical temperature of the Sommerfeld conduction theory, and this would yield absurdly high Curie points.

*Summary.* Although it is not yet possible to formulate quantitatively the exact criteria for a positive molecular field, all the foregoing con-

---

[30] Weiss, *J. de Physique*, **10**, 354 (1929).
[31] F. Bloch, *Zeits. f. Physik*, **57**, 545 (1929).
[32] A. Sommerfeld, *Zeits. f. Physik*, **47**, 1 (1928).
[33] E. C. Stoner, *Proc. Leeds Phil. Soc.* **2**, 50 (1930).

siderations make it clear that ferromagnetism is possible only if the exchange integrals are positive, and even then only under very special conditions of crystalline arrangement and spacing. This agrees with the fact that relatively few materials are ferromagnetic.

## 78. Proof of Formulae (22) and (23) for the Mean and Mean Square Energy

These formulae were first derived by Heisenberg with the rather involved machinery of group theory, but we shall show that Dirac's kinematical interpretation of the exchange effect as equivalent to a coupling ⟨9⟩ between spins frees us from the need of using this.

The square of the resultant crystalline spin vector is

$$\Big(\sum_{\text{whole crystal}} \mathbf{S}_i\Big)^2 = \sum \mathbf{S}_i^2 + \sum_{i \neq j} \mathbf{S}_i \cdot \mathbf{S}_j \doteq S'(S'+1). \tag{41}$$

Now the square $\mathbf{S}_i^2$ of the spin of any atom $i$ is a number $S(S+1)$, and, further, if we average over all the different states belonging to a given spin, the mean value (i.e. mean diagonal element) of $\mathbf{S}_i \cdot \mathbf{S}_j$ will by symmetry be independent of the indices $i, j$, provided $i \neq j$. There are $n$ terms in the single and $n(n-1)$ in the double sum in (41), as the crystal contains $n$ atoms. Therefore [34]

$$\overline{\mathbf{S}_i \cdot \mathbf{S}_j} = \frac{S'(S'+1) - nS(S+1)}{n(n-1)}. \tag{42}$$

The sum in ⟨16⟩ contains by definition $\tfrac{1}{2}nz$ terms, and so ⟨16⟩ becomes

$$W_{S'} = \overline{\mathscr{H}'} = -\frac{zJ}{n-1}[S'(S'+1) - nS(S+1)]. \tag{43}$$

In ferromagnetism we are interested in states which have large spin, so that $S'$ is of the order $n$. On the other hand, $S$ is of the order unity, as one atom contains only a limited number of electrons. Also, it is only necessary to retain the terms of highest order in $n$, and with this observation (43) yields (22) immediately.

We shall now calculate the mean square deviation $\Delta_{S'}^2$, but with the specialization $S = s = \tfrac{1}{2}$, which was not needed for (43).[35] When one

[34] The bars throughout § 78 are to be construed as denoting averages over all the states belonging to a given $S'$, with all such states weighted equally. Such averages should not be confused with the usual statistical averages wherein the various states are weighted with the Boltzmann factor.

[35] Besides the usual case of one valence electron per atom, the present calculation is applicable to atoms which are one electron short of a closed configuration, as here $S = \tfrac{1}{2}$ even though $S$ is not identical with the spin $s$ of an individual electron. Nevertheless it has seemed better in the ensuing equations to denote the spin of quantum number $\tfrac{1}{2}$ by $s$ rather than $S$ in order clearly to distinguish that the formulae, except Eq. (44), do not apply with an arbitrary $S$ substituted for $s$.

squares $\langle 16 \rangle$ one encounters three distinct types of terms having respectively two, three, and four unlike indices. It is very important to note that these three types hence have different mean values. When one counts the number of times these different kinds of products occur, one sees that the mean square of $\langle 16 \rangle$ is

$$\overline{\mathcal{H}'^2} = 4J^2\left[\frac{nz}{2}\overline{(\mathbf{s}_i \cdot \mathbf{s}_j)^2} + nz(z-1)\overline{(\mathbf{s}_i \cdot \mathbf{s}_j)(\mathbf{s}_i \cdot \mathbf{s}_k)} + \right.$$
$$\left. + \left(\frac{z^2n^2}{4} - nz^2 + \frac{zn}{2}\right)\overline{(\mathbf{s}_i \cdot \mathbf{s}_j)(\mathbf{s}_k \cdot \mathbf{s}_l)}\right]. \qquad (44)$$

Here and henceforth it is to be understood that no two subscripts are identical, so as to free us from the necessity of writing out explicitly $i \neq j$, $i \neq l$, &c. On p. 318 it was shown that the scalar product $\mathbf{s}_i \cdot \mathbf{s}_j$ of two electron spins has the characteristic values $\frac{1}{4}$, $-\frac{3}{4}$, and so always satisfies the algebraic equation $(\mathbf{s}_i \cdot \mathbf{s}_j - \frac{1}{4})(\mathbf{s}_i \cdot \mathbf{s}_j + \frac{3}{4}) = 0$, quite independently of whether or not one uses a system of representation in which this product is a diagonal matrix. Hence

$$\overline{(\mathbf{s}_i \cdot \mathbf{s}_j)^2} = -\frac{1}{2}\overline{\mathbf{s}_i \cdot \mathbf{s}_j} + \frac{3}{16} = -\left[\frac{S'(S'+1) - \frac{3}{4}n}{2n(n-1)}\right] + \frac{3}{16}. \qquad (45)$$

In the second form of this relation use has been made of (42) with $S = s = \frac{1}{2}$. The algebraic equation satisfied by $\mathbf{S}_i \cdot \mathbf{S}_j$ would be of higher order than the second if we did not take $S = \frac{1}{2}$, as $\mathbf{S}_i \cdot \mathbf{S}_j$ has $2S+1$ characteristic values, and this explains our making such a restriction.

The first kind of term in (44) is now evaluated. The method for the second is similar. We observe that the square $(\mathbf{s}_i + \mathbf{s}_j + \mathbf{s}_k)^2$ of the resultant of three electron spins has the characteristic values $S_3(S_3+1)$ with $S_3 = \frac{1}{2}, \frac{3}{2}$. As $\mathbf{s}_i^2 = \frac{3}{4}$, therefore $x = \mathbf{s}_i \cdot \mathbf{s}_j + \mathbf{s}_i \cdot \mathbf{s}_k + \mathbf{s}_j \cdot \mathbf{s}_k$ has the characteristic values $-\frac{3}{4}$, $+\frac{3}{4}$ and so always satisfies the algebraic equation $x^2 = \frac{9}{16}$. On squaring the left side of this equation one has three terms of the form $(i, j)^2$ and six of the form $(i, j)(i, k)$. Hence, with the aid of (45),

$$\overline{(\mathbf{s}_i \cdot \mathbf{s}_j)(\mathbf{s}_i \cdot \mathbf{s}_k)} = \frac{1}{6}[\frac{9}{16} - 3\overline{(\mathbf{s}_i \cdot \mathbf{s}_j)^2}] = \frac{S'(S'+1) - \frac{3}{4}n}{4n(n-1)}. \qquad (46)$$

To find the third term of (44) we note that in virtue of formula (41) for the resultant crystalline spin, we have

$$\left(\sum \mathbf{s}_i \cdot \mathbf{s}_j\right)^2 \doteq [S'(S'+1) - \frac{3}{4}n]^2,$$

as now $\sum \mathbf{S}_i^2 = \frac{3}{4}n$. Here the summation extends over the entire crystal. On reckoning the number of times the different kinds of terms occur in squaring out the left side, we find that

$$2n(n-1)\overline{(\mathbf{s}_i\cdot\mathbf{s}_j)^2}+4n(n-1)(n-2)\overline{(\mathbf{s}_i\cdot\mathbf{s}_j)(\mathbf{s}_i\cdot\mathbf{s}_k)}+$$
$$+n(n-1)(n-2)(n-3)\overline{(\mathbf{s}_i\cdot\mathbf{s}_j)(\mathbf{s}_k\cdot\mathbf{s}_l)}=[S'(S'+1)-\tfrac{3}{4}n]^2. \quad (47)$$

Substitution of (45) and (46) in (47) now yields

$$\overline{(\mathbf{s}_i\cdot\mathbf{s}_j)(\mathbf{s}_k\cdot\mathbf{s}_l)}=\frac{S'^2(S'+1)^2-(\tfrac{5}{2}n-3)S'(S'+1)+\tfrac{15}{16}n(n-2)}{n(n-1)(n-2)(n-3)}. \quad (48)$$

The mean square deviation is

$$\Delta^2_{S'}=\overline{\mathscr{H}'^2}-W^2_{S'}. \quad (49)$$

One can now substitute (45), (46), and (48) in (44) and then in turn (43) and (44) in (49). One then finds the Heisenberg result (23) if one keeps only the terms of highest order in $S'$ or $n$. These terms are those which increase as the first power of $n$ or $S'$ when $n$ and $S'$ become very great. To be sure, the highest-order terms in $\mathscr{H}'^2$ and $W^2_{S'}$ both increase as $n^2$, but they cancel each other in (49). To the approximation under consideration one may ignore the distinction between $n-1$ and $n$ in the denominators of (45) and (46), but in squaring (43) and in (48) one must use the somewhat better approximations $(n-1)^{-2}\sim(n+2)/n^3$ and $[n(n-1)(n-2)(n-3)]^{-1}\sim(n+6)/n^5$ respectively, as the corresponding terms in (49) are larger. In this fashion one finally arrives at (23).

One assumption which may well have bothered the reader is that we have supposed that all the scalar product terms in ⟨16⟩ have the same mean value as given in (42), despite the fact that ⟨16⟩ involves only neighbouring pairs, whereas we obtained (42) by averaging over all pairs of atoms in the crystal, whether adjacent or not. The legitimacy of this procedure is not immediately obvious, as the presence of the coupling potential ⟨16⟩ might conceivably make the mean of $\mathbf{s}_i\cdot\mathbf{s}_j$ for interacting pairs ($i,j$ neighbours) different than for the non-interacting pairs not involved in ⟨16⟩. Superficially this might seem the more likely since in the actual system of quantization the expression ⟨16⟩ is a diagonal matrix when the sum is taken over interacting pairs rather than over any arbitrary $\tfrac{1}{2}nz$ pairs. The following argument somewhat resembling one of Dirac's[36] removes this objection. The average value in question is proportional to the 'spur' or diagonal sum of the $\omega(S')$-dimensional matrix representing $\mathbf{S}_i\cdot\mathbf{S}_j$ for given $S'$. The invariance of the spur (§ 35) shows that this average is invariant of the mode of quantization, and by a proper transformation one can make a sum analogous to ⟨16⟩ a diagonal matrix for any $\tfrac{1}{2}nz$ pairs, rather than for the actual interacting pairs (neighbours). In virtue of this invariance such transformations will not affect the average of any $\mathbf{S}_i\cdot\mathbf{S}_j$. Therefore the mean value of $\mathbf{S}_i\cdot\mathbf{S}_j$ does not depend on whether it is

[36] P. A. M. Dirac, *Proc. Roy. Soc.* **123**A, 730 (1929), or *The Principles of Quantum Mechanics*, p. 211.

included in $\langle 16 \rangle$, and so all pairs are on a par as regards their mean values, regardless of whether or not they are neighbours.[37] One can similarly justify the assumption made in using (45), (46), (48) in connexion with (49) that these various mean products are the same regardless of whether $i$, $j$, $k$, $l$ are neighbours.

## 79. Magneto-caloric and Magnetostrictive Effects

Since a body in a magnetic field has a different energy than in its absence, and since the amount of magnetization changes with temperature, the application of such a field will produce a change in the specific heat. If measured per gramme mol., this change, which we shall call the 'magnetic specific heat', is given by

$$c_v - c_v^0 = L \frac{\partial}{\partial T}(\overline{\overline{W}} - \overline{\overline{W}}^0) = L \frac{\partial}{\partial T}\left[ kT^2 \frac{\partial \log Z/Z^0}{\partial T} \right], \qquad (50)$$

where $\overline{\overline{W}}$ and $Z$ are respectively the mean energy per molecule and the partition function in the presence of the field, and $\overline{\overline{W}}^0$, $Z^0$ are the corresponding expressions in its absence.

The third law of thermodynamics requires that the entropy $\mathfrak{S}$ remain finite at $T = 0$. As the specific heat at constant volume is $c_v = T\partial\mathfrak{S}/\partial T$, this means that the specific heat must approach the limit zero at $T = 0$. Contrary to this law, the magnetic specific heat in the Langevin theory has the non-vanishing value $Lk$ at $T = 0$, as is seen by using in (50) the Langevin partition function

$$Z/Z^0 = \tfrac{1}{2} \int_0^\pi e^{\mu H \cos\theta/kT} \sin\theta \, d\theta = \frac{kT}{\mu H} \sinh \frac{\mu H}{kT}.$$

On the other hand $c_v - c_v^0$ is indeed zero at $T = 0$ if one employs the Brillouin function demanded by quantum mechanics, for the Brillouin partition function is[38] $(x^{-J} - x^{J+1})/(1-x)$, where $x = e^{-g\beta H/kT}$, and this makes (50) vanish at $T = 0$. The compliance of the magnetic specific heat in quantum mechanics with the third law still remains true even if a Weiss molecular field is included to represent the effect of the Heisenberg exchange coupling, or if the Bloch modification of the Heisenberg theory appropriate to low temperatures is introduced. We omit explicit proofs, as all such results are merely special cases of the quite obvious result that any quantum distribution gives zero specific heat at $T = 0$.

[37] This is not to be construed as meaning that all pairs have the same mean value in problems where constraints are imposed on certain groups of electrons, such as e.g. Heisenberg's calculation cited in note 16. For instance, in atoms with $S > \tfrac{1}{2}$, the mean of $\mathbf{s}_i \cdot \mathbf{s}_j$ is different for inter-atomic than intra-atomic electron pairs because we constrain $S$ to one particular value rather than average over all values of $S$ consistent with given $S'$.

[38] This partition function is the same as the denominator evaluated on p. 257.

In fact, quantum partition functions are discrete summations $\sum e^{-W/kT}$, so that near $T = 0$ the expression $\log(Z/Z^0)$ is very approximately of the form $-(W_1 - W_1^0)/kT$, where $W_1 - W_1^0$ is the change in energy produced in the lowest state by the field. This form makes (50) vanish, whereas the classical distribution functions involving integration rather than summation do not have this property. The physical significance is that near $T = 0$ the molecules are not raised out of their quantum state of very lowest energy (including the spacial orientation of least energy) by increasing the temperature infinitesimally from the absolute zero. Instead $kT$ must be made comparable with the excitation energy of the next state before $c_v$ becomes appreciable.

The magnetic specific heat predicted by (50) is observed qualitatively in some ferromagnetic materials, usually with an adiabatic experimental method, whereby application of the field produces a change in temperature. We shall not give details, which have been discussed by Weiss,[39] and which he shows are nicely explained by his molecular fields. As we have seen that Heisenberg's theory gives results substantially equivalent to the Weiss theory (except for the difference between the Langevin and Brillouin functions), there is no difficulty in understanding in a general way these Weiss thermo-magnetic effects.

Even in the absence of a magnetic field, there should be a discontinuity in specific heat as one passes through the Curie point, a result first noted by Weiss.[39] In terms of the Heisenberg theory, this is because the states of high resultant spin are probable for the crystal below the Curie point, while those of very low spin gain the upper hand above the latter. In other words, the prevalent spin $S^\dagger$ is large for $T < T_C$, but is very small for $T > T_C$, as the crystal loses its spontaneous magnetization above the Curie point. To calculate this discontinuity in $c_v^0$ it will suffice, as a first approximation, to assume that all states of the same crystalline spin possess the same energy. An equivalent assumption was made in the original work of Fowler and Kapitza.[40] Also we may neglect the statistical distribution of various values of $S'$, as we saw in § 77 that the probability had a steep maximum at $S' = S^\dagger$. Thus for $T < T_C$, we may take $n\overline{\overline{W}}$ [41] equal to the expression $W_{S'}$ given in (22), with $S' = S^\dagger$, while for $T > T_C$ we take $\overline{\overline{W}} = 0$.

[39] Weiss and Beck, *J. de Physique*, **7**, 249 (1908); Weiss, Piccard, and Carrard, *Arch. des Sci. Phys. et. Nat.* **42**, 379 (1916); **43**, 113 and 199 (1917); P. Weiss, *J. de Physique*, **2**, 161 (1921); Weiss and Forrer, *Annales de Physique*, **15**, 153 (1926); Stoner, *Magnetism and Atomic Structure*, p. 289.

[40] R. H. Fowler and P. Kapitza, *Proc. Roy. Soc.* **124**A, 1 (1929).

[41] The factor $n$ appears here because (22) relates to a crystal of $n$ atoms.

Here, of course, we have disregarded additive terms in the energy which do not involve the spin interaction, and so are continuous at the Curie point. The discontinuity in specific heat at the Curie point is thus

$$\Delta c_v^0 = \frac{L}{n} \lim{}_{T \to T_C - 0} \frac{\partial W_{S'}}{\partial T} - 0 = -LzJS^2 \frac{\partial \zeta^2}{\partial T}\bigg|_{T=T_C}, \tag{51}$$

by (22) and (29). The value of $\partial \zeta^2/\partial T$ is found by differentiation of the first relation of (36) with respect to $T$ after setting $y = 2zJS^2\zeta/kT$. Since $\zeta$ approaches zero when $T$ does $T_C$, this gives

$$-\frac{1}{3} \frac{(S+1)}{S} \frac{1}{T_C} = \left(\frac{2zJ}{kT_C}\right)^2 \frac{d\zeta^2}{dT}\bigg|_{T=T_C} \left[\frac{(2S+1)^4 - 1}{720}\right]$$

and so, after use of (37), Eq. (51) becomes [42]

$$\Delta c_v^0 = \tfrac{5}{2} Lk \left[\frac{(2S+1)^2 - 1}{(2S+1)^2 + 1}\right]. \tag{52}$$

As $Lk \sim 2 \,\mathrm{cal.}$, the numerical values given by (52) for some particular values of $S$ are as follows in calories/gramme mol.:

$$\Delta c_v^0 = 3 \cdot 0 \ (S = \tfrac{1}{2}), \quad 4 \cdot 0 \ (S = 1), \quad 4 \cdot 41 \ (S = \tfrac{3}{2}), \quad 5 \cdot 0 \ (S = \infty). \tag{53}$$

The value for $S = \infty$ is, as we should expect, the same as in the classical theory of Weiss. Some experimental values are [43]

$$\Delta c_v^0 = 2 \cdot 2 \ (\mathrm{Ni}), \quad 6 \cdot 1 \ (\mathrm{Fe_3O_4}), \quad 6 \cdot 8 \ (\mathrm{Fe}). \tag{54}$$

---

[42] Fowler and Kapitza[40] derived (52) for the case $S = \tfrac{1}{2}$. The general expression (52) appears to have been first obtained in unpublished work of Landau, quoted by Dorfmann.[43] Stoner notes that, in the case of $S = \tfrac{1}{2}$, inclusion of a Gaussian distribution makes the theoretical value lower than (52) and so makes for poorer agreement with experiment (*Phil. Mag.* **10**, 27 (1930)). The resulting disagreement is not, however, as bad as represented by Stoner as his formula contains an extraneous factor $\tfrac{1}{2}$ because of an algebraic error. With the Gaussian distribution the theoretical value for $S = \tfrac{1}{2}$ is

$$\frac{3Lkz}{8}\left[\sqrt{\left(1 - \frac{8}{z}\right)} - 1 + \frac{8}{z}\right].$$

We have already mentioned that this distribution is not an especially good approximation, though doubtless better than neglecting the spread entirely, and so we need not be worried at quantitative discrepancies with experiment.

[43] These experimental values are from Weiss, Piccard, and Carrard, *l.c.*,[39] except that the determination for Ni is by Mme Lapp, *Annales de Physique*, **12**, 442 (1929). The agreement on Ni is ameliorated if, following Weiss, one writes (51) in the form

$$\Delta c_v^0 = -\tfrac{1}{2} T_C C^{-1} d(2L\beta S\dagger/n)^2/dT,$$

and uses merely empirical values of the Curie point $T$, the Curie constant $C$, and the saturation magnetization $2L\beta S\dagger/n$. The discrepancy is then only a few per cent. Accurate agreement with the theoretical form (52) of (51) is clearly out of the question since the saturation magnetization is only $0 \cdot 6$ as large as that to be expected from $S = \tfrac{1}{2}$.

By measuring changes in the Thomson heat, Dorfmann, Jaanus, and Kikoin (*Zeits. f. Physik*, **54**, 277, 289 (1929)) report a discontinuity of $2 \cdot 9$ cal. mol. in the 'specific heat of electricity' of nickel at the Curie point. The agreement with (53) for $S = \tfrac{1}{2}$ is closer than the probable accuracy of (53), as (53) neglects entirely the 'spreading' of energies for given $S'$. Also, especially there is the further difficulty that the discontinuity in the

The agreement between (53) and (54) as regards order of magnitude is gratifying. As the calculation is only a crude one, we need not worry over the want of quantitative agreement, or the fact, sometimes urged against the theory, that the experimental discontinuities are somewhat gradual rather than perfectly sharp at $T = T_C$. As also seen on p. 335, nickel seems to accord much better to $S = \frac{1}{2}$ than any other value of $S$, but too much weight should not be attached to this fact as precision is wanting in both theory and experiment.

The transition from large to small crystalline spins naturally implies a change of volume at the Curie point. Fowler and Kapitza [40] calculate that the order of magnitude of this change should be about 1 per cent., in accord with experiment. The reader is referred to their interesting paper for details. The sign of the observed change is such as to require $dJ/dV > 0$, or that the exchange integral increase with the volume. This seems at first thought a little mystifying, as one would expect $|J|$ to be greatest at small volumes, but is in accord with a theoretical prediction of Slater [28] that states of low crystalline spin have the least energy if the atoms are close enough together. This is more or less equivalent to saying that $J$ would become negative if the volume were sufficiently diminished, although this statement is a little misleading, as Slater's whole argument is based on the fact that the Heisenberg or Heitler-London perturbation theory is a poor approximation at small inter-atomic distances, so that one should use instead a method developed in Bloch's theory of conduction. In support of his view that sufficient concentration precludes ferromagnetism, Slater cites [44] the fact that in ferromagnetic bodies the ratio of the orbital radius of the $3d$ electrons to the inter-atomic distance in ferromagnetic bodies seems to be smaller than the usual ratio of the radius of the valence orbits to this distance in most materials. Fowler and Kapitza emphasize that the sign and small magnitude of the volume change at the Curie point show quite conclusively that the forces between the electrons which are responsible for ferromagnetism cannot be the 'cement' which holds the solid together. Instead, forces between other groups of electrons, presumably the outer or true valence electrons, as distinct from the 'ferromagnetic' electrons in inner incomplete shells, must be invoked.

electrical specific heat has the opposite sign from that which one would expect on ordinary elementary views. Hence the theoretical significance of Dorfmann's interesting measurements is at present a little obscure. In particular, they cannot be regarded as forcing the conclusion that the electrons responsible for ferromagnetism are conduction electrons.

[44] J. C. Slater, *Phys. Rev.* **36**, 57 (1930).

The same conclusion is reached independently on different grounds in Slater's work on cohesion.

The ordinary phenomenon of magnetostriction, i.e. the change in size observed on actually magnetizing ferromagnetic bodies, must be related to the change in volume at the Curie point in the same way as the thermo-magnetic effects of Weiss are related to the change of specific heat at this point. Both the Curie-point phenomena are primary effects resulting from the obliteration of the spontaneous molecular fields (or rather their quantum equivalents), whereas the others are secondary ones resulting from the superposition of the external on the molecular fields. Fowler and Kapitza show that in view of the observed magnitude and sign of the volume change at the Curie point, the observed magneto-strictive effects are of the right sign and order of magnitude (viz. the relative change in length calculated for iron on pseudo-saturation is $3 \cdot 5 \times 10^{-5}$, as compared to $2 \times 10^{-5}$ observed by Webster).

## 80. Feeble Paramagnetism

Numerous solids exhibit a feeble paramagnetism, which is comparable with diamagnetism in order of magnitude, and which is often independent of temperature, even though spectroscopic theory shows that the same materials would be strongly paramagnetic and conform approximately to Curie's law if present in the gaseous state. The researches of Honda and of Owen [45] show that a great many pure solid elements, e.g. the alkalis and earths, are of this category.

There is no difficulty in understanding theoretically the existence of such feeble paramagnetism. There are two possible explanations, viz. on the ground of inter-atomic interactions, which we shall consider first, and on the ground of the degeneracy phenomena in the Fermi-Dirac statistics. Actually both effects are doubtless to a certain extent superposed, but they are too complicated to discuss when together.

*Inter-atomic Interactions—'Exchange Demagnetization'*. We have shown at length in § 73 that if the spacial separation due to inter-atomic interaction is large compared to $kT$, the orbital magnetic moment is largely quenched, leaving only a small residual effect, due to 'high-frequency matrix elements', which has the desired independence of temperature. Unless the atoms happen to be in singlet states, it is also necessary to have some mechanism for quenching the spin. One possibility is the existence of such an intense magnetic coupling between spin and orbit within the atom that the inequality (4), Chap. XI, is

---

[45] K. Honda, *Ann. der Physik*, **32**, 1027 (1910); M. Owen, *ibid.* **37**, 657 (1912).

reversed. The inter-atomic forces are then unable to loosen sufficiently the coupling between spin and orbit, and the spin magnetic moment can hence be quenched along with the orbital (cf. p. 313). This is likely only in very heavy atoms, where the multiplet structures are wide, whereas many feebly paramagnetic solids are light (e.g. aluminium) or even exist in $S$ states devoid of multiplet structures (e.g. the alkalis).[46] A further difficulty is that Kramers' theorem (p. 296) shows that the quenching of the spin is necessarily only a partial one if the atom contains only an odd number of electrons.

It is probable that the spin is more commonly quenched through the operation of the Heisenberg exchange effect. If the exchange integral $J$ is negative, this effect favours the states of low crystalline spin, and so tends to efface any paramagnetism which would be present in the gaseous state. We then have 'exchange demagnetization', the exact opposite of ferromagnetism. Except for the change in sign, the discussion proceeds entirely as in Heisenberg's theory of ferromagnetism. If we neglect the refinement of the 'spread' of energy-levels belonging to a given $S'$, the susceptibility will be given by the expression (39), which can always be used since now always $T > T_C$ as $T_C < 0$. The molar susceptibility will thus be given by the expression

$$\chi_{\text{mol}} = \frac{4LS(S+1)\beta^2}{3k(T-T_C)} = 0{\cdot}496\,\frac{S(S+1)}{T+\Delta},$$

where

$$\Delta = -T_C = -\frac{2zJS(S+1)}{3k}$$

(cf. (37)). This susceptibility will be of the order of magnitude $10^{-5}$–$10^{-4}$ observed experimentally in feebly paramagnetic media, provided one assumes that $T_C$ is of the order $-10^4$. The temperature dependence is then very subordinate, as $\Delta \gg T$. Such a value of $T_C$ or $\Delta$ requires that the exchange integral $J$ be about $-1$ volt, a larger numerical value than in Heisenberg's theory of magnetism, where $T_C \sim 10^3$, $J \sim 0{\cdot}1$ volt. This difference does not seem too unreasonable, as the exchange integrals between the true valence orbits, especially the highly eccentric $s$ ones, may well be larger than between the nearly circular $d$ orbits responsible for ferromagnetism. Also one has Slater's [28, 44] somewhat allied suggestion that the ratio of the orbital radius to the interatomic distance is less than usual in ferromagnetic media.

Two points may be mentioned as favouring the above. One is that

---

[46] The alkali atoms have $^2S$ ground states, and hence have strong spin paramagnetism (given by Eq. (59) § 80) when free. The normal levels of earth atoms, such as Al, are of the type $^2P$ and hence possess both spin and orbital moments.

the relative abundance of feebly paramagnetic materials as compared
to ferromagnetic is in agreement with the Heitler-London idea that the
common bonds have negative $J$, also with Slater's proposition that low
crystalline spins predominate at high densities—not to mention the fact
that the Gaussian calculation, &c., shows that even with positive $J$ the
exchange effects may still not lead to ferromagnetism without the proper
crystalline arrangement, number of neighbours, &c. The second point
is that many feebly paramagnetic media, notably, of course, pure elements, are composed solely of naturally paramagnetic ions, so that
practically all neighbours have exchange couplings between their spins.
This is in marked contrast to the salts of the iron group, where we saw
that the large magnetic dilution made the exchange effects subordinate
and the spin hence free. We must, however, caution that there also
exist feebly paramagnetic complex ions, whose feeble paramagnetism
persists irrespective of the extent to which these ions are diluted in
other media. Such ions involve the theory for polyatomic molecules,
as discussed on pp. 272 and 293, and so are not to be confused with
the present discussion of solids composed of simple atoms. We can,
however, say that in the theory of these ions the complex ion is a unit
of structure corresponding in a certain sense to the whole micro-crystal
in the present discussion.

*Fermi-Dirac Statistics.* Pauli has shown [47] that it is possible to explain
the quenching of the spin in solids in quite a different way without
invoking the exchange forces between electrons if one assumes that all
the electrons not in closed shells participate to a certain extent in conduction or, in other words, are at least partially free, so that they can
be considered as wandering in, say, a cubical box of volume $V = l^3$.
Each electron has then three translational quantum numbers $n_1$, $n_2$, $n_3$
besides a fourth quantum number $m_s$ which gives the component of
spin along some axis. The Pauli exclusion principle states that no two
electrons have all four quantum numbers the same. At the absolute
zero the totality of electrons, regarded as one big system, will be in the
state of lowest energy. In the absence of external fields the dependence
of the energy on $m_s$ can be disregarded, and if there are $n$ conduction
electrons this means that at $T = H = 0$ there are two electrons for each
of the $n/2$ combinations of the quantum numbers $n_1$, $n_2$, $n_3$ which yield
the least energy. Each combination of these numbers, i.e. each translational state, we shall call a cell. Because of the exclusion principle, two
electrons in the same cell differ as to the sign of $m_s$ and compensate

---

[47] W. Pauli, Jr., *Zeits. f. Physik*, **41**, 81 (1927).

each other magnetically. Any paramagnetic alinement of the spins in a magnetic field, whereby more electrons have $m_s = -\frac{1}{2}$ than $m_s = \frac{1}{2}$, can be secured only by 'boosting' some of the electrons out of the $n/2$ originally occupied cells, and giving them higher values of the quantum numbers $n_1$, $n_2$, $n_3$. We now see qualitatively why much of the para-magnetism is suppressed in the Fermi-Dirac statistics based on the exclusion principle.

The readjustment in the distribution among the cells in a magnetic field does, however, take place to a certain slight extent even at low temperatures, leaving a small residual paramagnetism. The latter may be calculated at the absolute zero without delving into any of the intricacies of the Fermi-Dirac statistics,[48] such as, for instance, what is meant by temperature, which can no longer be defined as proportional to the mean translational kinetic energy. We shall follow a simple and elegant method due to Frenkel.[49] At the absolute zero the distribution is, of course, that of minimum energy. When a magnetic field is applied, this is no longer that in which the electrons are paired in the $n/2$ originally lowest cells. Instead we may suppose that the $n/2-k$ cells of least original energy have their full quota of two magnetically paired electrons, but that the next succeeding $2k$ cells each have a single electron with $m_s = -\frac{1}{2}$. As $k \ll n$, we may to a sufficient approximation regard these $2k$ cells as equally spaced in unperturbed energy, with the same spacing $\Delta W$ as that in the vicinity of the highest originally occupied cells, which we shall call the critical spacing. The change from the original complete pairing to the new distribution involves an increase of amount $k^2 \Delta W$ in the 'unperturbed' part of the energy, as taking an electron from cell $\frac{1}{2}n-x$ to $\frac{1}{2}n+x$ changes this energy by an amount $2x\Delta W$, and to a sufficient approximation $\sum_{x=1}^{k} x = k^2/2$. However, this change in the distribution diminishes by an amount $2k\beta H$ the part of the energy due to the magnetic field, as 'turning over' an electron from $m_s = \frac{1}{2}$ to $m_s = -\frac{1}{2}$ gives an alteration $-g\beta H = -2\beta H$. The value of $k$ appropriate to the absolute zero is that which minimizes the total energy $k^2 \Delta W - 2\beta k H + $ constant, and is hence $k = \beta H/\Delta W$. As $2k$ elec-trons now have spins alined along the field, the susceptibility per unit-volume is

$$\chi = \frac{2k\beta}{VH} = \frac{2\beta^2}{V\Delta W}. \tag{55}$$

[48] For exposition of these statistics see, for instance, Fowler's *Statistical Mechanics* Chap. XXI.

[49] J. Frenkel, *Zeits. f. Physik*, **49**, 31 (1928).

The value of the critical spacing $\Delta W$ will depend on whether we consider the conduction electrons as absolutely free, or consider the binding effect of the atoms through which they migrate. We shall first treat the case that they are absolutely free, as in Sommerfeld's theory of conduction. Here the unperturbed translational wave function of an electron is $\psi = A \sin(\pi n_1 x/l)\sin(\pi n_2 y/l)\sin(\pi n_3 z/l)$ as it vanishes at the walls of the box and satisfies the appropriate wave equation $h^2\nabla^2\psi+8\pi^2 mW\psi = 0$ provided

$$W = \frac{h^2(n_1^2+n_2^2+n_3^2)}{8ml^2} \qquad (n_1, n_2, n_3 > 0). \tag{56}$$

There is one cell at each corner of unit cubes in the $n_1$, $n_2$, $n_3$ space, and so the number of cells with energies inferior to some given value $W_{max}$ is approximately the volume $(4\pi/3)(2ml^2W_{max}/h^2)^{3/2}$ of one octant of a sphere of radius $(8ml^2W_{max}/h^2)^{\frac{1}{2}}$. The critical energy, or energy of the highest cell occupied at $T = H = 0$, is $(h^2/8ml^2)(3n/\pi)^{2/3}$, as it defines an octant of volume $n/2$. The spacing $\Delta W$ of the cells near the critical upper limit is $2dW/dn = (h^2/6ml^2)(9/\pi^2 n)^{\frac{1}{3}}$. Substitution of this value of $\Delta W$ in (55) yields

$$\chi = \frac{12m\beta^2}{h^2}\left(\frac{n}{V}\right)^{\frac{1}{3}}\left(\frac{\pi}{3}\right)^{\frac{2}{3}} \tag{57}$$

where $n/V$ is the number of conduction electrons per unit-volume. This is Pauli's celebrated formula, which marked the beginning of the quantum theory of electrons in metals. It will be compared with experiment at the end of § 81. By considering a second approximation in the Fermi-Dirac statistics of free electrons, Bloch [50] has shown that a more accurate formula than (57) is

$$\chi = \beta^2\left[\frac{12m}{h^2}\left(\frac{n}{V}\right)^{\frac{1}{3}}\left(\frac{\pi}{3}\right)^{\frac{2}{3}} - \frac{64\pi^4 Vm^3k^2T^2}{9nh^6}\right]$$

$$= 2\cdot20\times10^{-14}\left(\frac{n}{V}\right)^{\frac{1}{3}} - 1\cdot03\times10^7 T^2\left(\frac{V}{n}\right). \tag{58}$$

As $n/V$ is of the order $10^{22}$, the second term is negligible compared to the first at ordinary temperatures, so that (57) can be regarded as an adequate approximation or, in other words, it is legitimate to treat the electron gas as completely degenerate. The independence of temperature predicted by (57) or (58) is approximately confirmed in the measurements of McLennan, Ruedy, and Cohen,[51] which extend down to $-190°$ C.

[50] F. Bloch, *Zeits. f. Physik*, **53**, 216 (1929).
[51] J. C. McLennan, R. Ruedy, and E. Cohen, *Proc. Roy. Soc.* **116**A, 468 (1927).

As an alternative to the standard Sommerfeld theory based on free electrons, Bloch [52] has developed a theory of conduction based on bound electrons. Such electrons can pass from one atom to another because of the remarkable fact that in quantum mechanics there is a finite probability of a particle traversing a peak of potential energy greater than its own energy. In Bloch's theory an electron is in a 'valley' of potential energy when bound in an atom, and is continually playing leap-frog from one valley to another, thus giving an electric current. Bloch shows that the 'over-lapping' of the wave functions of adjacent atoms removes the degeneracy associated with the fact that electron-levels are identical in identical free atoms. An electron playing leap-frog thus has a variety of closely spaced energy states even though it has only one normal state when in a perfectly isolated atom. If the total splitting of these closely spaced levels (i.e. the 'critical energy' or total energy spread $W_C$ of the $n/2$ different levels occupied at $T = 0$) is large compared to $kT$, the 'degeneration' will be practically complete, and the susceptibility will be given by the expression (55), as the various steps used in the derivation of (55) retain their validity. The constant $\Delta W$ will, of course, have a different value than that calculated for free electrons in the preceding paragraph. Thus, if the over-lapping of the wave functions of adjacent atoms is sufficient, Bloch's theory also will give a feeble paramagnetism independent of temperature. This is encouraging, as Bloch's conduction mechanism probably comes closer to reality than that by free electrons in many cases. It must, however, be cautioned that it is not at all certain whether the 'over-lapping' in his theory is in many cases adequate to make the splitting or diffusion [53] $W_C$ in the ground state large compared to $kT$. If inadequate, Eq. (55) no longer applies. In the limit $W_C \ll kT$, the susceptibility is given by the same formula,

$$\chi = \frac{n\beta^2}{VkT},\tag{59}$$

as in the Boltzmann statistics, and the solid is strongly paramagnetic. In the Sommerfeld theory for free electrons, Eq. (59) also, of course, applies to the analogous limiting case $(h^2/8ml^2)(3n/\pi)^{2/3} \ll kT$, which is

[52] F. Bloch, *Zeits. f. Physik*, **52**, 555 (1928).

[53] This diffusion $W_C$ in Bloch's theory is not to be confused with the 'spacial separation' introduced in § 73, and will usually be much smaller than the latter or than the corresponding diffusion or critical energy $(h^2/8m)(3n/\pi V)^{\frac{2}{3}}$ for free electrons. The 'spacial separation' is associated with the removal of the spacial degeneracy for a single atom, and gives a splitting into $2L+1$ components (neglecting spin). The Bloch diffusion effect involves a further division of each of these $2L+1$ components, removing the degeneracy associated with the fact that these components are otherwise the same for all atoms.

usually realized only at extremely high temperatures. We have seen that the susceptibilities of rare earth and iron salts can be treated by the Boltzmann statistics. We now see that this implied that in these salts the Bloch leap-frog effect was so small that the Fermi-Dirac interference effects were negligible. Another way of saying the same thing is that the electrons could be regarded as firmly bound to an individual atom, for Bloch's theory is a sort of intermediary between that for isolated atoms and that for free electrons. This is in accord with the fact that these salts are much poorer conductors and have higher ionization potentials than, for instance, the feebly magnetic alkali metals.

## 81. The Diamagnetism of Free Electrons in Quantum Mechanics

Landau[54] has discovered the very remarkable fact that the orbital motions of free electrons give a diamagnetic contribution in quantum mechanics, whereas we saw in § 26 that classically they were without such an effect. This difference is a little hard to explain intuitively, but arises from the fact that the boundary electrons have different quantized velocities than those which do not touch the walls of the vessel, and so the magnetic moments of these two types of electrons do not compensate each other as in classical theory. (Classically, both types have the Maxwell-Boltzmann distribution of velocities.)

The calculation is most easily made by using cylindrical coordinates $\rho$, $z$, $\phi$, with the applied magnetic field along the $z$ direction. The $z$ component of motion can then be disregarded for our immediate purposes, as there is no force on the electron in this direction. We have then to deal with the two-dimensional wave equation

$$-\frac{h^2}{8\pi^2 m}\left(\frac{\partial^2\psi}{\partial\rho^2}+\frac{1}{\rho}\frac{\partial\psi}{\partial\rho}+\frac{1}{\rho^2}\frac{d^2\psi}{d\phi^2}\right)+\frac{Heh}{4\pi imc}\frac{\partial\psi}{\partial\phi}+\left(\frac{e^2H^2\rho^2}{8mc^2}-W\right)\psi=0, \quad (60)$$

as can be seen, for instance, by introducing cylindrical coordinates into (2), Chap. VI, and then ignoring the $z$ degree of freedom. As the solutions of (60) are clearly of the form $\psi = e^{in_1\phi}f(\rho)$, the term in (60) which is proportional to $\partial\psi/\partial\phi$ has merely the effect of displacing $W$ by an amount $hen_1H/4\pi mc$. Without this term, Eq. (60) is identical in form with that of a two-dimensional oscillator of frequency $\nu = He/4\pi mc$. The characteristic values of the latter are well known[55] to be

$$(2n_2+|n_1|+1)h\nu,$$

---

[54] L. Landau, *Zeits. f. Physik*, **64**, 629 (1930); also given by Pauli in the report of the 1930 Solvay Congress.

[55] See, for instance, Condon and Morse, *Quantum Mechanics*, p. 78.

where $n_1$, $n_2$ are integers. Hence, as $\beta = he/4\pi mc$,

$$W = (n_1 + |n_1| + 2n_2 + 1)\beta H. \tag{61}$$

Thus a free electron, even when not enclosed by bounding walls, has a discrete rather than continuous spectrum in a magnetic field. The magnetic moment corresponding to the stationary state (61) is

$$-\frac{\partial W}{\partial H} = -(n_1 + |n_1| + 2n_2 + 1)\beta. \tag{62}$$

Classically the azimuthal quantum number $n_1$ has the geometrical significance

$$n_1 = \frac{\pi e H}{hc}(r^2 - d^2), \tag{63}$$

where $r$ is the radius of the circle described by the electron under the influence of the field, and $d$ is the distance of its centre from the origin $\rho = 0$. To prove (63) we have only to note that [56]

$$p_\phi = m(x\dot{y} - y\dot{x}) - He(x^2 + y^2)/2c$$

and that classically we may take

$$p_\phi = n_1 h/2\pi, \qquad x = x_0 + r\cos(Het/mc), \qquad y = y_0 + r\sin(Het/mc),$$

as in the field the electron moves with an angular velocity [57] $He/mc$ in a circle about some point $x_0$, $y_0$. Of course the geometry of (63) is not to be taken too literally in wave mechanics, but will clearly have at least an asymptotic meaning for large quantum numbers, by means of which the most probable position of the statistical charge density can be approximately located.

In point of fact we must consider not ideally free electrons, as above, but rather those enclosed by some vessel, as we saw on p. 101 that reflection at the boundary played a very vital role. It is most convenient to take the vessel as a cylinder of radius $R$, with axis parallel to the field. In order to avoid the complication of distortion of characteristic values by the wall, the only case readily treated is that in which the classical radius of curvature $r = \sqrt{(2mc^2W/e^2H^2)}$ is much smaller than $R$ for the great bulk of electrons. (Whether the susceptibility would be the same in the case $r \geqslant R$ is at present uncertain, although the concept of spectroscopic stability suggests that perhaps it would be.) Since in Boltzmann statistics the prevalent energies are of the

---

[56] That this is the proper definition of the canonical generalized momentum associated with the coordinate $p_\phi$ can be seen from the theory given in § 8.

[57] Note that this angular velocity, which is readily deduced by elementary mechanics, is twice that corresponding to the Larmor frequency. This difference arises because Larmor's theorem neglects second order terms in $H$.

order $kT$, this condition $r \ll R$ becomes

$$R \gg \sqrt{(2mc^2 kT/e^2 H^2)} = 3\cdot 13 \times 10^{-2} T^{\frac{1}{2}}/H,$$

an inequality clearly satisfied for ordinary values of $T$, $H$, and $R$. Out of all the electrons within the vessel a fraction of the order $r/R$ have 'boundary' orbits which classically hit the wall. This shows that in quantum mechanics the overwhelming majority of common stationary states will not have their characteristic values appreciably distorted from (61) by the influence of the boundary, although there may be a very slight distortion because some of the charge wanders outside the classical limits.

*Boltzmann Statistics.* If we use Boltzmann statistics, the partition function is

$$Z = \sum_{n_1=-\pi e H R^2/hc}^{-1} \sum_{n_2=0}^{\infty} e^{-(n_1+|n_1|+2n_2+1)\beta H/kT} = \frac{\pi e H R^2}{hc} \sum_{n_2} e^{-(2n_2+1)\beta H/kT}. \quad (64)$$

Here the choice of the limits used in the summation over $n_1$ requires some discussion. Positive values of $n_1$ have been omitted because if $R \gg r$, only a negligible number of electrons have $r \gg d$ or, in other words, centres near the origin $\rho = 0$. It is very vital that, following Landau, we have taken the lower limit for the summation as $-\pi e H R^2/hc$ rather than $-\infty$. This value is obtained on the ground that the centre of the orbit cannot be distant more than approximately $R$ from the origin, and so we can exclude all values of $n_1$ which by (63) would give $d > R$. The sum over $n_2$ in (64) is readily evaluated, as it is merely a geometric series, and one finds $Z = 4\pi^2 R^2 m\beta H h^{-2}/(e^{\beta H/kT} - e^{-\beta H/kT})$. The moment per unit-volume is

$$M = \frac{n}{V} kT \frac{\partial \log Z}{\partial H} \quad (65)$$

and is hence

$$M = -\frac{n\beta}{V}\left[\coth\frac{\beta H}{kT} - \frac{kT}{\beta H}\right] = -\frac{n\beta}{V} L(\beta H/kT), \quad (66)$$

where $L(y)$ is the usual Langevin function, but the presence of the minus sign means that there is dia- instead of paramagnetism. In the limit $h = \beta = 0$ the right-hand side of (66) reduces to zero, in agreement with the fact that classically there is no diamagnetism for free electrons. This asymptotic agreement with classical theory can also be verified by replacing the sum by an integral in (64), as then $Z$ becomes independent of $H$. For the usual case $\beta H \ll kT$, Landau's formula (66) reduces to $\chi = M/H = -n\beta^2/3VkT$, and so the orbital diamagnetism is one-third as great as the spin paramagnetism (59), making the total resultant susceptibility $2n\beta^2/3VkT$.

The moment (66) is not the same as that furnished by the more immediate formula

$$M = \frac{n}{V} \frac{\sum_{n_1, n_2} (-\partial W/\partial H) e^{-W/kT}}{\sum_{n_1, n_2} e^{-W/kT}}, \tag{67}$$

if we use the same limits of summation as in (64) and same energy values as in (61). Eq. (67) then yields a preposterously large diamagnetism (viz. the first term alone in Eq. 66), as each of the states (61) has a strongly diamagnetic moment (62). This difference as compared with (66) arises because in (65) part of $\partial Z/\partial H$ comes from the fact that in (64) the limits of summation, or number of states, as well as the energy-levels $W$ are functions of $H$. (In our previous work $Z$ involved $H$ only through $W$ and as a matter of fact we derived (65) only for this special case, cf. p. 25). To obtain a proper expression for the moment by means of (67) it is very essential to include the 'boundary' electrons which are reflected at the walls of the cylinder (cf. Fig. 5, § 26). These electrons are few in number, but have enormously greater moments than do the inner orbits—so much greater in fact that they completely neutralize the latter in classical theory. If (66) is correct, the term in (65) resulting from the dependence of the limits on $H$ must be the same as that which results from inclusion of the boundary electrons in (67). Another way of saying the same thing is that Landau's use of (65) without boundary electrons to obtain (66) implies that these electrons make a negligible contribution to (65) despite the fact that they make a large one to (67). The states $n_1 < -\pi eHR^2/hc$ are those representing boundary electrons,[58] so that when they are included, the partition function contains a constant rather than variable number of states, and so involves $H$ only through $W$. There would thus be no doubt as to the applicability of (65) were the boundary electrons included therein. It is obvious that $Z$ itself would not be appreciably affected by including the boundary states, since, though great in number, they have such high energies that only a negligible fraction, of the order $r/R$, of the total number of electrons are located therein. It is, however, not quite so obvious (although justifiable on closer examination) that the boundary states make a negligible contribution to $\partial Z/\partial H$, since they have abnormally large moments $-\partial W/\partial H$. It is therefore reassuring to show that the moment (66) can also be calculated from (67). We shall follow a variant of a method due to Teller.[59] As $R \gg r$, the magnetic moment of a bound-

[58] This is most easily seen by regarding the wall as equivalent to a fictitious central field which is zero for $\rho \leqslant R$ but which increases to a very large value when $\rho$ slightly exceeds $R$. The dynamical problem is then one in central fields, where $n_1$, $n_2$ are respectively the azimuthal and radial quantum numbers. All positive and negative values of $n_1$ are allowable in this problem, and the range of values of $n_1$ not absorbed by the inner electrons must be due to the boundary electrons. Values of $n_1$ less than $-\pi eHR^2/hc$ rapidly take the electron into the region where this fictitious field is large, and so give large energies.

[59] E. Teller, *Zeits. f. Physik*, **67**, 311 (1931). Our procedure differs from his in the use of a cylindrical rather than infinite plane boundary. Still another method, which is quite simple, has been given by Darwin (Report of the 1930 Solvay Congress or *Proc. Camb. Phil. Soc.*, **27**, 86). Instead of using bounding walls, or the equivalent sudden repulsive field cited in note 58, he introduces a radial linear restoring force $-a\rho$ which, of course, becomes large only gradually. The wave equation for this system in a magnetic field is

ary electron is approximately [60] $(-e/2c)2\pi\omega_{n_1}R^2$ where $\omega_{n_1}$ is the frequency with which this electron creeps around the complete circumference of the wall. Further by the correspondence principle we have $\omega_{n_1} = \partial W/h\partial n_1$, a well-known kinematical result in the old quantum theory.[61] As the radius $R$ of the cylinder is large compared with the radius of an ordinary orbit, $h\omega_{n_1}/W$ is very small. Hence with given $n_2$ the states belonging to different consecutive values of $n_1$ lie very close together, and the summation over $n_1$ for the boundary electrons may be replaced by an integration. Hence the expression (67) becomes

$$M = \frac{n}{V} \frac{-\dfrac{\pi e H R^2}{hc} \displaystyle\sum_{n_2=0}^{\infty} (2n_2+1)\beta e^{-(2n_2+1)\beta H/kT} - \dfrac{\pi e R^2}{hc} \displaystyle\sum_{n_2=0}^{\infty} \int_{-\infty}^{-\pi e H R^2/hc} \dfrac{\partial W_B}{\partial n_1} e^{-W_B(n_1,n_2)/kT}\, dn_1}{(\pi e H R^2/hc) \displaystyle\sum e^{-(2n_2+1)\beta H/kT}}.$$

$$(68)$$

Here the first term in the numerator arises from the overwhelming number of inner electrons, and the second from the boundary ones, whose energies $W_B(n_1,n_2)$ would be difficult to determine explicitly. The summation over $n_1$ from $-\pi e H R^2/hc$ to $-1$ has already been performed for the former, and we have omitted the contribution of the latter to the denominator, which is clearly negligible on account of the high values of $W_B$. The integration of the second term over $n_1$ can immediately be performed. Furthermore $W_B$ has the value $\infty$ at $n_1 = -\infty$ and the value (61) at $n_1 = -\pi e H R^2/hc$, as at the latter limit the orbits just begin to touch the walls of the cylinder and so do not have their energies appreciably distorted from (61). The second term in the numerator thus becomes $kT/H$ times the denominator, and so the boundary electrons contribute the second term of the Langevin function in (66). It is easily seen that now the expression (68) assumes the desired value (66).

*Fermi-Dirac Statistics.* In actual solids the calculations should be made with the Fermi-Dirac rather than Boltzmann statistics. Here also the orbital diamagnetism proves to be one-third as great as the spin paramagnetism. Landau has shown that this is true regardless of whether or not the degeneracy is complete, but we shall give an elementary proof in which complete degeneracy is assumed, so that all orbital states may be supposed occupied by two electrons up to a certain critical energy $W_C$, and vacant thereafter. A similar assumption was made on p. 349 and is amply warranted at ordinary temperatures, for

readily integrated, as the harmonic form is preserved, and in the limit $a = 0$ Darwin finds the same expression for the susceptibility as Landau's.

[60] The boundary electrons have inordinately large moments because they encircle the origin when they make a circuit of the wall (Cf. Fig. 5, § 26). Hence in their case we may replace $m\rho^2\dot{\phi}$ by $m R^2\overline{\dot{\phi}} = 2\pi m R^2\omega_n$. On the other hand, the inner electrons usually do not encircle the origin, so that they have $\overline{\dot{\phi}} = 0$; their resultant moment (62) is due entirely to the fact that $\rho$ is different at different points of the orbit, a factor of subordinate importance in the case of the boundary electrons.

[61] Cf. for instance, J. H. Van Vleck, *Quantum Principles and Line Spectra*, p. 298. This relation will be a good approximation with the new mechanics, as the quantum number $n_1$ is large for the boundary electrons.

the density of electrons in ordinary conductors is sufficient to make $W_C/k$ of the order $10^{4\circ}$ C. Unlike the case of the Boltzmann statistics, the component of motion in the direction $z$ of the field $H$ cannot be entirely forgotten, as the exclusion principle can be applied only when we consider all components. If the cylinder has a length $l$, the characteristic values of the energy associated with the $z$ component are $h^2 n_3^2/8ml^2$ (cf. Eq. (56)), and consequently there are $\sqrt{8ml^2 W_{max}}/h^2$ values of $n_3$ for which this part of the energy does not exceed any given limit $W_{max}$. As there are two possibilities for the spin quantum number, and as a state is occupied if the $z$ component does not require more energy than $W_C - W$, the weight of a given state $n_1$, $n_2$ of motion in the $x$, $y$ plane is $2f(W)$, where $f = \sqrt{8ml^2(W_C - W)}/h^2$ if $W < W_C$, and $f = 0$ if $W > W_C$. As previously, we use $W$ to denote only the $x$-$y$ part of the energy. In Eq. (68) we must now replace the Boltzmann exponential factor by this $f(W)$. The integration of the boundary term over $n_1$ can be performed in the same fashion as previously explained in the Boltzmann case. The expression for the moment thus becomes

$$M = \frac{n}{V} \frac{\beta \sum_{n_2=0}^{n_C} [-(2n_C+1)(n_C-n_2)^{\frac{1}{2}} + \frac{10}{3}(n_C-n_2)^{\frac{3}{2}}]}{\sum (n_C - n_2)^{\frac{1}{2}}}, \tag{69}$$

with $2n_C + 1 = W_C/\beta H$. It is adequate to replace the sum by an integral in the denominator, but the numerator vanishes in classical theory, and here it is necessary to use the more accurate approximation formula [62]

$$\sum_{x=y_1}^{y_2} F(x) = \int_{y_1-\frac{1}{2}}^{y_2+\frac{1}{2}} F(x)\, dx - \frac{1}{24} F'(x)\Big|_{y_1-\frac{1}{2}}^{y_2+\frac{1}{2}}.$$ Eq. (69) thus gives $M = -n\beta/4Vn_C$.

By filling twice the $n/2$ lowest orbital states, one finds

$$W_C = (h^2/8m)(3n/\pi V)^{2/3}.$$

This is, as we should expect, the same value of $W_C$ as we calculated on p. 351 in the absence of the field. It is thus finally found that (69) becomes $\chi = -4m\beta^2 h^{-2}(n\pi^2/9V)^{1/3}$, so that the resultant susceptibility inclusive of both spin and orbit has two-thirds as large a value as (57).

It is to be emphasized that all these results apply only to electrons which are absolutely free. As soon as an electron becomes tightly bound

---

[62] Cf. Runge and Willers in *Encyl. der Math. Wiss.* ii. **2**, 92. We apply this approximation formula to our function $F$ despite the fact that this $F$ has a discontinuity in its first derivative at $n_2 = n_C$ since we must take $F = 0$ for $n_2 > n_C$. The justification for so doing lies in the fact that this discontinuity disappears as soon as one makes any allowance, however small, for the effect of temperature. In other words, if $T$ is greater than 0, but small compared to $W_C/k$ the distribution function diminishes exceedingly rapidly but not discontinuously in the vicinity of $W = W_C$.

to the atom, its diamagnetism will be given by the ordinary atomic formula $-e^2\overline{r^2}/6mc^2$ (cf. Eq. (2), Chap. VIII), even though occasionally it plays leap-frog from one atom to another. The freak case of bismuth, in which the electron seems to migrate around frequently from one atom to another, and so has an abnormally large radius and diamagnetism, has already been cited in § 23. In general one has no adequate theory for the intermediate case of feebly bound electrons.

It is tempting to calculate the susceptibilities for the alkali metals under the assumption that the valence electrons are completely free and conform to the Fermi-Dirac statistics. It is essential to include a correction for the diamagnetism of the residual positive ions ($Na^+$, &c.), which can be estimated by any of the methods given in § 52. This ionic diamagnetism we denote by $\chi_+$ in the following table, while $\chi_{-e}$ denotes two-thirds the expression (57), multiplied by the volume of a gramme mol. of the metal. We use Pauling's estimates of $\chi_+$ for $Li^+$, $Na^+$, and $K^+$, but Ikenmeyer's for $Rb^+$ and $Cs^+$ as the method of screening constants is probably more reliable for light atoms and the additivity method for heavy (see § 52).

CALCULATED AND OBSERVED MOLAR SUSCEPTIBILITIES OF ALKALI METALS

|  | Li | Na | K | Rb | Cs |
|---|---|---|---|---|---|
| $\chi_{-e}$ Calc. | $6{\cdot}8 \times 10^{-6}$ | $10{\cdot}2 \times 10^{-6}$ | $15{\cdot}7 \times 10^{-6}$ | $18{\cdot}2 \times 10^{-6}$ | $21{\cdot}5 \times 10^{-6}$ |
| $\chi_+$ Calc. | $-0{\cdot}6$ | $-\ 4{\cdot}2$ | $-16{\cdot}7$ | $-31{\cdot}3$ | $-45{\cdot}7$ |
| $\chi_{mol}$ Calc. | $5{\cdot}0$ | $6{\cdot}2$ | $-\ 1{\cdot}0$ | $-13{\cdot}1$ | $-24{\cdot}2$ |
| $\chi_{mol}$ Obs.: |  |  |  |  |  |
|   Honda & Owen[45] | $3{\cdot}5$–21 | 12 | 16–23 | 6 | $-13$ |
|   Sucksmith[63] | .. | 14 | 20 | 6 | $-\ 3$ |
|   McLennan, R. &     C.[51] | .. | 14 | 19 | 17 | 28 |
|   Lane[64] | .. | 15 | 21 | 18 | 29 |
|   Bitter[65] | 26 | .. | .. | .. | .. |

The discrepancy between the different observations shows that experimental as well as theoretical precision is difficult. It is possible that the susceptibility varies considerably with the physical treatment accorded the specimen, as Bitter[65] finds that stretching increases the susceptibility of copper almost 50 per cent. Hence no quantitative agreement with simple theory can be expected. The experimental values are invariably greater than the calculated, and this fact is probably to be explained on the ground that the electrons are not entirely free. Very tightly bound electrons have the strong spin para-

[63] W. Sucksmith, *Phil. Mag.* **2**, 21 (1926).

[64] C. Lane, *Phil. Mag.* **8**, 354 (1929); *Phys. Rev.* **35**, 977 (1930).

[65] F. Bitter, *Phys. Rev.* **36**, 978 (1930).

magnetism (59), which is $0 \cdot 372/T$ per gramme mol., and so even feeble binding might make the free value (57) too low. Also the exchange effects discussed on p. 348 may be important. At any rate, there is no difficulty in understanding qualitatively the marked contrast between the feeble paramagnetism of the solid alkali metals, and the strongly paramagnetic behaviour of their vapours, evidenced by Gerlach's confirmation of (59) in potassium vapour (§ 57).

# BRIEF SURVEY OF SOME RELATED OPTICAL PHENOMENA

## 82. The Kramers Dispersion Formula

This formula for the index of refraction $n$ is[1]

$$n^2 - 1 = 8\pi B \sum_{l,l'} \frac{\nu(l';l)|p_E^0(l;l')|^2}{h[\nu(l';l)^2 - \nu_0^2]} e^{-W_l^0/kT} \tag{1}$$

with

$$B = \frac{N}{\sum_l e^{-W_l^0/kT}}. \tag{2}$$

The frequency of the incident light is denoted by $\nu_0$, and its wave-length we suppose large compared to the atomic or molecular radius. The index $l$ or $l'$ denotes the totality of quantum numbers necessary to specify a stationary state, and the expressions $p_E^0(l;l')$ are the unperturbed matrix elements of the component of the atom's or molecule's electric moment in the direction of the electric vector $\mathbf{E}$ of the primary beam.

Eq. (1) was first obtained as an extrapolation from classical dynamics by means of the correspondence principle, but has since been deduced more rigorously with quantum mechanics.[2] It is hence *the* formula for dispersion. Classical theories of dispersion based on naïve harmonic oscillators owe their measure of success to the fact that each term in (1) has the same 'Sellmeier' form of dependence on the frequency $\nu_0$ as a conventional oscillator of appropriately chosen charge $e_i$ and mass $m_i$, viz. $e_i^2/m_i = 8\pi^2\nu(l';l)|p_E(l;l')|^2/h$.

Some features of (1) on which we may comment briefly are the following:

(a) *Presence of Negative Terms.* Any term with $\nu(l';l) < 0$ has a negative value of $e_i^2/m_i$ for the corresponding fictitious or 'virtual' oscillator. Such a term is said to give 'negative dispersion'.[3] This can

[1] H. A. Kramers, *Nature*, **113**, 673; **114**, 310 (1924); H. A. Kramers and W. Heisenberg, *Zeits. f. Physik*, **31**, 681 (1925). Except for the negative terms the formula was first proposed by Ladenburg, *Zeits. f. Physik*, **4**, 451 (1921).

[2] See Born, Heisenberg, and Jordan, *Zeits. f. Physik*, **35**, 570 (1926), or Born and Jordan, *Elementare Quantenmechanik*, p. 240; P. A. M. Dirac, *Proc. Roy. Soc.* **114**A, 710 (1927); E. Schrödinger, *Ann. der Physik*, **81**, 109 (1926); Sommerfeld, *Atombau, Wellenmechanisher Ergänzungsband*, p. 193.

[3] The negative terms are difficult to detect experimentally because of the difficulty of obtaining a sufficient concentration of atoms in excited states, but seem to be definitely established in neon. See Ladenburg, Carst, and Kopfermann, *Zeits. f. Physik*, **48**, 15, 26, 51, 192 (1927); Kopfermann and Ladenburg, *ibid.* **65**, 167; Ladenburg and Levy, *ibid.* **65**, 189 (1929).

exist only when there is an appreciable concentration of atoms or molecules in excited states, as $\nu(l';l)$ is necessarily positive if $l$ is the lowest
state. For this reason the negative dispersion is hard to detect experimentally.

(b) *Behaviour in Limit* $h = 0$. In this limit, as well as in that of very
large quantum numbers, Eq. (1), of course, merges asymptotically [4] into
the classical dispersion formula for the corresponding dynamical system,
which is in general a 'multiply periodic one', not a harmonic oscillator.
This requirement was, in fact, the clue to the initial discovery of (1).

(c) *Isotropic Media*. If there are no fields other than that of the
incident light, and if the dispersion is by a gas or even an isotropic
liquid or solid, a spacial averaging may be performed by means of the
principle of spectroscopic stability as on p. 193.

(d) *Invariance of Temperature*. Eq. (1) is a general expression not
yet requiring the hypothesis of § 46, that the quantum numbers can be
divided into three categories $n$, $j$, $m$ such that the effect of the index
$n$ on the energy is large, while that of $j$, and of the magnetic quantum
number $m$, is small compared to $kT$. If we make this hypothesis and
also that (c) of isotropy, the procedure on pp. 193–5 reduces (1) to

$$n^2 - 1 = \frac{8\pi N}{3h} \sum_{n'(n' \neq n)} \frac{\nu(n';n)|p^0(n;n')|^2}{\nu(n';n)^2 - \nu_0^2}, \tag{3}$$

provided further that the incident light is far enough from resonance
to permit assuming that the denominators in (1) are insensitive to the
indices $j$, $j'$. At constant density the expression (3) is independent of
temperature. This is in accord with experiment (see § 16). Eq. (3),
of course, involves the resultant amplitudes $p^0(n;n')$ in place of com-
ponents thereof as in (1). The expression $8\pi^3|p^0(n;n')|^2/3h^2$ is the same
as the Einstein absorption probability coefficient [5] $B_{n \to n'}$ for the transition $n \to n'$, with unresolved fine structure $j$, $j'$.

(e) *Behaviour in Limit* $\nu_0 = 0$. When $\nu_0 = 0$, Eq. (3) is the same as
the induced or non-polar part $4\pi N\alpha$ of the static dielectric constant
(see Eq. (28), Chap. VII). This agreement seems trivial to-day, but was
not secured in the last days of the old quantum theory in which refined
applications of the correspondence principle were used to obtain the
dispersion formula (1) for periodic fields, but in which straight classical

---

[4] For proof see Kramers and Heisenberg *l.c.*[1], or J. H. Van Vleck, *Phys. Rev.* **24**, 347
(1924).

[5] For discussion and references on the Einstein $A$ and $B$ coefficients and their relation
to the dispersion formula see Born and Jordan's *Elementare Quantenmechanik*, p. 240,
or the writer's *Quantum Principles and Line Spectra*, pp. 120, 161.

dynamics were used to calculate the orbits to be quantized in the analogous static case of the Stark effect.

(*f*) *Behaviour in Limit* $\nu_0 = \infty$. For very short incident wave-lengths Eq. (1) reduces to the classical Thomson formula for the dispersion by free electrons.[6] This means that, as we would expect, impressed forces of very high frequency are resisted more by the electron's own inertial reaction than by the forces binding the electron to the rest of the molecule. We shall give only the very simple proof appropriate to a one-electron system, although the theorem is much more general. Here the matrix elements of $p_E$ are the same as those of $-ez$ if we suppose $E$ directed along the $z$ axis. If we use Cartesian coordinates in the quantum condition $p_k q_k - q_k p_k = h/2\pi i$ (Eq. $\langle 12 \rangle$, Chap. VI) we may take $q_k = z$, $p_k = m\dot{z}$, so that $p_k(l; l') = 2\pi i m \nu(l; l') z(l; l')$. As $\nu(l; l') = -\nu(l'; l)$, we then have $(p_k q_k)(l; l) = -(q_k p_k)(l; l)$. The diagonal elements of this condition thus yield the 'Thomas-Kuhn relation'[7]

$$4\pi m \sum_{l'} \nu(l; l') |z(l; l')|^2 = -\frac{h}{2\pi}. \tag{4}$$

Eqs. (4) and (2) show that (1) will reduce to the Thomson formula[8]

$$n^2 - 1 = -\frac{Ne^2}{\pi m \nu_0^2}, \tag{5}$$

provided we can neglect $\nu(l; l')^2$ in comparison with $\nu_0^2$ in the denominators, as will be the case if the incident frequency is large compared to the atom's absorption frequencies. To prove (5) classically, we observe that the solution of the differential equation $m\ddot{z} = -eE$ for a free electron in a periodic field $E = E_0 \cos 2\pi\nu_0 t$ is $z = eE/4\pi^2 m \nu_0^2$, plus arbitrary terms $At + C$ not of interest to us. Hence $n^2 - 1 = 4\pi P/E = -4\pi Nez/E$ has the value (5).

(*g*) *Explicit Values of* (3). The various terms in (3) have been evaluated numerically in certain cases. Podolsky[9] and later Reiche[10] showed that in normal atomic hydrogen (3) becomes

$$n^2 - 1 = 2 \cdot 25 \times 10^{-4} (1 + 1 \cdot 228 \times 10^{-10} \lambda_0^{-2} + 1 \cdot 65 \times 10^{-20} \lambda_0^{-4} + \ldots)$$

at $0°$ C., 76 cm., provided the incident wave-length $\lambda_0$ is large compared to that $4/3R = 1216$ Å of the softest absorption line, thus permitting

[6] This asymptotic connexion was first proved by Kramers, *Physica*, **5**, 369 (1925), although in the old quantum theory Reiche and Thomas, also Kuhn,[7] proposed summation rules equivalent to (4) in order to secure this connexion.

[7] Thomas, *Naturwissenschaften*, **13**, 627 (1925); Thomas and Reiche, *Zeits. f. Physik*, **34**, 510 (1925); Kuhn, *ibid.* **33**, 408 (1925).

[8] See, for instance, A. H. Compton, *X-rays and Electrons*, p. 205.

[9] B. Podolsky, *Proc. Nat. Acad.* **14**, 253 (1928).

[10] F. Reiche, *Zeits. f. Physik*, **53**, 168 (1929).

use of a series development in descending powers of $\lambda_0$. Explicit calculations of (3) are usually difficult because in general the summation symbolizes an integration over the continuous spectrum beyond the 'series limit' besides the usual summation over the discrete one. Podolsky dodged this integration by an ingenious method due to Epstein,[11] while Reiche showed great computational skill by performing it explicitly. The various terms of (3) have also been estimated for some of the alkalis by various workers.[12] They confirm the experimental result that the first line of the principal series far overshadows succeeding lines in intensity. It is also calculated that the part of the dispersion due to the continuous spectrum is less important than in atomic hydrogen; the computed ratios of the continuous part to the total at very high incident frequencies being respectively: Li, 0·24; Na, 0·04; H, 0·44. This difference is primarily because the normal states of alkali valence electrons have principal quantum numbers greater than unity, for the corresponding value for the Balmer series of hydrogen is 0·12, against 0·44 for the Lyman series.[13]

(*h*) *Quadrupole Effects*. Eqs. (1) or (3) embody only the dipole part of the radiation. Both theoretically [14] and experimentally [15] the quadrupole part sometimes gives an appreciable effect, though usually very small.

(*i*) *Raman Scattering*. Eqs. (1) or (3) give the dispersive effect of the Rayleigh scattering, or resonance radiation which is emitted on return of the atom to its original state after excitation. There is also the now famous Raman scattering, first predicted by Smekal and by Kramers and Heisenberg,[16] in which the scattered light differs from the incident by an atomic (or molecular) frequency $\nu(l';l)$, and which arises from fluorescent radiation, either Stokes or anti-Stokes, whereby the atom reverts after excitation to a different state than the initial. As the Raman radiation has a different frequency from the primary, it does

[11] P. S. Epstein, *Proc. Nat. Acad.* **12**, 629 (1926).

[12] Hargreaves, *Proc. Cambr. Phil. Soc.* **25**, 75 (1929); B. Trumpy, *Zeits. f. Physik*, **57**, 787 (1929) and earlier papers (Li); Y. Sugiura, *Phil. Mag.* **4**, 495 (1927) (Na).

[13] Y. Sugiura, *J. de Physique*, **8**, 113 (1927).

[14] A. Rubinowicz, *Phys. Zeits.* **29**, 817 (1928); *Zeits. f. Physik*, **53**, 267 (1929); Bartlett, *Phys. Rev.* **34**, 1247 (1929); A. F. Stevenson, *Proc. Roy. Soc.* **128**A, 591 (1930).

[15] W. Prokofjew, *Zeits. f. Physik*, **57**, 387 (1929).

[16] A. Smekal, *Naturwissenschaften*, **11**, 873 (1923); **16**, 612 (1928); Kramers and Heisenberg, *l.c.*[1] The experimental literature on the Raman effect is too copious for us to cite, but we may mention that probably the most careful measurements on gases, as distinct from liquids, are those of Rasetti, *Proc. Nat. Acad.* **15**, 234, 515 (1929); *Phys. Rev.* **34**, 367 (1929); Dickinson, Dillon, and Rasetti, *ibid.* **34**, 582 (1929); and of Wood and Dieke, *Phys. Rev.* **35**, 1355; **36**, 1421 (1930).

not react coherently with the latter to give a dispersive effect or alteration of the primary velocity of propagation, and can be observed only
by analysing spectroscopically the scattered radiation. The intensity
of a Raman line of frequency $\nu_0 + \nu(l; l')$ can be shown proportional to
the expression

$$[\nu_0 + \nu(l; l')]^4 E^2 \sum_{q=x,y,z} \left| \sum_{l''} \left( \frac{p_q^0(l; l'') p_E^0(l''; l')}{\nu_0 + \nu(l''; l')} - \frac{p_E^0(l; l'') p_q^0(l''; l')}{\nu_0 + \nu(l; l'')} \right) \right|^2. \quad (6)$$

Here the $p_q^0(l; l')$ are the matrix elements of the various Cartesian components of the unperturbed electrical moment; while the $p_E^0(l; l')$ are
those of the component along the incident electric vector **E**. As (6)
involves the products $p^0(l; l'') p^0(l''; l')$ rather than $|p^0(l; l')|^2$, a necessary
condition for a Raman line is that it involve a displacement of energy-
levels obtainable by superposition of two consecutive allowed transitions. It need not be a possible emission or absorption line. The
necessary condition just given is not also a sufficient one, as the various
product terms in (6) may have such phases as to 'interfere destructively',
i.e. cancel each other when the summation is performed, even though
they do not vanish individually. For instance, it can be shown[17] that
the only Raman displacements for the rotational quantum number $J$
in molecular spectra are $\Delta J = 0, \pm 2$; the displacement $\Delta J = \pm 1$ is
impossible, even though there be $Q$ ($\Delta J = 0$) as well as $P$, $R$ branches
($\Delta J = \pm 1$) in the absorption or emission spectra. For a harmonic
oscillator the cancellation of the various terms in (6) (individually of
the form $\Delta n = 0, \pm 2$) is so great that there is no Raman effect. The
purely nuclear motions in diatomic molecules are to a first approximation simple harmonic. Hence the observed Raman displacements in the
vibrational quantum number $v$ in such molecules (usually $\Delta v = \pm 1$)
must owe their origin to 'intermediate states' $l''$ which represent 'electronic' rather than just vibrational excitation. When there are electron
transitions, the vibrational selection rules are governed by the Franck-
Condon principle, and are more complicated than for the harmonic
oscillator. This principle sometimes allows large transitions in $v$ in
electronic absorption bands, but the interference effects are such[18] that
the only appreciable Raman lines are those for which $\Delta v = 1$ ('fundamental') or $\Delta v = 2$ (first harmonic). The latter should be much fainter
than the former, and neither of them nearly as intense as the Rayleigh
line $\Delta v = 0$.

[17] E. C. Kemble and E. Hill, *Proc. Nat. Acad.* **15**, 387 (1929); this article contains an
excellent survey of the theory of the Raman effect.

[18] C. Manneback, *Naturwissenschaften*, **17**, 364 (1929); *Zeits. f. Physik*, **62**, 224; **65**,
574 (1930); J. H. Van Vleck, *Proc. Nat. Acad.* **15**, 754 (1929).

## 83. The Kerr Effect

When a static electric field $E'$ is applied (besides, of course, the periodic field $E$ of the incident light), the medium no longer has isotropic refractive properties. Instead, it becomes birefringent and the index of refraction $n$ has a different value $n_\perp$ when $E'$ is applied perpendicular to $E$ than that $n_\parallel$ when it is applied parallel thereto. The existence of this difference, i.e. influence of an electric field on dispersion, is known as the Kerr effect, and has been investigated in quantum mechanics by Kronig[19] and by Born.[20] The derivation of the Kramers dispersion formula (1), though not particularly difficult, would require us to develop the quantum mechanics of non-conservative systems. This is our main reason for omitting all mathematical analysis in the present chapter. We must, however, mention that once Eq. (1) is granted, the calculation of the Kerr effect is a straightforward, though rather tedious, piece of *static* perturbation theory. One simply uses in (1) not the amplitudes and frequencies for a free molecule, but rather those appropriate to a molecule in a constant electric field $E'$. These can be found by means of Eq. (37) and other relations of §§ 34–5, treating $E'$ as a perturbation parameter. The system perturbed by $E'$ becomes in turn the unperturbed system for calculating the polarization and attendant dispersion (1) produced by the periodic field $E$. If one makes the usual hypothesis, that the molecule's frequencies are all either small or large compared to $kT/h$, it is finally found that

$$n_\parallel^2 - n_\perp^2 = NE'^2\left(c_0 + \frac{c_1}{T} + \frac{c_2}{T^2}\right),\tag{7}$$

where $c_0$, $c_1$, $c_2$ are complicated sums of matrix elements involving also the incident frequency $\nu_0$. Calculation of explicit numerical values for $c_0$, $c_1$, $c_2$ would be very tiring, if not difficult, and so the quantum mechanics of the Kerr effect has as yet yielded little more than classical theory.[21] The constant $c_2$ vanishes if the molecule is non-polar or monatomic. The constant $c_1$ also vanishes for atoms in states devoid of

---

[19] R. de L. Kronig, *Zeits. f. Physik*, **45**, 458 (1927); **47**, 702 (1928).

[20] Born and Jordan, *Elementare Quantenmechanik*, p. 259.

[21] We do not attempt to include any of the classical theory of the Kerr and Faraday effects, or the experimental work. A good survey of this is given by Ladenburg in the Müller-Pouillet's *Lehrbuch der Physik*, 11th ed., vol. ii, second half, Chaps. XXXVI–XL. Much of the experimental work, especially in the case of the Kerr effect (except Stuart's recent data[23]), is for liquids rather than gases, and then there is the complication of possible association. Also the Clausius-Mossotti corrections, which we have omitted, then become important.

angular momentum.[22]   The Kerr effect should hence usually be larger
and vary more rapidly with temperature in polar molecules.  It is indeed
found experimentally that $n_{\parallel}^2 - n_{\perp}^2$ varies less rapidly with temperature
than $1/T$ in non-polar molecules (also in the polar ones bromo- and
chlorobenzol).  On the other hand, it varies more rapidly than $1/T$ in
the polar materials chloroform and ethyl ether, showing clearly the
effect of the term $c_2$.  It is particularly striking that recent experiments
of Stuart[23] on the Kerr effect in gases show that after reduction to
constant density $n_{\parallel}^2 - n_{\perp}^2$ is very nearly proportional to $1/T^2$ in ethyl
chloride and methyl bromide (polar), and to $1/T$ in carbon disulphide
(non-polar); in these cases the non-vanishing term of highest order in
$1/T$ ($c_2$ in polar, $c_1$ in non-polar molecules) thus has a preponderant
influence.  The second-order dependence on the field strength $E'$ demanded by (7) as well as by all earlier theories is, of course, confirmed
experimentally.

## 84. The Faraday Effect

If the applied field is magnetic rather than electric, one has formulae
analogous to (7) with $E'$ replaced by $H$ and with $c_2 = 0$ unless the
molecule is paramagnetic.  This is the Cotton-Mouton or Voigt effect,[24]
already discussed, like the Kerr effect, in § 31 for the static case or
limit $\nu_0 = 0$.  Because of the second-order dependence on $H$, it is hard
to measure, and the experimental data are rather meagre.

Far more important is the fact that a magnetic (but not an electric)
field applied parallel to the direction of propagation of the incident light
produces a rotation of the plane of polarization.  This is the so-called
Faraday effect, which is of the first rather than the second order in $H$.
The rotation $\Theta$ in a length $x$ is thus given by a formula of the form
$\Theta = RHx$.  The factor of proportionality is called the Verdet constant,
and is the same as $\pi\nu_0(n_+ - n_-)/Hc$, where $n_-$, $n_+$ are the refractive
indices for left- and right-handed circularly polarized beams.  Elementary classical theory based on Larmor's theorem and a rather too
simple atomic model yields the so-called Becquerel formula [25]

$$\Theta = CHx\nu_0 \frac{dn}{d\nu_0} \quad \text{with} \quad C = \frac{e}{2mc^2}. \tag{8}$$

[22] We are unable to agree with the statement on p. 267 of Born and Jordan's *Elementare Quantenmechanik* that $c_1$ vanishes for all types of atoms.

[23] H. A. Stuart, *Zeits. f. Physik*, **55**, 358; **59**, 13; **63**, 533 (1929–30), especially p. 538
of **63**.

[24] A survey of existing experimental work will appear in Professor Cotton's paper in
the report of the 1930 Solvay Congress.

[25] H. Becquerel, *Comptes Rendus*, **125**, 679 (1897).

*Faraday Effect in Atoms.* A quite complete quantum-mechanical treatment in the monatomic case has been given by Rosenfeld.[26] His calculations use many of the same general sorts of perturbation devices as in our preceding chapters, especially frequent use of the principle of spectroscopic stability and the measuring of multiplet intervals relative to $kT$. The results reduce to simple forms only in limiting cases, which we denote by $(a)$, $(b)$, $(c)$.

$(a)$ Multiplet width small compared to $kT$ and incident light well outside the multiplet. By the latter condition we mean that $\nu_0 - \nu(n'; n)$ is large in magnitude compared to the size of the multiplet, so that there is no especially small denominator or large 'resonance effect' for one particular multiplet component. Here Rosenfeld finds that

$$\Theta = \frac{4\pi e N H x \nu_0^2}{3mc^2} \sum_{n'} \left\{ \frac{\nu(n';n)|p^0(n;n')|^2}{h[\nu(n';n)^2 - \nu_0^2]^2} + \frac{f(L', L)|p^0(n;n')|^2}{\nu(n';n)^2 - \nu_0^2} \frac{L(L+1)}{3kT} \right\}. \quad (9)$$

The terms of (9) which are respectively independent of and inversely proportional to the temperature are usually, following Ladenburg,[27] called the diamagnetic and paramagnetic parts of the Faraday rotation, but this is not to be construed as meaning that they have opposite signs, for this is not necessarily the case. The factor $f$ in the second term has the value $3/4(L+1)$, $-3/4L$, or $-3/4(L^2+L)$ according as the change $L'-L$ in the azimuthal quantum number in the transition $n \to n'$ is 1, $-1$, or 0. As $n^2 - 1 \sim 2(n-1)$, comparison with (3) shows that the diamagnetic part of the rotation is given exactly by Becquerel's formula (8). In this particular case the spin anomaly has thus completely cancelled out, a result previously found in the old quantum theory by Darwin.[28] The need of adding a paramagnetic term to that given by Becquerel's formula was stressed by Ladenburg.[27] As it contains the factor $L(L+1)$, this term disappears if the atom is in an $S$ state, regardless of whether there is a spin paramagnetism.[29]

$(b)$ Incident light very close to resonance with one particular multiplet component.[30] Here we may omit the refractive effect of all lines but

---

[26] L. Rosenfeld, *Zeits. f. Physik*, **57**, 835 (1930).

[27] R. Ladenburg, *Zeits. f. Physik*, **34**, 898 (1925). The possible existence of a paramagnetic term appears also to have been intimated in previous work of Drude, Becquerel, and Dorfmann.        [28] C. G. Darwin, *Proc. Roy. Soc.* **112**A, 314 (1926).

[29] The explicit expressions for $f$ contain a factor $L$ in the denominator in the case of the transitions $L \to L-1$ and $L \to L$, but this occasions no difficulty even in $S$ states $(L = 0)$, as the amplitudes $p^0(n;n')$ vanish for these transitions if $L = 0$. States of negative $L$ are, in fact, non-existent, while the non-existence of the transition $L = 0 \to L = 0$ is a well-known selection rule.

[30] We, however, suppose throughout that the incident light is well outside the Zeeman pattern, i.e. that $\nu(n';n) - \nu_0$ is large in magnitude compared to $He/4\pi mc$.

this particular component. The expression for the rotation proves to be [31]

$$\Theta = \frac{4\pi e N_j H x v_0^2}{3mc^2} |p^0(nj; n'j')|^2 \left[ \frac{f_1 \nu(n'j'; nj)}{[\nu(n'j'; nj)^2 - \nu_0^2]^2} + \right.$$

$$\left. + \left( \frac{g_j^2 J(J+1)}{3kT} + \gamma_j \right) \left( \frac{f_2}{\nu(n'j'; nj)^2 - \nu_0^2} \right) \right]. \quad (10)$$

Because it contains a second rather than a first power of $\nu(n'j'; nj)^2 - \nu_0^2$ in the denominator, the diamagnetic part gives greater resonance than the paramagnetic, and so predominates except at very low temperatures. The paramagnetic part is present whenever the atom has a magnetic moment, and, unlike the previous case $(a)$, remains even in an $S$ state if the latter has a spin moment. Since in the present case one term in the summation in (1) has much the greatest resonance, Eq. (1) shows that $\nu_0 dn/d\nu_0$ is proportional to $\nu_0^2/(\nu(n'j'; nj)^2 - \nu_0^2)^2$. Hence the form of dependence on frequency for the diamagnetic part is such as to ensure the validity of Becquerel's formula (8), but in general with an anomalous value of $C$, viz. $ef_1/2mc^2$. The expressions $f_1, f_2, \gamma_j$ in (10) are functions of the quantum numbers which are too complicated for us to give explicitly, but we may mention that $f_1$ can be computed in an elementary manner [32] in which it is only necessary to consider the perturbing effect of the magnetic field on the frequencies and not on the amplitudes. In all other cases, e.g. $(a)$ and $(c)$ where there is less resonance to one particular component, it is vital to consider also the perturbations in amplitudes; neglect of this fact has led to many erroneous articles in the literature. The anomalous factor $f_1$ proves to be just the ratio of the mean Zeeman displacement for the various transverse components, weighted according to their intensity, to the normal Lorentz value $He/4\pi mc$. The most extensive experimental measurements for the present case $(b)$ appear to be those of Kuhn.[33] From the observed rotation he is even able to deduce the Einstein probability coefficients.

　　$(c)$ Multiplet large compared to $kT$, incident light outside the multi-

---

[31] The existence of the part of (10) involving the factor $\gamma_j$, also the third term of (11), which is of similar form as regards dependence on $\nu_0$, appears usually to be overlooked in the literature. This sort of term is, roughly speaking, the parallel of the part $N\alpha$ of the susceptibility which is independent of temperature (cf., for instance, Eq. (1) of Chap. IX). Except in exceptional cases it will hence be of subordinate importance compared to the term of 'Curie form' which is inversely proportional to temperature.

[32] For typical explicit calculations see the following reference to Kuhn.

[33] W. Kuhn, *Math. Phys. Comm. Dan. Acad.* vii. **12**, 11 (1926).

plet. Here the dependence of $\Theta$ on $T$ and $\nu_0$ is of the form

$$\Theta = NHx\nu_0^2 \sum_{n'} \left[ \frac{A_1(n';n)}{[\nu(n';n)^2 - \nu_0^2]^2} + \frac{A_2(n';n)}{T[\nu(n';n)^2 - \nu_0^2]} + \frac{A_3(n';n)}{\nu(n';n)^2 - \nu_0^2} \right], \quad (11)$$

and Becquerel's formula is not in general valid even with an anomalous value of $C$.

*Faraday Effect in Molecules.* Here an adequate analysis is wanting, although the beginnings of a theory for diatomic molecules have been made by Kronig.[34] About all one can say is that the dependence on $\nu_0$ and $T$ is of the general form (11), assuming one is not close to resonance with any one line. The second term vanishes in a non-paramagnetic state. It is a curious fact that the rotation for many molecules is represented quite well by a formula of the Becquerel form (8) but with an anomalous value of $C$. The anomaly in $C$ usually ranges from 0·50 to 0·70, but for $H_2$ it is 0·99, so that the unmodified Becquerel formula applies almost perfectly to hydrogen.[35] Eq. (11) gives a more complicated dependence on $\nu_0$ than (8) even with an anomalous value of $C$. The ability to represent many molecules approximately by the latter probably means that the second and third terms of (11) are usually small compared to the first, and that a group of absorption lines having nearly equal values of $\nu(n';n)$ have a predominant effect on the rotation. Oftentimes the dispersion and rotation are measured in the visible, while the lowest absorption lines are in the ultra violet; then Eq. (3) is not greatly different from a dispersion formula with only one assumed molecular frequency.

*Experimental Confirmation of Paramagnetic Term—Saturation Effects.* At very low temperatures the paramagnetic part, if present, should preponderate. This is confirmed especially well in the measurements of Becquerel and de Haas[36] on mixed crystals (tysonite and xenotime)

---

[34] R. de L. Kronig, *Zeits. f. Physik*, **45**, 508 (1927).

[35] For an excellent compilation of the experimental values of the constant $C$ see Darwin and Watson, *Proc. Roy. Soc.* **114**A, 474 (1927). These writers find that the behaviour of oxygen is anomalous, and its rotation cannot even be represented by a formula of the general form (11), at least if one assumes that there is only one important absorption frequency $\nu(n';n)$. The experimental work is also well surveyed in Ladenburg's article already cited.[21] In this article it is emphasized that in media in which the infra-red vibration bands are known to contribute appreciably to the dispersion, a formula of the form (8), even with an anomalous $C$, is found to be applicable only if one replaces $dn/d\nu$ by $dn'/d\nu$, where $n'$ is the part of the refractive index not arising from these bands. It is also then necessary to insert a correction factor $(n+2)^2 n'/(n'+2)^2 n$ whose origin is closely related to that of the ordinary Clausius-Mossotti correction in the case of static dielectric constants (§ 5). See pp. 2150, 2163 of Ladenburg, *l.c.*[21]

[36] J. Becquerel, *Le Radium*, **5**, 16 (1908); Becquerel and Onnes, *Leiden Communications*

containing rare earth atoms among the ingredients. We saw in Chapter IX that from a magnetic standpoint the rare earth ions behave as if free even when in solid compounds. Because of a factor $\nu(n';n)^2 - \nu_0^2$ rather than $[\nu(n';n)^2 - \nu_0^2]^2$ in the denominator, the paramagnetic rotation, unlike the diamagnetic, should change sign on passing through an absorption band, and this is verified experimentally.[37] The theoretical proportionality to $1/T$ is found to hold only approximately. In the case of tysonite the deviations from this law are not great (about 10 per cent.) down to $20°$ K., but the rotation at temperatures of liquid helium is about one-third less than one would expect if it were inversely proportional to the temperature. In xenotime the measurements show quite definitely that the rotation does not involve $H$ and $T$ only through the ratio $H/T$.

At very low temperatures one encounters the complication that the Faraday rotation is no longer linear in $H$, and instead saturation effects begin to enter, as $\beta H/kT$ is no longer small compared to unity. This saturation is indeed found by Becquerel and de Haas[38] at liquid helium temperatures. From the curvature of the saturation curves information can be deduced concerning the apparent Bohr magneton numbers. Unlike the case of susceptibilities, such information cannot be deduced from the initial slope, as the numerical values of the amplitudes and hence the absolute magnitudes of the right sides of Eqs. (9) and (10) are unknown. It can be shown that when saturation effects are considered, the paramagnetic parts of the rotations in cases $(a)$ and $(b, c)$ become, as we would expect, proportional to $B_L(\beta LH/kT)$ and $B_J(g_j J\beta H/kT)$ respectively instead of being linear in $H/T$ as in Eqs. (9), (10), and (11). Here $B(y)$ denotes the 'Brillouin function' defined in § 61. The elements responsible for the rotation in the mixed crystals tysonite and xenotime are cerium and gadolinium respectively, at least at the wave-lengths used by Becquerel and de Haas. In view of the Hund theory of the rare earths (§ 58) one should expect the saturation

103; Becquerel, Onnes, and de Haas, *ibid.* no. 177; Becquerel and de Haas, *ibid.* no 193, or *Zeits. f. Physik*, **52**, 568; **57**, 11 (1929); also further references cited in note 40.

[37] J. Becquerel, *Phil. Mag.* **16**, 153 (1908). The change in sign is found at ordinary temperatures, but with very low values of $T$ he finds that the absorption band seems to separate into two components such that the rotation is positive on both sides of one component, and negative on both sides of the other. The phenomena at low temperatures thus seem to be more complicated than contemplated by the usual simple theory. As the diamagnetic part of the rotation is necessarily positive, at least in atoms, the observation of a negative rotation in certain cases, notably $TiCl_4$, must mean that in these instances the influence of the paramagnetic part is quite appreciable.

[38] Becquerel and de Haas, *Zeits. f. Physik*, **52**, 678; **57**, 11 (1929), or *Leiden Communications* 193, 204.

curves for tysonite and xenotime to be proportional to $B_{5/2}(15\beta H/7kT)$ and $B_{7/2}(7\beta H/kT)$ respectively. Actually, at the temperatures of liquid helium they are found to be proportional to $B_{1/2}(\beta H/kT)$ and $B_{1/2}(7\beta H/kT)$ respectively. As noted by Becquerel and de Haas, Schütz,[39] and especially Kramers,[40] one obtains the empirical curve for tysonite if one assumes that the inter-atomic fields are so powerful as to quench the orbital angular momentum and leave only the spin free. The theory of § 73 shows that sufficiently large unsymmetrical fields will do this, but in our opinion any explanation by this mechanism is purely spurious. Because of the larger multiplet widths, even greater fields would be required than in the iron group (cf. especially Eq. (4), Chap. XI), whereas the close conformity of the susceptibilities of the rare earths to the gaseous theory undeniably evidences that the $f$ shells in rare earth ions are remarkably free. Instead, the clue to the saturation curves in tysonite is, we believe, to be found in the investigation of the distorting effects of fields, probably not of axial symmetry, which are larger than, or at least comparable with, $kT$ at the temperature of liquid helium, but still very small compared to the multiplet structure. This only requires fields whose effect is of the order 10 cm.$^{-1}$, and there is then no contradiction with susceptibility measurements at higher temperatures.[41] An explanation on this basis is now being attempted by Kramers in place of his original theory.

As regards xenotime, Kramers[40] has shown that one obtains the empirical curve if one assumes that the spin $S = \frac{7}{2}$ of the gadolinium atom is subject to an inter-atomic axial field sufficiently large to make $M_S = \pm\frac{7}{2}$ the only normal state at the temperature of liquid helium. There is the obvious difficulty that such a field, if purely electrostatic,

[39] Schütz, *Zeits. f. Physik*, **54**, 731 (1929).

[40] H. A. Kramers, *Proc. Amsterdam Acad.* **32**, 1176; **33**, 959 (1929–30), also Kramers and Becquerel, *ibid.* **32**, 1190 (1929); Becquerel, de Haas, and Kramers, *ibid.* **32**, 1206 (1929).

[41] Susceptibility measurements just completed at Leiden (*Communication* 210c) by de Haas and Gorter show that in the case of CeF$_3$ the Weiss-Curie formula $\chi = C/(T+\Delta)$ holds quite well down to about 70° K, with $\Delta = 62$, and with a value of $C$ which yields a magneton number 2·52 in excellent accord (1 %) with the Hund theory (§ 58). The value of $\Delta$ and the temperature 70° at which the cryomagnetic anomalies begin to appear are, as we should expect, considerably higher than for the hydrated sulphates usually measured. As the composition of tysonite is (La, Ce, Nd,+Pr)F, it is more analogous to the fluoride of cerium than to the sulphate, and so the susceptibility measurements demand, rather than preclude, an external energy of about 50 cm$^{-1}$. In short the measurements of the saturation rotation in tysonite are made at such low temperatures that one would hence expect great cryomagnetic anomalies, and so one cannot infer any contradiction between these measurements and the ordinary Hund theory of susceptibilities.

would have to be very large, as the energy coupling spins to electric fields is a second-order effect.[42] Possibly exchange forces between paramagnetic atoms and also inter-atomic magnetic forces have some influence; in this event the ultimate theory will be quite involved. At any rate the rotation measurements show indisputably that the spin of the gadolinium atom is much less free in xenotime than in hydrated gadolinium sulphate or gadolinium ethyl sulphate, where the susceptibility measurements confirm the gaseous theory remarkably well even at very low temperatures.

Further Faraday measurements on other materials at very low temperatures are in progress at Leiden. The saturation curves are apparently obtained more easily in this manner than by direct determinations of susceptibilities. Careful analysis of these curves should ultimately yield valuable quantitative information on the inter-atomic fields in rare earth crystals.

*Polarization of Resonance Radiation.* As the Faraday rotation is linear in $H$, it is appreciable only at large field strengths. On the other hand, a small field, 100 gauss or so, often has a tremendous effect on the polarization of resonance radiation. An elaborate theory of the polarization of scattered radiation was developed by Heisenberg and others [43] in the old quantum theory by means of the correspondence principle, and the new quantum mechanics has justified the method. The large influence of a small magnetic field (also of the hyper-fine structure [44]) on the polarization of scattered radiation does not contradict the principle of spectroscopic stability, though we have seen the latter demands that only exceedingly large magnetic fields appreciably distort the dielectric constant or index of refraction. This difference is because the principle in question imposes restraints on the total intensity but not on the polarization of the secondary radiation, except when there is excitation by isotropic rather than directed primary radiation.

---

[42] An additional difficulty is that $S$ states are without any paramagnetic rotary power if one neglects the influence of the inner quantum number $J$ on the energy. However, the excited states of the Gd ion may well have such large multiplet widths that one is not justified in replacing $v(n'j'; nj)$ by $v(n'; n)$ and then the paramagnetic part can persist even in $S$ states. It still seems a bit suprising that the great rotation found in Gd is thus due entirely to distortion of the orbital motion by the spin.

[43] W. Heisenberg, *Zeits. f. Physik*, **31**, 617 (1925); for further references and discussion see Ruark and Urey, *Atoms, Molecules, and Quanta*, pp. 353–60, or the writer's *Quantum Principles and Line Spectra*, pp. 171–9.

[44] A. Ellett, *Phys. Rev.* **35**, 588 (1930).

# INDEX OF AUTHORS

# SUBJECT INDEX

Absorption intensities, 47, 50, 51, 362.

Additivity relations, 57, 60, 77, 82–5, 207, 220–5.

Alkalis: diamagnetism and refractivity of ions, 222–5; magnetic susceptibility of solid, 347, 348, 359, 360;—of vapour, 238, 239; quantum defect, 217; Zeeman effect, 179.

Aluminum spectrum: resonance phenomenon, 219.

Ammonia molecule, 52, 71.

Angle and action variables, 37, 146.

Angular momentum: characteristic values of, 165; commutation rules for, 161; Fourier series for, 171; matrices for, 159–62, 167–72; behaviour in molecules, 262–4, 274, 277–81; quantization of, 106, 150, 164–5; quenching of orbital, 273–4, 287–97, 314, 324, 334; relation to magnetic moment, 4, 155, 174, 255, 256, 300; true $v$. canonical, 23–4, 145, 354; see also spin.

Anisotropy, magnetic (in crystals), 309–11.

Association, molecular, 17, 57, 58, 65, 294, 314; see also complexes.

Atom-core, polarization of, 215–20, 222.

'Atomic polarization', 46, 51, 52, 68.

'Austasch', see exchange effect.

Axis of quantization, 108, 114, 115, 140, 196.

Azimuthal quantum number, 159, 166, 203–4, 238, 354.

Band spectra: relation of dielectric constant to, 45–53, 72, 280.

Benzene molecule and derivatives, 72–81.

Birefringence, see Kerr effect.

Bismuth, diamagnetic susceptibility of, 92, 93.

Boltzmann distribution formula, 24–6, 96, 99, 102–4, 181, 196, 353, 355.

Brillouin function, 257–9, 325, 331, 332, 343, 371, 372.

Canonical: coordinates, 25; transformation, 138.

Carbon bonds, 72, 76, 84.

$CO_2$ molecule, 49–52, 70; $CS_2$, 70; $CCl_4$, 71.

Centrifugal expansion, 200.

Characteristic: functions, 123; values, 123, 143.

Charge: 'effective', 45, 47–52, 81, 200; electronic, 4; statistical density of, 129, 131, 354.

$ClO_2$ molecule, paramagnetism of, 275.

Chromium salts, 285, 301, 304, 306–8.

Classical theory and statistics, 1–104; absence of magnetism in pure, 94–102; inadequacy of, 102; quantum analogies with, 169–72, 184.

Clausius-Mossotti formula, 14, 16, 56, 87, 370.

Cobalt: pure metal, 335, 336; salts, 285, 297–9, 302, 304, 309.

Commutation rules, 119, 127–8, 161, 166, 258, 323.

Complexes, 293, 295, 301, 306, 314; complex atoms, 301, 304, 349.

Conduction electrons, 6, 100–2, 336, 339, 346, 349–60.

Contact transformation, 25, 138.

Continuity, equation of, 8, 10, 130.

Copper salts, 285, 297, 299, 300, 304.

Correspondence principle, 169–72, 107, 109, 110, 357, 361, 362, 373.

Corresponding states, Weiss theorem of, 334.

Cosine law, 162, 165, 174, 177, 230–2, 236, 318.

Coupling: $j$-$j$, 168; Russell-Saunders, 163–8, 173, 178, 229, 288; spin-orbit, 163, 237, 264, 267, 282, 295, 313, 317, 348; spin-spin, 311, 163, 237, 283, 318, 335; types (a)-(b) in molecules, 263.

Cryomagnetic anomalies, 249, 307–8, 333, 372.

Crystalline fields, 287–97, 309–11, 314–15, 372, 373.

Crystals, 2, 309–11, 323; liquid, 120; mixed, 370–3; single, 335.

Cubic symmetry, 291, 311, 324, 337, 338.

Curie's law, 89, 239, 249, 253–4, 267, 269; Weiss modification, 245, 253, 288, 300, 303–9, 314–15, 333, 372.

Curie point, 326, 331–3, 336–9, 344–8.

Current density in quantum mechanics, 130.

Degenerate electron gas, 349–52, 357–9.

Degenerate systems, 134–7, 112, 124, 182, 280; nearly degenerate, 137, 175, 179; non-degenerate, 132–4; invariance theorems in, 139–42; relation to symmetry of field, 290–7, 273, 274; required with odd no. of electrons, 296, 297, 348.

Density, dependence on, see Clausius-Mossotti formula, dilution.

Diagonal: matrices, 127, 142–3, 171, 172; matrix elements, significance of, 129, 143; sum (invariance of), 142, 177, 342.

Diamagnetism: of atoms and ions, 90–4, 99, 206–15, 220–5; of free electrons, 100–2, 353–60; of molecules, 276–9; pressure dependence, 110, 113; diamagnetic correction to paramagnetic susceptibility, 227, 243, 252, 359; diamagnetic Zeeman term, 178–80.

Diatomic molecules: electric moment, 27, 66; magnetic moment, 262–72, 276–81; spectral notation, 262; dumb-bell and top models, 147–55, 183–5, 32–7, 115.

PRINTED IN GREAT BRITAIN AT THE UNIVERSITY PRESS, OXFORD
BY JOHN JOHNSON, PRINTER TO THE UNIVERSITY